14-120-1351

Under the General Editorship of

MARSHALL D. KETCHUM

University of Chicago

Houghton Mifflin Adviser in Finance

MATHEMATICS

OF FINANCE

SECOND EDITION

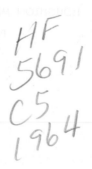

HF
5691
C5
1964

ROBERT CISSELL

Xavier University

and

HELEN CISSELL

HOUGHTON MIFFLIN COMPANY • BOSTON

NEW YORK • ATLANTA • GENEVA, ILL. • DALLAS • PALO ALTO

HOUGHTON MIFFLIN COMPANY • BOSTON

Printed in the U.S.A.

GENERAL EDITOR'S
INTRODUCTION

Decisions as to courses of action in finance, as in everything else, involve forecasts of the future, and all forecasts must be based on judgment as to what the future will bring. The conclusion of this syllogism is that financial decisions must be made on the basis of judgment. While this is true, it is just as true that success in the making of judgments requires a thorough understanding of the past and the present, the setting within which the problem arises.

This book is designed to enable the financial analyst to evolve the facts on which his decision must be made. The financial vice-president of a corporation, faced with the problem of possible refunding of a bond issue, must make a forecast of the future of interest rates, but he must first know what amortization of the debt under present contractual arrangements is costing him. The individual, in making personal investment decisions, must forecast how capitalization rates on earnings and dividends are likely to change; but before making a decision, he must have a knowledge of what these capitalization rates are at present.

In this book, the authors show the student how to reduce a problem to the comparison of two figures: one figure based on the situation as it exists now, and the second figure based on assumptions as to what will prevail in the future. Or, stated more completely, the analyst will make his decision on the basis of a comparison of the present figure with the figure derived from the assumptions as to the future that are most likely to prevail.

This second edition facilitates the problem of determination of the correct figures for comparison by introducing techniques that have been devised since the first edition was published, and by taking account of changes in financial law and practice with which the analyst must deal. A thorough study of the book will make anyone working with financial problems a better decision-maker.

MARSHALL D. KETCHUM
University of Chicago

Our objective in revising this text has been to provide a practical and up-to-date treatment of the mathematics used in modern business transactions. This text is especially suitable for students of economics and business administration. To meet the needs and interest of all students, including those taking liberal arts and general college courses, the book emphasizes financial transactions that are important to individuals and families.

Students who take a course in the mathematics of finance will in later life borrow money, buy a car, home, or other item on time, and take out life insurance. Many of them will put their savings in bonds, stocks, or other investments. A knowledge of the mathematics of finance will enable them to borrow or invest more wisely.

Throughout the book, practical problems are used to illustrate the application of the formulas and tables. Many of the problems are based on data taken from actual business transactions. Students are interested in discovering that "easy" credit terms may actually conceal a very high rate which can be determined accurately by the methods given in this book. Students find the mathematics of finance more interesting when they know that they will benefit financially from what they are learning.

In a mathematics of finance course, most of the problems are word or thought problems. Because students have had trouble with word problems in algebra, they expect the mathematics of finance to be a succession of very difficult problems. Fortunately, most of the thought problems are not difficult if the student will do two things: make a time diagram of the problem and use an equation of value. Both of these are used extensively in the examples throughout this book.

Algebraic derivations are accompanied or illustrated by numerical examples. This is particularly helpful to students who have a limited knowledge of algebra and find it difficult to follow a derivation that is presented only in general terms.

So that the student can check on his progress, answers are given to many of the problems. Since the answer to a problem in the mathematics of finance usually does not help in determining the method of solution, the answers are given at the end of the problem to save time that would otherwise be spent looking in the back of the book. Answers to the even-numbered problems and suggestions about what to include or omit in varying circumstances are given in the teacher's manual.

Most of the additional material in the first nine chapters consists of more examples and more explanation of points suggested by teachers who have used the text. We have added in Chapter 7 a discussion of the mathematics involved in the important management function of capital budgeting. This additional material is offset, in part at least, by a simpler treatment of depreciation in line with the latest government regulations. Thus past users of the text should find that the topics which they covered in the past can be treated in about the same length of time.

The chapter on stocks is a major feature of the revision. A modern treatment of the mathematics of finance would be incomplete without a discussion of stocks which are important in both corporate financing and in the financial planning of many individuals and families. Since the mathematics required in the stock chapter is covered in detail earlier in the book, students should be able to understand the material on stocks even if there is no time for formal coverage in class.

Tables are an indispensable part of a mathematics of finance text. The tables in this text have been carefully selected to acquaint students with those used in modern business firms. Because these tables are well organized and include all necessary functions, they save valuable time which can be used to work more problems. The mathematical tables are also useful sources of data for other courses and for solving practical business problems. Tables 2, 3, and 4 are reproduced from the excellent Compound Interest Tables of the Financial Publishing Company with the permission of Mr. Charles H. Gushee, President. Tables 5 and 6 are reproduced from publications of the Society of Actuaries with permission of Mr. Walter L. Grace, Secretary of the Society. Table 7 is taken from the *Mathematics of Business, Accounting, and Finance* by Kenneth L. Trefftzs and E. J. Hills, published by Harper & Brothers. These excellent tables of logarithms are used with the permission of Professor Trefftzs who prepared them. Because most problems require the use of one or more functions from the tables, they have been printed on colored paper to save the student's time. Table 8, Reciprocals, was taken from the twelfth edition of the Chemical Rubber Company Standard Mathematical Tables by permission of Robert C. Weast, Editor.

To insure that the book will be in line with present commercial practices and of the greatest practical value to students, the material has been checked by authorities in banking, insurance, investments, and other financial fields. Suggestions from practical financiers and teachers, listed separately on pages xi and xii, have helped insure the inclusion of the latest commercial practices in a teachable way.

We wish to express our appreciation to the Rev. Victor C. Stechschulte, S.J., late Chairman of the Department of Mathematics at Xavier University, and to Dr. P. D. Edwards of Ball State Teachers College. These gentlemen read the entire manuscript for the first edition and made many valuable suggestions for improvements. Especially is sincere appreciation due to Mr. Odin Nielsen of Horwath and Horwath, accountants and auditors. From his detailed analysis of the first edition have come many ideas which help to make this edition a more effective means for teaching the mathematics of finance.

ROBERT CISSELL

HELEN CISSELL

Cincinnati, Ohio

ACKNOWLEDGMENTS

We are grateful to the following persons for many valuable suggestions. The businessmen in this list are using mathematics of finance in their work and have helped us prepare a text which is in line with current business practices. Some of the teachers used the first edition and have suggested improvements for making the second edition clearer and more interesting to the students. Other teachers in related fields, such as accounting and finance, have checked the text to see that it provides the mathematical preparation which students need for their courses.

J. F. Curry, Head, Department of General Business, Mississippi State University.

Arthur C. Daniels, Vice-President, Institute of Life Insurance.

Lawrence Fitzgerald, Vice-President, Merrill Lynch, Pierce, Fenner and Smith.

Dr. Allen O. Felix, Manager, School and College Relations, New York Stock Exchange.

Miles C. Hartley, Chairman, Department of Mathematics, University of Tampa.

Walter P. Heinzman, Professor, New Mexico State University.

Dr. Gerald E. Harriman, Chairman, Department of Finance, Xavier University.

Victor E. Henningsen, Vice-President and Actuary, The Northwestern Mutual Life Insurance Company.

Dr. Marshall D. Ketchum, Professor of Finance, The University of Chicago.

Harry R. Maly, C.P.A., Assistant Professor of Accounting, Xavier University.

Dr. A. James Meigs, Economist of the New York Stock Exchange.

Dr. Z. I. Mosesson, F.S.A.

Dr. Frank M. Phillips, Professor of Mathematics, Stetson University.

Dr. Charles F. Pinzka, University of Cincinnati.

Emmett S. Sams, Department of Mathematics, Mars Hill College.

Jacob W. Schweitzer, Assistant Professor of Accounting, Xavier University.

William E. Smith, Assistant Professor of Accounting, Xavier University.

Russell J. Walker, C.P.A., Assistant Dean, College of Business Administration, Xavier University.

Edward F. Wilz, C.P.A., Chairman, Department of Accounting, Xavier University.

Dr. George A. Wing, Assistant Professor of Finance, Xavier University.

Stella D. Yates, North Idaho Junior College.

CONTENTS

MATHEMATICS OF FINANCE

1

SIMPLE INTEREST
AND BANK DISCOUNT

1.1 Simple Interest

Money paid for the use of money is called interest. To compute interest a person must know how much money is borrowed, the rate of interest and the term of the loan.

The **principal** is the sum of money which is borrowed. The **rate** is the per cent of the principal which is charged for its use. The **time** or **term of the loan** is the period during which the borrower has the use of the principal.

Simple interest is computed entirely on the original principal. **Compound interest** is based on a principal which is increased each time interest is earned.

Simple interest is computed by simply multiplying together the principal, rate and time. This leads to the simple interest formula,

$$I = Prt \tag{1}$$

I = the simple interest in dollars
P = the principal in dollars
r = the interest rate per unit of time expressed as a decimal
t = the time in units that correspond to the rate

Note that r and t must correspond. That is, if the rate is an annual rate the time must be in years; if the rate is a monthly rate, the time must be in months. Unless stated otherwise, rates are assumed to be annual rates. An interest rate is usually given as a percentage. This must be converted to

1

a decimal or a fraction when substituting in the simple interest formula. Thus interest at 4% means that for each dollar which is borrowed for a year, 4 cents interest will be charged. If this rate is used in Formula (1) r would be replaced by .04 or 4/100.

EXAMPLE 1: What is the simple interest on $1000 at 5% for 3 months?

SOLUTION: Since nothing is said to the contrary, the 5% is an annual rate. Therefore the time, when substituted in the simple interest formula, must be in years. Substituting $P = 1000$, $r = .05$ and $t = \frac{3}{12}$ or $\frac{1}{4}$ year in Formula (1),

$$I = 1000 \times .05 \times \tfrac{1}{4} = \$12.50$$

EXAMPLE 2: A man buys a home and gets a loan for $10,000. The interest rate is $5\frac{1}{2}$%. What is the interest for the first month?

SOLUTION: Substituting $P = 10,000$, $r = .055$, and $t = \frac{1}{12}$ in (1),

$$I = 10,000 \times .055 \times \tfrac{1}{12} = \$45.83$$

EXAMPLE 3: The interest paid on a loan of $500 for 4 months was $12.50. What was the interest rate?

SOLUTION: When a rate is required, we ordinarily get it correct to the nearest hundredth of 1%. We substitute $I = 12.50$, $P = 500$ and $t = \frac{4}{12}$ or $\frac{1}{3}$ in (1). It makes no difference which member of an equation is to the left of the equal sign. Many people find it easier to solve equations when the unknown is on the left as shown below.

$$500 \times r \times \tfrac{1}{3} = 12.50$$
$$r = \frac{3 \times 12.50}{500} = .075 = 7\tfrac{1}{2}\%$$

EXAMPLE 4: A man gets $63.75 every 6 months from an investment which pays $4\frac{1}{4}$% interest. How much money does he have invested?

SOLUTION: Substituting $I = 63.75$, $r = .0425$ and $t = \frac{1}{2}$ in (1),

$$P \times .0425 \times \tfrac{1}{2} = 63.75$$
$$P = \frac{63.75 \times 2}{.0425} = \$3000.00$$

EXAMPLE 5: How long will it take $5000 to earn $50 interest at 6%?

SOLUTION: Substituting $I = 50$, $P = 5000$ and $r = .06$ in (1),

$$5000 \times .06 \times t = 50$$

$$t = \frac{50}{5000 \times .06} = \tfrac{1}{6} \text{ year or 2 months}$$

EXAMPLE 6: General Mills $100 par value 5% preferred stock was quoted at 115. At this price, what rate of interest or yield will a buyer receive on his investment?

SOLUTION: In this problem, two rates of interest are involved. The return in dollars is the stated rate times the par value or $.05 \times 100 = \$5.00$. This amount will be paid to the owner of the stock regardless of what he paid for it. To find the yield rate received by a buyer who paid $115, substitute in (1),

$$115 \times r \times 1 = 5.00$$

$$r = \frac{5.00}{115} = .0435 = 4.35\%$$

Had the buyer obtained this stock for less than $100, his rate of return would be more than 5%.

1.2 Amount

The sum of the principal and the interest is called the **amount,** symbol S. This definition leads to the formula,

$$S = P + I$$
$$= P + Prt$$

Factoring, we have $\qquad S = P(1 + rt) \qquad\qquad (2)$

EXAMPLE: A man borrows $350 for 6 months at 8%. What amount must he repay?

SOLUTION: Substituting $P = 350$, $r = .08$ and $t = \tfrac{1}{2}$ in Formula (2),

$$S = 350(1 + .08 \times \tfrac{1}{2}) = 350(1.04) = \$364.00$$

This problem could have been worked by getting the simple interest and adding it to the principal.

$$I = Prt = 350 \times .08 \times \tfrac{1}{2} = \$14.00$$
$$S = P + I = 350.00 + 14.00 = \$364.00$$

Many problems in the mathematics of finance can be solved by more than one method. Students should look for the easiest way, thereby reducing both labor and the risk of numerical errors. It is often desirable to work a problem different ways as a check.

As this example shows, the dollar value of a sum of money will vary in accordance with the time and rate. Students who are accustomed to thinking of money only in terms of so much cash, must now get into the habit of taking into account these other variables. A debt of $1000 due in one year with interest at 6% should be considered as an obligation of $1060 due in one year. If a time is not stated, we shall assume that the designated sum is the present or cash value. Thus if a problem states that the price of a car is $2000, this means the cash price. If a sum is due in the future "without interest" or if a rate is not stated, we shall assume that the given value is the maturity value of the obligation. Thus "$3000 due in 6 months" means that 6 months hence the debtor must pay $3000. In the business world, this obligation would be worth less than $3000 before the end of 6 months.

Students also need to learn that different amounts of money may be *equivalent in value*. At 5% interest, $100 now is equivalent in value to $105 in a year. What this means in practice is that a borrower is willing to repay $105 one year hence if he can get the use of $100 immediately. The lender is willing to lose the use of $100 for a year if he gets $5 interest. The equivalent values of different sums is the basis for the useful equations of value used throughout the mathematics of finance.

Another way of expressing an interest rate is to say that "money is worth so much." This expression is often used in problems to specify the rate which the parties to a transaction have agreed to use in arriving at a settlement. In practical business usage this rate is usually the current rate for that type of transaction in the particular locality.

1.3   Rounding

Money answers in mathematics of finance are rounded off to values that can be paid in standard coinage. In this book, unless stated otherwise, answers are rounded to the nearest cent. Calculated values ending in exactly half a cent or more are rounded up.

Calculated Value	*Rounded Value*
$45.789	$45.79
45.443	45.44
45.375	45.38
45.4650	45.47
45.6749	45.67

Note that in the last case .6749 is rounded down to .67. Since we are rounding to the nearest cent, it would be wrong to make the 4 a 5 in one step and round to 45.68 in a second step.

While exceptions to the above rule are noted as we come to them, we mention a couple now to illustrate how commercial practices affect rounding. Mortgage lenders customarily round up any fraction of a cent. Thus a monthly payment of $85.142 would be rounded up to $85.15. Had the fraction of a cent been dropped, the deficiency which accumulates over a long series of payments would all be made up on the concluding payment, making this payment larger than the others. By rounding up, the reverse is true, and the concluding payment will be somewhat smaller. This probably makes for happier customers. Some lenders even round up to the nearest dime. A monthly payment of $112.125 would be rounded up to $112.20. Again no injustice is done as the overpayment of a few cents each month is offset by the smaller concluding payment.

When data are approximate, rounding should not imply a degree of accuracy that is not possible with the data. Suppose that the market value of a stock has been increasing at about 10% a year. With so many uncertainties involved in the stock market, it would be foolish to predict the price a year from now to the nearest cent. A reasonable procedure would be to round off the answer to the nearest dollar and then qualify this as only a prediction.

Another practical question is how many decimal places to retain when a factor involves an unending decimal. If we want the amount of $4800 at 4% for 1 month, we can substitute in Formula (2),

$$S = 4800(1 + .04 \times \tfrac{1}{12}) = 4800(1.003333\ldots)$$

The second factor must be terminated somewhere. A good working rule is to round such factors to the same number of decimal places as there are digits in the sum of money *including the cents*. In $4800.00 there are 6 digits, so we have,

$$S = 4800(1.003333) = 4815.9984 = \$4816.00$$

Note that in this problem it is simpler to get the interest from Formula (1) and then add principal and interest to get the amount.

$$I = 4800 \times .04 \times \tfrac{1}{12} = \$16.00$$
$$S = 4800 + 16 = \$4816.00$$

1.4 Time Diagram

An easy and accurate way to keep track of the varying dollar values of sums of money is to use a time diagram which shows the sums and the points in time at which they have particular dollar values. Students will find such diagrams of great help in the analysis and solution of problems. The simple time diagram below shows how the different dollar values of an obligation are placed at the corresponding points in time.

```
┌─────────────────────────────────────────────────────────┐
│                                                           │
│         Equivalent values at 5% interest                  │
│    $100                                        $105       │
│    └─────────────────────────────────────────┘           │
│    Now                                       1 year       │
│                                                           │
└─────────────────────────────────────────────────────────┘
```

Exercise 1a

1. Find the simple interest on $750 for 2 months at 7% and the amount.
($8.75, $758.75)

2. Find the simple interest on $1225 for 3 months at $3\frac{1}{2}\%$ and the amount.

3. If $3500 is invested at 5% for 6 months, how much interest will be earned and what will be the amount?   ($87.50, $3587.50)

4. If a company borrows $9830 for 4 months at $4\frac{1}{2}\%$, how much interest will be charged and what amount must be repaid when the loan matures?

5. A man borrows $10,000 to buy a home. The interest rate is 6% and the monthly payment is $64.43. How much of the first payment goes to interest and how much to principal?   (Interest $50.00; principal $14.43)

6. A $15,000 home loan is to be repaid with monthly payments of $100. If the interest rate is 5%, how much of the first payment goes to interest and how much to principal?

7. A building and loan advertises a rate of $4\frac{1}{2}\%$. Deposits made by the 10th of the month earn interest from the 1st of that month. Deposits made after the 10th earn interest from the 1st of the following month. Interest is credited on June 30 and December 31. A depositor had $2045 in his account on June 30, 1966. He deposited $1120 on September 7, 1966. How much will he have in his account on December 31, 1966?   ($3227.81)

8. A man has an account in a building and loan that pays 4.8%. Interest dates are June 30 and December 31. Money deposited by the 10th of a month earns interest from the 1st of that month. Deposits after the 10th earn interest from the first of the following month. This man had a balance of $1600 on

December 31, 1967. He deposited $400 on February 8, 1968, and $600 on April 25, 1968. Find the final entry in his passbook after interest is credited on June 30, 1968.

9. A man borrowed $150 for two months and paid $9.00 interest. What was the annual rate?   (36%)

10. A mechanic borrowed $125 from a licensed loan company and at the end of 1 month paid off the loan with $128.75. What annual rate of interest did he pay?

11. If a person loans $6000 at 5%, how long will it take him to get $75.00 interest?   (3 months)

12. How long will it take $8400 to earn $24.50 interest at 3.5%?

13. How long a time will be required for $625 to earn $25 interest at 4.8%?
                                                                    (10 months)

14. How long will it take $1800 to earn $63.75 interest at $4\frac{1}{4}$%?

15. What is the amount if $3.6 million is borrowed for 1 month at $2\frac{7}{8}$%?
                                                                   ($3,608,625)

16. What is the amount if $14.4 million is borrowed for 2 months at $3\frac{1}{4}$%?

17. A man borrows $95. Six months later he repays the loan, principal and interest, with a payment of $100. What interest rate did he pay?   (10.53%)

18. A loan shark made a loan of $5 to be repaid with $10.50 at the end of one month. What was the annual interest rate?

19. A waitress, temporarily pressed for funds, pawned her watch and diamond ring for $55. At the end of 1 month she redeemed them by paying $59.40. What was the annual rate of interest?   (96%)

20. A loan shark was charging $10 interest for a $50 loan for a month. What was the annual interest rate?

21. A teacher borrowed $100 from the credit union to which she belonged. Every month for 4 months she paid $25 on the principal and interest at the rate of 1% a month on the balance at the beginning of the month. The first interest payment would be 1% of $100, the second interest payment would be 1% of $75, and so on until the loan was repaid. What was the total interest paid on this loan?   ($2.50)

22. A person borrowed $900 from a credit union which charges $\frac{3}{4}$% per month on the outstanding balance of a loan. Every month for 6 months he paid $150 on the principal plus interest on the balance at the beginning of the month. Find the total interest.

23. Cincinnati Gas and Electric $100 par value, 4% preferred stock was quoted at 94. At this price what is the yield rate?   (4.26%)

24. Philadelphia Electric $100 par value, 4% preferred stock was quoted at 103. What was the yield rate?

25. White Sewing Machine preferred stock with a par value of $50 and a $3 annual dividend was quoted at 42. What was the yield rate?   (7.14%)

26. Use current data from your local paper to complete the table below for preferred stocks designated by your instructor. See Chapter 10 for directions on how to read stock tables.

Stock and Dividend	High	Low	Close	Yield Rate in Per Cent Based on Closing Price

1.5 Exact and Ordinary Interest

When the time is in days and the rate is an annual rate, it is necessary to convert the days to a fractional part of a year when substituting in the simple interest formulas. Interest computed using a divisor of 360 is called **ordinary interest.** When the divisor is 365 or 366, the result is known as **exact interest.**

EXAMPLE: Get the ordinary and exact interest on a 60-day loan of $300 if the rate is 8%.

SOLUTION: Substituting $P = 300$ and $r = .08$ in (1), we have

$$\text{Ordinary interest} = 300 \times .08 \times \tfrac{60}{360} = \$4.00$$
$$\text{Exact interest} \quad = 300 \times .08 \times \tfrac{60}{365} = \$3.95$$

Note that ordinary interest is greater than exact interest. Also it is easier to compute when the work must be done without a calculator. It is probably for these reasons that ordinary interest is used more frequently.

1.6 Exact and Approximate Time

There are two ways to compute the number of days between calendar dates. The more common method is the **exact** method which includes all days except the first. A simple way to determine the exact number of days is to use Table 1 in the green pages, which gives the serial numbers of the days in the year. Another method is to add the number of days in each month during the term of the loan, not counting the first day but counting the last one. The **approximate** method is based on the assumption that all of the full months contain 30 days. To this number is added the exact number of days that remain in the term of the loan.

EXAMPLE: Find the exact and approximate time between March 5 and September 28.

SOLUTION: From Table 1 we find that September 28 is the 271st day in the year and March 5 is the 64th day. Therefore the exact time = 271 − 64 = 207 days. If a table of calendar days is not available, we can set up a table as follows:

$$
\begin{array}{lll}
\text{March} & 26 & (31 - 5) \\
\text{April} & 30 & \\
\text{May} & 31 & \\
\text{June} & 30 & \\
\text{July} & 31 & \\
\text{August} & 31 & \\
\text{Sept.} & \underline{28} & \\
\text{Total} & 207 \text{ days} &
\end{array}
$$

To get the approximate time we count the number of months from March 5 to September 5. This gives us $6 \times 30 = 180$ days. To this we add the 23 days from September 5 to September 28 to get a total of 203 days.

1.7 Commercial Practices

Since we have exact and ordinary interest and exact and approximate time, there are four ways to compute simple interest:

1. Ordinary interest and exact time (Bankers' Rule)
2. Exact interest and exact time
3. Ordinary interest and approximate time
4. Exact interest and approximate time

This brings out the fact that in computing simple interest, as in all problems in the mathematics of finance, both parties to the transaction should understand what method is to be used. In this book, when the time is in days, we use ordinary interest and exact time unless another method is specified. This is known as **Bankers' Rule** and is the common commercial practice.

When an obligation has a stated time to run, it is necessary to determine the due date. If the time is stated in days, the due date is the exact number of days after the loan begins. If the time is stated in months, the due date is the same as the date on which the term of the loan begins unless the date of the loan is larger than the last date of the month in which the loan matures. When this happens, we take as the maturity date the last date of the month. Examples,

Date of Loan	Term of Loan	Maturity Date
June 15, 1964	60 days	August 14, 1964
June 15, 1964	2 months	August 15, 1964
Dec. 10, 1964	4 months	April 10, 1965
Dec. 10, 1964	120 days	April 9, 1965
Dec. 10, 1963	120 days	April 8, 1964
		(1964 is a leap year)
Dec. 28, 29, 30 or 31, 1964	2 months	Feb. 28, 1965
Dec. 29, 30 or 31, 1963	2 months	Feb. 29, 1964

EXAMPLE 1: On November 15, 1965, a man borrowed $500 at 5%. The debt is repaid on February 20, 1966. Find the simple interest using the four methods.

SOLUTION: We first get the exact and approximate time.

Exact Time	*Approximate Time*
From Table 1:	
November 15 is the 319th day	November 15 to February 15 is
February 20 is the 51st day	three months
In 1965 there are $365 - 319 = 46$ days	Three months $\times$ 30 days = 90 days
In 1966 there are 51 days	February 15 to 20 = 5 days
Total time 97 days	Total time 95 days

Ordinary interest and exact time (Bankers' Rule) $I = 500 \times .05 \times \frac{97}{360} = \$6.74$

Exact interest and exact time $I = 500 \times .05 \times \frac{97}{365} = \$6.64$

Ordinary interest and approximate time $I = 500 \times .05 \times \frac{95}{360} = \$6.60$

Exact interest and approximate time $I = 500 \times .05 \times \frac{95}{365} = \$6.51$

To encourage prompt payment of bills, many merchants allow discounts for payments in advance of the final due date. Terms of 2/10, $n/30$ mean that if the bill is paid within 10 days, 2% of the amount of the bill can be deducted. Otherwise the full amount of the bill becomes due on the 30th day. A buyer who takes advantage of cash discounts in effect lends money to the seller and receives as interest the discount. Interest rates earned in this way are so high, as the following example shows, that it is good business practice to take advantage of such discounts.

EXAMPLE 2: A merchant receives an invoice for $1000 with terms 2/10, $n/30$. If he pays on the 10th day, he earns what rate of interest?

SOLUTION: The discount is $20 making the principal $980. Substituting in Formula (1),

$$980 \times r \times \frac{20}{360} = 20$$

$$r = \frac{20 \times 360}{980 \times 20} = .367 = 36.7\%$$

Exercise 1b

1. Find the ordinary and exact interest on $750 for 100 days at 3%.
($6.25, $6.16)

2. Find the ordinary and exact interest on $6080.50 for 60 days at $3\frac{1}{4}\%$.

3. Find the ordinary and exact interest on $1200 for 45 days at $4\frac{1}{2}\%$.
($6.75, $6.66)

4. If $P = \$9800$ and $r = 2\frac{1}{8}\%$, get the ordinary and exact interest for a 120-day loan.

5. Use exact time and find the ordinary and exact interest on $300 at 5% from May 5, 1966, to September 12, 1966.   ($5.42, $5.34)

6. Use exact time and find the ordinary and exact interest on $500 from November 30, 1966, to March 15, 1967 using a rate of $7\frac{1}{2}\%$.

(Use Bankers' Rule in Problems 7 to 14)

7. What amount must be repaid on November 21, 1967, if $7000 is borrowed at 7% on November 1, 1967?   ($7027.22)

8. A man borrows $7760 on December 15, 1966. He repays the debt on March 3, 1967 with interest at $6\frac{1}{2}\%$. Find the amount repaid.

9. A debt of $500 is due on June 15, 1966. After that date the borrower is required to pay 5% interest. If the debt is settled on January 10, 1967, what must be repaid?   ($514.51)

10. On May 1, 1966, a man borrows $1850 which he promises to repay in 4 months with interest at 3%. If he does not pay on time his contract requires him to pay 8% on the unpaid amount for the time after the due date. Determine how much he must pay to settle the debt on December 15, 1966.

11. A man borrows $3050 on December 15, 1967, at $3\frac{1}{4}\%$. What amount must he repay on April 8, 1968? Note that for leap years, the number of the day after February 28 is one more than the number in Table 1. ($3081.66)

12. A man borrows $5000 on November 11, 1963, at $5\frac{1}{2}\%$. What amount must he repay on March 10, 1964?

13. Bank A which is deficient in reserves borrows $4.5 million for 1 day from Bank B which has excess reserves. If the market rate for such loans is 3%, how much interest must Bank A remit to Bank B on the following day? ($375.00)

14. Bank A borrows $800,000 from Bank B for 3 days. If the interest rate is $3\frac{1}{4}\%$, what will be the interest in dollars?

15. On December 31 a man has $3000 in his account in a building and loan. His money will earn interest at $4\frac{1}{2}\%$ if it is left on deposit until the next interest date which is June 30. Money withdrawn before June 30 does not get any interest. On May 1 the man needs $1000. Instead of drawing the money out of his account, he makes a passbook loan using his passbook as security. He plans to repay this loan from his account on June 30 when he gets his interest. If the building and loan charges 6% for a passbook loan, this plan will save the man how much money as of June 30? ($12.50)

16. Get the answer to Problem 15 if the loan is for $1500 and is made on March 31.

17. The United States Government sells short-term securities known as Government Bills. These securities carry no stated interest rate but are sold on a discount basis in open bidding. A bank wants to purchase $10 million of these bills that will mature in 91 days and it bids $9,920,000. This offer is accepted. What annual rate of interest will the bank earn if it holds the bills to maturity? (3.19%)

18. A bank bids $4,912,500 for $5 million of Government Bills which will mature in 182 days. If the offer is accepted and the bank holds the bills to maturity, what rate of interest will be earned?

19. A merchant receives an invoice for $2000 with terms 2/10, $n/60$. If he pays on the 10th, he will earn what rate of interest? (14.7%)

20. An invoice for $5000 has terms 3/10, $n/45$. What rate of interest is earned if payment is made on the 10th?

1.8 Present Value at Simple Interest

To get the amount of a principal invested at simple interest, we use the formula, $S = P(1 + rt)$. If the amount is known and we want to get the principal, we solve the formula for P.

$$P = \frac{S}{1 + rt} \qquad (3)$$

EXAMPLE: If money is worth 5%, what is the present value of $105 due in one year?

SOLUTION: Substituting $S = 105, r = .05,$ and $t = 1$ in (3),

$$P = \frac{105}{1 + .05 \times 1} = \$100.00$$

This means that $100 invested now at 5% should amount to $105 in a year. Substituting in the amount formula verifies this.

$$S = 100(1 + .05 \times 1) = \$105.00$$

Getting the present value of a sum due in the future is called **discounting.** When the simple interest formula is used to get the present value, the difference between the amount and present value is called **simple discount.** Note that the simple discount on the future amount is the same as the simple interest on the principal or present value.

1.9 Use of Reciprocals

Only by working many problems and checking the results, can a person acquire an understanding of the mathematics of finance. To make it possible for students to work a greater diversity of problems, we use data that simplify computations. Division, which is often the most time-consuming arithmetic operation, can sometimes be done more rapidly by multiplying by the reciprocal of the divisor from Table 8 in the green pages.

EXAMPLE 1: If money is worth 7%, what is the present value of $2000 due in 1 year?

SOLUTION: Substituting $S = 2000, r = .07$ and $t = 1$ in Formula (3),

$$P = \frac{2000}{1.07} = 2000 \times \frac{1}{1.07}$$

To get $1/1.07$, we can write $1/1.07 = 100 \times 1/107$

$$= 100 \times .00934\ 5794$$
$$= .934\ 579$$

Practically it is usually easier and most students prefer to locate the decimal point by inspection. In any case, the answer is found by a simple multiplication.

$$P = 2000 \times .934\ 579 = \$1869.16$$

EXAMPLE 2: If money is worth 4%, what is the present value of $5000 due in 2 months?

SOLUTION: Substituting in Formula (3),

$$P = \frac{5000}{1 + .04 \times \frac{1}{6}} = \frac{5000}{1.006667}$$

To divide this out would be a lot of work. However, to use the reciprocal tables, the denominator must have 3 or less significant figures. By multiplying numerator and denominator by 6,

$$P = \frac{30,000}{6.04} = 30,000 \times .165\ 5629 = \$4966.89$$

1.10 Use Your Head

All answers should be subjected to a common-sense check. Many mistakes are whoppers, resulting from such common slips as misplaced decimal points and inverted fractions. There is no disgrace in making such mistakes. Not catching them is another matter. The student who is looking for the present value at 4% of $5000 due in 2 months and writes down $49,668.87 should not expect credit because he got everything right except the decimal point. Common sense should tell him to expect an answer somewhat less than $5000.

1.11 What Is It Worth, Now?

The mathematics of finance can be used to find the best answer to many practical business problems. Typical of the many important questions which we consider in this and later chapters are: Should we pay cash or use credit? Is it better to buy or lease? Will a new machine pay for itself?

A good way to compare different plans is to get all of them on a present value basis. Just as we can compare two items when we know their cash prices, so are we helped to choose between more complicated alternatives when we know what each is worth *now*.

EXAMPLE: A man can buy a piece of property for $5000 cash or $5300 in a year. He has the cash and can invest it at 5%. Which is better and by how much now?

SOLUTION: The propositions as they stand cannot be compared because they are at different points in time. Formula (3) enables us to find that at 5% the $5300 due in a year has a present value of,

$$P = \frac{5300}{1.05} = \$5047.62$$

This means that the buyer would have to invest $5047.62 now at 5% to have $5300 in a year. (Check: 5047.62 × 1.05 = $5300.00). By paying cash, the buyer saves $47.62 now.

If he could get another rate of return on his money, there might be a different decision. For example,

Rate of Return	Present Value of $5300 Due in 1 Year	Better Plan
5%	$5047.62	Save $47.62 now by paying cash
6%	5000.00	Plans are equivalent
7%	4953.27	Save $46.73 now by paying $5300 in 1 year

Exercise 1c

1. What is the present value of $1500 due in 9 months if money is worth 4%? ($1456.31)

2. At an interest rate of $4\frac{1}{2}\%$ what is the present value of $4300 due in 3 months?

3. At 6% interest what is the present value of $600 due in 6 months? ($582.52)

4. What is the present value of $600 due in 6 months at: (a) 2%; (b) 3%; (c) 4%?

5. What is the present value of $100 due in 1 year at: (a) 4%; (b) 5%; (c) 6%? [(a) $96.15; (b) $95.24; (c) $94.34]

6. At 5% find the present value of $2000 due in: (a) 3 months; (b) 6 months; (c) 9 months.

7. A man can get a lot for $3000 cash or $3100 in one year. He has the cash but can invest it at 4%. Which is more advantageous to him and by how much now? (By paying $3100 in a year he saves $19.23 now)

8. If a person can earn $4\frac{1}{2}\%$ on his money, is it better to pay $1990 cash for an item or to pay $2090 in a year? Give the cash equivalent of the savings resulting from adopting the better plan.

9. A man may discharge an obligation by paying either $200 now or $208 in 6 months. If money is worth 4% to the man, what is the cash equivalent of choosing the better plan?   (By paying $200 cash he saves $3.92 now)

10. A man can settle a debt by paying either $1475 now or $1500 in 3 months. If the man can earn 4% on his money, which plan is more advantageous and by how much now?

1.12   Present Value of Interest-Bearing Debt

We must first get the maturity value of interest-bearing debts, using the stated interest rate for the term of the loan. Then we get the present value of this maturity value for the time between the day it is discounted and the due date using the rate specified for discounting. Since two rates and two times may be involved in discounting an interest-bearing debt, a time diagram helps to prevent errors.

EXAMPLE: A debtor signs a note for $2000 due in 6 months with interest at 4%. One month after the debt is contracted, the holder of the note sells it to a third party who determines the present value at 6%. How much is received for the note?

SOLUTION: A time diagram is made. The maturity value is obtained, and then discounted for the five months between the discount date and the due date.

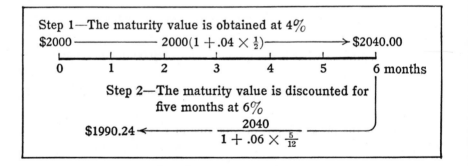

A common error in problems of this type is to use the time between the original loan and the discount date for getting the present value. That would be one month in this example. The person who buys the note is not interested in how long it has run, but in how long it still has to run. In this example, the buyer of the note is loaning $1990.24 to the holder of the note. The $2040 he gets five months later is a return of his principal with interest at 6%.

1.13 Equations of Value

Sometimes it is desired to replace one or more obligations with one or more payments at different times that will be equivalent in value to the original obligations. For example, a man may owe the same creditor $200 due now and $106 due in a year. He has cash with which he can settle all his obligations. However, he would be foolish to make a cash payment of $306 because part of the debt is not due now. He will want the creditor to make some allowance for the early payment of the $106 due in a year. If simple interest is to be used in arriving at a settlement, the two parties must agree on a rate. Suppose they decide to use 6%. Then we simply get the present value at 6% of $106 due in a year.

$$P = \frac{106}{1 + .06 \times 1} = \$100$$

We can add this to the $200 due now to get a total cash settlement of $300. Note that two sums of money cannot be added *until they have been brought to the same point in time*.

Suppose in the above example that the man did not have the cash and asked his creditor to allow him to settle all the debts in a year. Now he must expect to pay interest on the $200 due now. If the agreed rate is 6%, the $200 would amount to $212 in a year. Because it is at the same point in time as the $106 the two could be added making the total debt *at that time* $318. The three alternatives we have discussed can be summarized as follows:

$$\left. \begin{array}{l} \$200 \text{ now and } \$106 \text{ in a year} \\ \$300 \text{ now} \\ \$318 \text{ in a year} \end{array} \right\} \begin{array}{l} \text{are equivalent in} \\ \text{value if money is} \\ \text{worth } 6\% \end{array}$$

We have gone into this point in detail because of its fundamental importance in the mathematics of finance and the difficulty it causes students. ALWAYS bring obligations to the same point using the specified rate before combining them. This common point is called a **focal date** or **comparison date**. When everything has been brought to a focal date, an **equation of value** can be set up and unknown quantities determined. If any obligations are interest bearing, maturity values must be determined before moving them to the focal date.

A very effective way to solve many problems in the mathematics of finance is to make a time diagram, select a focal date, and then use an equation of value in which the original obligations are set equal to the payments after *both* have been brought to the focal date using the specified interest rate.

If a student draws a good time diagram, he will often find that the equation of value practically writes itself.

In simple interest problems the answer will vary slightly depending on the location of the focal date. In compound interest problems the location of the focal date does not affect the answer. Students should recognize that the focal date is simply an arbitrary point in time which we must have so that all obligations and payments can be brought to the same time and an equation of value obtained.

EXAMPLE 1: A man owes $200 due in 6 months and $300 due in 1 year. He and his creditor agree that he can make a cash settlement of both debts using a simple interest rate of 5% and putting the focal date now. Get the size of the cash settlement.

SOLUTION: A time diagram with the original debts on one side of the line and the new obligations on the other side will make it easy to obtain the correct equation.

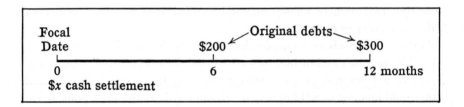

To get the $200 to the focal date we discount it for 6 months. The $300 must be discounted for 1 year. Since the unknown payment is at the focal date it simply equals x. Now that everything is at the same point in time, we can set up the equation of value:

$$x = \frac{200}{1 + .05 \times \frac{1}{2}} + \frac{300}{1 + .05 \times 1} = 195.12 + 285.71 = \$480.83$$

EXAMPLE 2: Solve the above problem using 12 months hence as the focal date.

SOLUTION: The $200 must be accumulated for 6 months, the $300 is at the focal date, and the unknown payment must be accumulated for 1 year. This leads to the equation of value:

$$x(1 + .05 \times 1) = 200(1 + .05 \times \tfrac{1}{2}) + 300$$
$$1.05x = 205 + 300 = 505$$
$$x = \frac{505}{1.05} = \$480.95$$

This example shows that in simple interest problems the answer varies slightly with the location of the focal date so that both parties must agree on both the rate and the focal date.

EXAMPLE 3: A man owes $1000 due in 1 year with interest at 6%. He wants to discharge this obligation with two equal payments in 3 and 9 months respectively. What will be the size of these payments if he and the creditor agree to use an interest rate of 6% and a focal date 1 year hence?

SOLUTION: First get the maturity value of the $1000 debt.

$$S = 1000(1 + .06 \times 1) = \$1060$$

No further use will be made of the original debt of $1000. Now make a time diagram, move everything to the focal date, and set up the equation of value.

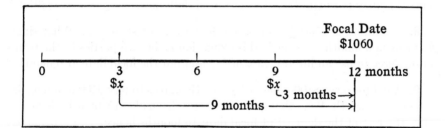

$$x(1 + .06 \times \tfrac{3}{4}) + x(1 + .06 \times \tfrac{1}{4}) = 1060$$
$$1.045x + 1.015x = 1060$$
$$2.06x = 1060$$
$$x = \frac{1060}{2.06} = \$514.56$$

Exercise 1d

1. A man owes $200 due in 4 months and $800 due in 8 months. What single payment 6 months hence will discharge these obligations if the settlement is based on an interest rate of 4% and the focal date is 6 months hence?

($996.03)

2. A man owes $350 due in 3 months and $525 due in 6 months. If money is worth 5%, what single payment in 6 months will settle both obligations. Put the focal date at 6 months.

3. A person owes $200 due in 6 months and $400 due in 1 year. What cash payment will retire both debts if money is worth 5%? Use now as the focal date. ($576.07)

4. Debts of $500 and $1500 are due in 3 and 6 months respectively. What cash settlement will settle these debts if it is based on an interest rate of 6% and the time of the cash settlement is used for the focal date?

5. The Rettig Hardware Co. owes $400 due in 3 months. If money is worth 4%, what equal payments in 2 and 6 months will discharge the debt? Put the focal date 6 months hence. ($200.66)

6. The Valley Hardware Company owes a jobber $625 due in 4 months. If money is worth 5%, what equal payments in 2 and 4 months will settle this debt? Put the focal date at 4 months.

7. A man owes $200 due in 6 months with interest at 6% and $200 due in 1 year without interest. What single payment now will discharge both debts if money is worth 3%? Put the focal date now. ($397.13)

8. A man owes $550 due in 6 months with interest at 6%. What single payment in 3 months will settle this obligation if the two parties to the transaction agree to use an interest rate of 5% and put the focal date at 6 months?

9. A debtor owes $1000 due in 1 year. He agrees to pay $500 in 3 months. If money is worth 4%, what payment must he make 15 months hence to retire the rest of the debt? Put focal date 15 months hence. ($490.00)

10. A man owes $4000. He and his creditor agree that he can pay $2000 now and the balance in 6 months. Find the payment in 6 months if the settlement is based on an interest rate of 4% and the focal date is 6 months hence.

11. On June 1, 1967, a man incurs a debt for $1500 due in 3 months with interest at $4\frac{1}{2}$%. On July 1, 1967, he pays $500 on the debt. What balance will he owe on the original due date if the two parties to the transaction agree to use $4\frac{1}{2}$% in arriving at a settlement? Use the due date as the focal date and approximate time and ordinary interest. ($1013.13)

12. On April 1, 1965, a man buys merchandise and agrees to pay $2000 in 2 months. On May 1, 1965, he pays $800 on the debt. What balance will he owe on the due date if the creditor agrees to use 5% in arriving at a settlement? Use the due date as the focal date and approximate time and ordinary interest.

1.14 Partial Payments

When a person borrows money, it is desirable to have an agreement with his creditor under which he can reduce the interest by making partial payments before the due date. There are two common ways to allow interest credit on short-term transactions: **Merchants' Rule** and **United States Rule.** Under the Merchants' Rule the entire debt earns interest to the final settlement date. Each partial payment also earns interest from the time it is made to the final settlement date. The balance due on the final date is simply the difference between the amount of the debt and the sum of the amounts of the partial payments. Note that this is essentially a focal date problem using the given interest rate and putting the focal date at the final settlement date. Merchants' Rule is used frequently with short-term obligations.

Under the United States Rule the interest on the outstanding principal is computed each time a partial payment is made. If the payment is greater than the interest, the difference is used to reduce the principal. If the payment is less than the interest, it is held without interest until another partial payment is made. The two payments are then added. If they exceed the interest at that time, the difference is used to reduce the principal. The final settlement is the last outstanding principal carried to the final settlement date.

EXAMPLE 1: A debt of $1000 is due in 1 year with interest at 6%. The debtor pays $300 in 4 months and $200 in 10 months. Find the balance due in 1 year using the Merchants' Rule and the United States Rule.

Merchants' Rule

Original debt			$1000.00
Interest on $1000 for 1 year			60.00
			$1060.00
First payment	$300.00		
Interest on $300 for 8 months	12.00		
		$312.00	
Second payment	$200.00		
Interest on $200 for 2 months	2.00		
		$202.00	
Sum of partial payments accumulated to the final settlement date			514.00
Balance due on final settlement date			$ 546.00

United States Rule

Original debt	$1000.00
Interest on $1000 for 4 months	20.00
Amount due after 4 months	$1020.00
Deduct first payment	300.00
New balance due	$ 720.00
Interest on $720 for 6 months	21.60
Amount due after 10 months	$ 741.60
Deduct second payment	200.00
New balance due	$ 541.60
Interest on $541.60 for 2 months	5.42
Balance due on final settlement date	$ 547.02

Note that the two methods lead to different concluding payments. Again we see why the two parties to a business transaction must agree on the method.

EXAMPLE 2: On June 15, 1967, a man borrows $5000 at 5%. He pays $2000 on July 10, 1967, $50 on November 20, 1967, and $1000 on January 12, 1968. What is the balance due on March 10, 1968, by United States Rule?

United States Rule

Debt on June 15, 1967		$5000.00
Interest at 5% on $5000 from		
June 15 to July 10 (25 days)		17.36
Amount due		$5017.36
Payment of $2000 on July 10, 1967		2000.00
Balance as of July 10, 1967		$3017.36
Interest on $3017.36 from July 10 to November 20, 1967 (133 days), is $55.74. Since this is more than the $50 payment on November 20, this payment is held without interest and no deduction is made.		
Interest on $3017.36 from July 10, 1967 to January 12, 1968 (186 days)		77.95
Amount due		$3095.31
Payments: November 20, 1967	$ 50.00	
January 12, 1968	1000.00	1050.00
Balance as of January 12, 1968		$2045.31
Interest on $2045.31 from January 12, 1968, to March 10, 1968 (58 days). Note extra day for leap year.		16.48
Balance due on March 10, 1968		$2061.79

Exercise 1e

(When calendar dates are given and all payments are made on the same day of the month, base interest computations on approximate time and ordinary interest. For example, take the time between June 1 and September 1 as 3 months or $\frac{1}{4}$ year, etc. In all other calendar date problems use Bankers' Rule.)

1. A man borrows $5000 at 5%. He pays $2000 in 2 months and $2000 in 4 months. How much would he have to pay in 6 months to cancel the debt by Merchants' Rule? By U.S. Rule?   ($1075.00, $1075.91)

2. A debt of $7000 is due in 6 months with interest at 4%. Partial payments of $1500 and $2000 are made in 2 and 4 months respectively. What is the balance due on the final settlement date by Merchants' Rule? By U.S. Rule?

3. The Main Hardware Co. was in arrears in their account with the Reliance Supply Corp. to the extent of $1200 on June 1 and were required to pay 8% interest from that date. On July 1 they paid $400 and on August 1 they paid $300. What was the balance due on September 1 by Merchants' Rule? By U.S. Rule?   ($516.67, $516.81)

4. An obligation of $650 is due on April 15, after which the borrower must pay interest at $4\frac{1}{2}$%. If he pays $200 on June 15 and $100 on August 15, how much will he have to pay on October 15 to discharge the obligation if the final settlement is based on Merchants' Rule? On U.S. Rule?

5. A man borrows $3000 at 4% on August 15, 1966. He pays $600 on September 15, 1966; $800 on October 15, 1966; and $600 on December 15, 1966. If he makes a final settlement on February 15, 1967, how much will he have to pay by Merchants' Rule? By U.S. Rule?   ($1035.33; $1035.68)

6. A couple purchased a lot on June 1, for $1200 and paid $500 down. They agree to pay interest on the balance at 5%. If they pay $300 on August 15 and $200 on September 30, how much must they pay on November 1 to own the lot by Merchants' Rule? By U.S. Rule?

7. What is the balance due by Merchants' Rule for Example 2 on page 22?
                                                    ($2060.20)

8. On June 1, 1966, a man borrowed $1000 at 3% for 1 year. If not paid on the due date, the maturity value of the debt was to bear interest at 8% from the due date. The borrower paid $300 on July 15, 1967, $15 on November 20, 1967, and $200 on January 10, 1968. What payment would be required on April 30, 1968, to settle the debt by Merchants' Rule? By U.S. Rule?

1.15   Bank Discount

The charge for many business loans is based on the final amount rather than the principal or present value. This charge is called the **bank discount** or **discount.** The money which the borrower receives is called the **bank proceeds** or **proceeds.** The percent used in computing the discount is called the **bank discount rate** or **discount rate.**

As an illustration of a bank discount transaction, consider the case of a man who wants to borrow $100 for a year from a lender who uses a discount rate of 6%. The lender will take 6% of $100 from the $100 and give the borrower $94. Thus the computation of bank discount is exactly the same as the computation of simple interest except that it is based on the amount rather than the principal. This leads to the bank discount formula:

$$D = Sdt \qquad (4)$$

D = the bank discount in dollars
S = the amount or maturity value
d = the discount rate per unit of time expressed as a decimal
t = the time in units that correspond to the rate

Since the proceeds or present value of the loan is the difference between the amount and the discount, we can say

$$P = S - D$$
$$= S - Sdt$$

Factoring, we have $\qquad P = S(1 - dt) \qquad (5)$

Solving this expression for S results in a formula which is useful when a borrower wants a certain amount of cash and the problem is to determine the size of the loan to be discounted.

$$S = \frac{P}{1 - dt} \qquad (6)$$

EXAMPLE 1: A man borrows $600 for 6 months from a lender who uses a discount rate of 8%. What is the discount and how much money does the borrower get?

SOLUTION: Substituting $S = 600$, $d = .08$ and $t = \frac{1}{2}$ in (4), we have

$$D = 600 \times .08 \times \tfrac{1}{2} = \$24.00$$

Since the proceeds are the difference between the maturity value and the discount, the borrower will get $600.00 - 24.00 = \$576.00$.

EXAMPLE 2: A man wants to get \$2000 cash with the loan to be repaid in 6 months. If he borrows the money from a bank that charges a 6% discount rate, what size loan should he ask for?

SOLUTION: Substituting $P = 2000$, $d = .06$, and $t = \frac{1}{2}$ in (6)

$$S = \frac{2000}{1 - .06 \times \frac{1}{2}} = \frac{2000}{.97} = \$2061.86$$

CHECK: $D = 2061.86 \times .06 \times \frac{1}{2} = \$61.86$
Proceeds $= 2061.86 - 61.86 = \$2000$

Bank discount is sometimes called interest in advance because it is based on the future amount rather than on the principal or present value. Because it requires only multiplication, bank discount is easier to compute than discount at a simple interest rate which requires division. A given bank discount rate results in a larger money return to a lender than the same simple interest rate. For these reasons, the bank discount method is the one commonly used to discount sums of money for periods of time of a year or less.

EXAMPLE 3: Get the present value of \$100 due in 1 year at a simple interest rate of 6%. At a bank discount rate of 6%.

SOLUTION: For a simple interest rate of 6% we substitute $S = 100$, $r = .06$ and $t = 1$ in (3):

$$P = \frac{100}{1 + .06 \times 1} = \frac{100}{1.06} = \$94.34$$

For a bank-discount rate of 6% we substitute $S = 100$, $d = .06$ and $t = 1$ in (4):

$$D = 100 \times .06 \times 1 = \$6.00$$

Present value or proceeds $= 100 - 6.00 = \$94.00$

Note that the present value at 6% bank discount is 34 cents less for the same maturity value than if the present value were based on a 6% interest rate.

1.16   Interest Rate Equivalent to a Bank Discount Rate

As the previous example shows, the present value at a given discount rate is less than the present value based on the same interest rate. For comparison purposes, it is desirable to be able to determine the interest rate which is equivalent to a given discount rate. This is the case if the discount rate and the interest rate both result in the same present value for an amount due in the future. To get the relationship between r and d, all we have to do is get the present value of an amount S due in the future by Formula (3) and set it equal to the present value of the same amount S by Formula (5).

$$\frac{S}{1 + rt} = S(1 - dt)$$

Dividing both sides by S,
$$\frac{1}{1 + rt} = 1 - dt$$

Inverting both sides,
$$1 + rt = \frac{1}{1 - dt}$$

Subtracting 1 from both sides and simplifying,

$$rt = \frac{1}{1 - dt} - 1 = \frac{1 - 1 + dt}{1 - dt} = \frac{dt}{1 - dt}$$

Dividing both sides by t,
$$r = \frac{d}{1 - dt} \tag{7}$$

In a similar way we find that the discount rate corresponding to a given interest rate is

$$d = \frac{r}{1 + rt} \tag{8}$$

EXAMPLE 1: A bank discounts a $200 note due in a year using a bank discount rate of 6%. What interest rate are they getting?

SOLUTION: Substituting $d = .06$ and $t = 1$ in (7),

$$r = \frac{.06}{1 - .06 \times 1} = \frac{.06}{.94} = .0638 \text{ or } 6.38\%$$

EXAMPLE 2: A lender charges a discount rate of $7\frac{1}{2}\%$ for discounting a note for $600 due in 2 months. What is the equivalent interest rate?

SOLUTION: Substituting $d = .075$, and $t = \frac{1}{6}$ in (7),

$$r = \frac{.075}{1 - .075 \times \frac{1}{6}} = \frac{.075}{.9875} = .0759 = 7.59\%$$

EXAMPLE 3: To earn an interest rate of 6% on a 6 months' loan, a lender should charge what discount rate?

SOLUTION: Substituting $r = .06$ and $t = \frac{1}{2}$ in (8),

$$d = \frac{.06}{1 + .06 \times \frac{1}{2}} = \frac{.06}{1.03} = .0583 = 5.83\%$$

To avoid division we could use the reciprocal of 1.03.

$$d = .06 \times .9709 = .05825 = 5.83\%$$

Exercise 1f

1. Get the bank discount and the proceeds if $1500 are discounted for 3 months at a discount rate of 6%.　　　　　　　($22.50, $1477.50)

2. Get the bank discount and the proceeds if $4400 are discounted at a discount rate of 8% for 2 months.

3. Get the discount on $3200 for 60 days at $4\frac{1}{2}\%$ discount. What are the proceeds?　　　　　　　($24.00, $3176.00)

4. Get the discount on $568.30 for 120 days at $3\frac{1}{2}\%$ discount. What are the proceeds?

5. Find the bank discount and the present value of $5000 due in 5 months using a discount rate of 5%.　　　　　　　($104.17, $4895.83)

6. An obligation of $6040 is due in 10 months. What is the present value of this obligation at a bank discount rate of $4\frac{1}{4}\%$?

7. A bank charges 6% for discounting loans. If a man agrees to repay $1200 in 3 months, how much does he receive now?　　　　　　　($1182.00)

8. An obligation of $650 is due on August 10. What is its value on April 6 if it is discounted at a discount rate of $3\frac{1}{2}\%$?

9. Find the bank discount and the proceeds if $450 are discounted for 30 days at 6%.　　　　　　　($2.25, $447.75)

10. Find the bank discount and the proceeds if $250,000 are discounted for 60 days at 4%.

11. A man wants $5000 for 3 months. What size loan should he get if his bank charges a discount rate of 5%?　　　　　　　($5063.29)

12. A man wants $800 for 6 months. What size loan should he ask for if his bank charges a discount rate of $4\frac{1}{2}\%$?

13. George Wilson needs $800 on February 10. He plans to repay the money on June 30. What size loan should he request if his bank's discount rate is 6%? ($819.11)

14. A borrower needs $4000 on June 1. He expects to repay the loan on July 16. What size loan should he request from a lender whose discount rate is 6%?

15. A bank discounts a sum which is due in 1 year. If the discount rate is 8%, what is the equivalent interest rate? (8.70%)

16. If a sum is due in 90 days, what is the interest rate equivalent to a discount rate of 6%?

17. If a sum is due in 6 months, what is the interest rate equivalent to a discount rate of 5%? (5.13%)

18. If a sum is due in 1 month, what is the interest rate equivalent to a discount rate of 5%?

19. A lender wants to get an 8% interest rate on a loan which he is making for 6 months. What discount rate should he use? (7.69%)

20. To get 7% interest on 120-day loans, a lender should charge what discount rate?

1.17 Promissory Notes, Drafts, and Trade Acceptances

When a person borrows money, he may be required to sign a **note** promising to make payment at some specified time in the future. While various forms are used for notes, the following is a typical example of the commercial forms in use today.

A Promissory Note

The expressions used when dealing with notes are defined below and illustrated with the note shown.

Expression	*Example*
Face value is the amount loaned or borrowed. This is usually given in figures and in words.	$600.00
Date is the date the note is made.	June 1, 1966
Term is the time from the date of the note to the maturity or due date.	Sixty days
Rate is the per cent at which interest is to be calculated. Unless stated otherwise, this is understood to be an annual rate. Notes may be non-interest-bearing.	5%
Payee is the person or firm to whom the note is due.	William Rettig
Maker is the person or firm executing the note. The one who owes the money.	Robert Boster
Maturity date is the date the note is due. This is calculated from the date and term of the note.	July 31, 1966
Maturity value is the face value plus interest if any. If no interest rate is given in a note, it is non-interest-bearing and the maturity value equals the face value. This does not necessarily mean that the original debt did not bear interest. It merely means that the interest, if any, has been added to the principal and the note has been drawn for the maturity of the debt.	$605.00

As an illustration of the way notes are used in business, let us consider what Mr. Rettig might do with the above note. If he does not need cash, he will probably hold the note until its maturity date when Mr. Boster will pay him the $600 plus interest for 60 days at 5%.

If Mr. Rettig needs cash before the due date, and if his standing with his bank is good, he can get the note discounted. Suppose that he takes this note to his bank on June 26. The bank determines that the note will have a maturity value of $605 on July 31, 1966.

The time between June 26, the day the note is discounted, and July 31, the day it matures, is 35 days. If, in this case, the bank discount rate is 6% the charge for discounting the note from Formula (4) would be

$$D = 605 \times .06 \times \tfrac{35}{360} = \$3.53$$

Therefore the proceeds are $605.00 − 3.53 = $601.47. What the bank has done is loan Mr. Rettig $601.47. They will get their money back with interest when they collect $605 from Mr. Boster on July 31. All that remains is for Mr. Rettig to endorse the note on the back to acknowledge payment and to guarantee that he will reimburse the bank if Mr. Boster fails to pay the bank.

When working note problems students should remember that:

(1) Interest, if the note is interest-bearing, is based on the face value of the note, the interest rate stated in the note, and the time from the day the note is made to the maturity date.

(2) The discount is based on the maturity value of the note, the discount rate specified by the lender, and the time from the day the note is discounted to the maturity date.

If a student has trouble getting the times correct in note problems, a time diagram is helpful. The sketch shows how a diagram could be made for the preceding problem.

```
Face Value ──────── Add interest for ───────→ Maturity Value
                    60 days at 5%
  $600.00                                          $605.00
    └──────────────────┴────────────────────────────┘
   June 1             June 26                      July 31
              Proceeds ←──── Subtract discount ────┘
              $601.47        for 35 days at 6%
```

A *draft* is a written order by a first party (drawer) directing a second party (drawee) to make a certain payment to a third party (payee). There are three parties to a draft, but only two persons may be involved. Thus the drawer may make himself the payee. The drawee becomes liable after he writes "accepted" on the draft and signs it.

A sight draft is payable on presentation of the draft and the payee receives the face value of the draft. An aftersight draft is payable a stated time after acceptance. Since this determines the maturity date, the drawee writes the date of acceptance when he signs the draft. An after-date draft is payable a stated time after the date of the draft so the date of acceptance need not be shown. After-date and after-sight drafts are due in the future and may be sold or discounted.

A *trade acceptance* is a draft that arises from the sale of merchandise. The seller draws a trade acceptance on the purchaser who is ordered to make payment to a third party who may be the seller or his bank.

EXAMPLE 1: On December 10, 1965, Thomas Willer discounts the note shown at a bank which charges a discount rate of 6%. How much does he receive?

A Non-interest-bearing Note

$ 1530.00 _____   November 1 _____ 19 65

Ninety days ____ *after date* I ___ *promise to pay to*

the order of Thomas Willer _____

Fifteen hundred and thirty and no/100 - - - - - *Dollars*

Payable at Miami, Florida _____

Value received

No. 75 ____ *Due* January 30, 1966   *J. N. Wilson*

SOLUTION: In this case the maturity value of the note equals the face value given in the note. Since the time is given in days, use exact time to get the maturity date. Ninety days after November 1, 1965, is January 30, 1966. Now we determine the exact time from the day of discount, December 10, 1965, to the maturity date. This is 51 days. Substituting $S = 1530$, $d = .06$ and $t = \frac{51}{360}$ in (4),

$$D = 1530 \times .06 \times \tfrac{51}{360} = \$13.01$$

Therefore Mr. Willer gets $1530.00 - 13.01 = \$1516.99$

EXAMPLE 2: On August 10, 1965, John A Blalock discounts the note shown at a bank which charges a discount rate of 5%. How much does he receive?

An Interest-bearing Note

$ 3000.00 _____   June 1 _____ 19 65

Six months _____ *after date* I ___ *promise to pay to*

the order of John A. Blalock _____

Three thousand and no/100 - - - - - - - - - - *Dollars*

Payable at Albany, New York _____

Value received with interest at 4%

No. 11 ____ *Due* December 1, 1965   *C. M. Moose*

SOLUTION: First we get the maturity value, substituting $P = 3000$, $r = .04$ and $t = \frac{1}{2}$ in (1),

$$I = 3000 \times .04 \times \tfrac{1}{2} = \$60.00$$
$$S = 3000.00 + 60.00 = \$3060.00$$

This note matures on December 1, 1965. The exact time from August 10 to December 1 is 113 days. Substituting $S = \$3060$, $d = .05$ and $t = \frac{113}{360}$ in (4),

$$D = 3060 \times .05 \times \tfrac{113}{360} = \$48.03$$
$$\text{Proceeds} = 3060.00 - 48.03 = \$3011.97$$

EXAMPLE 3: In some cases the problem is to determine the maturity value of a note which will result in the desired proceeds. A merchant receives $1000 worth of goods with terms 2/10, n/60. To take advantage of the 2% discount for paying on or before the 10th day, he decides to borrow the money from a lender charging a discount rate of 8%. For what amount should a 50-day non-interest-bearing note be made to provide proceeds of $980?

SOLUTION: Substituting $P = 980$, $d = .08$ and $t = 50/360$ in (6),

$$S = \frac{980}{1 - .08 \times \frac{50}{360}} = \frac{980}{1 - \frac{1}{90}} = \frac{90 \times 980}{90 - 1} = \$991.01$$

Check: $D = 991.01 \times .08 \times \frac{50}{360} = \$11.01$

$$\text{Proceeds} = 991.01 - 11.01 = \$980.00$$

Borrowing money at a discount rate of 8% results in a net savings of $8.99 as of the final due date. It usually pays to take advantage of cash discounts even if it means borrowing to get the cash.

Exercise 1g

(If the time in a note is given in months, the due date is the same date of the month as the date of the note. A three months' note dated March 1 would be due on June 1. If the time is given in days use exact time when getting the maturity date. When getting the discount, use exact time from the discount date to the due date and a 360-day year.)

1. On August 5, 1966, A. E. Spraul discounts the note (top of page 33) at a bank which charges a discount rate of 6%. What are the proceeds? ($753.10)

2. What are the proceeds if Mr. Spraul discounts the note in Problem 1 on July 1, 1966, at a bank charging a discount rate of 6%?

```
$ 750.00 _____                    _____ July 1,  19 1966
  Sixty days _____ after date  I  promise to pay to
the order of A. E. Spraul _____
  Seven hundred and fifty and no/100 - - - - - - Dollars
Payable at Denver, Colorado _____
Value received with interest at 5%
No. 110   Due August 30, 1966   R. D. Fellinger
```

3. On February 1, 1965, John P. Foley discounts the note below at a bank which charges a discount rate of 6%. How much does he get?   ($7962.67)

```
$ 8000.00 _____                  _____ January 15  19 65
  Forty-five days  after date  I  promise to pay to
the order of  John P. Foley _____
  Eight thousand and no/100 - - - - - - - - - - Dollars
Payable at Austin, Texas _____
Value received
No. 6   Due March 1, 1965       D. D. Clack
```

4. What are the proceeds if Mr. Foley discounts the note in Problem 3 on February 15, 1965, at a bank charging a discount rate of $5\frac{1}{2}$%?

5. On December 20, 1966, F. A. Collins discounts the note below at a bank which charges a discount rate of 5%. How much does he receive?   ($3033.28)

```
$ 3000.00 _____                  _____ October 1  19 66
  Ninety days  after date  I  promise to pay to
the order of F. A. Collins _____
  Three thousand and no/100 - - - - - - - - - Dollars
Payable at  Frankfort, Kentucky _____
Value received with interest at 5%
No. 8   Due December 30, 1966   John F. Kelley
U.S. Bond
```

6. What are the proceeds if Mr. Collins discounts the note in Problem 5 on October 15, 1966, at a bank charging a discount rate of 5%?

7. The Gibson Hardware Co. has a note for $1200 dated November 15, 1967. The note is due in 6 months with interest at 5%. If the Gibson Co. discounts the note on January 30, 1968, at a bank charging a discount rate of 6%, what will be the proceeds?   ($1208.27)

8. A merchant receives a note for $1245.40 which is due in 60 days with interest at $4\frac{1}{2}$%. He discounts it immediately at a bank which charges 5% discount. What are the proceeds?

9. A company holds the following non-interest-bearing notes. They are all taken to the bank on August 14, 1964, and the proceeds deposited to the company's account. Get the total proceeds if the discount rate is 6%.

($5777.33)

Date of Note	Term	Face Value
July 15, 1964	90 days	$1000
Aug. 14, 1964	45 days	800
June 25, 1964	60 days	4000

10. A company holds the following non-interest-bearing notes. They were taken to the bank on November 5, 1965, and the proceeds deposited to the company's account. Get the total proceeds if the discount rate is 6%.

Date of Note	Term	Face Value
Sept. 6, 1965	90 days	$2000
Oct. 16, 1965	60 days	2500
Oct. 12, 1965	30 days	4800

11. A company holds the following interest-bearing notes. They were discounted at 6% on June 1, 1964. Find the total proceeds.   ($3013.18)

Date of Note	Term	Face Value	Rate
April 2, 1964	90 days	$2000	5%
June 1, 1964	30 days	1000	4%

12. A company holds the following interest-bearing notes. They were discounted at 6% on July 15, 1963. Find the total proceeds.

Date of Note	Term	Face Value	Rate
May 16, 1963	120 days	$4200	5%
June 10, 1963	45 days	6000	4%

13. A man buys merchandise costing $340. He wants to give a 30-day non-interest-bearing note which, if his creditor discounts it immediately at 4%, will result in proceeds of $340. For what amount should he make the note?   ($341.14)

14. The owner of a store needs $500 cash for a business transaction. He arranges to get the money from a bank which charges a discount rate of 4%. If the note is for 90 days, it should have what face value if the proceeds are to be $500?

15. On April 10, a man obtains a loan from his bank to be repaid on June 29. If the bank's discount rate is 5%, what must be the face value of a non-interest-bearing note which will have proceeds of $860?   ($869.66)

16. On July 10 a man needs $2350 which he plans to repay on September 18. He gets the loan from a bank which has a bank discount rate of 4%. What will be the face value of the non-interest-bearing note which he signs?

17. On June 1, Fanger and Rampke buy merchandise amounting to $3000. If they pay cash they will get a 2% cash discount. To take advantage of this cash discount, they sign a 60-day non-interest-bearing note at their bank which charges a discount rate of 6%. What should be the face value of this note to give them the exact amount they need to pay cash for the merchandise?
          ($2969.70)

18. The Economy Appliance store buys merchandise totaling $4560. A 3% discount will be allowed for cash payment. They get the cash by signing a 30-day non-interest-bearing note at a bank which charges a discount rate of 4%. Get the face value of the note.

2

COMPOUND INTEREST
AND DISCOUNT

2.1 Compound Interest

An investment of $1000 at 4% simple interest earns $40 per year. In three years the simple interest would amount to $120. However, if the interest as it is earned is added to the principal and this new principal draws interest, the investment increases more rapidly than with simple interest. Interest paid on an increasing principal in this way, is known as **compound interest.** The following example shows the increase in an investment of $1000 if the interest rate is 4% compounded annually.

Original principal	$1000.00
Interest for first year at 4%	40.00
Principal at the start of the second year	1040.00
Interest for second year at 4%	41.60
Principal at the start of the third year	1081.60
Interest for third year at 4%	43.26
Amount at the end of three years	$1124.86

Thus, the compound interest earned on the original investment is $124.86 as compared to the $120.00 which would be earned at simple interest in the same length of time. The difference of $4.86 is interest earned on interest. The total, $1124.86, is called the **compound amount.**

From now on compound interest is used in all problems in this book except when the time is a single period or a part of a period.

Note that compound interest is simply a repeated application of simple interest. If a long time is involved, say two or three hundred interest payments, the computations using the above system would be very laborious. Fortunately it is easy to develop a formula that gives the final amount without the intermediate computations.

2.2 Compound Amount Formula

In the preceding example the interest was computed and added to the principal every year. In many business transactions the interest is computed annually, semiannually, quarterly, monthly, or at some other time interval. The time between successive interest computations is called the **conversion** or **interest period.** This is the basic unit of time in all compound interest problems. The important rate is the **interest rate per conversion period** which is designated by the symbol i. The symbol for the total number of conversion periods is n.

In most business transactions the practice is to quote an annual interest rate and the frequency of conversion. From this information the rate per period is determined. Thus 6% compounded semiannually means that 3% interest will be earned every six months. The quoted annual rate is called the **nominal rate** and is indicated by the symbol j. The number of conversion periods per year is indicated by the symbol m. The equation relating m, j and i is $j = mi$ or $i = j/m$. When no conversion period is stated in a problem, assume that the interest is compounded annually.

The following table shows a few examples of quoted or nominal rates and the corresponding conversion periods per year and rate per period.

Quoted or Nominal Rate	Conversion Periods per Year	Rate per Period $i = j/m$	
j	m	Per Cent	Decimal
6% compounded annually	1	6	.06
6% compounded semiannually	2	3	.03
6% compounded quarterly	4	$1\frac{1}{2}$	.015
6% compounded monthly	12	$\frac{1}{2}$	.005
3% compounded quarterly	4	$\frac{3}{4}$	.0075
5% compounded semiannually	2	$2\frac{1}{2}$	.025
5% compounded monthly	12	$\frac{5}{12}$	.004167

To eliminate the tedious period-by-period computations used in the example at the beginning of this chapter, we invest P dollars for n periods at a rate of i per period and derive a formula for the final amount. Because many students find it difficult to follow a derivation in terms of symbols alone, a numerical example is used to illustrate the steps. In this example $P = \$1000$, $i = .04$ and $n = 2$. The principal at the end of the first period will be indicated by P_1; at the end of the second period by P_2; and so on.

Original principal	P	$1000
Interest	Pi	$1000 \times .04$
P_1	$P + Pi = P(1 + i)$	$1000 + 1000 \times .04 = 1000(1.04)$
Interest	$P(1 + i)i$	$1000(1.04).04$
P_2	$P(1 + i) + P(1 + i)i$	$1000(1.04) + 1000(1.04).04$
	$= P(1 + i)(1 + i)$	$1000(1.04)(1.04)$
	$= P(1 + i)^2$	$= 1000(1.04)^2$

It is evident that as we continue the problem each new principal will be $(1 + i)$ times the preceding value. At the end of n periods the final amount, for which the symbol is S, would equal the original principal times $(1 + i)^n$. This gives us the basic formula for compound interest,

$$S = P(1 + i)^n \tag{9}$$

$S =$ the amount at compound interest
$P =$ the principal
$i =$ the rate per conversion period
$n =$ the number of conversion periods

The factor $(1 + i)^n$ is called the **accumulation factor** or **Amount of 1**. It is sometimes designated by the symbol s. The numerical value of $(1 + i)^n$ can be computed by successive multiplication, by logarithms, or by the binomial theorem. In practical business usage it is usually obtained from previously computed tables. In this book values of $(1 + i)^n$ for common interest rates will be found in the *Amount of* 1 column of Table 2. The columns of data in Table 2 have descriptive headings which tell what the various columns are in a few simple words. At the bottom of each column of data, symbols are given to help the student select the correct factor for a particular problem.

The usefulness of Table 2 is easily appreciated when we consider how much time it saves. Carrying a sum of money forward by getting the simple interest for each period and adding to the principal means two arithmetic operations for each period. This means a lot of work, and many chances to make mistakes if many periods are involved. Table 2 makes it possible to carry money forward 20, 30, or more periods just as easily as making one simple interest computation. The example on the next page shows how to get the correct factor from Table 2.

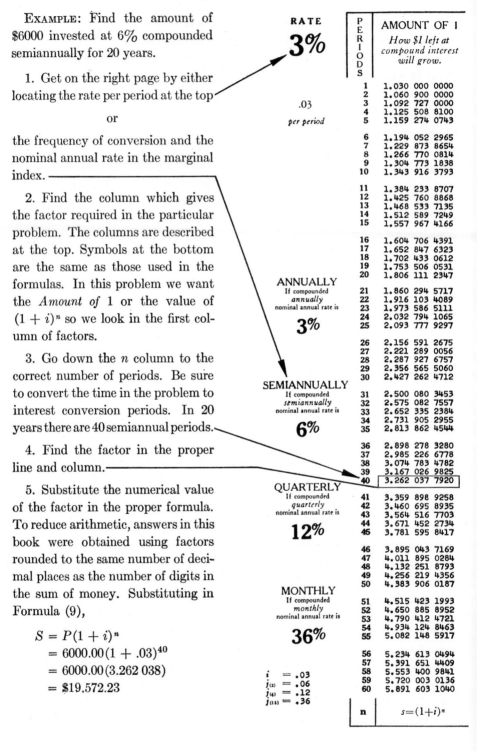

EXAMPLE: Find the amount of $6000 invested at 6% compounded semiannually for 20 years.

1. Get on the right page by either locating the rate per period at the top

or

the frequency of conversion and the nominal annual rate in the marginal index. ───

2. Find the column which gives the factor required in the particular problem. The columns are described at the top. Symbols at the bottom are the same as those used in the formulas. In this problem we want the *Amount of* 1 or the value of $(1 + i)^n$ so we look in the first column of factors.

3. Go down the n column to the correct number of periods. Be sure to convert the time in the problem to interest conversion periods. In 20 years there are 40 semiannual periods.

4. Find the factor in the proper line and column. ───

5. Substitute the numerical value of the factor in the proper formula. To reduce arithmetic, answers in this book were obtained using factors rounded to the same number of decimal places as the number of digits in the sum of money. Substituting in Formula (9),

$$S = P(1 + i)^n$$
$$= 6000.00(1 + .03)^{40}$$
$$= 6000.00(3.262\ 038)$$
$$= \$19,572.23$$

RATE	PERIODS	AMOUNT OF 1
3%		*How $1 left at compound interest will grow.*
.03 *per period*	1	1.030 000 0000
	2	1.060 900 0000
	3	1.092 727 0000
	4	1.125 508 8100
	5	1.159 274 0743
	6	1.194 052 2965
	7	1.229 873 8654
	8	1.266 770 0814
	9	1.304 773 1838
	10	1.343 916 3793
	11	1.384 233 8707
	12	1.425 760 8868
	13	1.468 533 7135
	14	1.512 589 7249
	15	1.557 967 4166
	16	1.604 706 4391
	17	1.652 847 6323
	18	1.702 433 0612
	19	1.753 506 0531
ANNUALLY *If compounded annually nominal annual rate is* **3%**	20	1.806 111 2347
	21	1.860 294 5717
	22	1.916 103 4089
	23	1.973 586 5111
	24	2.032 794 1065
	25	2.093 777 9297
	26	2.156 591 2675
	27	2.221 289 0056
	28	2.287 927 6757
	29	2.356 565 5060
SEMIANNUALLY *If compounded semiannually nominal annual rate is* **6%**	30	2.427 262 4712
	31	2.500 080 3453
	32	2.575 082 7557
	33	2.652 335 2384
	34	2.731 905 2955
	35	2.813 862 4544
	36	2.898 278 3280
	37	2.985 226 6778
	38	3.074 783 4782
	39	3.167 026 9825
	40	3.262 037 7920
QUARTERLY *If compounded quarterly nominal annual rate is* **12%**	41	3.359 898 9258
	42	3.460 695 8935
	43	3.564 516 7703
	44	3.671 452 2734
	45	3.781 595 8417
	46	3.895 043 7169
	47	4.011 895 0284
	48	4.132 251 8793
	49	4.256 219 4356
MONTHLY *If compounded monthly nominal annual rate is* **36%**	50	4.383 906 0187
	51	4.515 423 1993
	52	4.650 885 8952
	53	4.790 412 4721
	54	4.934 124 8463
	55	5.082 148 5917
$i = .03$ $j_{(2)} = .06$ $j_{(4)} = .12$ $j_{(12)} = .36$	56	5.234 613 0494
	57	5.391 651 4409
	58	5.553 400 9841
	59	5.720 003 0136
	60	5.891 603 1040
	n	$s = (1+i)^n$

2.3 How Many Places?

The factors in Table 2 are given to 10 decimal places making them adequate for handling large sums of money. In the examples worked in the tables published by the Financial Publishing Company, the complete factor is used and the answer is rounded to the cent. If a calculator is available, as it usually is in a business, this is the sensible way to work a problem as it insures maximum accuracy without any troublesome questions about the number of decimal places to use to get answers correct to the nearest cent.

Since most students have to do calculations manually, we use simple sums in most problems to minimize routine arithmetic. To further conserve the student's time, we give answers which were obtained by rounding the factors to the same number of decimal places as there are digits in the sum of money given in the problem *including the cents*. Thus a principal of $25,000 would mean rounding the factor to 7 decimal places, while 4 places would be used for a principal of $25. This usually gives an answer that is the same as or within a penny or two of what would be obtained using the entire factor.

EXAMPLE 1: Find the compound amounts of $25, $2500, and $2,500,000 invested at 6% converted quarterly for 5 years.

SOLUTION:

$$25(1.015)^{20} = 25 \times 1.3469 = \$33.67$$
$$2500(1.015)^{20} = 2500 \times 1.346\ 855 = \$3367.14$$
$$2{,}500{,}000(1.015)^{20} = 2{,}500{,}000 \times 1.346\ 855\ 007 = \$3{,}367{,}137.52$$

EXAMPLE 2: A principal of $1000 is deposited at 4% for 10 years. How much will the depositor have to his credit and what will be the compound amount if the interest was compounded annually, semiannually, quarterly, monthly?

SOLUTION: The required factors and final results are summarized below.

Frequency of Compounding	Rate per Period i	Number of Conversion Periods n	Amount of 1 $(1+i)^n$	Compound Amount S	Compound Interest $S-1000$
Annually	.04	10	1.480 244	$1480.24	$480.24
Semiannually	.02	20	1.485 947	1485.95	485.95
Quarterly	.01	40	1.488 864	1488.86	488.86
Monthly	.00333	120	1.490 833	1490.83	490.83

As the frequency of conversion is increased, interest is added to principal more often, so the depositor has a larger amount to his credit.

EXAMPLE 3: A depositor planned to leave $2000 in a building and loan paying $4\frac{1}{2}\%$ compounded semiannually for a period of 5 years. However, at the end of $2\frac{1}{2}$ years he had to withdraw $1000. What will he have in his account at the end of the original 5-year period?

SOLUTION: We first get the amount in his account at the end of $2\frac{1}{2}$ years.

$$S = 2000(1.0225)^5 = 2000 \times 1.117\ 678 = \$2235.36$$

After withdrawing $1000, he has a remainder of $1235.36. During the remainder of the 5 years this will grow to,

$$S = 1235.36(1.0225)^5 = 1235.36 \times 1.117\ 678 = \$1380.73$$

ALTERNATE SOLUTION: We could draw a time diagram, select a focal date, and solve using an equation of value.

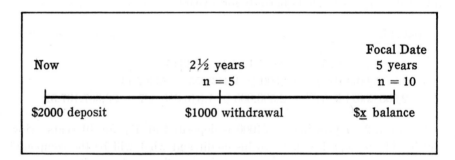

Carrying everything to the focal date,

$$
\begin{aligned}
x &= 2000(1.0225)^{10} - 1000(1.0225)^5 \\
&= 2000 \times 1.249\ 203 - 1000 \times 1.117\ 678 \\
&= 2498.41 - 1117.68 = \$1380.73
\end{aligned}
$$

In compound interest problems, the answer does not depend on the location of the focal date. By a skillful selection of focal date, a student can work problems and check results with a minimum of work.

2.4 Law of Organic Growth

The compound interest law is often called the *law of organic growth*. It can be applied to anything that is changing at a constant rate. There are many situations in nature, science and business where the compound interest law is useful, provided good judgment is used in applying it. The investigator must be careful about extending past rates into the future. If something has been increasing at approximately a constant rate for several years, that rate can be useful for getting predicted values for the next few years. The same rate might lead to absurd long-term predictions. Rates determined under one set of conditions may not apply in another situation. Rats and bugs may increase at certain rates in the laboratory where they are protected from their natural enemies. But there is no justification for applying these rates to the usual environment with its cats, birds and other limiting factors.

EXAMPLE 1: During the period 1950–1960, the population of a city increased at a rate of about 3% a year. If the population in 1960 was 300,000, what is the predicted population in 1970?

SOLUTION: Substituting $P = 300,000$, $i = .03$ and $n = 10$ in (9),

$$S = 300,000(1.03)^{10} = 300,000 \times 1.343\ 916 = 403,175$$

In dealing with approximate data, the prediction should usually be rounded off to a reasonable value such as 403,000.

EXAMPLE 2: During the period 1957–1962, the net income per share of Sears Roebuck common stock increased about 7% a year. The net income in 1962 was $3.08 per share. Assuming that the same rate of increase continues, predict the net income per share for 1965.

SOLUTION: Substituting $P = 3.08$, $i = .07$, and $n = 3$ in (9),

$$S = 3.08(1.07)^3 = 3.08 \times 1.225 = \$3.77$$

EXAMPLE 3: During the period 1950–1960, the population of a city increased 8%. If the population was 500,000 in 1960, what is the estimated population for 1980 assuming that the same rate of growth continues?

SOLUTION: The conversion period is the basic unit of time in compound interest problems. In financial problems, this is usually 1 year or less. In organic problems it may be many years or it may be a few seconds or less. In this problem it is a decade, so for 20 years, $n = 2$. Substituting in (9),

$$S = 500,000(1.08)^2 = 500,000 \times 1.166\ 400 = 583,200$$

Exercise 2a

1. Fill in the conversion periods per year and the rate per period columns.

Quoted or Nominal Rate j	Conversion Periods per Year m	Rate per Period i	
		Per Cent	Decimal
4%			
4% compounded semiannually			
4% compounded monthly			
5% compounded monthly			
$3\frac{1}{2}$% compounded semiannually			
$1\frac{3}{4}$% compounded semiannually			

2. What is the compound amount and the compound interest if $100 is invested at 6% for 20 years?

3. Find the compound amount and the compound interest if $1000 is invested for 10 years at 2%. ($1218.99; $218.99)

4. Find the compound amount and the compound interest if $24,500 is borrowed for 3 years at 5% converted monthly.

5. The day a boy was born, his father invested $200 at $3\frac{1}{2}$% compounded semiannually. Find the value of the fund on the boy's 18th birthday.

($373.48)

6. On a girl's 8th birthday her parents placed $250 in her name in an investment paying $3\frac{1}{2}$% compounded semiannually. How much will she have to her credit on her 21st birthday?

7. A town increased in population 2% a year during the period 1950 to 1960. If the population was 18,000 in 1960, what is the estimated population to the nearest hundred for 1970, assuming that the rate of growth remains the same? (21,900)

8. The sales of a business have been increasing at the rate of 3% a year. If the sales in 1965 are $250,000, what are the estimated sales to the nearest thousand dollars for 1970?

9. Find the amount of $6000 for 8 years at 4% nominal, compounded: (a) annually; (b) semiannually; (c) quarterly; (d) monthly.
[(a) $8211.41; (b) $8236.72; (c) $8249.65; (d) $8258.37]

10. Find the amount of $10,000 for 10 years at 6% compounded: (a) annually; (b) semiannually; (c) quarterly; (d) monthly.

11. On June 1, 1965, a man borrows $1200 at 8% compounded semiannually. How much must he repay on December 1, 1968? ($1579.12)

12. A man borrows $560 on September 15, 1966. If he pays interest at 6% converted monthly, how much must he repay on June 15, 1969?

13. What amount of money will be required to repay a loan of $6000 on December 31, 1970, if the loan was made on December 31, 1964, at a rate of 5% compounded semiannually?   ($8069.33)

14. On June 1, 1959, a man incurred a debt of $3000 which was to be repaid on demand of the lender with interest at 3% converted semiannually. If the lender demanded payment on December 1, 1967, how much would he receive?

15. On June 30, 1959, a man deposited $850 in a building and loan paying $4\frac{1}{2}$% compounded semiannually. How much will he get if he draws out his money on June 30, 1966?   ($1160.66)

16. What amount of money will be required to repay a loan of $1835.50 on July 1, 1969, if the loan was made on October 1, 1965, at an interest rate of 5% compounded quarterly?

17. A person put $2500 in a savings and loan association paying 4% converted quarterly. He planned to leave the money there 6 years and then use it for a trip. At the end of 2 years he had to withdraw $500. What was the amount in his account at the end of the original 6-year period?   ($2588.05)

18. What would be the answer to Problem 17 if the $500 withdrawal was made at the end of 4 years?

19. On July 1, 1965, a man put $5000 in a savings and loan association paying 4% converted semiannually. On January 2, 1967, he withdrew $2500 from his account. What was the balance in his account on January 2, 1970?   ($3160.06)

20. Interest dates for a bank are May 1 and November 1. Interest on savings accounts is 3% converted semiannually. A depositor opens an account on May 1, 1964, with a deposit of $1500. He withdraws $500 on November 1, 1965, and deposits $1000 on May 1, 1967. What is the balance in his account on May 1, 1968?

21. The compound interest tables can be used to solve problems involving the currencies of other nations. A man in London borrows 1000 pounds at 5% converted semiannually for 5 years. Find the amount of this obligation. One pound = 20 shillings; 1 shilling = 12 pence.
                                    (1280 pounds, 1 shilling, 8 pence)

22. Find the amount of a loan of 2500 pounds for 4 years at 4% converted quarterly.

23. The annual earnings per share of Potomac Electric Power have been increasing at about 4% a year. If the earnings in 1962 were $1.04, the same rate of increase would result in what predicted earnings for 1967?   ($1.27)

24. The annual earnings per share of Southern Indiana Gas and Electric Company have been increasing at about 5% a year. If the earnings in 1962 were $3.03 a share, the same rate of increase would result in what predicted earnings for 1967?

2.5   Effective Interest Rate

The same nominal interest rate will result in different amounts of interest depending on the number of conversions per year. To put different rates and conversion periods on a comparable basis, we determine the **effective rate, r.** The number of conversion periods per year is indicated by the symbol m. The effective rate is the rate converted annually that will produce the same amount of interest per year as the nominal rate converted m times per year. We use the compound interest formula to determine the effective rate equivalent to a given nominal rate and number of conversions per year.

If the nominal rate is 6% converted annually, the effective rate will also be 6%. But if the nominal rate is 6% converted semiannually, the amount of $1 at the end of one year will be $(1.03)^2 = \$1.0609$. This is simply the accumulation factor for a rate per period of 3% and two periods. The interest on $1 for one year is then $\$1.0609 - 1.0000 = \$.0609$. This is equivalent to an annual rate of 6.09%. Thus 6.09% converted annually would result in the same amount of interest as 6% converted semiannually. The computations used to get the effective rate of 6.09% in this case can be summarized as follows:

$$1.0609 = (1.03)^2$$

$$r = 1.0609 - 1 = .0609$$

Putting the above relationship in the form of a general equation, we have

$$1 + r = (1 + i)^m$$
$$r = (1 + i)^m - 1 \tag{10}$$

Using the above formula, a nominal rate of 6% with various conversions per year results in the following effective rates:

Conversion periods or m	1	2	4	12	52	365
Effective rate in per cent	6	6.09	6.136	6.168	6.180	6.183

Notice that the increases in the effective rate are not large as we get to weekly and daily compounding. It can be shown by more advanced mathematics that even if the interest is compounded continuously, the limiting effective rate is 6.18365%.

Because three rates are used in compound interest work, it is well at this point to summarize the meaning of each.

The nominal rate (symbol j) is the quoted or stated rate. If interest is to be converted other than annually, the conversion period is specified when the nominal rate is given.

The rate per period (symbol i) equals the nominal rate divided by the number of conversion periods per year (j/m). The rate per period is the value used when getting factors from the compound interest tables.

The effective rate (symbol r) is the rate actually earned in a year. It is used to get different nominal rates and conversion periods on a common basis for comparison purposes.

EXAMPLE: Find the effective rate of interest equivalent to 8% converted semiannually.

SOLUTION: The rate per period $= 4\%$ or .04, and $m = 2$. In getting the effective rate it is usually sufficiently accurate to take the accumulation factor from Table 2 to four decimal places. Substituting in Formula (10),

$$r = (1.04)^2 - 1$$
$$= 1.0816 - 1.0000 = .0816$$

Thus 8.16% compounded annually will produce the same amount of interest as 8% compounded semiannually.

Exercise 2b

1. What is the effective rate of interest equivalent to 10% converted quarterly?   (10.38%)

2. What is the effective rate of interest equivalent to 7% converted: (a) semiannually; (b) quarterly?

3. Find the effective rate of interest equivalent to 9% converted quarterly.   (9.31%)

4. Which gives a better return, 9% converted monthly or $9\frac{1}{2}\%$ effective?

5. Which gives the better annual return on an investment, $6\frac{1}{8}\%$ converted annually or 6% converted quarterly? Show the figures on which you base your answer.   (6% converted quarterly)

6. Which rate of interest gives the better annual yield, 4% compounded monthly or $4\frac{1}{2}\%$ compounded semiannually? Show the figures on which you base your answer.

7. Get the effective rate of interest equivalent to 5% converted: (a) semi-annually; (b) quarterly; (c) monthly.　　[(a) 5.06%; (b) 5.09%; (c) 5.12%]

8. Get the effective rate of interest equivalent to 24% converted: (a) quarterly; (b) monthly.

2.6　Interest for a Part of a Period

When deriving the compound interest formula, we assumed that the time would be an integral number of conversion periods. When there is a part of a period, the usual practice is to allow simple interest for this time on the compound amount at the end of the last whole period.

EXAMPLE: At 4% compounded semiannually, $2000 will amount to how much in 3 years and 5 months?

SOLUTION: The total time in this case is six whole periods and five months left over. The compound amount at the end of the six whole periods is

$$S = 2000(1.02)^6 = 2000 \times 1.126162 = \$2252.32$$

The simple interest for the remaining five months is

$$2252.32 \times \tfrac{5}{12} \times .04 = \$37.54$$

Therefore the amount at the end of 3 years and 5 months is

$$2252.32 + 37.54 = \$2289.86$$

Note that in getting the simple interest we use the nominal annual rate and the time in years. A common mistake is to use the rate per period.

The procedure used to get the total amount for a problem involving a part of a period is illustrated. The series of dots indicate that part of the time scale has been omitted.

2.7   Amount at Changing Rates

If the interest rate on an investment changes, the final amount can be found by getting the amount each time there is a change in rate and then carrying this value forward at the new rate until there is another change. All that this means is that we have a series of compound interest problems. The amount at the end of one stage becomes the principal at the beginning of the next stage.

In this text when a problem has two or more stages, we round intermediate answers to the nearest cent. This makes the arithmetic as simple as possible. If a calculator is available, some people prefer to either carry more places in the intermediate steps or first to multiply the factors together.

EXAMPLE: A principal of $900 earns 4% converted quarterly for 4 years and then 5% converted semiannually for 2 more years. Find the final amount.

SOLUTION: We first find the amount at the end of 4 years using a factor rounded to 5 decimal places.

$$900(1.01)^{16} = 900 \times 1.17258 = \$1055.32$$

We now go forward 2 more years at 5% converted semiannually. Since there are 6 digits in the new principal, we round the factor to 6 decimal places.

$$1055.32(1.025)^4 = 1055.32 \times 1.103\,813 = \$1164.88$$

If this problem were worked by first multiplying the complete factors together, we would have,

$$900 \times 1.172\,578\,6449 \times 1.103\,812\,8906 = 900 \times 1.294\,307\,4241 = \$1164.88$$

Exercise 2c

1. On June 30, 1963, Charles Moser borrowed $3000 at 4% converted semiannually. How much would he have to repay on September 28, 1970? Use Bankers' Rule for simple interest computation.   ($3998.02)

2. Find the amount of $750 for $4\frac{1}{2}$ years at 5% effective.

3. If $6000 is borrowed for 5 years and 4 months at $4\frac{1}{2}$% converted semiannually, what amount would be required to repay the debt?   ($7607.65)

4. What is the amount of $40,000 for 6 years and 3 months at $4\frac{1}{2}$% converted semiannually?

5. To what sum of money does $2000 accumulate in 3 years and 5 months at 6% compounded semiannually?   ($2447.80)

6. On June 1, 1966, a debt of $4000 was incurred at a rate of 6%. What amount will be required to settle the debt on September 15, 1970? Use Bankers' Rule for simple interest computation.

7. A savings and loan association advertises "instant interest." Funds received by the 10th of the month earn interest from the 1st. Interest is paid at the rate of 4% converted quarterly. Interest dates are March 31, June 30, September 30, and December 31. Interest is paid to the date funds are withdrawn. A man deposits $2000 on January 7, 1964. If he closes out his account on January 30, 1966, how much will he get? Allow simple interest for 1 month.
                                                                          ($2172.93)

8. Another depositor put $5000 on April 8, 1965, in the savings and loan association in Problem 7. He closed out his account on November 30, 1968. What was the balance at that time? Allow simple interest for 2 months.

9. Four thousand dollars were invested for 12 years. During the first 5 years the interest rate was 5% converted semiannually. The rate then dropped to $4\frac{1}{2}\%$ converted semiannually for the remainder of the time. What was the final amount?   ($6991.74)

10. A principal of $6500 earns 4% effective for 3 years and then $3\frac{1}{2}\%$ compounded semiannually for 4 more years. What is the amount at the end of the 7 years?

11. William H. Maguire bequeathed $400,000 to a university for the construction of a science building. The university got 4% on this investment for 9 years. The rate then dropped to $3\frac{1}{2}\%$. If the building was built 25 years after the gift was received, how much was in the fund at that time?
                                                                          ($987,201.12)

12. An investment of $3000 earns 3% for 2 years, then $2\frac{1}{2}\%$ compounded semiannually for 4 more years, then 4% compounded semiannually for 2 years. Get the amount at the end of the 8 years.

2.8   Present Value at Compound Interest

In business transactions there are many times when it is necessary to determine the **present value** of some sum of money due in the future. The present value is defined as the principal that will amount to the given sum at the specified future date. The difference between the future amount and its present value is the **compound discount**. To get the present value of a future amount, we simply solve the compound interest formula for P:

$$P = \frac{S}{(1+i)^n}$$

This is often expressed using negative exponents:

$$P = S(1 + i)^{-n} \tag{11}$$

P = the principal or present value
S = the amount due in the future
i = the rate per period
n = the number of periods

The quantity $\dfrac{1}{(1 + i)^n}$ or $(1 + i)^{-n}$ is called the **discount factor** or **Present Worth of 1**. It is also indicated, particularly in insurance problems, by the symbol v^n. Numerical values of the discount factor for common interest rates are given in the *Present Worth of 1* column in Table 2. In our examples we shall follow the common practice of using a negative exponent to indicate that a sum due in the future is to be discounted. Then the present value can be obtained by simply multiplying by the factor from Table 2.

EXAMPLE 1: Find the present value of $5000 due in 4 years if money is worth 4% compounded semiannually.

SOLUTION: Substituting $S = 5000$, $i = .02$ and $n = 8$ in (11) and using the *Present Worth of* 1 factor from Table 2, we have

$$P = 5000(1.02)^{-8} = 5000 \times .853490 = \$4267.45$$

This means that if $4267.45 were put at interest for 4 years at 4% compounded semiannually, the amount would be $5000. A good exercise for students is to carry money backwards and forwards in this way to show that the results do check.

When the time involves a part of a conversion period, we bring S back for the minimum number of periods that includes the given time and then compute the simple interest on the principal up to the point where the present value is wanted.

EXAMPLE 2: A note with a maturity value of $1000 is due in 3 years and 8 months. What is its present value at 6% compounded semiannually?

SOLUTION: We first bring the $1000 back 4 years or 8 periods, the minimum number of periods that includes 3 years and 8 months.

$$1000(1.03)^{-8} = 1000 \times .789\ 409 = \$789.41$$

This is now taken forward 4 months at simple interest.

$$789.41 \times .06 \times \tfrac{1}{3} = \$15.79$$

Adding principal and interest, we get $805.20 as the present value.

On problems like this where it is necessary to move money backwards and forwards, or keep track of several sums of money, it is suggested that the student make a time diagram which will show the exact point in time that a given sum of money has a certain value. The above problem can be sketched.

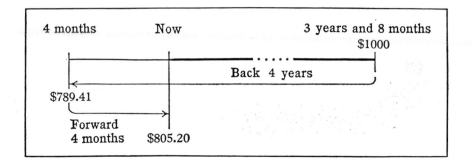

In the preceding examples the maturity value of the obligation was known and it was only necessary to discount this amount. Many times, however, the original debt will be interest-bearing and the maturity value will not be given. Then the *maturity value at the given interest rate must be determined*. Finally the present value of this maturity value is obtained by discounting at the rate specified for discounting. The two rates may be and frequently are different.

EXAMPLE 3: On August 5, 1964, Mr. Kane loans Mr. Hill $2000 at 6% converted semiannually. Mr. Hill gives Mr. Kane a note promising to repay the loan with accumulated interest in 6 years. On February 5, 1968, Mr. Kane sells the note to a buyer who charges an interest rate of 8% converted semi-annually for discounting. How much does Mr. Kane get?

SOLUTION: We must first determine the maturity value of the debt.

$$S = 2000(1.03)^{12} = 2000 \times 1.425761 = \$2851.52$$

Now the original time and the original interest rate have no more bearing on the problem. All that the buyer of the note is interested in is the maturity value, how long he will have to wait to collect, and what the note is worth to him at his discount rate.

The note matures on August 5, 1970. From February 5, 1968, to this maturity date is $2\frac{1}{2}$ years or 5 periods of 6 months each. Therefore the value of the note at 8% compounded semiannually is

$$P = 2851.52(1.04)^{-5} = 2851.52 \times .821927 = \$2343.74$$

Note that the time for discounting is from the time the buyer buys the note to the maturity date. The time when the original debt was contracted does not enter into this part of the problem except to establish the maturity date. A time diagram will prevent many of the common errors with this type of problem.

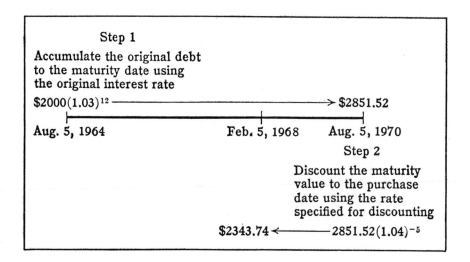

EXAMPLE 4: A man can buy a piece of property for $4500 cash or for $2000 down and $3000 in 3 years. If the man has money on which he is earning 4% converted semiannually, which is the better plan for him and by how much now?

SOLUTION: We get the present value at 4% compounded semiannually of $3000 due in 3 years.

$$P = 3000(1.02)^{-6} = 3000 \times .887\ 971 = \$2663.91$$

Adding this to the $2000 down payment makes the present value of the time payment plan $4663.91. By paying $4500 cash, the man saves $163.91 now.

Exercise 2d

(Use Bankers' Rule for simple interest computations for a part of a period.)

1. What principal is needed to accumulate $3000 in 8 years at $3\frac{1}{2}\%$ converted semiannually?   ($2272.85)

2. What is the present value at $4\frac{1}{2}\%$ compounded semiannually of $3460 due in 18 months?

3. Find the present value of $5000 due in 4 years if money is worth 3% compounded semiannually.   ($4438.56)

4. Find the present value of $450.80 due in $2\frac{1}{2}$ years if money is worth 6% compounded semiannually.

5. What is the present value at 3% compounded quarterly of $12,000 due in 18 months?   ($11,473.90)

6. Find the present value of $3500 due in $4\frac{1}{2}$ years if money is worth 5%.

7. A man owns a note for $2500 due in 5 years. What should a buyer pay for the note if he wishes to earn 5% converted quarterly on his money? What is the compound discount?   ($1950.02; $549.98)

8. An obligation of $5000 is due on December 1, 1970. What is the value of this obligation on October 1, 1965, at 4% compounded semiannually?

9. On September 3, 1964, Mr. Lovett buys some equipment for $3000 from the Excello Company. He signs a note promising to pay the $3000 with interest at 6% compounded semiannually in 18 months. On December 3, 1964, the Excello Company sells the note to a finance company that charges an interest rate of 8% converted quarterly for discounting. How much does the Excello Company get for the note?   ($2969.15)

10. A note dated June 1, 1965, calls for the payment of $850 in 6 years. On March 15, 1968, it is sold at a price that will yield the buyer 4%. How much is paid for the note?

11. Mr. Durkin gets a note which calls for repayment of $3000 in 5 years, together with compound interest at 4% converted quarterly. He immediately sells the note to a buyer who charges an interest rate of 6% converted semiannually for discounting. How much does Mr. Durkin get for the note?   ($2723.81)

12. A note dated September 15, 1964, calls for the payment of $400 with interest at 6% per annum in 4 years. On December 20, 1966, the note is sold at a price that will yield $4\frac{1}{2}\%$ compounded semiannually. Get the selling price.

13. A note for $800 is due in 5 years with interest at 4%. At the end of 3 years it is discounted at 5%. What are the proceeds at the time of discounting? ($882.83)

14. A debt of $2500 is due on September 15, 1968. What payment must be made on July 17, 1966, to repay the debt if the borrower is permitted to discount the debt at 3% compounded semiannually?

15. On August 9, 1964, Mr. Lufkin borrows $4000 from Mr. Feld. He gives Mr. Feld a note promising to repay the money in 5 years with interest at 5%. On February 9, 1966, Mr. Feld sells the note to a buyer who charges a rate of 7% compounded semiannually for discount purposes. How much does Mr. Feld get for the note? ($4012.59)

16. A note for $2000 dated June 1, 1967, is due with compound interest at 5% compounded semiannually 3 years after date. On December 1, 1968, the holder of the note has it discounted by a lender who charges 6% compounded semiannually. What are the proceeds?

17. Find the present value of $2000 due in 15 months if money is worth 7% converted semiannually. ($1835.46)

18. Thirty-five hundred dollars are due on October 30, 1967. At $2\frac{1}{2}$% compounded semiannually, what is the value of this obligation on August 1, 1965?

19. Mr. Wurtz sells the note below on March 16, 1967 to a lender who charges 6% compounded semiannually for discounting. How much does he receive? ($2005.66)

20. If the above note is discounted on September 21, 1967, by a lender who charges 8% converted quarterly, how much will Mr. Wurtz receive?

21. A man can buy a lot for $2800 cash or for payments of $1500 down and $1500 in 2 years. If he can earn $4\frac{1}{2}$% converted semiannually on his money, which plan is better? (Saves $72.26 now by paying cash)

22. What would be the better plan for the man in Problem 21 if he can earn 6% converted annually on his money?

2.9   Extension of the Tables

When a problem has a greater number of periods than is given in the tables, the tables can be extended by using the law of exponents for factors with a common base: $a^m \times a^n = a^{m+n}$. Applying this law in reverse order to the *Amount of* 1 factor, we get: $(1 + i)^{m+n} = (1 + i)^m \times (1 + i)^n$. Note that while the individual exponents add to the total exponent, the required factor is obtained by *multiplying* the individual factors.

EXAMPLE 1: Find the compound amount of $100 for 20 years at 6% compounded monthly.

SOLUTION: n is 240 and the table goes only to 180. However, $(1.005)^{180} \times (1.005)^{60} = (1.005)^{240}$. Using these two factors, we have

$$S = 100 \times 2.45409 \times 1.34885 = \$331.02$$

When n is an even number the work can be simplified by using the same factor more than once. In this example $(1.005)^{120} \times (1.005)^{120} = (1.005)^{240}$. Substituting accumulation factors, we have

$$S = 100 \times 1.81940 \times 1.81940 = \$331.02$$

The required multiplications may be done in any order.

EXAMPLE 2: In his will, an alumnus appointed a trust company to handle his estate. The decedent instructed the trust company to set aside a sum in a separate account sufficient to pay his alma mater $250,000 at the end of 40 years. What sum should the trust company deposit in the separate account if it earns 3% converted monthly?

SOLUTION: Substituting $S = 250,000$, $i = .0025$ and $n = 480$ in (11),

$$P = 250,000(1.0025)^{-480}$$

The *Present Worth of* 1 factor must be broken down into factors with powers no larger than 180 since this is the largest n in our tables. One solution would be,

$$250,000(1.0025)^{-180}(1.0025)^{-180}(1.0025)^{-120}$$

Since we are dealing with a large sum of money for a long time, complete factors were substituted and calculations made on a desk calculator.

$$P = 250{,}000 \times .637\ 986\ 3214 \times .637\ 986\ 3214 \times .741\ 095\ 6173 = \$75{,}411.40$$

To show how an alternate choice of factors would lead to the same result with less work, the problem is reworked below with the n of 480 divided into 3 equal parts.

$$P = 250{,}000[(1.0025)^{-160}]^3 = 250{,}000(.670\ 654\ 7320)^3 = \$75{,}411.40$$

EXAMPLE 3: A sum of $75,411.40 was deposited in an account paying 3% converted monthly. Find the amount. The result will be a check on our answer to Example 2.

SOLUTION: Substituting $P = \$75{,}411.40$, $i = .0025$, and $n = 480$ in (9),

$$S = 75{,}411.40(1.0025)^{480} = 75{,}411.40[(1.0025)^{160}]^3$$
$$= 75{,}411.40(1.491\ 080\ 2120)^3 = \$250{,}000.00$$

With a calculator, these calculations can be done quickly and we have a check on our work even though we are dealing with hundreds of thousands of dollars and hundreds of conversion periods.

Exercise 2e

1. Find the compound amount if $250 is invested at 4% compounded semiannually for 40 years. ($1218.86)

2. What is the compound amount of $4500 invested at 5% compounded monthly for 16 years?

3. If $35,000 is invested at 3% compounded semiannually for 50 years, what will be the amount? ($155,121.59)

4. If $355.60 is invested at 5% compounded quarterly, what will be the amount in 20 years?

5. Find the amount of $4000 invested for 25 years at 6% converted monthly. ($17,859.89)

6. Find the amount of $14,000 invested at 4% compounded monthly at the end of 22 years and 3 months.

7. How much must be invested today at 4% compounded semiannually to amount to $10,000 in 50 years? ($1380.33)

8. How much must be invested today at 4% compounded quarterly to amount to $5000 in 25 years?

9. How much must be deposited now in an investment paying 3% converted monthly to amount to $100,000 in 20 years?   ($54,922.27)

10. How much must be deposited now in an investment paying 4% converted monthly to amount to $100,000 in 20 years.

2.10   Finding the Rate

In the basic formula for compound interest, $S = P(1 + i)^n$, there are four quantities.   We have shown how to determine the amount and the present value using Table 2. When the amount, principal and time are known, the approximate rate can be found by simple interpolation. Since the rate is usually wanted only for information or purposes of comparison, this method is sufficiently accurate for most practical purposes. If a rate must be determined to several decimal places, refined methods of interpolation will be found in the Compound Interest and Annuity Tables published by the Financial Publishing Company. Logarithmic tables can also be used following the method given on page 71.

EXAMPLE: If $500 amounts to $700 in 5 years with interest compounded quarterly, what is the rate of interest?

SOLUTION: Substituting in the compound interest formula,

$$500(1 + i)^{20} = 700$$
$$(1 + i)^{20} = \tfrac{700}{500} = 1.4000$$

We must now find the value of i for which $(1 + i)^{20} = 1.4000$. We go along line 20 in Table 2 until we find an *Amount of* 1 of 1.4000 or, as is usually the case, values on each side of the one we are looking for. We put the results in tabular form and let d represent the desired difference.

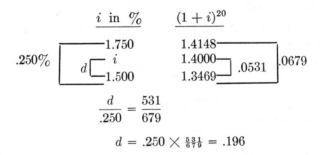

$$\frac{d}{.250} = \frac{531}{679}$$

$$d = .250 \times \tfrac{531}{679} = .196$$

Therefore the desired rate per period is $1.5000 + .196 = 1.696\%$. The nominal rate, compounded quarterly, is $4i$ or $4 \times 1.696 = 6.78\%$.

It is not necessary to write the difference between 1.4148 and 1.3469 as
.0679. We can write 679 with the decimal point and zero understood. The
number 679 is called the *tabular difference*. Omitting leading zeros is the usual
practice and is the one we follow from now on.

Had we wanted only the nominal rate, we could have solved for it directly.
The symbol $j_{(m)}$ stands for the nominal rate j compounded m times per year.
With these simplifications, the problem becomes,

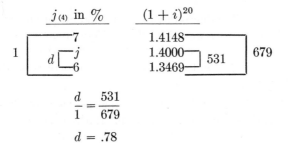

$$\frac{d}{1} = \frac{531}{679}$$

$$d = .78$$

Therefore the nominal annual rate compounded quarterly is $6 + .78 = 6.78\%$.

Exercise 2f

(Unless the problem states otherwise, rates should be computed to two
decimal places when expressed as a per cent.)

1. For a sum of money to double itself in 15 years, what must be the rate
of interest converted annually?   (4.72%)

2. If an investment increases from $5000 to $6000 in 5 years, what was
the nominal rate of interest compounded semiannually?

3. If $750 accumulates to $850 in 6 years, find the nominal rate converted
semiannually.   (2.10%)

4. The sales of a business increased from $30.4 million in 1961 to $43.5
million in 1966. What was the annual rate of increase, assuming that it was
constant from year to year? (Answer to .1%)

5. If an investment increases 50% in 12 years, what is the effective rate
of interest?   (3.43%)

6. If the population of a city increases from 400,000 to 490,000 at approximately a constant rate during a decade, what is the annual rate of
increase?

7. A firm organized in 1943 had sales of $30,000 that year. In 1963 the
sales were $120,000. What was the annual rate of increase, assuming that
it was approximately constant from year to year?   (7.2%)

8. The sales of a business increased at approximately a constant rate from $5.8 million in 1962 to $7.9 million in 1967. What was the annual rate of increase?

9. A man bought a house for $8000. In addition to the cost of the house he paid $100 for legal fees and $50 for a survey. Three years later he sold the house for $10,000 from which the real estate agent deducted 5% commission. The increased net selling price represents what annual rate of return on the original total cost? (5.24%)

10. A man purchased 10 shares of Cincinnati and Suburban Bell Telephone Stock in 1957 when the price was $77 a share. Commissions and other buying costs totaled $10. He sold the stock in 1963 when the price was $104 a share. Selling costs totaled $12. Find the average annual increase in the net value of his investment.

11. During the period 1959–1962, the earnings per share of Duquesne Light increased at approximately a constant rate. If the earnings were $1.44 in 1959 and $1.65 in 1962, what was the annual rate of increase? (4.6%)

12. During the period 1957–1962, the earnings per share of General Public Utilities increased at approximately a constant rate from $1.34 a share in 1957 to $1.64 a share in 1962. Find the annual rate of increase to the nearest tenth of 1 per cent.

2.11 Finding the Time

We now find the time when the principal, amount, and rate are known. To do this we determine the numerical value of the *Amount of 1* factor, $(1 + i)^n$, and then locate this factor, or the values on both sides of it, in Table 2. If interest is allowed only on conversion dates, we take the value of n corresponding to the factor which is closest to the computed value of $(1 + i)^n$. If simple interest is allowed for a part of a period, we can use either the simple interest formula or interpolation to get the exact answer.

EXAMPLE: How long will it take $200 to amount to $350 at 3% compounded semiannually?

SOLUTION: Substituting in the compound interest formula, we have

$$200(1.015)^n = 350$$
$$(1.015)^n = \tfrac{350}{200}$$
$$(1.015)^n = 1.75$$

We now look under 1.5% for an accumulation factor of 1.75. As is usually the case, we do not find this exact value. If n is 37 the factor is 1.735, and if n is 38 the factor is 1.761. The nearest time is therefore 38 periods or

19 years. If this is a savings account or other investment on which interest is paid only on conversion dates, the closest amount to $350 would be $200(1.015)^{38} = \$352.16$.

If simple interest is allowed for a part of a period, we can get the compound amount at the end of 37 periods and then carry this forward a sufficient time to get $350. For 37 periods $S = 200(1.015)^{37} = 200 \times 1.73478 = \$346.96$. Now we must determine how long it takes this amount to draw $3.04 simple interest. Using the simple interest formula, $I = Prt$, we have $3.04 = 346.96 \times .03 \times t$. Solving this for t we get .292 years or 105 days (based on a 360-day year). We can also get the answer by interpolating between the two values.

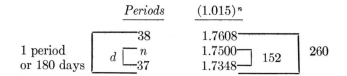

In the above diagram d is used to indicate the desired difference. Since the periods in this problem are 180 days, we have,

$$\frac{d}{180} = \frac{152}{260}$$

$$d = 180 \times \tfrac{152}{260} = 105$$

Thus the time for $200 to amount to $350 at 3% compounded semiannually is $18\frac{1}{2}$ years plus an additional 105 days if simple interest is allowed for a part of a period.

Exercise 2g

1. How long will it take any sum of money to double itself at $2\frac{1}{2}\%$? Give answer to the nearest year.   (28 years)

2. How long will it take an investment to increase 50% in dollar value if money is worth 5%? Give answer to the nearest year.

3. How long will it take $750 to accumulate to $1000 at 5% converted semiannually? Give answer to the nearest period.   (12)

4. How long will it take $4000 to amount to $5000 at $3\frac{1}{2}\%$ converted semiannually? Give answer to the nearest period.

5. A child 8 years old is left $1600. Under the conditions of the will, the money is to be invested until it amounts to $2500. If the money is invested at $3\frac{1}{2}\%$, how old will the boy be when he gets the $2500? Give answer to the nearest birthday.   (21 years old)

6. A man invests $1000 at 6% compounded semiannually on June 1, 1964. No interest is allowed for a part of a period. On what date will this account have at least $2000 in it?

7. How long will it take $3000 to amount to $3600 at 3% converted semi-annually? Assume that simple interest is allowed for a fraction of a period and give answer to the nearest day.   (6 years and 44 days)

8. In what time will $200 amount to $250 at 5%? Allow simple interest for a fraction of a period and get the answer to the nearest day.

9. The population of a city has been increasing at the rate of 3% a year. If the population is now 425,000, how long will it take the city to grow to a population of 500,000, assuming that the annual rate of increase remains at 3%?   (5+ years)

10. The sales of a business have been increasing at approximately 7% a year. If the sales in 1964 were $14.2 million, when will sales reach $20 million assuming that the rate of increase remains at 7%? Give answer to the nearest year.

11. A loan company charges 36% a year compounded monthly on small loans. How long will it take to triple money at this rate? Give answer to the nearest month.   (37 months)

12. An alumnus leaves $75,000 to a university with the provision that it is to be invested until it amounts to $100,000. From then on the interest is to be used each year for scholarships. If the school gets 3% compounded annually how many years after they receive the gift will the fund first amount to at least $100,000?

13. How long will it take an investment to increase 33% if it draws interest at 6% compounded quarterly?   (19 periods)

14. It is estimated that a piece of property will increase in value at the rate of 5% a year. If the property is purchased for $45,000 in 1961, what is its predicted value for the year 1966?

15. Five hundred dollars is put in a savings deposit on June 1, 1964. Interest is allowed at $2\frac{1}{2}$% compounded semiannually, but no interest is paid for a part of a period. What is the date when this account will have at least $750 in it? What will be the amount at that time?   (Dec. 1, 1980; $753.37)

16. A man invests $2000 at 7% compounded semiannually on September 1, 1965. No interest is allowed for a part of a period. On what date will this investment first amount to at least $3000 and what will be the amount at that time?

17. During the period 1959–1962, the dividends paid by Public Service Electric and Gas increased at about 8% a year. If this rate of increase continues, in how many years will the annual dividend be doubled?   (9)

18. Dividends paid by Cleveland Electric Illuminating have been increasing at about 6% a year. In 1962 the dividend was $2.00. If the present rate of increase continues, when can the dividend be expected to reach $3.00?

2.12 Equations of Value

In business transactions it is often necessary to exchange one set of obligations for another set of different amounts due at different times. To do this it is necessary to bring all of the obligations to a common date called a **focal date.** We then set up an **equation of value** in which all of the original obligations at the focal date equal all of the new obligations at the focal date. This procedure is based on the fact that the value of any sum of money can be found at any time by accumulating it at compound interest if we take it into the future, or discounting it if we bring it back in time. The equation of value should be thoroughly understood because it is the most effective way to solve many investment problems, particularly the more complicated ones.

EXAMPLE 1: A man owes $200 due in 1 year and $300 due in 2 years. The lender agrees to let him settle both obligations with a cash payment. Before the problem can be worked, the two parties must agree on an interest rate or value of money to be used in setting up the equation of value. In this case we assume that the lender specifies that 4% compounded semiannually will be used. If this is as much or more than the borrower can get elsewhere, he would be wise to use his cash to cancel the debts. Assume that the borrower is satisfied with this rate of interest and determine the size of the cash payment.

SOLUTION: The first thing to decide is the location of the focal date. In compound interest problems the answer will be the same regardless of the location of the focal date. Therefore, the only consideration is making the work a minimum. If there is only one unknown payment, putting the focal date at the time that payment is made will eliminate long division.

Most students find a sketch similar to the one below helpful in getting times correct in focal date problems. If the original obligations are put on one side of the time scale and the payments on the other side, the equation of value can be quickly and correctly determined from the sketch.

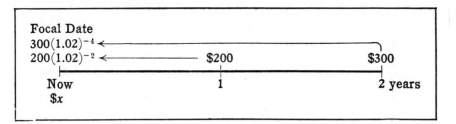

The sketch shows that the $200 must be discounted for 2 periods and the $300 for 4 periods to transfer them to the focal date. Because the focal date is at the point where the unknown payment is made, we can set up the equation of value:

$$x = 200(1.02)^{-2} + 300(1.02)^{-4}$$
$$= 200 \times .96117 + 300 \times .92385$$
$$= 192.23 + 277.16 = \$469.39$$

Thus a cash payment of $469.39 will equitably settle debts of $200 and $300 due in 1 and 2 years if money is worth 4% compounded semiannually.

Because the focal date method of solving problems is so useful in the mathematics of finance, it is important that students both understand and have confidence in this method. To show that we do have a fair and correct answer to this problem, let us consider it in another way. Suppose that the borrower had invested the $469.39 at 4% compounded semiannually, the rate he and the lender agreed on. At the end of 1 year this would amount to $469.39(1.02)^2$ or $488.35. If he deducts the $200 he now owes, this will leave a balance of $288.35. Carrying this forward for another year would result in an amount of $288.35(1.02)^2$ or $300.00. It is a good idea for students to check several problems in this way until they are convinced of the utility and the accuracy of the focal date and the equation of value.

EXAMPLE 2: A man owes $500 due now. The lender agrees to let him settle this obligation with 2 equal payments in 1 and 2 years respectively. Find the size of these payments if the settlement is based on 6%.

SOLUTION: Since there are 2 unknown payments, it will not be possible to avoid division in the final step. However, if the focal date is put at 2 years, the coefficient will be as simple as possible and the work will be less than if the focal date were put anywhere else. A sketch shows what factors are needed to get everything to the focal date.

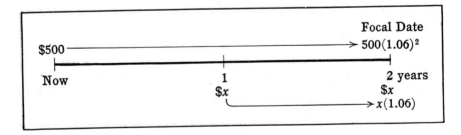

Since the two payments are equal we shall designate each of them by x. The value of the first one *at the focal date* is $x(1.06)$. Since the second one is already at the focal date, its value at that point is x.

We now set up an equation of value in which the payments carried to the focal date equal the original obligation at the focal date.

$$x(1.06) + x = 500(1.06)^2$$
$$2.06x = 500 \times 1.12360 = 561.80$$
$$x = \frac{561.80}{2.06} = \$272.72$$

Thus payments of \$272.72 in one and two years will equitably settle a debt of \$500 due now if money is worth 6%. Sometimes students think that this answer should be accumulated or discounted from the focal date to the time the payment is made. This is incorrect. The equation of value gives the size of the payment at the time the payment is made.

EXAMPLE 3: A man owes \$200 due in 2 years and \$400 due in 5 years. He wants to settle these obligations with a payment of \$300 in 3 years and the remainder in 4 years. If money is worth 4%, what is the size of the payment in 4 years?

SOLUTION: The man is getting the \$200 for a longer time than originally planned, so he should have to pay interest for this change. On the other hand he is repaying the \$400 sooner than originally called for, so he should be allowed to discount this obligation. This apparently complex situation can be handled quite easily by bringing everything to a focal date which in this case is put at 4 years to minimize computations. The time diagram and the equation of value are shown.

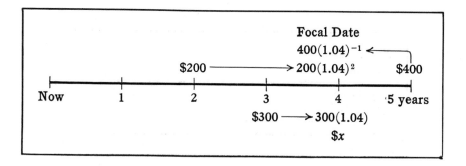

$$300(1.04) + x = 200(1.04)^2 + 400(1.04)^{-1}$$

$$\begin{aligned} x &= 200 \times 1.08160 + 400 \times .96154 - 300 \times 1.04 \\ &= 216.32 + 384.62 - 312.00 \\ &= \$288.94 \end{aligned}$$

EXAMPLE 4: If any obligations bear interest, it is first necessary to compute the maturity values. A man owes $1000 due in 3 years with interest at 5% compounded quarterly, and $500 due in 5 years with interest at 4%. If money is worth 6%, what single payment 6 years hence will be equivalent to the original obligations?

SOLUTION: First get the maturity values of the debts:

$$1000(1.0125)^{12} = 1000 \times 1.160754 = \$1,160.75$$
$$500(1.04)^5 = 500 \times 1.21665 = \$608.33$$

Now sketch the problem and set up the equation of value:

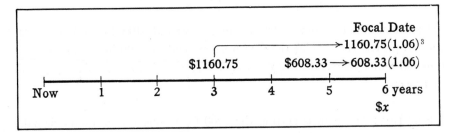

$$\begin{aligned} x &= 1160.75(1.06)^3 + 608.33(1.06) \\ &= 1160.75 \times 1.191016 + 608.33 \times 1.06 \\ &= 1382.47 + 644.83 = \$2027.30 \end{aligned}$$

EXAMPLE 5: Instead of taking $3000 cash from an insurance policy, a beneficiary chooses to take three annual payments, the first to be made now. If the insurance company pays 3% on money left with them, what is the size of the payments?

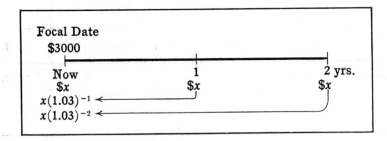

SOLUTION: Putting the focal date now, we have

$$x + x(1.03)^{-1} + x(1.03)^{-2} = 3000$$
$$x + .970874x + .942596x = 3000$$
$$2.913470x = 3000$$
$$x = \frac{3000}{2.913470}$$
$$= \$1029.70$$

Exercise 2h

1. A man owes $300 due in 2 years and $500 due in 4 years. If money is worth 4% converted semiannually, what single payment 3 years hence will settle the obligations? ($792.71)

2. On June 1, 1967, a man owes $4000 which he is unable to repay. His creditor charges him 8% converted semiannually from that date. If the debtor pays $2000 on June 1, 1968, how much would he have to pay on June 1, 1969, to discharge the rest of his obligation?

3. Hull owes Graves $300 due at the end of 2 years and $300 due at the end of 3 years. He wishes to replace these two obligations with a single payment due at the end of $2\frac{1}{2}$ years. If the two agree that money is worth 5% converted semiannually, what will be the size of the payment? ($600.18)

4. Wilson owes Smith $500 due at the end of 2 years and $1000 due at the end of 4 years. Both men agree that Wilson may settle his obligations with a single payment at the end of 3 years using an interest rate of 7%. Solve this problem putting the focal date at 3 years. Solve a second time using 4 years for the focal date.

5. A man leaves $10,000 to his 2 children with the provision that they are to get equal amounts when they reach age 21. If the children are 12 and 17 when the man dies, how much will each receive? The money is invested at $3\frac{1}{2}$% compounded semiannually. ($6241.45)

6. A man leaves an estate of $30,000 which is invested at 4% compounded semiannually. At the time of his death, he has three children aged 13, 15, and 19. Each child is to receive an equal amount from the estate when he reaches age 21. How much does each get?

7. Suppose that the man in Problem 5 had left each child $5000 with the provision that the money be invested at $3\frac{1}{2}$% compounded semiannually and the compound amount given to each child upon reaching age 21. How much would each get? (12-year old, $6832.66; 17-year old, $5744.41)

8. Assume that each of the three children in Problem 6 received $10,000 upon the father's death with the provision that the money was to be invested at 4% compounded semiannually until the child reaches age 21. How much would each receive?

9. A man owes $3000 due in 3 years with interest at 4% and $2000 due in 6 years with interest at 3% converted semiannually. If money is worth 5%, what single payment in 1 year will settle the two obligations?   ($4934.45)

10. A man owes $500 due in 1 year with interest at 7%, $700 due in 18 months without interest, and $500 due in 3 years with interest at 4% compounded quarterly. If money is worth $2\frac{1}{2}$% compounded semiannually, what single payment in 1 year will settle the debts?

11. Instead of taking $3000 cash, the beneficiary of an estate takes 2 equal payments due in 1 and 2 years respectively. If the investment pays interest at 3% converted quarterly, what will be the size of each payment?

($1568.60)

12. A father invests $2000 at 4% compounded semiannually on his son's 12th birthday. If the money is paid to the son in 4 equal annual payments starting on his 18th birthday, what will be the size of each payment?

13. A building is sold for $18,000. The buyer pays $3000 cash. He signs a note with a maturity value of $5000 due in 1 year, and a second note with a maturity value of $5000 due in 2 years. If the seller charges interest on the debt at 4%, what should be the maturity value of a third note due in 3 years that will pay off the remainder of the debt?   ($6264.96)

14. A man borrows $5000 on March 1, 1965, agreeing to pay 6% compounded semiannually. He pays $2000 on September 1, 1966. How much will he have to pay to settle the debt on October 16, 1967?

15. On August 1, 1964, a man bought $300 worth of merchandise and signed a note promising to pay the $300 without interest in 6 months. On November 1, 1964, he bought $500 worth of merchandise and signed a note promising to pay $500 without interest in 6 months. On December 1, 1964, the holder of the notes sold them to a finance company that charged 6% converted monthly. How much does the finance company pay for the notes?
($784.71)

16. On June 1, 1965, a man bought $400 worth of goods and gave a note for $400 to be paid in 6 months without interest. On August 1, 1965, he got $300 worth of goods and signed a 6 months non-interest-bearing note for this amount. On November 1, 1965, the company that holds the notes has them discounted by a finance company that charges 6% converted monthly. How much is received for the two notes?

17. A man owes $500 due now and $1000 due in 15 months. His creditor will allow him to pay both debts in 18 months provided the settlement is based on 8% converted quarterly. What payment in 18 months will settle both obligations?   ($1583.08)

18. A man buys machinery worth $6000. He pays $2000 down and agrees to pay the balance in 2 equal payments in 3 and 6 months respectively. If interest is charged at 6% converted monthly, what will be the size of each payment?

19. A piece of property can be purchased for $28,500 cash or for $10,000 down and two equal payments of $10,000 at the end of 1 and 2 years respectively. To pay cash, the buyer would have to withdraw the money from an investment which is paying him 4% converted semiannually. How much will the buyer save by choosing the better method of payment?

(By paying cash he saves $350.14 now)

20. If the buyer in Problem 19 has his money in stocks which are currently yielding 6% on their market value, would you recommend that he sell the stocks and pay cash? Explain your answer in terms of probable savings by adopting your recommendation.

2.13 Use of Logarithms

Logarithms can be used to solve problems when compound interest tables are not available or when the time or rate is not in the table.

When the total time is obtained using logarithms, the assumption is that compound interest is earned for the fraction of a period as well as for the number of whole periods. This will lead to slightly different results than are obtained using the factors from Table 2 and simple interpolation. If time is determined by logarithms and simple interest is to be used for the remaining fraction of a period, the amount should be determined for the integral number of periods. Then the simple interest formula can be used to get the additional time needed for this sum to equal the final amount.

When logarithms are used to get the rate, the result is theoretically correct and not an approximation, as was the case using factors from Table 2 and simple interpolation. Under ordinary business conditions when the rate is needed only for comparison purposes, Table 2 leads to sufficiently accurate results.

The examples below show how logs can be used to solve the four types of compound interest problems. Six-place tables have been used for these problems. Although the method remains the same, more extensive tables are needed to get accurate results with large sums of money.

EXAMPLE 1: If \$545 is invested at $3\frac{4}{5}\%$, what will be the amount in 7 years?

SOLUTION: Substituting $P = 545$, $i = .038$, and $n = 7$ in (9), we have

$$S = 545(1.038)^7$$

Since the rate is not in the tables, we take the logarithm of both sides:

$$\log S = \log 545 + 7 \log (1.038)$$

$\log 545$		$= 2.736397$
$7 \log (1.038) = 7 \times .016197$	$=$	$.113379$
$\log S$ (adding)		$= 2.849776$

Looking up the antilog of 2.849776, we have $S = \$707.58$

EXAMPLE 2: Find the present value of \$600 due in 8 years if money is worth 5.2% compounded semiannually.

SOLUTION: Substituting $S = 600$, $i = .026$, and $n = 16$ in (11), we have

$$P = 600(1.026)^{-16}$$

Taking the logarithm of both sides,

$$\log P = \log 600 - 16 \log (1.026)$$

$\log 600$		$= 2.778151$
$16 \log (1.026) = 16 \times .011147$	$=$	$.178352$
$\log P$ (subtracting)		$= 2.599799$

Looking up the antilog of 2.599799, we have $P = \$397.92$

EXAMPLE 3: How many years will it take \$175 to amount to \$230 at 4.4%?

SOLUTION: Substituting $S = 230$, $P = 175$ and $i = .044$ in (9), we have

$$230 = 175(1.044)^n$$

from which $(1.044)^n = \frac{230}{175}$

Taking the logarithm of both sides,

$$n \log (1.044) = \log 230 - \log 175$$

$$n = \frac{\log 230 - \log 175}{\log 1.044} = \frac{2.361728 - 2.243038}{.018700} = 6.347 \text{ years}$$

This means that if compound interest is paid for a part of a period the time would be 6.347 years. Since this is not common in practice, the time would usually be used in one of the following ways. If the interest is paid only on conversion dates, we would say that the closest time is 6 years which would result in an amount somewhat less than $230. This means that if we want at least $230 the money would have to be left on deposit for 7 years. If simple interest is paid for part of a period, we would take the amount at the end of 6 years and use the simple interest formula to get the additional time necessary for this to accumulate to $230.

EXAMPLE 4: If a speculative investment increased in value from $30,000 to $80,000 in 5 years, what was the annual compounded rate of growth?

SOLUTION: Substituting $S = 80,000$, $P = 30,000$ and $n = 5$ in (9), we have

$$80,000 = 30,000(1 + i)^5$$

$$(1 + i)^5 = \frac{80,000}{30,000}$$

Taking logarithms of both sides,

$$5 \log (1 + i) = \log 80,000 - \log 30,000$$

$$\log (1 + i) = \frac{\log 80,000 - \log 30,000}{5}$$

$$= \frac{4.903090 - 4.477121}{5} = \frac{.425969}{5} = .085194$$

Looking up the antilog of .085194, we find that

$$1 + i = 1.2167$$

From which $$i = .2167 = 21.67\%$$

The compound interest law can also be applied to something which is decreasing at a constant rate. An example in nature is the decay of a radioactive substance. The book value of an asset, depreciated according to the double declining balance method (page 192), follows the compound interest law. When a quantity is decreasing, the rate will be negative and we find its value using logarithms.

EXAMPLE 5: The value of the dollar dropped from $1.19 in 1950 to $.94 in 1962. Assuming that the drop was at approximately a constant rate, what was the annual per cent change?

SOLUTION: Substituting $P = 1.19$, $S = .94$ and $n = 12$ in (9),

$$1.19(1 + i)^{12} = .94$$

Taking the logarithm of both sides,

$$\log(1 + i) = \frac{\log .94 - \log 1.19}{12}$$

$$= \frac{(.973\ 128 - 1) - (.075\ 547)}{12}$$

When working with logarithms, we must end with a positive mantissa and an integral characteristic. To achieve this, we can change the form of a logarithm provided we do not change its numerical value. If we add 119 to the first term in the first logarithm and then subtract 119 from the second term in the same logarithm, we can complete the problem.

$$\log(1 + i) = \frac{(119.973\ 128 - 120) - (.075\ 547)}{12}$$

$$= \frac{119.897\ 581 - 120}{12} = 9.991\ 465 - 10$$

Looking up the antilog, $1 + i = \quad .981$

From which $i = -.019 = -1.9\%$

Thus for the period 1950–1962, the value of the dollar decreased about 2% a year.

Exercise 2i

1. If an investment pays $9\frac{1}{2}\%$ return, what will be the amount of $100 in 5 years?   ($157.42)

2. What will be the amount of $234.50 in 8 years at 4.8% compounded semiannually?

3. If an investment pays 10%, how much must be invested today to amount to $250 in 10 years?   ($96.39)

4. How much must be invested at 7.6% converted quarterly to amount to $500 in 4 years?

5. How long does it take $350 to amount to $500 at 4.15% converted annually? Give answer to the nearest year.   (9 years)

6. How many years will it take $45,000 to amount to $72,000 at 3.8% converted annually?

7. How long does it take an investment to triple itself at 9.5%? Give answer to nearest year. (12 years)

8. How long will it take a principal of $42,000 to amount to $60,000 at 4.8% converted quarterly? Give answer to nearest period.

9. What is the annual rate of interest if an investment of $3500 amounts to $45,000 in 40 years? (6.6%)

10. An investment of $6700 amounted to $32,000 in 14 years. What was the annual rate of return correct to .1%?

11. A piece of property was purchased in 1950 for $32,000. In 1965 it was sold for $255,000. What annual rate of return was received on this investment? (14.8%)

12. What is the nominal rate of return converted semiannually, if $6780 amounts to $18,550 in $8\frac{1}{2}$ years?

13. Over the past several years a business has been increasing at an approximately constant rate of 10% a year. If the business had sales of $2.5 million in 1953, what are the estimated sales for 1963 assuming that the business continues to increase at about the same rate? ($6.5 million)

14. The net income of a business has been increasing at about 12% a year. If the net income in 1964 was $23.6 million, what is the estimated net income for 1968?

15. A man estimates that a piece of property will be worth $185,000 in 6 years. If he expects a return of $8\frac{1}{2}$% on his investment, what is the property worth to him today to the nearest thousand dollars? ($113,000)

16. The estimated value of a piece of property in 5 years is $75,000. What would it be worth today to a speculator who expects a rate of return of 10% on his money?

17. The sales of a business were $38,000,000 in 1965 and $74,000,000 in 1969. Assuming that sales increased at approximately a constant rate, what was the annual compounded rate of growth? (18%)

18. If the population of a country increases from 130 million to 144 million in 10 years, what is the annual rate of increase correct to .1%?

19. A man put $17,500 in a speculative investment in June 1952. In June 1966, the investment was valued at $75,000. What annual per cent return did he earn on his investment? (11%)

20. An illegal money lender makes a loan of $100. Three months later his victim repays $133.10. What rate of interest is the lender getting per month?

21. When Secretary of State William Seward purchased Alaska for less than 2 cents an acre in 1867, some dubbed it "Seward's Icebox," others "Seward's Folly." Since that time, Alaska has yielded nearly 100 times its price in gold alone. If the $7.2 million which the U.S. paid Russia for Alaska in 1867 had been invested at $4\frac{1}{2}\%$ compounded semiannually, how much would the investment amount to in 1967.   ($616.5 million)

22. In 1626, Peter Minuit bought Manhattan Island from the Indians for trinkets valued at 60 guilders or $24. Had this money been put into a savings account paying 4.6% converted semiannually, how much would be in the account in 1966? Answer to nearest $10,000.

23. From 1954 to 1962, the net earnings per share of IBM common stock increased from $1.87 to $8.72. What was the average annual rate of increase on a compound interest basis?   (21%)

24. During the period 1959–1962, the earnings per share of Public Service Electric and Gas increased from $2.16 a share to $3.74. What was the average annual rate of increase to the nearest per cent?

3

ORDINARY ANNUITIES

3.1 Types of Annuities

When most people buy a home, they borrow money and agree to repay it in monthly payments over a period that may range from 10 to 30 years. It would be very laborious to try to handle 120 to 360 payments by the methods given in the preceding chapter. To simplify computations, we develop formulas which enable us to handle problems of many payments as easily as we worked with a single payment in the chapter on compound interest.

The series of equal monthly payments which a person makes in buying a home is called an **annuity.** Interest payments on bonds, premiums on insurance, payments on installment purchases are familiar examples of annuities. In general, any set of equal payments made at equal intervals of time form an annuity.

Annuities are divided into **annuities certain** and **contingent annuities.** An **annuity certain** is one for which the payments begin and end at fixed times. The payments on a home form an annuity certain because the buyer agrees to make the first payment on a certain date and continue the payments until the required number has been made. Even if the buyer of the home dies, any outstanding debt on the home must be paid.

A **contingent annuity** is one for which the date of the first or last payment or both depends upon some event. Many life insurance policies are examples of contingent annuities.

The **payment interval** or **rent period** is the length of time between successive payments. Payments may be made annually, semiannually, monthly, weekly, or at any fixed interval. The **term** of an annuity is the time between the start of the first rent period and the end of the last rent period. The **periodic rent** is the size of each payment in dollars and cents.

In this chapter we shall work with the **ordinary annuity** which has the periodic payments made at the *end* of each period. In the next chapter we discuss the **annuity due** which has the payments made at the *beginning* of each period.

3.2 Amount of an Ordinary Annuity

The final value or **amount of an annuity** is the sum of all the periodic payments accumulated to the end of the term using compound interest. In the case of an ordinary annuity, this will be the value of the annuity on the date of the last payment.

EXAMPLE: Starting 1 year from now, a man deposits $500 a year in an account paying 4% compounded annually. What amount does he have to his credit just after making the 4th deposit?

SOLUTION: A sketch is often helpful in visualizing annuity problems. In this case we put the focal date at 4 years because we want the amount of all the payments at that time.

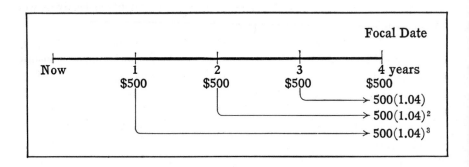

Starting with the last payment and accumulating all of them to the focal date, we have

4th payment			$500.00
3rd	"	$500(1.04)$	520.00
2nd	"	$500(1.04)^2$	540.80
1st	"	$500(1.04)^3$	562.43
Amount of the annuity			$2123.23

3.3 Amount Formula

If there are many payments, the above method for getting the amount would require too much work. We now derive a general formula for the amount of an annuity of n payments of $1 each and a rate of i per period. As in the preceding example, we accumulate each payment to the end of the term. At this point the last payment will, of course, be $1 as it has had no time to earn interest. The next to the last payment will be $1(1 + i)$ or simply $(1 + i)$ because it has earned interest for one period. The payment before this will amount to $(1 + i)^2$ and so on. The first payment will amount to $(1 + i)^{n-1}$ because it earns interest for one period less than the number of payments.

The diagram for this ordinary annuity of $1 per period is shown below. The dots show that some of the payments do not appear on the sketch. The symbol $s_{\overline{n}|}$ (read "s sub n" or "s angle n") is used to represent the amount of n payments of $1 each when the interest rate per period is i. Students sometimes prefer to write this as $s_{\overline{n}|i}$ and put in the rate per period as they set up a problem. This helps them to remember what rate to use when they get the numerical value of the factor from Table 2. This practice is followed in some of the examples in this book.

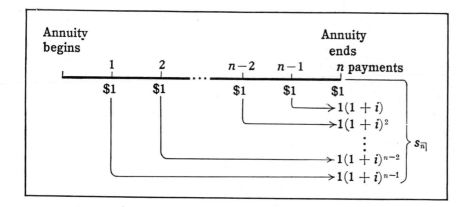

Starting with the last payment and writing the sum of all the payments accumulated to the end of the annuity, we have

$$s_{\overline{n}|} = 1 + (1 + i) + (1 + i)^2 + \cdots + (1 + i)^{n-2} + (1 + i)^{n-1}$$

The expression on the right is a geometric progression in which the first term is 1, the common ratio is $(1 + i)$ and the number of terms is n. In algebra it is shown that the sum of the terms in a geometric progression is

$$s = \frac{a(r^n - 1)}{r - 1}$$

where a is the first term and r is the common ratio. Substituting values from the annuity problem in this general formula, we get

$$s_{\overline{n}|} = \frac{1[(1+i)^n - 1]}{(1+i) - 1} = \frac{(1+i)^n - 1}{i}$$

Values of $s_{\overline{n}|}$ for common interest rates are given in the *Amount of 1 per Period* column of Table 2. If the periodic rent is $R per period instead of $1, we indicate the total amount of the payments by the symbol S_n. All we have to do to get the amount of an annuity of $R per period is to multiply R by $s_{\overline{n}|}$. Thus the basic formula for the amount of an ordinary annuity is

$$S_n = Rs_{\overline{n}|} = R\,\frac{(1+i)^n - 1}{i} \tag{12}$$

S_n = amount of an ordinary annuity of n payments
R = periodic payment or rent
$s_{\overline{n}|}$ = *Amount of 1 per Period* for n periods at the rate i per period

Some workers prefer to work with $j_{(m)}$, the nominal annual rate converted m times a year. They use the marginal index to get on the right page of the compound interest and annuity tables.

EXAMPLE 1: Starting 1 year from now, a man deposits $500 a year in an account paying 4% interest compounded annually. What amount does he have to his credit just after making the 4th deposit?

SOLUTION: Substituting $R = 500$, $n = 4$, and $i = 4\%$ in formula (12),

$$S_4 = 500 s_{\overline{4}|4\%} = 500 \times 4.24646 = \$2123.23$$

This is the same as the problem on Page 76 which took several multiplications and an addition when each deposit was handled separately.

EXAMPLE 2: A man deposits $300 at the end of each 6 months in a building and loan association that pays $3\frac{1}{2}\%$ compounded semiannually. How much will he have to his credit at the end of 10 years?

SOLUTION: Substituting $R = 300$, $n = 20$, and $i = 1\frac{3}{4}\%$ in formula (12),

$$S_{20} = 300 s_{\overline{20}|1\frac{3}{4}\%} = 300 \times 23.70161 = \$7110.48$$

The deposits total $300 \times 20 = \$6000$. Thus the total compound interest is $1110.48.

3.4 Amount After an Annuity Ends

The formula for the amount of an ordinary annuity gives the value of all payments and accumulated interest just after the last payment is made. If no more payments are made, but if the accumulated amount continues to earn interest, the *Amount of* 1 column of Table 2 can be used to get the final amount.

EXAMPLE: A man deposits $300 at the end of each 6 months for 3 years in an account paying 3% converted semiannually. If he makes no more deposits, how much will he have in his account 2 years after the last deposit is made? An annuity which earns interest for 2 or more periods after the last payment is sometimes called a *forborne* annuity.

SOLUTION: Substituting $R = 300$, $n = 6$ and $i = 1\frac{1}{2}\%$ in (12),

$$S_6 = 300s_{\overline{6}|1\frac{1}{2}\%} = 300 \times 6.22955 = \$1868.87$$

This amount now becomes the principal which is accumulated for 2 years. Substituting $P = \$1868.87$, $n = 4$ and $i = .015$ in (9),

$$S = 1868.87(1.015)^4 = 1868.87 \times 1.061364 = \$1983.55$$

ALTERNATE SOLUTION: As an illustration of how a careful analysis of a problem can result in an independent check of the answer, the above problem is worked assuming that payments were also made during the last 2 years. This results in an ordinary annuity of 10 payments and makes the answer too large by the amount of the last 4 payments. The effect of these payments is offset by subtracting the amount of an annuity of 4 payments. This can all be done quite easily by subtracting factors as shown below.

$$S_6 = 300(s_{\overline{10}|} - s_{\overline{4}|}) = 300(10.70272 - 4.09090)$$
$$= 300(6.61182) = \$1983.55$$

While the theory of this method may be somewhat more complicated than the first method, the arithmetic is simpler. A time diagram, focal date approach helps to determine the most efficient way to work a problem. The sketch below shows how the addition and subtraction of fictitious payments enables us to solve the problem using only *Amount of* 1 *per Period* factors from Table 2.

$s_{\overline{10}|}$ takes all payments to the focal date — Focal Date

$-s_{\overline{4}|}$ subtracts amount of 4 fictitious payments

6 real payments   4 fictitious payments

Exercise 3a

1. Find the amount of an annuity of \$500 per year for 12 years at: (a) 1%; (b) 2%; (c) 3%; (d) 4%. All rates are converted annually.
[(a) \$6341.25; (b) \$6706.04; (c) \$7096.01; (d) \$7512.90]

2. Find the amount of an annuity of \$1200 at the end of each 6 months for 5 years if money is worth: (a) 4%; (b) 5%; (c) 6%. All rates are converted semiannually.

3. A man puts \$100 every 6 months in a savings account that pays $3\frac{1}{2}$% compounded semiannually. If he makes his first deposit on June 1, 1960, how much will he have in his account just after he makes his deposit on December 1, 1969? (\$2370.16)

4. Every 6 months a family puts \$50 in a savings account that pays 3% compounded semiannually. If they make the first deposit on August 1, 1960, how much will be in their account just after they make their deposit on February 1, 1970?

5. What is the amount of an annuity of \$100 at the end of each month for 6 years if money is worth 4% compounded monthly? (\$8122.26)

6. Find the amount of an annuity of \$35 at the end of each month for 12 years if money is worth 5% converted monthly.

7. To provide for his son's education, a man deposits \$150 a year at the end of each year for 18 years. If the money draws 3% interest, how much does the fund contain just after the 18th deposit is made? If no more deposits are made, but if the amount in the fund is allowed to accumulate at the same interest rate, how much will it contain in 3 more years?
(\$3512.17; \$3837.84)

8. Two hundred dollars at the end of each year for 6 years is equivalent in value to what single payment at the end of 6 years if the interest rate is 6% effective?

9. A child 12 years old received an inheritance of $400 a year. This was to be invested and allowed to accumulate until the child reached the age of 21. If the money was invested at 4% effective and if the first payment was made on the child's 12th birthday and the last payment on his 21st birthday, what amount did he receive when he reached the age of 21?

($4802.44)

10. A man deposits $125 at the end of each 3 months for 5 years in a fund that pays 5% converted quarterly. How much will he have to his credit just after the last deposit is made?

11. A man deposits $300 at the end of each year for 3 years in an investment paying 3% converted annually. He then allows his account to accumulate for 2 more years without making any more deposits. What is the amount in his account at the end of the 5 years?

($983.74)

12. On March 1, 1960, a man deposited $150 in an investment that pays 3% converted semiannually. He continues to make $150 deposits every 6 months until September 1, 1966, when he makes his final deposit. If he lets the money continue to draw interest, how much will he have in his account on March 1, 1968?

13. A family has been paying $75.50 a month on their home. The interest rate on the mortgage is 5% compounded monthly. Because of sickness they miss the payments due on May 1, June 1, July 1, and August 1. On September 1 they want to make a single payment which will reduce their debt to what it would have been had they made all payments on time. What single payment on this date will be equivalent to the 5 payments from May to September inclusive?

($380.66)

14. A dealer purchased merchandise and agreed to pay $200 on August 1, September 1, October 1, November 1, and December 1. He was to be charged 6% converted monthly on any payments not made on time. He made the August payment, but let all the others go to December 1. At that time what payment did he have to make to settle all his obligations?

15. A person has an income of $250 every 6 months from preferred stocks. He deposits this in a savings and loan association paying $4\frac{1}{2}\%$ converted semiannually with interest dates on June 30 and December 31. If he makes his first deposit on June 30, 1965 and his last deposit on December 31, 1969, how much will be in his account just after he makes the last deposit? ($2768.93)

16. In 1949, a man put $500 in common stocks. He continues to make the same deposit every year. If the stocks increase in market value at about 4% a year, what will be the value of the man's portfolio just after he makes his purchase in 1966?

17. To provide for a son's education, a man opens an account with a deposit of $300 in a savings and loan association which pays $4\frac{1}{2}\%$ converted semiannually. The first deposit is made on the boy's 6th birthday on June 23, 1960. (This deposit will earn interest from July 1.) Additional deposits of $100 each are made every 6 months. How much will be in the account on the interest date immediately following the boy's 18th birthday?   ($3648.47)

18. The father in Problem 17 makes the last deposit on the boy's 16th birthday. How much will be in the account on July 1, 1972?

3.5   Present Value of an Ordinary Annuity

The **present value** of an annuity is the sum of the present values of all the payments of the annuity. To get the present value we shall assume an annuity of n payments of $1 each and a rate of i per period. We then discount each payment to the beginning of the annuity. The sum of these discounted values is designated by the symbol $a_{\overline{n}|}$.

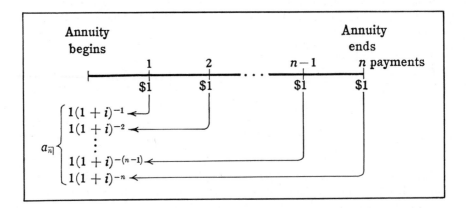

Writing the sum of all the payments discounted to the beginning of the annuity, we have

$$a_{\overline{n}|} = (1+i)^{-1} + (1+i)^{-2} + \cdots + (1+i)^{-(n-1)} + (1+i)^{-n}$$

The expression on the right is a geometric progression in which the first term is $(1+i)^{-1}$, the common ratio is $(1+i)^{-1}$, and the number of terms is n. Substituting these values in the formula for the sum of a geometric progression, we have

$$a_{\overline{n}|} = \frac{(1+i)^{-1}\{[(1+i)^{-1}]^n - 1\}}{(1+i)^{-1} - 1}$$

Multiplying numerator and denominator by $(1 + i)$ gives

$$a_{\overline{n}|} = \frac{(1 + i)^{-n} - 1}{1 - (1 + i)} = \frac{(1 + i)^{-n} - 1}{1 - 1 - i} = \frac{(1 + i)^{-n} - 1}{-i}$$

$$= \frac{1 - (1 + i)^{-n}}{i} = \frac{1 - v^n}{i}$$

Values of $a_{\overline{n}|}$ are given in the *Present Worth of 1 per Period* column of Table 2. If the periodic rent is $\$R$ per period instead of $\$1$, we indicate the present value of the annuity by the symbol A_n. To get the value of A_n in dollars all we need to do is to multiply R by $a_{\overline{n}|}$. Thus the basic formula for the present value of an ordinary annuity is

$$A_n = Ra_{\overline{n}|} = R\frac{1 - (1 + i)^{-n}}{i} = R\frac{1 - v^n}{i} \tag{13}$$

$A_n =$ present value of an ordinary annuity of n payments

$R =$ periodic payment or rent

$a_{\overline{n}|} =$ *Present Worth of 1 per Period* for n periods at the rate i per period

$v^n =$ *Present Worth of 1*. Another symbol for $(1 + i)^{-n}$

Note that we have given the formulas for the amount and present value of an annuity in two forms — one using the factors $s_{\overline{n}|}$ and $a_{\overline{n}|}$, the other using the exponential form as obtained in the original derivation. Whenever possible, problems should be worked by using the $s_{\overline{n}|}$ and $a_{\overline{n}|}$ factors from Table 2. When the rate for a given problem is not in the table, the exponential form of the formula can be used and evaluated using logarithms. In practical business usage it is seldom necessary to use logarithms because the rate can usually be found in the extensive compound interest and annuity tables published by the Financial Publishing Company.

EXAMPLE 1: A man wants to provide a $\$300$ scholarship every year for 10 years. The first scholarship is to be awarded one year from now. If the school can get a 3% return on their investment, how much money should the man give now?

SOLUTION: Substituting in the present value formula, we have

$$A_{10} = 300 \times a_{\overline{10}|}$$
$$= 300 \times 8.53020 = \$2559.06$$

Note that $3000 in scholarships will actually be paid from this gift. What happens is that the school will immediately invest the $2559.06 at 3%. At the end of the first year, interest will be added to the fund and the first $300 scholarship taken out. This will go on for 10 years when the last interest payment plus the balance in the fund at that time will be just sufficient for the last scholarship. When we consider amortization schedules in Chapter 5 this procedure will be illustrated in detail.

From the annuity problems worked thus far, the student should recognize that the annuity formulas, like the compound interest formulas, make it possible to shift financial obligations from one point in time to another point. This is so important that it is worth while restating in summary form the basic principles underlying the mathematics of finance. These are:

1. *Except in cash transactions, the date on which a given sum of money has a certain dollar value must be specified.*

2. *Once the dollar value on a certain date has been specified, the dollar value on any other date can be determined by using the stated interest rate and the appropriate formula.*

3. *Two or more items* must not be *equated unless they have been brought to the same point in time.*

EXAMPLE 2: Wilson agrees to pay Smith $1000 at the end of each year for 5 years. If money is worth 3%, what is the cash equivalent of this debt? If Wilson does not make any payments until the end of 5 years, how much should he pay at that time if this single payment is to be equivalent to the original payments using an interest rate of 3%?

SOLUTION: The original debt is $1000 at the end of each year. Thus *as each payment is made* it has a dollar value of $1000. If a payment is made before it is due, its dollar value will be less than $1000. If the entire debt is settled immediately, Smith will have the use of the money from one to five years sooner than would otherwise have been the case. Therefore, he will be willing to write off the entire debt if he gets the *present value* of the payments. This is given by Formula (13):

$$A_5 = 1000a_{\overline{5}|3\%} = 1000 \times 4.579707 = \$4579.71$$

If a payment is made after it is due, the dollar value will be increased by the interest. If all of the debt is settled at the end of 5 years, Smith will expect the *amount* of the payments at that time. This is given by Formula (12):

$$S_5 = 1000s_{\overline{5}|3\%} = 1000 \times 5.309136 = \$5309.14$$

Thus $4579.71 now is *equivalent in value* to the five $1000 payments at the end of each year if money is worth 3%. Likewise $5309.14 in five years is *equivalent in value* to the original obligations. As an interesting check on our work let us see if $4579.71 now is equivalent to $5309.14 in 5 years. Substituting in Formula (9), we have

$$4579.71(1.03)^5 = 4579.71 \times 1.159274 = \$5309.14$$

Exercise 3b

1. Find the present value of an ordinary annuity of $500 per year for 12 years at: (a) 1%; (b) 2%; (c) 3%; (d) 4%. All rates are converted annually. Carry the present value for the 1% rate forward 12 years. How does the accumulated amount compare with the amount of an annuity of $500 a year as determined in Problem 1 (a) in Exercise 3a?

[(a) $5627.54; (b) $5287.67; (c) $4977.00; (d) $4692.54]

2. Find the present value of an ordinary annuity of $750 at the end of each year for 8 years at: (a) 2%; (b) 4%; (c) 6%; (d) 8%.

3. Find the present value of an ordinary annuity of $1200 at the end of each 6 months for 5 years if money is worth: (a) 4%; (b) 5%; (c) 6%. All rates are converted semiannually.

[(a) $10,779.10; (b) $10,502.48; (c) $10,236.24]

4. If money is worth $4\frac{1}{2}\%$ converted semiannually, what is the present value of $145.50 due at the end of each 6 months for 2 years?

5. A television set is bought for $50 cash and $18 a month for 12 months. What is the equivalent cash price if the interest rate is 24% converted monthly? ($240.36)

6. A refrigerator can be purchased for $57.47 down and $20 a month for 24 months. What is the equivalent cash price if the rate is 30% converted monthly?

7. Find the cash value of a car that can be bought for $400 down and $80 a month for 24 months if money is worth 18% converted monthly. ($2002.43)

8. An heir receives an inheritance of $500 every half year for 20 years, the first payment to be made in 6 months. If money is worth $4\frac{1}{2}\%$ converted semiannually, what is the cash value of this inheritance?

9. A contract for the purchase of a home calls for the payment of $81.90 a month for 20 years. At the beginning of the 6th year (just after the 60th payment is made) the contract is sold to a buyer at a price which will yield 5% converted monthly. What does the buyer pay? ($10,356.68)

10. A man wants to provide a $3000 research fellowship at the end of each year for the next 4 years. If the school can invest money at 4%, how much should the man give them now to set up a fund for the 4 scholarships?

11. A home was purchased for $3000 down and $100 a month for 15 years. If the monthly payments are based on 6% converted monthly, what was the cash price of the house?   ($14,850.35)

12. An apartment was purchased for $6,000 down and $500 at the end of each 6 months for 8 years. If the payments are based on 5% converted semi-annually, what was the cash price of the apartment?

13. If a person can get 4% converted semiannually on his invested money, is it better for him to pay $11,500 cash or $3000 down and $1000 every 6 months for 5 years for a store building?

(Saves $482.59 now by paying cash)

14. Answer Problem 13 if the buyer can get 5% converted semiannually on his savings.

3.6   Extension of Tables

In some problems the number of payments is greater than can be found directly in the tables. Such problems can be solved by dividing the annuity into parts and then accumulating or discounting the amount or present value of each part of the annuity to the desired point in time.

EXAMPLE 1: Find the amount of an annuity of $100 at the end of each month for 30 years at 6% converted monthly.

SOLUTION: There are 360 payments, so we divide the annuity into 2 annui-ties of 180 payments each. The last 180 payments form an ordinary annuity which has an amount of,

$$S_{180} = 100 s_{\overline{180}|\frac{1}{2}\%} = 100 \times 290.818\ 71 = \$29,081.87$$

The amount of the first 180 payments just after the 180th payment is also $29,081.87. At the time of the 180th payment, this single sum is equivalent in value to the 180 payments. To get the value of the first 180 payments at the end of the term, we take this equivalent single sum forward at compound interest.

$$S = 29,081.87 \times (1.005)^{180}$$
$$= 29,081.87 \times 2.454\ 0936 = \$71,369.63$$

Adding the two amounts gives a total amount of $100,451.50.

A time diagram helps in analyzing and setting up problems of this type.

To Get the Amount of 360 Payments

Separate into two annuities of 180 payments each

| Payments 1 to 180 | Payments 181 to 360 | Focal Date |

| 0 | 1 | 2 | 179 | 180 | 181 | 182 | 359 | 360 |

$100 $100 $100 $100 $100 $100 $100 $100

Amount of first annuity earns interest for 180 periods ——— $29,081.87(1.005)^{180}

Amount of second annuity = $ 29,081.87

$$29{,}081.87(1.005)^{180} \longrightarrow 71{,}369.63$$

Total amount = $100,451.50

Had there been more than 360 payments, we would have separated the annuity into three or more annuities.

EXAMPLE 2: Find the present value of an annuity of $100 at the end of each month for 30 years at 6% converted monthly.

SOLUTION: We divide the annuity into 2 annuities of 180 payments each. The first 180 payments form an ordinary annuity which has a present value of,

$$A_{180} = 100a_{\overline{180}|\frac{1}{2}\%} = 100 \times 118.503\,51 = \$11{,}850.35$$

At a point in time one period before the 181st payment, the value of the last 180 payments is also $11,850.35. We now replace payments 181 to 360

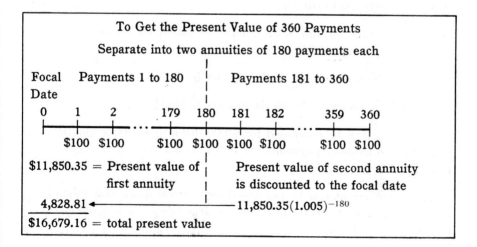

To Get the Present Value of 360 Payments

Separate into two annuities of 180 payments each

| Focal Date | Payments 1 to 180 | Payments 181 to 360 |

| 0 | 1 | 2 | 179 | 180 | 181 | 182 | 359 | 360 |

$100 $100 $100 $100 $100 $100 $100 $100

$11,850.35 = Present value of first annuity

Present value of second annuity is discounted to the focal date

4,828.81 ◄——— 11,850.35(1.005)^{-180}

$16,679.16 = total present value

with this single sum. To get the value of the last 180 payments at the beginning of the term, we discount this equivalent single sum.

$$P = 11,850.35(1.005)^{-180}$$
$$= 11,850.35 \times .407\ 4824 = \$4828.81$$

Adding the two results gives a total present value of $16,679.16.

A time diagram helps in finding a systematic solution of the problem.

Whenever possible, the simplest solution is to divide the annuity into equal parts as was done in these examples. If we had 325 payments, we could separate them into annuities of 180 and 145 payments or any other combination which totals 325 with each part 180 or less.

EXAMPLE 3: Check the answers to Examples 1 and 2.

SOLUTION: Since both examples involved the same annuity, we check by taking the present value from Example 2 forward 30 years at 6% converted monthly.

$$S = 16,679.16(1.005)^{360} = 16,679.16(1.005)^{180}(1.005)^{180}$$
$$= 16,679.16(2.454\ 0936)^2 = \$100,451.50$$

which is the same as the amount in Example 1.

Exercise 3c

1. Find the amount of an annuity of $40 at the end of each year for 80 years if money is worth 3%.   ($12,854.52)

2. What is the amount of an annuity of $60 at the end of each month for 30 years at a rate of 5% converted monthly?

3. Find the present value of the annuity in Problem 1.   ($1208.03)

4. Find the present value of the annuity in Problem 2.

5. A home can be purchased for $5000 down and $200 a month for 20 years. If the monthly payments are based on 5% converted monthly, find the total cash price of the house.   ($35,305.06)

6. An apartment can be purchased for $10,000 down and $1000 every 3 months for 18 years. If the payments are based on 5% converted quarterly, find the total cash price.

3.7   Periodic Payment of an Annuity

In practical business problems the amount or present value of an annuity is frequently known and the periodic payment is to be determined. This can be done by solving the amount and present value formulas for R.

Solving Formula (12), $S_n = Rs_{\overline{n}|}$, for R,

$$R = \frac{S_n}{s_{\overline{n}|}} = S_n \times \frac{1}{s_{\overline{n}|}} \tag{14}$$

R = periodic payment or rent

S_n = amount of annuity of n payments

$\dfrac{1}{s_{\overline{n}|}}$ = periodic deposit that will grow to \$1 in n payments

Use Formula (14) when the future amount is known.

Solving Formula (13), $A_n = Ra_{\overline{n}|}$, for R,

$$R = \frac{A_n}{a_{\overline{n}|}} = A_n \times \frac{1}{a_{\overline{n}|}} \tag{15}$$

R = periodic payment or rent

A_n = present value of annuity of n payments

$\dfrac{1}{a_{\overline{n}|}}$ = periodic payment necessary to pay off a loan of \$1 in n payments

Use Formula (15) when the present value is known.

While R could be found by dividing S_n or A_n by the correct factor, problems of this type occur so frequently in practice that the reciprocals of these factors have been determined. The numerical values of $\dfrac{1}{s_{\overline{n}|}}$ are given in the *Sinking Fund* column of Table 2 and $\dfrac{1}{a_{\overline{n}|}}$ in the *Partial Payment* column. This means that the periodic rent can be determined by multiplying as indicated in the final form of the above formulas. When setting up problems, the rate per period is often included as a subscript. When in doubt about which formula to use, draw a time diagram and see if the known sum is an amount or a present value. It is then easy to see whether the payments are to be taken forward or brought back to equal in value the given sum.

EXAMPLE 1: If money is worth 4% compounded semiannually, how much must a man save every 6 months to accumulate $3000 in 4 years?

SOLUTION: A time diagram shows that the $3000 is an amount in the future.

4 years, 8 payments							Amount $3000	
0	1	2	3	4	5	6	7	8 payments
	R	R	R	R	R	R	R	R

Substituting $S_8 = 3000$, $n = 8$, and $i = 2\%$ in Formula (14),

$$R = 3000 \times \frac{1}{s_{\overline{8}|2\%}}$$
$$= 3000 \times .116510 = \$349.53$$

Note that 8 payments of $349.53 total $2796.24. The balance needed to produce an amount of $3000 comes from the accumulated interest on each payment from the time it is made to the end of the problem 4 years hence.

EXAMPLE 2: A man wants to buy a home costing $13,000. If he pays $3000 cash, how much will the monthly payments be if he gets a 15-year mortgage with a rate of 6% compounded monthly?

SOLUTION: A time diagram shows that the $10,000 is a present value.

Present value $10,000		15 years, 180 payments					
0	1	2	3	178	179	180	payments
	R	R	R	R	R	R	

Substituting $A_{180} = 10,000$; $n = 180$; and $i = \frac{1}{2}\%$ in Formula (15),

$$R = 10,000 \times \frac{1}{a_{\overline{180}|\frac{1}{2}\%}}$$
$$= 10,000 \times .008439 = \$84.39$$

Note that 180 payments of $84.39 amount to $15,190.20 making the total interest $5190.20.

It is interesting to see what would happen if the man could borrow the $10,000 at 5% compounded monthly.

$$R = 10,000 \times \frac{1}{a_{\overline{180}|\frac{5}{12}\%}} = \$79.08$$

Repaying the $10,000 will now cost $180 \times 79.08 = \$14,234.40$ making the total interest $4234.40. Thus a reduction of one percentage point in the rate has resulted in a reduction of $5190.20 - 4234.40 = \$955.80$ in the total interest charges. This is not, of course, equivalent to a total cash savings of this amount as the savings are spread over 180 months at the rate of $5.31 per month. The equivalent cash savings will depend on the value of money to the person. For example, at 3% converted monthly it would be,

$$5.31 \times a_{\overline{180}|\frac{1}{4}\%} = 5.31 \times 144.805 = \$768.91$$

Whether we make the comparison on the basis of the total savings in interest or on the equivalent cash value of the savings, there is no doubt that before borrowing money, a person should shop around to find the most reasonable rate. An apparently small difference in the rate may mean saving hundreds of dollars.

Another thing to note in the above problem is that even with a 5% rate, the interest totaled over $4000. This shows that people should save their money so that they will have to do as little borrowing as possible.

3.8 Extension of Tables

The simplest way to find the value of $\frac{1}{s_{\overline{n}|}}$ or $\frac{1}{a_{\overline{n}|}}$ for an n beyond those given in the tables is to compute $s_{\overline{n}|}$ or $a_{\overline{n}|}$ using the method in Section 3.6 and then take the reciprocal.

EXAMPLE 1: How much must be deposited each quarter in an account paying 4% converted quarterly to accumulate $10,000 in 20 years?

SOLUTION: Substituting $S = 10,000$, $i = 1\%$, and $n = 80$ in (14),

$$R = 10,000 \times \frac{1}{s_{\overline{80}|1\%}}$$

We get $s_{\overline{80}|}$ by using 2 annuities of 40 payments each.

Amount of last 40 payments $= s_{\overline{40}|}$ $\qquad$ $=$ $\quad$ 48.886 3734

Amount of first 40 payments $= s_{\overline{40}|}(1.01)^{40}$

$$= 48.886\ 3734 \times 1.488\ 8637 = \underline{72.785\ 1468}$$

$$s_{\overline{80}|} = 121.671\ 5202$$

$$\frac{1}{s_{\overline{80}|}} = \quad .008\ 2189$$

$$R = 10,000 \times .008\ 2189 = \$82.19$$

EXAMPLE 2: To help finance the purchase of a home, a couple borrows $20,000. The loan is to be repaid in equal monthly payments over 20 years. If the rate is 6% converted monthly, find the size of the monthly payment.

SOLUTION: Substituting $A_n = 20,000$, $i = \frac{1}{2}\%$, and $n = 240$ in (15),

$$R = 20,000 \times \frac{1}{a_{\overline{240}|\frac{1}{2}\%}}$$

We get $a_{\overline{240}|}$ using 2 annuities of 120 payments each.

Present value of first 120 payments $= a_{\overline{120}|}$ $\qquad$ $=$ $\quad$ 90.073 4533

Present value of second 120 payments $= a_{\overline{120}|}(1.005)^{-120}$

$$= 90.073\ 4533 \times .549\ 6327 = \underline{49.507\ 3153}$$

$$a_{\overline{240}|} = 139.580\ 7686$$

$$\frac{1}{a_{\overline{240}|}} = \quad .007\ 1643$$

$$R = 20,000 \times .007\ 1643 = \$143.29$$

Exercise 3d

1. A man wants to accumulate $3000 in 6 years. He makes equal deposits at the end of each 6 months in a savings account paying 3% converted semiannually. What is the size of each deposit?   ($230.04)

2. Find the annual payment of an ordinary annuity if the amount is $5000, payments are made for 10 years, and the interest rate is 4%.

3. A man buys a refrigerator which sells for $350 cash. He pays $50 down and the balance in 18 equal monthly payments. If the seller charges 24% converted monthly for time payments, what is the size of the monthly payment?   ($20.01)

4. A loan company charges 36% converted monthly for small loans. What would be the monthly payment if a loan of $150 is to be repaid in 12 payments?

5. A man buys a car which lists at $2500. He pays $700 down and the balance in 24 monthly payments. If the interest rate is 12% converted monthly, what is the size of the payments? ($84.73)

6. What would be the monthly payment in Problem 5 if the rate is 24% converted monthly?

7. An heir receives $5000. He takes $1000 in cash and invests the remainder at 5% on June 1, 1964, with the understanding that this investment will be paid to him in equal payments every year for 3 years with the first payment to be made on June 1, 1965. What is the size of each of these payments? ($1468.84)

8. What would be the size of each payment in Problem 7 if the heir received 6% converted annually on his investment?

9. On June 1, 1965, a widow takes the $10,000 benefits from her husband's insurance policy and invests the money at 3% converted monthly with the understanding that she will receive 120 equal monthly payments. If she is to get her first check on July 1, 1965, what will be the size of each monthly payment? ($96.56)

10. If the widow in Problem 9 could invest the money at 4% converted monthly, how much would she get each month?

11. A couple expects to need about $3000 in 3 years for a down payment on a house. They plan to accumulate this amount by making equal payments every 6 months in a building and loan association that pays $4\frac{1}{2}$% converted semiannually. If the first deposit is made on July 1, 1965, and the last deposit on July 1, 1968, what is the size of the semiannual payment? They want to have the $3000 just after the last deposit. ($400.50)

12. Find the quarterly payment for an ordinary annuity to amount to $4500 in 4 years at 6% converted quarterly.

13. Eight thousand dollars are invested on June 1, 1964, at 4% converted monthly. The investment is to be paid out in 96 equal monthly payments with the first payment to be made on July 1, 1964. What is the size of the monthly payment? ($97.51)

14. If the investment in Problem 13 is paid out in 48 equal monthly payments, what would be the size of each payment?

15. A family needs to get a loan of $8000 to buy a new home. One lender charges 5% converted monthly. A second lender offers 4% converted monthly. If the monthly payments are to run for 12 years, what would be the total interest for the two rates? ($2654.56 at 5%; $2085.76 at 4%)

16. A mortgage for $12,000 is to be repaid in monthly payments over a period of 15 years. What would be the total savings in interest if the loan is financed at 5% converted monthly rather than 6%?

17. A family buys a home costing $15,000. They pay $3000 down and get a 30-year mortgage for the balance at 5% converted monthly. What is the size of their monthly payments? What is the total interest that they will pay on this loan?

($64.42 a month; $11,191.20 interest)

18. A man gets a loan for $8000 to be repaid in monthly payments over a period of 25 years. If the interest rate is 6% converted monthly, what is the size of the monthly payment and the total interest?

19. A $30,000 life insurance policy matures on June 1, 1964 with the death of the insured. The beneficiary is to receive 192 equal monthly payments with the first payment on July 1, 1964. Find the size of the monthly payment and the date of the concluding payment if interest is earned at 3% converted monthly. ($196.93, June 1, 1980)

20. What would be the size of the monthly payment if the money in Problem 19 earned 4% converted monthly?

21. A man wants to accumulate a $20,000 retirement fund. He plans to make semiannual deposits in a savings and loan association which pays 4% converted semiannually. If his first deposit is made on June 30, 1965, and his plan calls for the last deposit to be made on December 31, 2000, what should be the size of each deposit? ($126.54)

22. Work Problem 21 if the man can get 4½% converted semiannually.

3.9 Finding the Term of an Annuity

In some problems the amount or present value, the size of the payments, and the rate are specified. This leaves the number of payments to be determined. When an integral number of payments is not exactly equivalent to the original amount or present value, one of the following procedures is followed in practice. The last regular payment can be increased by a sum which will make the payments equivalent to the amount or present value. Or a smaller concluding payment can be made one period after the last full payment. In this book we follow the latter procedure unless the problem states that the last full payment is to be increased. Sometimes, when a certain amount of money is to be accumulated, a smaller concluding payment will not be required because the interest after the last full payment will equal or exceed the balance needed.

EXAMPLE 1: A man wants to accumulate $5000 by making payments of $1000 at the end of each year. If he gets 3% on his money, how many regular payments will he make and what is the size of the last payment?

SOLUTION: Using Formula (12) for the amount of an annuity,

$$1000s_{\overline{n}|3\%} = 5000$$

Solving for $s_{\overline{n}|}$,
$$s_{\overline{n}|3\%} = \frac{5000}{1000} = 5.0000$$

We look in Table 2 under 3% for the factor 5.0000 in the *Amount of 1 per Period* column. We find that for 4 periods the factor is 4.1836 and for 5 periods it is 5.3091. Therefore the man will have to make 4 deposits of $1000 and a fifth smaller deposit now to be determined. To get the size of this deposit we use an equation of value.

Instead of taking the four $1000 payments separately to the focal date, we get the amount of these four payments at the end of 4 years.

$$S_4 = 1000s_{\overline{4}|3\%}$$
$$= 1000 \times 4.183627 = \$4183.63$$

We now take this amount to the focal date and set up the equation of value.

$$4183.63(1.03) + x = 5000$$
$$x = 5000.00 - 4309.14 = \$690.86$$

Thus if the man deposits $1000 for four years and $690.86 at the end of 5 years, he will have exactly $5000 in his account. Note that in problems like this the last deposit will never be larger than the other deposits.

It is also possible to get the 4 payments to the focal date by looking up $s_{\overline{5}|}$ and subtracting 1 to allow for the fact that no full payment is made at the end. Then the amount becomes

$$1000(5.309136 - 1.000000) = \$4309.14$$

This leaves a balance of $690.86 to be paid at the end of 5 years.

This method will be discussed in more detail under annuities due in the next chapter.

EXAMPLE 2: A man wants to accumulate $9000 by annual payments of $1000 invested at 3%. How many full payments must he make and what will be the size of the concluding payment?

SOLUTION: Substituting in (12),

$$1000s_{\overline{n}|} = 9000$$

Solving for $s_{\overline{n}|}$, $s_{\overline{n}|} = 9.0000$

The *Amount of 1 per Period* column of Table 2 shows that 8 full payments will be required. The amount of these payments is

$$S_8 = 1000 \times 8.892336 = \$8892.34$$

Since this is close to the required amount, we compute the simple interest for 1 year, getting $266.77. This results in a final amount of $9159.11, so no smaller concluding payment is required in this problem.

EXAMPLE 3: A man dies and leaves his widow an estate worth $5000. Instead of taking the cash, she is to get monthly payments of $50. How many regular payments will she receive and what smaller payment one period after the last regular payment will settle the transaction equitably? The company will pay interest at 3% compounded monthly on the balance left with them.

SOLUTION: Using Formula (13) for the present value of an annuity,

$$50a_{\overline{n}|\frac{1}{4}\%} = 5000$$

Solving for $a_{\overline{n}|}$, $a_{\overline{n}|\frac{1}{4}\%} = \dfrac{5000}{50} = 100$

We look in Table 2 under $\frac{1}{4}\%$ for the factor 100 in the *Present Worth of 1 per Period* column. We find that for 115 periods the factor is less than 100 and for 116 periods it is greater. Therefore the widow will receive 115 payments of $50 and a 116th payment that is smaller than $50. To find the size of this concluding payment we set up an equation of value.

We first get the amount of the 115 regular $50 payments:

$$S_{115} = 50s_{\overline{115}|\frac{1}{4}\%}$$
$$= 50 \times 133.0450$$
$$= \$6652.25$$

We now take this amount and the $5000 to the focal date and set up the equation of value:

$$6652.25(1.0025) + x = 5000(1.0025)^{116}$$
$$x = 5000 \times 1.335944 - 6652.25(1.0025)$$
$$x = 6679.72 - 6668.88 = \$10.84$$

In this case the person will receive 115 payments of $50 and a 116th payment of $10.84.

As pointed out at the end of Example 1, it is also possible to get the 115 payments to the focal date by looking up $s_{\overline{116}|}$ and subtracting 1. The amount of 115 payments at the end of 116 periods then becomes,

$$50(134.3776 - 1.0000) = \$6668.88$$

Exercise 3e

1. Mr. Freeman can afford to set aside $200 every 6 months from his salary. He plans to buy a resort cottage when he has accumulated $3600. How long will it take him if he can invest the money at $3\frac{1}{2}\%$ converted semi-annually? Give answer to the nearest payment.   (16 payments)

2. How many payments of $50 at the end of each month will be required to accumulate $3000 if interest is earned at 5% converted monthly? Give answer to the nearest payment.

3. How many annual payments of $12,000 each and what final smaller payment must be made to accumulate $35,000 if the money gets interest at 4%?   (Two full payments; a concluding payment of $9540.80)

4. A couple deposits $250 at the end of each 6 months in a building and loan paying 4% converted semiannually. To accumulate $4500, they must make how many full payments and what will be the size of the concluding payment if one is needed?

5. A man leaves his wife an estate of $25,000. The money is invested at 3% compounded monthly. How many monthly payments of $200 would the widow receive and what would be the size of the concluding payment?
              (150 full payments; a concluding payment of $12.94)

6. An heir invests her inheritance of $15,000 at 4% converted monthly. If she takes the money out in monthly payments of $125, how many full payments will she get and what will be the size of the concluding payment?

7. The present value of an annuity is $7500. Semiannual payments of $500 are made from the $7500 which is invested at 4% compounded semi-annually. How many full payments will be made and what is the size of the concluding payment?   (18 full payments; a concluding payment of $5.80)

8. A man has $3000 in a building and loan association. If he gets $4\frac{1}{2}\%$ converted semiannually, how many withdrawals of $500 can he make at the end of each 6 months and what will be the size of the concluding withdrawal if it is made 6 months after the last full withdrawal?

9. Since the concluding payment in Problem 7 would be so small if made one period after the last full payment, it might be sent with the last regular payment. If this is done what is the size of the last check received by the annuitant?   ($505.69)

10. If, in Problem 5, the concluding payment was sent with the last regular payment, what total payment would the widow get at that time?

11. A man invests $20,000 on June 1, 1963, at 3% converted monthly. He is to receive monthly payments of $250 with the first payment to be made on July 1, 1963. How many full payments will he receive? What will be the size and date of the concluding payment if it is made 1 month after the last $250 payment?
    (89 full payments; a concluding payment of $92.31 on December 1, 1970)

12. Ten thousand dollars are invested on August 1, 1964, at 3% converted monthly. The investment is to be paid out in monthly payments of $200 with the first payment to be made on September 1, 1964. How many full payments will be made and what will be the size and date of the last payment if it is made 1 month after the last full payment?

13. A house is for sale for $13,500. A couple can pay $4500 down and $80 a month. If they get a loan at 5% converted monthly, how many $80 payments must they make and what will be the size of the concluding payment?   (152 regular payments and a 153rd payment of $9.74)

14. How many full payments and what would be the size of the concluding payment in Problem 13 if the rate is 4% converted monthly?

15. A couple can save $150 at the end of each 6 months. How long will it take them to accumulate $3500 if they get 3% converted semiannually on their savings? If they need a partial deposit 6 months after the last $150 deposit, how large should it be?   (20 full deposits; no partial deposit needed)

16. Work Problem 15 using a rate of 4% converted semiannually.

17. A piece of property is purchased for $360,000. The buyer pays $60,000 down and agrees to pay $40,000 at the end of each year. If the interest rate is 5%, how many full payments must be made and what will be the size of the concluding payment 1 year after the last full payment?

(9 full payments and a concluding payment of $25,552.70)

18. A firm buys a store costing $180,000. They pay $30,000 down and $20,000 at the end of each year. If the interest rate is 4%, how many full payments must they make and what will be the size of the concluding payment?

3.10   Finding the Interest Rate

A very practical application of the amount and present value formulas is finding the interest rate. In many business transactions the true interest rate is concealed in one way or another, so it is desirable that the customer be able to determine the rate. In this way he can compare one proposition with another and select the one that is least expensive for him. The rate can be determined approximately, but with sufficient accuracy for most practical purposes, by interpolation using factors from Table 2.

EXAMPLE 1: Find the rate of interest per period and the nominal rate converted semiannually at which payments of $150 every 6 months will amount to $2000 in 6 years.

SOLUTION: Substituting in formula (12) for the amount of an annuity, we have

$$150s_{\overline{12}|} = 2000$$

$$s_{\overline{12}|} = \frac{2000}{150} = 13.3333$$

We refer to Table 2 and go across the row for $n = 12$ until we find the factor 13.3333 or, as is usually the case, values on each side of this factor. We record these values below.

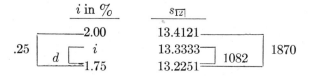

The rate per period in our problem lies between 1.75% and 2%. Using d to indicate the difference between 1.75% and the desired rate, we set up the proportion,

$$\frac{d}{.25} = \frac{1082}{1870}$$

$$d = .25 \times \frac{1082}{1870} = .144$$

From which $i = 1.75 + .144 = 1.894\%$

This is the rate per period. To get the approximate nominal rate converted semiannually we double this value so that the final answer is

$$2 \times 1.894 = 3.788 = 3.79\%$$

If only the nominal rate is wanted, we can get it as follows.

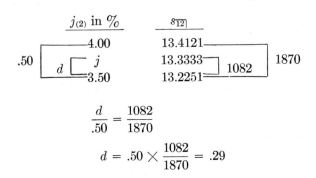

$$\frac{d}{.50} = \frac{1082}{1870}$$

$$d = .50 \times \frac{1082}{1870} = .29$$

The approximate nominal rate converted semiannually is $3.50 + .29 = 3.79\%$.

EXAMPLE 2: A used car can be purchased for $500 cash or $50 down and $35 a month for 18 months. Find the rate per month and the nominal annual rate.

SOLUTION: Subtracting the down payment gives us a present value of $450. Substituting in Formula (13) for the present value of an annuity, we have

$$35a_{\overline{18}|} = 450$$

$$a_{\overline{18}|} = \frac{450}{35} = 12.8571$$

We refer to Table 2 and look in row 18 until we find either 12.8571 or factors on both sides of this value in the *Present Worth of 1 per Period* column. The results are recorded below. Note that $a_{\overline{n}|}$ decreases as i increases.

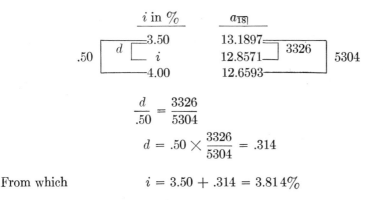

$$\frac{d}{.50} = \frac{3326}{5304}$$

$$d = .50 \times \frac{3326}{5304} = .314$$

From which $i = 3.50 + .314 = 3.814\%$

To convert this to an approximate annual rate we multiply by 12

$$12 \times 3.814 = 45.8\%$$

Because rates on installment purchases and small loans are often quite high, a buyer should always check the true rate before signing a contract.

EXAMPLE 3: To show how it is possible to conceal the true rate of interest from the customer, consider the following case based on data from a lender in a Midwestern city. A customer wants to borrow $100. The lender says the rate is 6% and charges him $6.00 "interest." Then he adds a fee of $2.00 for investigation. Any such fees are actually a part of the cost of the loan and should be so considered no matter what the lender may call them. The lender now divides $108 by 12 and informs the buyer that he is to repay the loan in 12 monthly installments of $9.00 each. Most customers still think they are getting money at 6%, but an analysis using the present value formula shows an entirely different situation.

SOLUTION: $9.00a_{\overline{12}|} = 100$

$$a_{\overline{12}|} = \frac{100}{9} = 11.1111$$

i in %		$a_{\overline{12}|}$	
	⎡1.00	11.2551⎤	
.25	d ⎣ i	11.1111⎦ 1440	1758
	⎣1.25	11.0793	

$$\frac{d}{.25} = \frac{1440}{1758}$$

$$d = .205$$

$$i = 1.000 + .205 = 1.205\%$$

From which the approximate nominal rate is

$$12 \times 1.205 = 14.5\%$$

This means that the customer who thought he was paying 6% is actually paying over twice that amount. The reason is that instead of having the full loan of $100 for a year, the borrower has the full amount for only one month after which he starts repaying part of the principal each month. A good exercise for students is to obtain data on a small loan or installment purchase and then compute the true interest rate and see how it compares with the value stated by the lender.

EXAMPLE 4: A trombone is priced on the tag at $100. It can be purchased for $8 down and $5 a week for 20 weeks. Or it can be obtained for cash at a 10% discount. What nominal interest rate converted weekly is charged the installment buyer?

SOLUTION: First we must get the *true* cash price which is not $100 but $100 less 10% or $90. This makes the original unpaid balance $82. ($90 less the $8 down payment). Now we substitute in (13),

$$5a_{\overline{20}|} = 82$$

From which

$$a_{\overline{20}|} = 16.4000$$

	i in %		$a_{\overline{20}|}$		
		1.75	16.7529		
.25	*d*	*i*	16.4000	3529	4015
		2.00	16.3514		

$$\frac{d}{.25} = \frac{3529}{4015}$$

$$d = .25 \times \frac{3529}{4015} = .22$$

$$i = 1.75 + .22 = 1.97\% \text{ per week}$$

This makes the approximate nominal rate $52 \times 1.97 = 102\%$.

3.11   Check the Rate

The examples in the preceding section show how to determine the interest rate. That this is important in practice is indicated by the following study in one state of 105 cases in which 6% was quoted:

```
1 case came to 6%
6 cases were between 7 and 10%
61 cases were between 11 and 20%
19 cases were between 21 and 30%
10 cases were between 31 and 100%
8 cases were between 101 and 679%
```

Because most students will have to at least occasionally borrow money, it is important for them to know about the more common sources of credit. In this section we shall consider consumer loans and installment credit. Large loans for homes and businesses will be discussed in Chapter 5.

The following table gives the common rates for various sources of small loans. While this will be a help in locating the most economical source of credit, the borrower should still check the rate himself as some lenders vary considerably from the typical values given below.

Source of Credit	Common Rates
Insurance policies	4–6%
Credit unions	9–12%
Commercial banks	12–18%
Automobile finance companies	12–24%
Licensed small loan companies	24–42%
Installment sellers	12–25% and up!
Loan sharks	120–1200% and up!

The person who borrows on his **life insurance** is in effect getting the use of his own cash reserve which will be discussed in Chapter 9. While an insurance policy may be the cheapest source of a small loan, the borrower should remember that, if he dies, the benefits will be reduced by the amount of the loan.

A **credit union** is really a people's bank. The members of a business, union, church or other group who have savings put the money on deposit in the credit union and receive interest. Members of the same group who need cash borrow from the credit union. Because operating, investigation and collection costs are low, a credit union can make small loans at a rate that is usually lower than those charged by commercial sources of credit.

While consumer loan rates charged by **banks** are not high, as modern credit goes, they are likely to be considerably higher than the stated rate and should be checked using the methods given in the preceding section.

Automobile finance companies usually charge rates that range from approximately 12 to 24% converted monthly. However, there are a few unethical companies in this field that resort to excessive packing (arbitrary amounts added to the financing charges) that can make the true interest rate much higher.

The **licensed small loan companies** charge rates which range from 2 to $3\frac{1}{2}$% a **month**. While these rates are high, perhaps unnecessarily so at times, these companies perform a useful service in granting credit to people who could not get a loan from one of the less expensive agencies mentioned above. People should not let the advertising emphasis of some of these companies on how easy it is to get a loan cause them to forget how hard it is to repay it at the usual rates.

Rates for **installment sales** vary from what is supposed to be zero when there is no charge for credit up to very high rates in other cases. However, if a discount can be obtained for cash, even the "no charge for credit" propositions may actually conceal a high rate of interest based on the *true* cash price.

Loan sharks operate outside the law and will charge whatever they can get away with. Because of their high rates and brutal methods, they should be avoided completely.

We can sum up the wise use of credit by saying that people should pay cash when possible, shop for credit if they must borrow, check the true rate of interest, and avoid being swindled by following the rule below.

Read and understand the contract and check financing costs before signing. Be sure that all blanks are filled in and get a complete copy of the contract.

Exercise 3f

1. The total cost of a car is $2673.54 cash. The down payment is $873.54. Payments of $70 a month are to be made for 30 months. What is the true annual interest rate converted monthly? Show answer between the two closest table values.   (12–15% converted monthly)

2. A lathe priced at $120 was sold on easy terms for a down payment of $40 and 10 monthly payments of $9. What is the true annual interest rate converted monthly? Show answer between the two closest table values.

3. If $500 periodic payments per year for 8 years amount to $4500, what is the effective rate of interest?   (3.34%)

4. Deposits in a building and loan association of $200 at the end of each 6 months for 5 years amounted to $2160. What was the average nominal rate of interest converted semiannually earned on this account?

5. A couple started to save $150 every 6 months in June, 1951. If they have $6400 in their account just after making the deposit in June, 1967, what nominal rate of interest converted semiannually did they earn on their savings?   (3.10%)

6. At the end of each month for 5 years a man put $50 in an investment. If his account then amounted to $3300, what rate of interest converted monthly did he earn on his investment?

7. On his 26th birthday Walter Artmeyer put $300 in a savings account. He continues to deposit the same amount every year. If he has $27,000 in his account just after he makes his deposit on his 65th birthday, what average annual rate of return had he earned on his investment?   (3.76%)

8. A rifle selling for $55 cash can be purchased for $10 down and $10 a month for 5 months. What is the nominal interest rate converted monthly rounded to the nearest .1%?

9. An electric range lists for $300. Sales tax is 3%. The range may be purchased on time for $25 down and 18 payments of $18.50 a month. What is the nominal interest rate?   (20.8%)

10. A used car is priced at $730. It can be purchased for $64 down and $45 a month for 18 months. What is the nominal rate of interest converted monthly for this time payment plan? Round answer to the nearest .1%.

11. The cash price of a refrigerator is $360. A buyer can pay $160 down and $12 a month for 24 months. What is the nominal rate converted monthly?   (37.8%)

12. A sofa can be purchased for $100 cash. If it is bought on time the down payment is $10 and the balance is paid in 11 monthly payments of $9 each. Get the nominal interest rate rounded to .1%.

13. A suite of furniture for 3 rooms can be purchased for $431.47 cash, or for $31.47 down and 18 monthly payments of $26 each. What is the nominal rate converted monthly?   (20.5%)

14. A refrigerator lists for $407.47. It can be purchased for $57.47 down and 24 monthly payments of $20 each. What is the nominal rate rounded to .1%?

15. A gravestone can be purchased for $180 cash or $45 down and $7.50 a month for 24 months. What is the nominal rate of interest?   (29.3%)

16. An engagement ring can be purchased for $110. Or it can be obtained with no down payment and monthly payments of $20 at the end of each month for 7 months. Get the nominal rate converted monthly rounded to .1%.

17. A store advertised a suite of furniture for $300. The ad said that there was no charge for easy terms since the furniture could be purchased for $50 down and $25 a month for 10 months. However, a cash customer could get a 10% discount by asking for it. What nominal rate of interest was actually paid by the installment buyer?   (28.7%)

18. A jewelry store advertised: "No carrying charge for time payments and no down payment." A watch with a price tag of $60 could be purchased for $5 a month for 12 months. When a customer asked for a cash discount, he got the watch for $50. Based on the true cash price, what was the nominal interest rate rounded to .1%?

19. A home freezer is listed at $350. If a customer pays $100 down, the balance plus a carrying charge of $20 can be paid in 12 equal monthly payments. If the customer pays cash, he can get a discount of 5% off the list price. What is the nominal rate converted monthly if the freezer is bought on time?   (28.6%)

20. A store offers to sell a watch for $60 or for $5 down and $5 a week for 11 weeks. If this same watch can be purchased for $50 cash at another store, the first store is actually charging what nominal rate of interest under their "no carrying charge plan"?

21. A store claims that their credit costs are very low. For example, a $220 washing machine can be bought for $20 down and $17.20 a month for 12 months. Under this plan they claim that the buyer is paying only 6% interest. A competitor claims that these carrying charges are low only because the washing machine is overpriced by $15. If this is correct, what nominal interest rate converted monthly is paid by an installment buyer at the first store?   (20.7%)

22. A man borrows $150 from a licensed small loan company and agrees to pay $15.07 a month for 12 months. What is the nominal rate of interest correct to the nearest percent?

23. A man needs $75 immediately for medical care for one of his children. He gets the money from a small loan company and agrees to pay $9.02 a month for 10 months. What is the nominal rate of interest?   (42%)

24. Shop for some item and get the following information:

Item. . . . .
Cash price. . . . .
Tax (if any) . . . .
Total cost . . . .
Cash discount (if one is allowed). . . . .
Down payment . . . .
Number and size of payments. . . . .
Interest rate as stated by the seller . . . .

Now compute the nominal rate using Table 2.

4

OTHER ANNUITIES CERTAIN

4.1 The Annuity Due

Formula (12), $S_n = Rs_{\overline{n}|}$, and the *Amount of 1 per Period* column in Table 2 enable us to find the amount of an annuity at the time of the last payment. Formula (13), $A_n = Ra_{\overline{n}|}$, and the *Present Worth of 1 per Period* column enable us to find the present value of an annuity one period before the first payment. If we want the value of an annuity at any other time, we can use these formulas to convert the annuity into an equivalent single sum and then move this sum to the desired point in time using compound interest or compound discount. In some cases we follow this procedure. In other cases, it is more efficient to use the formulas derived in this chapter for other types of annuities that occur frequently in business transactions.

An **annuity due** is one in which the payments are made at the beginning of the payment interval, the first payment being due at once. Insurance premiums and property rentals are examples of annuities due. To get the amount and present value formulas for the annuity due, we modify the formulas already derived for the ordinary annuity so that the ordinary annuity tables can be used with very simple corrections.

The sketch on the following page illustrates an annuity due. Note that it starts with a payment and ends one period after the last or nth payment. Also included in the sketch is the corresponding ordinary annuity.

The sketch shows that if we obtain the amount of an ordinary annuity of $n + 1$ payments, we would have the amount of the corresponding annuity due except that we have included a final payment which is not actually made at the end of the last period of the annuity due. Therefore all we have to do is subtract one payment to permit us to use the ordinary annuity tables to

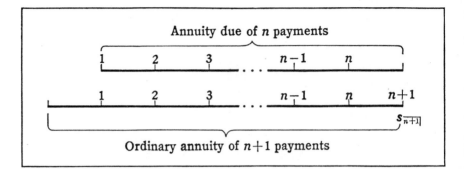

get the amount of an annuity due. This leads to the following formula:

$$S_n = R s_{\overline{n+1}|} - R$$
$$\mathbf{S_n = R(s_{\overline{n+1}|} - 1)} \tag{16}$$

The rather complex appearing quantity which is to be multiplied by R is quite simple to get in practice. First we add 1 to the number of payments in the annuity due, and use the resulting value when we go to the table. This means that if there are 10 payments we look up the value for 11. Then we subtract 1 from the factor. For an interest rate of 2% and 11 periods the factor is 12.1687 (correct to 4 decimal places). To get the amount of an annuity due of 10 payments we would use 11.1687 for the factor. All of these steps can be done mentally.

To get the present value of an annuity due, we again make a sketch with the corresponding ordinary annuity.

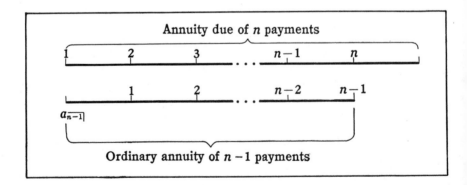

Note that we again match the annuity due with an ordinary annuity as closely as we can. If we obtain the present value of an ordinary annuity of

$n - 1$ payments, we would have the present value of the corresponding annuity due except that we would not be including a payment which is made at the beginning of the term of the annuity due. Therefore all we have to do is add this first payment. This leads to the following formula for the present value of an annuity due:

$$A_n = Ra_{\overline{n-1}|} + R$$
$$A_n = R(a_{\overline{n-1}|} + 1) \tag{17}$$

Again it is simple to use the ordinary annuity tables. First we subtract 1 from the number of payments in the annuity due, and use the resulting value when we go to the table. This means that if there are 8 payments in an annuity due we look up the value for 7. Then we add 1 to the factor. For an interest rate of 3% and 7 periods the factor is 6.2303. We then change this to 7.2303 to get the present value of an annuity due of 8 payments and a rate of 3%.

EXAMPLE 1: A man invests $200 at the beginning of each year for 10 years. If he gets interest at $3\frac{1}{2}\%$ effective, how much does he have to his credit at the end of 10 years?

SOLUTION: Substituting $R = 200$, $n + 1 = 11$, and $i = 3\frac{1}{2}\%$ in (16),

$$S_{10} = 200(s_{\overline{11}|} - 1)$$
$$= 200 \times 12.14199 = \$2428.40$$

EXAMPLE 2: A student wants to have $600 four years from now. How much must he invest at the beginning of each year starting now if he gets 3% compounded annually on his savings?

SOLUTION: Substituting in (16) and solving for R,

$$600 = R(s_{\overline{5}|} - 1) = R \times 4.30914$$
$$R = \frac{600}{4.30914} = \$139.24$$

ALTERNATE SOLUTION: We can check the answer by using an equation of value with the focal date at the time of the last deposit. The 4 payments are brought to the focal date as an ordinary annuity, and the $600 is brought to the focal date by discounting it for one period.

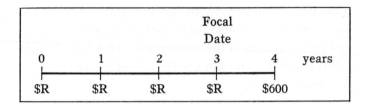

$$Rs_{\overline{4}|} = 600(1 + i)^{-1}$$

$$R = 600(1.03)^{-1} \times \frac{1}{s_{\overline{4}|}}$$

$$= 600 \times .97084 \times .23903 = \$139.24$$

This method requires an additional multiplication but no division.

EXAMPLE 3: The premium on a life insurance policy is $60 a quarter payable in advance. Find the cash equivalent of a year's payments if the insurance company charges 6% converted quarterly for the privilege of paying this way instead of all at once for the year.

SOLUTION: Substituting $R = 60$, $n - 1 = 3$ and $i = 1\frac{1}{2}\%$ in (17),

$$A_4 = 60(a_{\overline{3}|} + 1)$$
$$= 60 \times 3.9122 = \$234.73$$

While paying by the quarter is convenient, the savings represented by annual payments are substantial.

EXAMPLE 4: The beneficiary of a life insurance policy may take $10,000 cash or 10 equal annual payments, the first to be made immediately. What is the annual payment if money is worth $2\frac{1}{2}\%$?

SOLUTION: Substituting in (17) and solving for R,

$$10,000 = R(a_{\overline{9}|} + 1) = R \times 8.9708655$$
$$R = \frac{10,000}{8.9708655} = \$1114.72$$

ALTERNATE SOLUTION: An equation of value with the focal date at the time of the last payment enables us to check the above answer. The 10 payments are brought to the focal date as an ordinary annuity since the focal date is at the time of the last payments. The $10,000 is brought forward 9 (not 10) periods. A time diagram is very helpful in getting the correct values of n in problems like this.

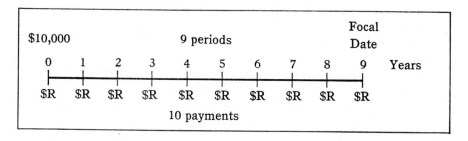

$$Rs_{\overline{10}|} = 10,000(1.025)^9$$

$$R = 10,000(1.025)^9 \times \frac{1}{s_{\overline{10}|}}$$

$$= 10,000 \times 1.248\ 8630 \times .089\ 2588 = \$1114.72$$

This method eliminates the division at the expense of an additional multiplication.

Exercise 4a

1. If money is worth 4% converted semiannually, what is the present value of an annuity due of $500 every 6 months for 5 years? ($4581.12)

2. At 5% converted monthly, what is the present value of an annuity due of $45 every month for 12 years?

3. What is the amount of the annuity due in Problem 1? ($5584.36)

4. What is the amount of the annuity due in Problem 2?

5. On July 6, 1963, a man deposited $250 in a savings and loan association paying $4\frac{1}{2}\%$ converted semiannually. Interest dates are June 30 and December 31, and deposits made by the 10th of a month earn interest for the entire month. This man continues to make $250 deposits every 6 months up to and including January 4, 1969, when he makes his last deposit. How much will be in his account after interest is credited on June 30, 1969? ($3477.07)

6. On June 1, 1961, a man deposits $200 in a building and loan association that pays 3% converted semiannually. He continues to make $200 deposits every 6 months. If he makes his last deposit on December 1, 1965, how much will be in his account on June 1, 1966?

7. A couple expects to need $4000 in June, 1968. In June, 1964, they make the first of 4 equal annual deposits in an investment paying 4%. What is the size of each deposit needed to accumulate the desired amount?

($905.73)

8. A debt of $7500 is due in 10 years. The debtor agrees to settle this debt with 10 equal annual payments, the first payment to be made now. Find the size of the payment if money is worth 4%.

9. The annual premium on a life insurance policy is $250 payable in advance. However, payments may be made quarterly in advance in which case the insurance company charges interest at 6% converted quarterly. Find the size of the quarterly payment. ($63.90)

10. The annual premium on a life insurance policy is $185 payable in advance. What would be the monthly premium based on 6% converted monthly?

11. A man has $5000 in a building and loan association which pays $3\frac{1}{2}$% compounded semiannually. If he withdraws $500 at the beginning of each half year, how many such withdrawals can he make? What will be the size of the concluding withdrawal?

(Ten $500 withdrawals and an 11th withdrawal of $439.80)

12. In Problem 11 how many $250 withdrawals could be made and what would be the size of the concluding withdrawal?

13. Instead of taking $5000 from an inheritance, a person decides to take 60 monthly payments with the first payment to be made immediately. If interest is allowed at 3% converted monthly, what will be the size of each payment? ($89.62)

14. Instead of taking $20,000 cash from an inheritance, the heir elects to receive quarterly payments for 10 years with the first payment to be made right away. If the money is invested at 4% converted quarterly, what will be the size of each payment?

15. A man wants to take out enough life insurance to provide 120 monthly payments certain of $150 each to his family. If the first payment is to be made upon proof of the man's death, he should take out what size policy? Round the answer to the nearest $1000. The insurance company pays 3% converted monthly on money left with them. ($16,000)

16. A man is planning an insurance program which will pay 180 monthly payments certain of $200 each to his widow. The insurance company will pay 3% converted monthly on money left with them. If the first payment is to be made upon proof of the man's death, he should take out what size policy? Round answer to nearest $1000.

17. A store can be rented for $300 a month payable in advance. If the renter pays 3 months in advance, the owner will allow interest at 5% converted monthly. What is the size of the payment at the beginning of each 3 months that is equivalent to $300 at the beginning of each month?

($896.27)

18. A store can be rented for $350 per month payable in advance. The landlord will accept a single cash payment at the beginning of a year for a year's lease if interest is computed at 5% converted monthly. What would be the cost of a year's lease?

19. A man knows that if he dies his wife will not get any social security benefits until she reaches age 62. He has several insurance policies. One for $10,000 is to be used to provide a monthly income for her between the time he dies and she reaches age 62. She is 55 at the time he dies and she elects to get 84 equal monthly payments from this policy with the first payment to be made immediately. What will be the size of each payment if 4% converted monthly is paid on the proceeds of this policy?   ($136.23)

20. The widow in Problem 19 decides to wait until age 65 to start receiving social security payments so they will be larger. She elects to get 120 equal monthly payments from the $10,000 policy with the first payment to be made immediately. Find the size of the payments.

21. On June 1, 1963, a man opened a savings account for his daughter with a deposit of $25 in a bank paying 3% converted semiannually. If he continues to make semiannual deposits of $25 until December 1, 1970, when he plans to make the last deposit, how much will be in the account on June 1, 1971?   ($455.04)

22. A man invests $300 every year, making his first deposit on August 1, 1958, and his last deposit on August 1, 1968. How much will be in his account on August 1, 1969, if he gets interest at 3% compounded annually?

23. A man aged 25 is considering two types of life insurance policies. The first is an ordinary life with an annual premium of $200 for a $10,000 policy. The second is a twenty-year endowment with an annual premium of $510. He decides to take out the ordinary life and deposit the difference in premiums each year in an investment paying 3% compounded annually. If he dies just before making his 17th deposit, how much will be in his savings account? Allow interest for the year after the 16th deposit.   ($6436.09)

24. A man aged 30 is considering two $15,000 insurance policies. The first is an ordinary life with an annual premium of $277. The second is a 20-pay life with an annual premium of $410. He decides to take out the ordinary life and put the difference in premiums in an investment paying $3\frac{1}{2}\%$. How much will his family get from this investment if he dies after interest is earned on the 15th deposit but before he makes the 16th deposit?

25. A factory owner has a fire insurance policy for which the annual premium is $300 payable in advance. If interest is 6% converted annually, what would be the equivalent single premium which would provide insurance for 5 years? ($1339.53)

26. A home owner has been paying his insurance at the beginning of each year. The annual premium is $60. At 8% converted annually, what would be the equivalent premium for a three-year policy?

4.2 Deferred Annuities

A deferred annuity is one in which the first payment is not made at the beginning or end of the first period but at some later date. When the first payment is made at the end of 10 periods, the annuity is said to be deferred 9 periods. Similarly, an annuity which is deferred for 12 periods will have the first payment at the end of 13 periods. It is important that the student understand that *the interval of deferment ends one period before the first payment.* In practice this point causes considerable trouble because in some problems the interval of deferment is given, in others the time of the first payment. When the time of the first payment is given, the student must determine the interval of deferment before substituting in the present value formula. For example, if payments are made quarterly and the first payment is made in 4 years, the interval of deferment is 15 periods.

The sketch shows a deferred annuity of n payments which is deferred for m periods.

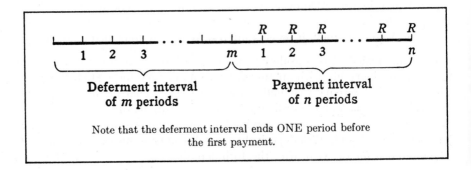

Note that the deferment interval ends ONE period before the first payment.

To get the formula for the present value of a deferred annuity, we begin by assuming that a payment is made at the end of each period during the interval of deferment. If this were the case, we would have an ordinary annuity of $m + n$ payments and the present value would be $Ra_{\overline{m+n}|}$. This value, of course, is too large because it includes the assumed payments during the interval of deferment. These assumed payments also form an ordinary annuity and their present value is $Ra_{\overline{m}|}$. Therefore, to get the present value of a deferred annuity all we have to do is subtract the present value of the m assumed payments from the present value of the $m + n$ payments. This leads to

$$A_n = Ra_{\overline{m+n}|} - Ra_{\overline{m}|}$$

$$A_n = R(a_{\overline{m+n}|} - a_{\overline{m}|}) \tag{18}$$

To get the present value of a deferred annuity, we look up $a_{\overline{m+n}|}$ and $a_{\overline{m}|}$ in the *Present Worth of 1 per Period* column of Table 2, subtract the smaller from the larger, and multiply this difference by the periodic payment.

The present value of a deferred annuity can also be obtained by using Formula (13) for the present value of an ordinary annuity to get the value of the payments one period before the first payment is made and then discounting this equivalent single sum for the m periods in the interval of deferment. This leads to,

$$A_n = Ra_{\overline{n}|}(1 + i)^{-m} \tag{19}$$

This form of the deferred annuity formula is useful when logarithms are used. It also makes it possible to obtain R without doing any dividing since

$$R = A_n(1 + i)^m \times \frac{1}{a_{\overline{n}|}} \cdot$$

EXAMPLE 1: Find the present value of a deferred annuity of $500 a year for 10 years deferred 5 years. Money is worth 3%.

SOLUTION: The deferment interval is given and equals 5 years. The number of payments is also given and is 10. To get the present value all we need do is substitute in formula (18) and get values under *Present Worth of 1 per Period* in Table 2 for a rate of 3%.

$$A_{10} = 500(a_{\overline{5+10}|} - a_{\overline{5}|})$$
$$= 500(11.93794 - 4.57971)$$
$$= 500 \times 7.35823 = \$3679.12$$

EXAMPLE 2: Find the present value of an annuity of $50 every 3 months for 5 years if the first payment is made in 3 years. Money is worth 4% converted quarterly.

SOLUTION: Here $n = 20$ and i is 1%. To get the interval of deferment we drop back 1 period from the first payment, so $m = 11$.

$$A_{20} = 50(a_{\overline{11+20}|} - a_{\overline{11}|})$$
$$= 50(26.5423 - 10.3676)$$
$$= 50 \times 16.1747 = \$808.74$$

EXAMPLE 3: A woman inherits $20,000. Instead of taking the cash, she invests the money at 3% converted semiannually with the understanding that she will receive 20 equal semiannual payments with the first payment to be made in 5 years. Find the size of the payments.

SOLUTION: The interval of deferment is 9 periods, the present value of the annuity is $20,000, and i is $1\frac{1}{2}\%$. Substituting in (18),

$$20,000 = R(a_{\overline{9+20}|} - a_{\overline{9}|}) = R(23.3760756 - 8.3605173)$$

$$R = \frac{20,000}{15.0155583} = \$1331.95$$

ALTERNATE SOLUTION: Using (19) solved for R,

$$R = A_n(1 + i)^m \times \frac{1}{a_{\overline{n}|}}$$

$$R = 20,000(1.015)^9 \times \frac{1}{a_{\overline{20}|}}$$

$$R = 20,000 \times 1.1433900 \times .0582457 = \$1331.95$$

This method of solution eliminates division but requires 2 multiplications.

Exercise 4b

1. Find the present value of a deferred annuity of $500 a year for 6 years deferred 5 years if money is worth 4%.   ($2154.33)

2. Find the present value of an annuity of $45 a month for 96 months if the first payment is made 2 years hence, and money is worth 4% converted monthly.

3. Find the present value of a deferred annuity of $1200 a year for 10 years deferred 5 years if money is worth 3%.   ($8829.87)

4. Find the present value of a deferred annuity of $200 every 6 months for 8 years if money is worth 4% converted semiannually and the interval of deferment is $4\frac{1}{2}$ years.

5. Find the value on September 1, 1964, of a series of $80 monthly payments, the first of which will be made on September 1, 1968, and the last on December 1, 1970, if money is worth 6% compounded monthly.   ($1649.63)

6. Find the value on June 1, 1963, of a series of payments of $425 every 6 months if the first of these payments is to be made on December 1, 1966, and the last on June 1, 1973. Use an interest rate of $4\frac{1}{2}\%$ converted semiannually.

7. What amount put aside on a boy's 12th birthday will provide 4 annual payments of $800 for college tuition if the first payment is made on the boy's 18th birthday? The fund will earn interest at 3%. ($2565.12)

8. What sum of money should be set aside today to provide an income of $150 a month for a period of 5 years if the first payment is to be made 4 years hence and money is worth 6% compounded monthly?

9. A child aged 12 wins $8000 on a quiz program. It is placed in a trust fund earning 3% converted annually. If she takes the money in 4 equal annual payments with the first payment to be made 6 years later, what will be the size of each payment? ($2495.01)

10. Under the terms of a will, a child on his 18th birthday will receive $12,000. He will get $2000 of this in cash. The remainder will be set aside to provide a monthly income from his 21st to his 25th birthday inclusive ($n = 49$). If the money is invested at 4% compounded monthly, what will be the size of the monthly payments?

11. On his wife's 59th birthday, her husband makes provision for her to receive $150 a month for 5 years with the first payment to be made on her 65th birthday. If the investment earns 4% converted monthly, how much money must he set aside? ($6430.90)

12. On his 57th birthday a man wants to set aside enough money to provide an income of $150 a month for 10 years with the first payment to be made on his 60th birthday. If he gets 3% compounded monthly on his money, how much will this pension plan cost on his 57th birthday?

13. On June 1, 1964, a man deposits $3000 in a bank paying 3% compounded annually. On June 1, 1970, he makes the first of 4 equal annual withdrawals from his account. Find the size of the withdrawals so that the account will be closed with the last withdrawal. ($935.63)

14. If the account in Problem 13 had earned $3\frac{1}{2}$% interest, what would be the size of the annual withdrawal?

15. A philanthropist gives a college $40,000 on September 1, 1950, with the provision that the money is to be used to provide annual scholarships of $2500 with the first scholarship to be awarded on the September 1 following his death. The money is invested at $2\frac{1}{2}$%. If the donor dies on June 18, 1965, how many full scholarships can be awarded? (33)

16. A widow decides to take the $10,000 proceeds from an insurance policy in payments of $200 a month with the first payment to be made in 5 years. How many full payments will she get if the insurance company allows 3% converted monthly on the money left with them?

17. On June 1, 1960, a minor receives an inheritance of $6500. This is placed in a trust fund earning 3% compounded semiannually. On December 1, 1965, the child reaches age 18 and is paid the first of 8 equal semiannual payments from the fund. What is the size of each payment?   ($1007.69)

18. A school receives $40,000 in 1964. This is to be used to provide annual scholarships of $3000 with the first scholarship to be awarded in 1970. If the money is invested at 4%, how many full scholarships can be awarded? How much will be left in the fund one year after the last full scholarship to apply to a partial scholarship?

4.3 Perpetuities

In some investments only the interest is used and the principal is kept intact. For example, if a philanthropist wants to provide an annual scholarship of $1000 indefinitely, he must give as an endowment enough money to earn $1000 interest every year. When it is assumed that the regular payments will go on forever, the annuity is called a **perpetuity.** Other examples of perpetuities are dividends on preferred stock (provided all dividends are paid), interest on perpetual bonds, and the endowment funds of endowed institutions such as libraries, museums, etc., that are established with a sum of money that is supposed to maintain them "in perpetuity."

In practice all perpetuities must end sometime, but the *forever assumption* still underlies the mathematical treatment of perpetuities. It is, of course, impossible to get the accumulated amount of a perpetuity. Getting the present value is both possible and easy. We shall first consider the case where the interest period coincides with the payment period.

To get the present value of a perpetual scholarship of $1000 a year, we have to know what rate of interest can be expected on the endowment. Suppose the school can expect a return of 4%. Then the philanthropist would have to give $25,000 because it takes this amount to earn $1000 interest each year at 4%. As long as only the interest is used and the endowment earns 4%, the $1000 scholarships can be awarded indefinitely. In more general terms we can say

$$A_\infty i = R$$

$$A_\infty = \frac{R}{i} \tag{20}$$

The subscript ∞ is the mathematical symbol for **infinity.** In this case A_∞ denotes the present value of a series of payments that continue indefinitely. The size of each payment is R and the rate per period is i.

Now suppose that instead of using the interest as it is earned, we let it accumulate for more than one period. We shall use the letter n to indicate the number of conversion periods that elapse before the interest is drawn off leaving the original principal intact. Letting the present value of this perpetuity accumulate for n periods we have an amount of

$$A_\infty (1 + i)^n$$

We now subtract the periodic payment and again have the original present value,

$$A_\infty (1 + i)^n - R = A_\infty$$

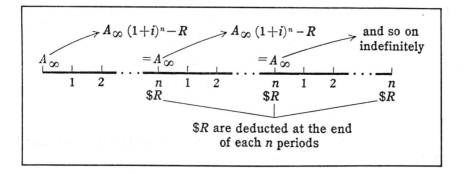

$R are deducted at the end
of each n periods

To solve the above formula for A_∞ we proceed as follows:

$$A_\infty (1 + i)^n - A_\infty = R$$
$$A_\infty [(1 + i)^n - 1] = R$$
$$A_\infty = \frac{R}{(1 + i)^n - 1}$$

Multiplying numerator and denominator by i and rearranging, we have

$$A_\infty = \frac{R}{i} \times \frac{i}{(1 + i)^n - 1}$$

Since $\dfrac{i}{(1 + i)^n - 1} = \dfrac{1}{s_{\overline{n}|}}$ this can be simplified as follows,

$$A_\infty = \frac{R}{i} \times \frac{1}{s_{\overline{n}|}} \qquad\qquad (21)$$

We can now solve this type of perpetuity with a minimum of work because the factor $\dfrac{1}{s_{\overline{n}|}}$ can be obtained from the *Sinking Fund* column in Table 2.

EXAMPLE 1: An alumnus wants to provide a perpetual $300 a year scholarship with the first scholarship to be given in 1 year. If the money can be invested at 3%, how large must the grant be?

SOLUTION: This is the first type of perpetuity and the solution is very simple.

$$A_{\infty} = \frac{300}{.03} = \$10,000$$

EXAMPLE 2: If the money in Example 1 could be invested at 3% converted semiannually, how large a grant would be needed?

SOLUTION: Here we must use the second perpetuity formula because the interest is converted twice a year while it is used only once a year.

$$A_{\infty} = \frac{300}{.015} \times \frac{1}{s_{\overline{2}|1\frac{1}{2}\%}}$$

$$= \frac{300}{.015} \times .4962779$$

$$= \$9925.56$$

It is interesting to see just how this initial grant provides the $300 annual scholarships.

Initial grant	$9,925.56
$1\frac{1}{2}\%$ interest for 6 months	148.88
New principal	10,074.44
$1\frac{1}{2}\%$ interest for the second 6 months	151.12
New principal	10,225.56
First scholarship is deducted	300.00
Principal at start of second year	9,925.56

Thus the school will be able to provide annual scholarships of $300 indefinitely if they continue to get 3% converted semiannually on the original grant of $9925.56.

This problem also illustrates why, at current interest rates, even a very large endowment does not provide much income. This means that an organization, such as a private school, which does not have enough income from tuition to meet expenses, must conduct fund raising campaigns from time to time to provide funds for operation and expansion.

EXAMPLE 3: Find the rate of return on a 4%, $100 preferred stock with dividends payable semiannually if the stock is selling at $105.

SOLUTION: In this problem the stock will pay 2% every six months on $100. Thus the person who gets the stock will obtain a perpetuity of $2 every six months regardless of what he pays for the stock. However, the rate of return on his investment will depend on the purchase price. The purchase price becomes the present value of the perpetuity and the \$2 dividends are the periodic payments. Solving the perpetuity formula for i, we have

$$i = \frac{R}{A_\infty} = \frac{2.00}{105} = .019 = 1.9\%$$

The nominal rate is $2 \times 1.9 = 3.8\%$.

If the stock had been purchased at less than \$100 the rate of return would be more than 4%.

EXAMPLE 4: How much must an alumnus give a college to provide an annual scholarship of \$500 for an indefinitely long period if the endowment can be invested at 4% and if the first scholarship will be provided: (a) 1 year from now; (b) immediately; (c) 5 years from now?

SOLUTION: (a) If the first scholarship is to be awarded in 1 year, the required grant will be

$$A_\infty = \frac{500}{.04} = \$12,500$$

(b) If the first scholarship is to be awarded immediately the grant is simply the sum of the above perpetuity and \$500 or \$13,000.

(c) If the first scholarship is to be awarded in 5 years, the fund will have to contain \$12,500 in 4 years. At that time it begins to function as a perpetuity and will earn \$500 a year interest from then on. The question then is what sum now will amount to \$12,500 in 4 years at 4%. This can be obtained from (11).

$$P = 12,500(1.04)^{-4} = 12,500 \times .8548042 = \$10,685.05$$

In problems like this it is a good idea to use a time diagram to avoid errors in determining the various times that are involved. A sketch like the following shows each point in time and the corresponding dollar value of the endowment.

Exercise 4c

1. A man wants to provide $1000 every 6 months indefinitely toward the support of an orphanage. If the first payment will be made in 6 months and if the fund draws interest at 4% converted semiannually, what size endowment will be needed?   ($50,000)

2. What is the present value of a perpetuity of $125 a month if money is worth 6% converted monthly and the first payment is to be made in 1 month?

3. If money is worth 4% converted semiannually, find the present value of an annual scholarship of $1200 a year if the first scholarship is to be awarded 1 year from now? (Round answer to the nearest dollar.)   ($29,703)

4. What is the present value of a perpetuity of $750 a year if the first payment is to be made in 1 year and the interest rate is 3% converted semi-annually?

5. A school receives a gift of $200,000 to provide annual scholarships to needy students. If 20 scholarships will be awarded each year starting in 1 year, and if the money is invested at $4\frac{1}{2}$% converted semiannually, what will be the size of each scholarship?   ($455.06)

6. What would be the size of each scholarship in Problem 5 if the rate is 3% converted semiannually?

7. Mr. Berger wants to provide a research fellowship of $1800 annually. If money can be invested at $2\frac{1}{2}$% compounded semiannually, and if the first fellowship will be awarded in 5 years, how much should Mr. Berger give the school?   ($64,783.79)

8. What sum of money invested at 3% converted semiannually will provide a perpetual income of $3000 at the end of each 2 years?

9. On September 1, 1960, a college receives a grant of $30,000 which is invested at 4%. If annual scholarships are awarded for 20 years from this grant, what is the size of the scholarship if the first one is awarded on (a) September 1, 1960; (b) September 1, 1970? If the scholarships are to be awarded indefinitely, what will be the size of the scholarship if the first one is awarded on (c) September 1, 1960; (d) September 1, 1970?
                    [(a) $2122.55; (b) $3141.89; (c) $1153.85; (d)$1707.97]

10. In 1950 an alumnus gave a university $20,000 which was invested at a rate that would provide $1000 scholarships at the end of each year indefi-nitely. (a) What interest rate was the school earning on the investment at that time? (b) After the scholarship was awarded in 1962, the school had to reinvest the fund at $3\frac{1}{2}$%. If they want to continue to award scholarships indefinitely, they will have to change the value of each scholarship to what amount? (c) If they want to continue to award $1000 scholarships, the fund will provide how many full scholarships at the new rate?

11. What is the present value of a perpetuity of $800 at the end of each year if money is worth: (a) $2\frac{1}{2}\%$; (b) $2\frac{1}{2}\%$ compounded semiannually?

[(a) $32,000; (b) $31,801]

12. What would be the size of the grants in Problem 9 if the school can invest the money at 5%?

13. What sum of money invested at 2% converted semiannually, will provide $200 at the end of each 2 years indefinitely?   ($4925.62)

14. How much will it take to provide a hospital with an annual research grant of $5000 indefinitely if the first grant is to be made immediately and if the endowment which is to make the grants possible can be invested at 4%?

15. A school can invest money at 4% converted semiannually. How large a grant would be needed to provide a $1500 research fellowship at the end of each year indefinitely? (Round answer to the nearest dollar.)   ($37,129)

16. What size grant would provide the fellowship in Problem 15 if $3\frac{1}{2}\%$ compounded semiannually is earned on the invested funds?

17. A share of preferred stock has a par value of $100 and pays 6% interest annually. If it is purchased for $94, what yield rate would the investor get?   (6.38%)

18. If the stock in Problem 17 was purchased for $106, what would be the yield rate?

19. A man gives a school $15,000 to provide an annual scholarship indefinitely. The first scholarship is to be awarded 1 year after the grant is received. If the fund earns 4% converted semiannually, what will be the size of each scholarship? (When solving practical business problems, always look for the most direct method. While this is a perpetuity, the perpetuity formulas do not provide the easiest method of solution. Carry the original grant forward 1 year at compound interest and keep back a sum equal to the original grant. The difference will be the accumulated interest which can be given as a scholarship without touching the original principal.)   ($606.00)

20. If the institution in which the fund in Problem 19 is invested starts paying 4% compounded quarterly, what will be the size of the annual scholarship?

4.4 The General Case

When payments are made more or less frequently than the compounding period, the annuity comes under the **general case**. The first step in solving general annuity problems is to get the payments and the compounding periods to coincide. Then the problem can be completed by using the factors from Table 2 in the same way that we have been using them for simple annuities in which the payments are made at the time interest is earned.

One way to solve general annuities is to convert the given interest rate into an equivalent rate for which the conversion period is the same as the payment period. The second way is to change the original payments to equivalent payments made on the stated interest conversion dates. In this book we shall follow the latter practice of altering the original payments into equivalent payments which coincide with the compounding periods. This results in simpler computations in some cases.

We shall now consider problems which have interest compounded more frequently than payments are made. For example, payments may be made annually and interest compounded semiannually; or payments may be made semiannually and interest compounded monthly.

EXAMPLE 1: Find the amount of an ordinary annuity of $500 per year for 10 years if money is worth 4% compounded semiannually.

SOLUTION: A good way to analyze a problem of this type is to sketch one payment interval and the corresponding conversion periods.

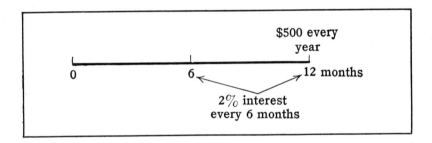

We now replace the original payments with payments of $R on each interest date.

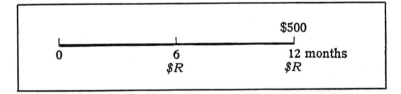

Since the new payments form an ordinary annuity of $R per payment accumulating at 4% converted semiannually, we can set up the following equation of value using Formula (14),

$$R = 500 \times \frac{1}{s_{\overline{2}|2\%}} = 500 \times .4950495 = \$247.52$$

(In the exercises and examples in this section we usually round the equivalent payment to the nearest cent. This results in answers that will be the same as those obtained by students who do not have access to computing machines and round intermediate answers to save time. In practical business situations where computing machines are available, entire factors can be used throughout the problem without additional labor and the final answer rounded to the cent.)

We now replace the original payments of $500 every year by payments of $247.52 every 6 months. The problem can then be completed as an ordinary annuity. Note in particular that there are 20 payments in the final annuity because each of the original 10 payments has been replaced by 2 payments. Therefore the final amount using Formula (12) is,

$$S_{20} = 247.52 s_{\overline{20}|2\%}$$
$$S_{20} = 247.52 \times 24.29737 = \$6014.09$$

EXAMPLE 2: Find the present value of an ordinary annuity of 20 semiannual payments of $1000 each if money is worth 6% converted monthly.

SOLUTION: A sketch of one payment interval shows that it contains 6 interest conversion periods.

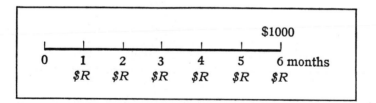

The original payment is to be replaced by 6 equal monthly payments which are equivalent in value to $1000 at the end of 6 months. Substituting in (14),

$$R = 1000 \times \frac{1}{s_{\overline{6}|\frac{1}{2}\%}} = 1000 \times .164595 = \$164.60$$

We now have an annuity of $20 \times 6 = 120$ payments of $164.60. At 6% converted monthly the present value of this annuity is

$$A_{120} = 164.60 a_{\overline{120}|\frac{1}{2}\%} = 164.60 \times 90.07345 = \$14,826.09$$

We now consider problems in which payments are made more frequently than interest is compounded. For example, payments may be made semiannually and interest compounded annually; or payments may be made monthly and interest compounded semiannually.

The problem now is to convert the payments made during an interest conversion period into an equivalent single payment made on an interest conversion date. In doing this, as in all problems in the mathematics of finance, careful attention must be given to the practical conditions that pertain to the problem.

A typical illustration of the practical rules followed by a financial institution can be found in the passbook of a bank or savings and loan association. We might find that a bank pays 3% compounded semiannually on May 1 and November 1. Money deposited between these dates earns simple interest. If money is deposited by the 10th or before, interest is credited from the 1st of that month. If deposited after the 10th, interest is credited from the 1st of the following month. Money withdrawn before the semiannual payment date gets no interest for that period. When we work a problem for this particular bank, these are the rules we must follow.

EXAMPLE 3: A man resolves to deposit $100 from his pay at the end of each month in a bank which pays interest as described in the preceding paragraph. If he makes his first deposit on May 31, 1964, how much will he have in his account after interest is credited on May 1, 1969?

SOLUTION: The first step is to get the semiannual payment which is equivalent to the 6 monthly deposits. A time diagram for the first 6 deposits shows how long each deposit earns simple interest.

The diagram shows that the last deposit does not earn any simple interest, the 5th deposit earns interest for one month and so on. A table like the following one will simplify the interest computations:

Deposit	Months Simple Interest is Earned	Interest	Amount
6th	0	0	$100.00
5th	1	$100 \times .03 \times \frac{1}{12} = .25$	100.25
4th	2	$100 \times .03 \times \frac{2}{12} = .50$	100.50
3rd	3	$100 \times .03 \times \frac{3}{12} = .75$	100.75
2nd	4	$100 \times .03 \times \frac{4}{12} = 1.00$	101.00
1st	5	$100 \times .03 \times \frac{5}{12} = 1.25$	101.25
	15	Total	$603.75

An equivalent and condensed way to get the simple interest is to assume that one deposit of $100 has earned 15 months interest.

$$100 \times .03 \times \tfrac{15}{12} = \$3.75$$

We now replace the 60 monthly deposits of $100 each with 10 semiannual deposits of $603.75 and work the problem as an ordinary annuity.

$$S_{10} = 603.75 s_{\overline{10}|1\frac{1}{2}\%} = 603.75 \times 10.70272 = \$6461.77$$

In the preceding example simple interest was credited for a part of a period. It is also possible to have compound interest for a part of a period. All that we need do is take the basic formula for compound interest, $S = P(1 + i)^n$, and substitute the proper value for n.

If $1 is placed at 6% compound interest for 6 months the amount would be

$$S = 1.00(1.06)^{\frac{1}{2}} = 1.02956$$

Values for $(1 \times i)^n$ when n is a fraction can be found using logarithms or in the auxiliary tables published by the Financial Publishing Company. In this text, values for compound interest for a part of a period for the more common interest rates are given in Table 3 under the column heading *Amount of* 1.

Going back to the above illustration, suppose that the dollar had been placed at 6% simple interest for 6 months. Then the amount would have been $1.03. This is more than the amount at 6% compound interest for 6 months. Most people know that money increases more rapidly at compound interest than at the same rate of simple interest if it is left on deposit for more than one interest period. This is the result of interest being earned on interest. But it is not generally known that for less than a conversion period, compound interest results in a smaller amount than simple interest. The difference is not great but it is one which should be taken into account.

Compound interest for a part of a period is used more frequently in annuity problems than in dealing with single sums. For such problems Table 3, Auxiliary Tables taken from the extensive tables of the Financial Publishing Company, can be used to simplify computations. An example will show how these tables are used.

EXAMPLE 4: What is the amount of 60 payments of $100 at the end of each month at 3% converted semiannually?

SOLUTION: The interest conversion period is 6 months and the rate per period is $1\frac{1}{2}\%$. The time interval for payments is 1 month or $\frac{1}{6}$ of a conversion period. We now go to the auxiliary table for $1\frac{1}{2}\%$ and look opposite 1–6 where we find the factor 6.037391 in the *Equivalent per Period to a Payment of* 1 column. This means that a payment of $6.037391 every 6 months is equivalent to a payment of $1 every month if money is worth 3% compounded semiannually. Since our monthly payments are $100, the equivalent semiannual payment is

$$100 \times 6.037391 = \$603.7391$$

and the amount of 60 deposits is

$$S_{10} = 603.7391 s_{\overline{10}|1\frac{1}{2}\%} = 603.7391 \times 10.70272 = \$6461.64$$

This example was worked using the factors to several decimal places to show that the auxiliary tables result in an answer close to, but not identical with the one obtained when simple interest is used for a part of a period. The answer to this example is 13 cents smaller than the answer to Example 3 which used the same data with simple interest for a part of a period. The fact that there is a difference, even if it is not large, shows that problems must be worked using rules which apply to the particular transaction.

EXAMPLE 5: An insurance company pays 3% compounded annually on money left with them. What would be the cost of an annuity of $200 at the end of each month for 10 years?

SOLUTION: In the 3% auxiliary table opposite 1–12, we find the factor 12.16412. Therefore, the annual payment equivalent to 12 monthly payments is

$$200 \times 12.16412 = \$2432.82$$

We now get the present value of an ordinary annuity of $2432.82 a year for 10 years at 3%.

$$A_{10} = 2432.82 a_{\overline{10}|3\%} = \$2432.82 \times 8.530203 = \$20{,}752.45$$

Exercise 4d

1. Find the present value and the amount of an annuity of $40 every 6 months for 12 years if money is worth 5% converted quarterly.
($714.32; $1296.74)

2. Find the present value and the amount of an annuity of $150 a year for 8 years at 3% converted semiannually.

3. What single payment now is equivalent at 6% converted monthly to payments of $100 at the end of each 6 months for 6 years? ($993.19)

4. Compute the present value of an ordinary annuity of $50 at the end of each quarter for 7 years if money is worth 5% converted monthly.

5. Get the amount of the annuity in Problem 3.   ($1422.29)

6. Get the amount of the annuity in Problem 4.

7. Find the present value and the amount of payments of $25 at the end of each month for 9 years if money is worth 3% compounded semiannually.
($2365.62; $3092.67)

8. Find the present value and the amount of payments of $50 at the end of each month for 6 years if money is worth 4% compounded semiannually.

9. What is the present value and the amount of an annuity of $450 at the end of each 6 months for 10 years if the interest rate is 4% compounded annually?
($7372.08; $10,912.47)

10. An insurance company pays 3% compounded annually on money left with them. What would be the cost of an annuity of $125 at the end of each month for 10 years?

4.5   Finding the Periodic Payment

When the amount or present value of a general annuity is known, the **periodic payment** can be found by first getting the equivalent payment per interest conversion period and then converting this into the payments made on the actual payment dates.

EXAMPLE 1: A widow has $10,000 with which she wants to buy an annuity that will provide her a monthly income for 15 years. If she can get 3% converted semiannually on her money, what will be the size of the monthly payments?

SOLUTION: First we get the equivalent payment at the end of each 6 months.

$$R = 10,000 \times \frac{1}{a_{\overline{30}|1\frac{1}{2}\%}} = 10,000 \times .0416392 = \$416.39$$

We must now convert this semiannual payment into an equivalent monthly payment. Since 6 payments are made during an interest period, we look in Table 3 for $1\frac{1}{2}$% and time interval of 1–6. The factor is 6.03739. Since this is for a payment of 1 per period our problem becomes,

$$R \times 6.03739 = 416.39$$

$$R = \frac{416.39}{6.03739} = \$68.97$$

This problem can be solved without division by using the *Payment Equivalent to 1 per Period* column and multiplying. The payment at the end of each month equivalent to $1 at the end of each 6 months is $.16563. Therefore the payment every month equivalent to $416.39 every 6 months is

$$R = 416.39 \times .16563 = \$68.97$$

EXAMPLE 2: A couple would like to accumulate $3000 in 5 years by making deposits at the end of each month in an account paying $3\frac{1}{2}\%$ compounded semiannually. What is the size of each deposit?

SOLUTION: The equivalent semiannual deposit is

$$R = 3000 \times \frac{1}{s_{\overline{10}|1\frac{1}{4}\%}} = 3000 \times .092375 = \$277.13$$

Since 6 payments are made during each interest period, we look in Table 3 for $1\frac{3}{4}\%$ opposite 1–6 and find the factor .165464 in the *Payment Equivalent to 1 per Period* column.

Therefore $R = 277.13 \times .165464 = \$45.86$

Exercise 4e

1. A man leaves his widow a $5000 insurance policy. What monthly income would this provide for 8 years if the insurance company pays 3% converted semiannually? Payments are made at the end of each month.
($58.60)

2. The present value of an annuity is $12,000. It is to be used to provide a quarterly income for 6 years. What will be the size of the payments if the interest rate is 4% converted annually?

3. What periodic payment at the end of each month for 10 years will be required to accumulate $15,000 if the fund earns interest at $3\frac{1}{2}\%$ compounded semiannually?   ($104.72)

4. A city wants to accumulate $250,000 in 15 years to redeem an issue of bonds. What payment will be required at the end of each 6 months to accumulate this amount if interest is earned at 3% converted annually?

4.6   Other General Annuities

Many special formulas have been developed for handling particular situations involving general annuities. These include the unusual cases in which the number of payments is not a divisor of the conversion period nor is the conversion period a divisor of the payment interval. Special formulas are not given here because in an introductory course in the mathematics of finance the important thing is for the student to understand the theory of general annuities. The best way to do this is to analyze each problem and then determine the equivalent payment per interest period that will reduce the general case to one of the simpler annuities with which he is already familiar. Should his later work require him to solve many general annuities, a knowledge of the theory of this type of problem will enable him to develop the formulas he needs or locate them in advanced publications on financial mathematics.

The following examples show how other types of general annuities can be worked using equivalent payments.

EXAMPLE 1: Get the present value and the amount of an annuity due of $200 at the beginning of each year for 3 years if money is worth 6% compounded semiannually.

SOLUTION: First we make a time diagram of the problem.

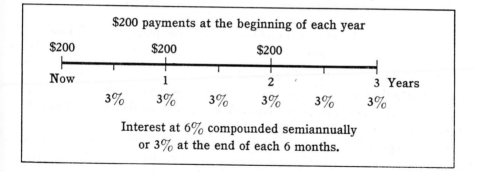

We replace each of the $200 payments with a set of equivalent payments every 6 months. This can be done by letting the $200 be the present value of an ordinary annuity of 2 payments and getting the value of R from (15).

$$R = 200 \times \frac{1}{a_{\overline{2}|3\%}} = 200 \times .52261 = \$104.52$$

The problem can now be illustrated by a diagram.

This is solved as a simple annuity.

From (13) $A_6 = 104.52 \times a_{\overline{6}|3\%} = 104.52 \times 5.41719 = \$566.20$

From (12) $S_6 = 104.52 \times s_{\overline{6}|3\%} = 104.52 \times 6.46841 = \$676.08$

Check: $566.20(1.03)^6 = 566.20 \times 1.19405 = \$676.07$

EXAMPLE 2: Find the present value of an annuity of \$250 at the beginning of each month for 10 years if money is worth 4% converted semiannually.

SOLUTION: The six \$250 payments must be replaced with an equivalent payment made on an interest conversion date. A time diagram of the first 6 payments is a help in making this substitution.

Again we emphasize that in a problem like this the practical conditions that pertain to the problem must be taken into account. Here are the possibilities:

(a) No interest is allowed for a part of a period. The first payment would earn 6 months interest or \$5.00 and the other payments would not earn any interest. This would make the equivalent payment at the end of 6 months $255 + (5 \times 250) = \$1505$.

(b) Simple interest is allowed for a part of a period. We would then take each payment forward at simple interest to 6 months and add them. This would give an equivalent payment of \$1517.50. (See Example 3, Section 4.4).

(c) Compound interest is allowed for a part of a period. To find the equivalent payment we go to Table 3 for 2% and look opposite 1–6 because the payment interval is one sixth of a conversion period. Multiplying the *Equivalent per Period to a Payment of* 1 factor by the size of our payment we have

$$250 \times 6.049807 = \$1512.45$$

Since Table 3 gives us the equivalent payment at the time the last payment is made, we must allow interest on this value for $\frac{1}{6}$ of a period to get it to coincide with an interest conversion period. Using the *Amount of* 1 factor from Table 3 for 1–6 period, we have

$$1512.45 \times 1.003306 = \$1517.45$$

Note that this is very close to the value for simple interest. We now use (13) to get the present value:

$$A_{20} = 1517.45a_{\overline{20}|2\%} = 1517.45 \times 16.351433 = \$24,\!812.48$$

Exercise 4f

(In this exercise assume that compound interest is allowed for a part of a period.)

1. Find the present value and the amount of an annuity due of $600 at the beginning of each year for 12 years if money is worth 3% converted semi-annually. ($6144.73; $8783.90)

2. What is the present value of payments of $350 at the beginning of each 6 months for 5 years if money is worth 5% converted monthly?

3. Four hundred dollars are invested at the beginning of each 3 months at 6% compounded annually. What is the amount at the end of 5 years? ($9355.09)

4. What is the present value of an annuity of $60 at the beginning of each month for 8 years if money is worth 3% compounded semiannually?

4.7 Summary of Ordinary, Due, and Deferred Annuities

The most effective way for a student to solve an annuity problem is to make a sketch, determine at what point in time he wants the value of the annuity, and then substitute in the proper formula. This is much better than just reading a problem and then trying to "type" it. Students should recognize that the same series of payments might be treated as one type of annuity at one time and another type at another time. For example, if we want the value of a series of payments one period before the first payment we would use the present value formula for an ordinary annuity. But if we want the value of the same series of payments one period after the last payment, we would use the amount formula for an annuity due. By comparing his sketch with the diagram on page 134, the student can eliminate guesswork in solving annuity problems.

The focal date approach is very useful for annuity problems. The student should, of course, select a focal date that will minimize computations. Good judgment in choosing a focal date will come from observation and experience. Students should also note that even complicated problems can usually be broken down into simple parts. Too often students try to take a word problem of several sentences and immediately set up an equation that will give the final answer. Do one part at a time. Every problem can be broken down into single payments and annuities which can be moved to any point in time and an equation of value set up.

In this and the preceding chapter we discussed the common types of annuities certain. All of these have one thing in common — a series of equal payments equally spaced. The various formulas which were derived were for convenience in getting the value of the annuity at different times with a minimum of work. The sketch below shows how the formulas we now have enable us to get the value of an annuity at any time.

① To get the value several periods before the first payment use the present value formula for a deferred annuity:

$$A_n = R(a_{\overline{m+n}|} - a_{\overline{m}|}) \qquad \textbf{(18)} \text{ page 115}$$

If computations are to be done with logarithms use,

$$A_n = Ra_{\overline{n}|}(1 + i)^{-m} \qquad \textbf{(19)} \text{ page 115}$$

② To get the value one period before the first payment use the present value formula for an ordinary annuity:

$$A_n = Ra_{\overline{n}|} \qquad \textbf{(13)} \text{ page 83}$$

③ To get the value at the time the first payment is made use the present value formula for an annuity due:

$$A_n = R(a_{\overline{n-1}|} + 1) \qquad \textbf{(17)} \text{ page 109}$$

④ To get the value at the time the last payment is made use the amount formula for an ordinary annuity:

$$S_n = Rs_{\overline{n}|} \qquad \textbf{(12)} \text{ page 78}$$

⑤ To get the value one period after the last payment use the amount formula for an annuity due:

$$S_n = R(s_{\overline{n+1}|} - 1) \qquad\qquad \text{(16) page 108}$$

⑥ Methods for getting the value of an annuity several periods after the last payment are discussed in Section 3.4, page 79. We can get the amount of an annuity of $n + p$ periods and then subtract the amount of an annuity of p periods. This can be done easily in terms of *Amount of 1 per Period* factors as shown below.

$$S_n = R(s_{\overline{n+p}|} - s_{\overline{p}|})$$

Another method, particularly useful if logarithms are being used, is to get the amount of an ordinary annuity and carry this forward using compound interest.

$$S_n = Rs_{\overline{n}|}(1 + i)^p$$

Let us work an example to show how a step-by-step approach using focal dates can solve a problem that at first seems quite difficult.

EXAMPLE: A man deposits $2000 today at 3% interest. One year from now he makes the first of 19 annual deposits of $100 each in a fund paying 4%. Twenty years from now he draws out both of his investments, adds $100 cash to their sum, and buys an annuity of $200 a month, the first payment to be made one month after he buys the annuity. The insurance company allows him 3% converted monthly on his deposit with them. How many $200 payments does he get? What is the size of the concluding payment 1 month after the last full payment?

SOLUTION: First we make a sketch of his deposits and find how much he has when he buys the annuity 20 years hence.

We put the focal date at 20 years and carry everything to that point. This means that we allow 3% compound interest on the $2000, get the amount of an annuity due of 19 payments at 4%, and add $100.

$$
\begin{aligned}
2000(1.03)^{20} &= 2000 \times 1.806111 &&= \$3612.22 \\
100(s_{\overline{20}|4\%} - 1) &= 100 \times 28.77808 &&= 2877.81 \\
\text{Final cash payment} & &&= \underline{100.00} \\
\text{Total for purchase of annuity} & && \$6590.03
\end{aligned}
$$

This $6590.03 now becomes the present value of an ordinary annuity of $200 per month. The student should note that the same sum of money may be an amount at one stage in the problem and a present value at another stage. Using the present value formula for an ordinary annuity, we have

$$6590.03 = 200a_{\overline{n}|}$$
$$a_{\overline{n}|} = 32.95$$

Reference to Table 2 shows that there will be 34 full payments and a smaller 35th payment. To get the size of the concluding payment we shall take the $6590.03 forward 34 periods and get the amount of an annuity of $200 a month for 34 months. We then allow simple interest on the difference for 1 month.

$$6590.03(1.0025)^{34} = 6590.03 \times 1.088602 = \$7173.92$$
$$200s_{\overline{34}|} = 200 \times 35.44064 = \underline{7088.13}$$
$$85.79$$

$$\text{Interest on \$85.79 for 1 mo.} = 85.79 \times \tfrac{1}{12} \times .03 = \underline{\quad .21}$$
$$\$\quad 86.00$$

Thus the man will receive 34 payments of $200 and a 35th payment of $86.00.

To show how the same problem can be solved in more than one way, we could get the 35th payment by putting a focal date at this point and bring the 34 payments forward as an annuity due.

$$x = 6590.03(1.0025)^{35} - 200(s_{\overline{34+1}|} - 1)$$
$$= 6590.03 \times 1.091323 - 200 \times 35.52924$$
$$= 7191.85 - 7105.85 = \$86.00$$

In this problem the two methods gave exactly the same answer. Sometimes there will be a difference of a few cents if the answers to the intermediate steps are rounded to the nearest penny.

4.8   Summary of Perpetuities

A perpetuity is an annuity which results from using only the interest on an investment. We have only present value formulas for perpetuities because the payments are assumed to go on indefinitely so that no final amount can be computed. If the interest is used as soon as it is earned, the present value of the perpetuity simply equals the periodic payment divided by the rate per period.

$$A_\infty = \frac{R}{i} \qquad\qquad \textbf{(20)} \text{ page } 118$$

If the interest is allowed to accumulate for n periods before being used, the present value becomes

$$A_\infty = \frac{R}{i} \times \frac{1}{s_{\overline{n}|}} \qquad\qquad \textbf{(21)} \text{ page } 119$$

4.9   Summary of General Annuities

When the payment interval does not coincide with the interest conversion period, a new payment should be obtained which falls on interest conversion dates. This new payment must be equivalent to the original payments at the given rate of interest. This equivalence can be obtained using simple interest, the *Sinking Fund* column in Table 2, or Table 3, Auxiliary Tables, depending on the problem. After these equivalent payments are obtained, the problem can be completed using the regular annuity formulas. Note in particular that the number of payments will now be determined by the interest conversion periods because payments are now on this basis.

5

AMORTIZATION
AND SINKING FUNDS

5.1 Amortization of a Debt

One of the most important applications of annuities in business transactions is the repayment of interest-bearing debts. First we consider the **amortization** method. When a debt is repaid by this method, a series of periodic payments, usually equal in amount, pay the interest outstanding at the time the payments are made and also repay a part of the principal. As the principal is gradually reduced in this way, the interest on the unpaid balance decreases. This means that as time goes on, an increasing portion of the periodic payments is available to reduce the debt. Sooner or later most of the students who study this material will purchase a car, home, or other item on time and will amortize the debt. An understanding of how debts are amortized and the ability to determine the costs involved can save a person many dollars by enabling him to make a wise selection of a lender and a repayment plan.

5.2 Finding the Payment

When a debt is amortized by equal payments at equal intervals, the debt becomes the present value of an annuity. We determine the size of the payment by the methods used to get the periodic rent in the annuity problems in the preceding chapters.

EXAMPLE 1: A man buys a $13,000 home and pays $5000 down. He gets a 15-year mortgage for the balance. If the lender charges 6% converted monthly, what is the size of the monthly payment?

SOLUTION: Here we have an ordinary annuity with $A_n = 8000$, $n = 180$, and $i = \frac{1}{2}\%$. From formula (15) on page 89 for the rent of an ordinary annuity we find,

$$R = 8000 \times \frac{1}{a_{\overline{180}|\frac{1}{2}\%}}$$
$$= 8000 \times .008439 = \$67.51$$

When a debt is amortized, the common commercial practice is to round up any fraction of a cent. This insures complete amortization in the time specified. If each payment were low by a fraction of a cent, there would still be a small outstanding debt after the specified number of payments had been made. Instead of rounding up to the cent, a lender may round up to the dime, dollar, or other unit of money. This does not injure the borrower since the higher periodic payment will be offset by a smaller concluding payment.

EXAMPLE 2: A debt of \$10,000 bearing interest at 5% converted semiannually is to be amortized in 20 semiannual payments. Find the concluding payment if the semiannual payment is rounded up to: (a) the cent; (b) the dime; (c) the dollar.

SOLUTION: Substituting $A_{20} = 10,000$; $i = 2\frac{1}{2}\%$, $n = 20$ in (15),

$$R = 10,000 \times \frac{1}{a_{\overline{20}|2\frac{1}{2}\%}} = 10,000 \times .064\,1471 = \$641.471$$

Making a time diagram, we see that the simplest method of solution is to set up an equation of value with the focal date at the 20th payment. Then the concluding payment is simply the difference between the \$10,000 carried to the focal date and an annuity *due* of 19 regular payments.

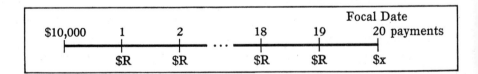

(a) If the payment is rounded up to the cent,

$$x = 10,000(1.025)^{20} - 641.48(s_{\overline{20}|} - 1)$$
$$= 10,000(1.638\,6164) - 641.48(24.54466)$$
$$= 16,386.16 - 15,744.91 = \$641.25$$

(b) If the payment is rounded up to the dime,

$$x = 10{,}000(1.025)^{20} - 641.50(s_{\overline{20}|} - 1) = \$640.76$$

(c) If the payment is rounded up to the dollar,

$$x = 10{,}000(1.025)^{20} - 642.00(s_{\overline{20}|} - 1) = \$628.49$$

5.3 Outstanding Principal

It is often important to know the principal outstanding at a certain time. The borrower may want to pay off the rest of the debt in a lump sum, or the lender may want to sell what is still owed him. To get the principal outstanding at any time we can get the value of the remaining payments at that time.

EXAMPLE 1: To pay off an $8000 mortgage, a man got a 15-year loan at 6% converted monthly. How much does he still owe on his home after he has paid on it for 5 years?

SOLUTION: In Example 1 in the preceding section, we found that the monthly payment is $67.51. To find the outstanding principal we use an equation of value and compare the original debt with the payments that have been made. We put the focal date at the 60th payment and bring everything to this point.

$$x = 8000(1.005)^{60} - 67.51 \times s_{\overline{60}|}$$
$$= 8000 \times 1.348850 - 67.51 \times 69.7700$$
$$= 10{,}790.80 - 4710.17 = \$6080.63$$

This means that the principal has been reduced by only 8000.00 − 6080.63 = $1919.37 although the man has paid $4050.60 (60 payments × $67.51). During the early years of a long-term amortization program, a large part of the money paid goes for interest. This leads to the practical point that the buyer of a home should try to borrow from a lender who offers the lowest rate of interest and who will permit the borrower to pay off the mortgage faster than the contract requires without charging a fee. Frequently a borrower will find that an increase in income or an inheritance will put him in a position to pay more per month on his mortgage than he had originally agreed. Since he probably cannot invest this money at as high a rate as he is paying on his mortgage, it is to his advantage to use it to reduce his debt. It is disconcerting to discover that a small print provision, which he had not read in his contract, imposes a penalty for this advance payment.

ALTERNATE SOLUTION: In this problem, we can get a good check on our answer by getting the present value of the remaining 120 payments which form an ordinary annuity.

$$A_{120} = 67.51 a_{\overline{120}|\frac{1}{2}\%}$$
$$= 67.51 \times 90.0735$$
$$= 6080.86$$

This differs by 23 cents from the preceding result because the monthly payment was rounded up to the nearest cent. Carrying the monthly payment to several decimal places would give a closer check, but there is no reason to do this since the payment must be rounded in practical problems.

This method of checking could not be used if the payment had been rounded up to the dime or dollar because then the concluding payment would differ greatly from the other payments.

EXAMPLE 2: On May 15, 1965, a man borrowed $10,000 at 6% converted monthly. He plans to repay the debt in equal monthly payments over 15 years with the first payment on June 15, 1965. The 12 payments during 1967 will reduce the principal by how much? What was the total interest paid in 1967?

SOLUTION: We use (15) to get the monthly payment.

$$R = 10,000 \times \frac{1}{a_{\overline{180}|\frac{1}{2}\%}} = \$84.39$$

The total reduction in principal in 1967 will be the difference between the outstanding principal in December, 1966, and December, 1967. A time diagram shows that the outstanding principal must be determined after the 19th and the 31st payments. This requires two equations of value using these points as focal dates.

Outstanding on 12/15/66 = $10,000(1.005)^{19} - 84.39 s_{\overline{19}|} = \$9316.34$
Outstanding on 12/15/67 = $10,000(1.005)^{31} - 84.39 s_{\overline{31}|} = \underline{\$8849.95}$
Principal reduction during 1967 = $\$\ 466.39$

		Focal Date	Focal Date	
5/15/65	6/15/65	12/15/66	12/15/67	
$10,000	1	19	31	Payments
	$84.39	$84.39	$84.39	

To get the total interest paid in 1967, we subtract the amount applied to principal from the total payments which equal $12 \times 84.39 = \$1012.68$. Total interest $= 1012.68 - 466.39 = \$546.29$.

5.4 Amortization Schedule

When debts are repaid using the amortization method, it is important to know what portion of each payment goes for interest and how much is applied to reducing the principal. That interest can be a substantial part of the periodic payment can be seen from the following example.

EXAMPLE 1: A man buys a home and gets a 25-year, 6% mortgage for $10,000. The monthly payments are $64.44. When the buyer goes in to the lending institution to make his first monthly payment, he probably thinks he is buying a house with it. How much house is he actually getting?

SOLUTION: The interest rate is $\frac{1}{2}\%$ a month. This means that the interest for the first month will be $50. Deducting this from the monthly payment leaves only $14.44 to be applied to the principal. Thus the "home owner" starts the second month owing $10,000.00 - 14.44 = \$9985.56$. The second month's interest is figured on this principal and amounts to $49.93. As he continues the payments, more and more of each payment will be applied to the debt. Thus when the debt gets down to approximately $1000 the interest will be only about $5 and most of the payment will actually go for house. Again we see the importance of reducing a debt as rapidly as possible.

A person who buys a home on an amortization plan should get a periodic statement from the lender showing how much interest he has paid and how much the mortgage has been reduced, or he should get an amortization schedule which will show exactly where he stands at any time. The interest column will show the buyer how much interest can be deducted in a calendar year when computing income tax. The same column will show the lender how much he must report as income. Since there is not space here to show an amortization schedule for 300 periods, we use a shorter problem. The schedule for this problem will include all the steps necessary to construct any amortization schedule.

EXAMPLE 2: A debt of \$5000 is to be amortized by 5 semiannual payments made at the end of each six months. If interest is charged at the rate of 6% convertible semiannually, find the periodic payment and construct an amortization schedule. Round the payment up to the cent.

SOLUTION: Substituting in (15),

$$R = 5000 \times \frac{1}{a_{\overline{5}|3\%}} = \$1091.775 = \$1091.78$$

Amortization Schedule

Period	Outstanding Principal at Beginning of Period	Interest at End of Period	Payment	Principal Repaid
1	\$5000.00	\$150.00	\$1091.78	\$ 941.78
2	4058.22	121.75	1091.78	970.03
3	3088.19	92.65	1091.78	999.13
4	2089.06	62.67	1091.78	1029.11
5	1059.95	31.80	1091.75	1059.95
				\$5000.00

As this example shows, the concluding payment may differ from the other payments by a few cents.

Exercise 5a

Unless stated otherwise, periodic payments were obtained by rounding up to the cent. Outstanding balances were obtained by carrying all obligations and payments forward to a focal date.

1. A \$6000 loan is to be amortized with 6 equal annual payments. If the interest rate is 5%, find the annual payment and construct an amortization schedule. $(R = \$1182.11)$

2. A loan of \$1200 is to be amortized with 12 equal monthly payments. Find the monthly payment and construct a schedule if the rate is 12% converted monthly.

3. A debt of \$30,000 with interest at 6% is to amortized with 4 equal annual payments. Find the size of the payment and construct an amortization schedule. $(R = \$8657.75)$

4. Construct an amortization schedule for a debt of \$30,000 to be repaid with equal payments at the end of each 6 months over a 5-year period. The rate is 4% converted semiannually.

5. A debt of $8000 with interest at 6% converted semiannually is being amortized with 10 equal semiannual payments. Find the size of the periodic payment and the outstanding principal just after the fifth payment.

($937.85; $4295.01)

6. A debt of $8500 with interest at 5% converted monthly is being amortized with monthly payments over a period of 15 years. Find the size of the payment and the outstanding principal just after the 90th payment.

7. A man buys a $13,000 home and pays $3000 down. He gets a 12-year mortgage for the balance. (a) If the lender charges 6% converted monthly, determine the monthly payment rounded up to the nearest dime. (b) How much of the first payment goes for interest and how much toward reducing the principal? (c) How much does the man still owe just after making the 72nd payment? (d) How much of the 100th payment goes for interest and how much for principal?   [(a) $97.60; (b) $50.00 interest, $47.60 principal; (c) $5886.93; (d) $19.61 interest, $77.99 principal.]

8. A house worth $16,000 is purchased with a down payment of $6000 and monthly payments for 15 years. If the interest rate is 6% compounded monthly, find the size of the monthly payment rounded up to the nearest dime. Complete the first three lines of the amortization schedule. How much is still owed on the house just before making the 90th payment?

9. A $2400 car is purchased with a down payment of $800 and equal monthly payments for 24 months. If the interest rate is 12% compounded monthly, find the size of the monthly payment and complete the first three lines of the amortization schedule. How much is still owed on the car just before making the 12th payment?   ($R = \$75.32$; $922.99 still owed)

10. Work Problem 9 for a rate of 24% converted monthly.

11. A man purchases a home costing $13,300 and makes a down payment of $2300. He gets a mortgage for the balance at 6% converted monthly. This is to be repaid in equal monthly payments over a 15-year period. If he gets the loan in September, 1965, and makes the first monthly payment one month later, how much interest can he deduct when preparing his income tax statement for 1965? By how much is the mortgage reduced in 1965? Base your answers on an amortization schedule.

(Tax deduction $164.43; principal reduced by $114.06)

12. A family buys a home for $13,000. They make a 20% down payment and get a 10-year, 4% loan for the balance which is to be paid off in equal monthly payments. If they make their first payment in November, 1966, how much interest can they deduct from their 1966 income when they prepare their income tax report for 1966?

13. A debt of $20,000 bearing interest at 4% converted quarterly is to be amortized with payments every 3 months for 10 years. Find the concluding payment if the quarterly payment is rounded up to (a) the cent; (b) the dime; (c) the dollar.   [(a) \$608.72; (b) \$604.89; (c) \$566.58]

14. Work Problem 13 for a rate of 5% converted quarterly.

15. On October 20, 1964, a man borrowed \$20,000 at 5% converted monthly. The debt was to be repaid in equal monthly payments over 15 years with the first payment on November 20, 1964. The monthly payment was rounded up to the dime. The 12 payments during 1965 will reduce the principal by how much? What will be the total interest in 1965?

(Principal reduction \$926.95; Interest \$971.45)

16. Use the data in Problem 15 to get the principal reduction and interest for 1970.

5.5   Refinancing

After a long term loan has been partially paid off, it is sometimes possible to get the balance due refinanced at a lower rate which will result in a considerable reduction in the total interest charges. The present value of these interest savings should be balanced against any costs involved in refinancing to see if the change would be a profitable one.

EXAMPLE: A man purchased a home and signed a mortgage contract for \$10,000 which required repayment in equal monthly payments over 12 years based on 6% converted monthly. Just after making the 60th payment, he has the balance refinanced at 5% converted monthly. If the number of payments remains unchanged, what will be the new monthly payment and what will be the total savings in interest?

SOLUTION: Using (15) to get the monthly payment,

$$R = 10,000 \times \frac{1}{a_{\overline{144}|\frac{1}{2}\%}} = \$97.59$$

Outstanding balance after 60 payments $= 10,000(1.005)^{60} - 97.59 s_{\overline{60}|\frac{1}{2}\%} =$ 13,488.50 − 6808.85 = \$6679.65.

This balance becomes the present value of an ordinary annuity of 84 payments. From (15) the new monthly payment is,

$$R = \$6679.65 \times \frac{1}{a_{\overline{84}|\frac{5}{12}\%}} = \$94.42$$

The difference per month is \$3.17 making the total savings in interest \$266.28 over 84 months. If money is worth about 4% converted monthly to the person, the present value of these savings is, $3.17 \times a_{\overline{84}|\frac{1}{3}\%} = \$231.91$.

If the cost of refinancing is less than \$231.91, it will pay the man to re-finance. In this analysis, no allowance was made for the concluding payments being slightly smaller than the regular payments since the difference would be about the same for both plans.

5.6   Amortization with Specified Payments

In some transactions the size of the payment is specified. Often this will be some rounded value such as \$50, \$1000, etc. This means that the number of payments must be determined.

EXAMPLE 1: A debt of \$5000 is to be amortized with payments of \$1000 at the end of each year. Find the number of payments if the interest rate is 3%.

SOLUTION: Substituting in Formula (13),

$$5000 = 1000a_{\overline{n}|}$$

$$a_{\overline{n}|} = \frac{5000}{1000} = 5.00$$

Reference to Table 2 shows that the factor 5.00 lies between 5 and 6 periods. Thus 5 full payments plus a part of a payment will be required to amortize the debt.

The concluding irregular payment may be added to the last regular pay-ment or it may be made one interval after the last full payment. If the con-cluding payment is small, some lenders prefer to add it to the last full pay-ment. In this book, unless the problem specifies otherwise, follow the com-mon practice of making this payment one period after the last full payment, regardless of size. This means that simple interest must be allowed at the specified rate for one period on this payment.

EXAMPLE 2: Find the size of the concluding payment in the previous example.

SOLUTION: First we get the balance due just after the last regular payment by accumulating the original debt to the 5th year and getting the amount of the 5 regular payments. A time diagram is helpful in problems of this type.

$$5000(1.03)^5 - 1000s_{\overline{5}|} = 5796.37 - 5309.14 = \$487.23$$

This \$487.23 could be added to the 5th payment and a total of \$1487.23 paid at that time. Or it could be carried forward one period at simple inter-est. The size of the payment then equals,

$$487.23 + 487.23 \times .03 = \$501.85$$

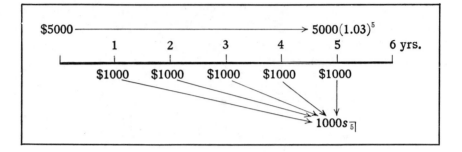

EXAMPLE 3: Construct an amortization schedule for this problem.

Amortization Schedule

Period	Outstanding Principal at Beginning of Period	Interest at End of Period	Payment	Principal Repaid
1	$5000.00	$150.00	$1000.00	$ 850.00
2	4150.00	124.50	1000.00	875.50
3	3274.50	98.24	1000.00	901.76
4	2372.74	71.18	1000.00	928.82
5	1443.92	43.32	1000.00	956.68
6	487.24	14.62	501.86	487.24
				$5000.00

The value of the concluding payment differs from that previously determined by one cent. This is the result of rounding all entries in the schedule to the nearest cent. When an amortization schedule is constructed, the value of the concluding payment will be determined from the schedule.

Exercise 5b

(Round periodic payments up to the cent)

1. A 10-year mortgage for $8000 is being amortized with monthly payments at 6% converted monthly. Just after making the 60th payment, the borrower has the balance refinanced at 5% converted monthly with the term of the loan to remain the same. What will be the total savings in interest?
(Original monthly payment $88.82; New monthly payment $86.70;
Total savings in interest $127.20)

2. A man gets a $10,000 mortgage on a new home to be repaid in 144 monthly payments at 6% converted monthly. Instead of making the regular 96th payment, he applies $2000 from an inheritance on the mortgage. At the same time he gets the balance of the debt refinanced at 5% converted monthly with the first payment under the new plan to be made in 1 month. If the duration of the loan remains the same, what is the size of the new monthly payment? If the size of the payments remains the same, how many full payments must he make to pay off the balance and what will be the size of the final payment?

3. On September 15, 1964, a couple buys a home. Their loan is to be repaid in 180 payments of $50 each with the first payment to be made on October 15, 1964. If the rate is 5% converted monthly, how much would it cost to pay off the debt on July 15, 1969? Include the payment due on July 15, 1969.   ($4824.41)

4. In 1956 a family borrowed $9000 at 6% converted monthly to finance a home. The term of the loan was 15 years. The first payment was made in June of 1956 and all payments were made on time up to and including the one in August of 1965. In September of 1965 the borrower paid $1000 on the loan instead of the usual monthly payment and arranged with the lender to refinance the balance at 5% converted monthly. In October of 1965 he is to make the first of 60 equal monthly payments under the new conditions. What is the size of the new monthly payment?

5. A debt of $8000 is to be amortized with annual payments of $500. If interest is charged at 4%, how many full payments will there be and what will be the size of the concluding payment made 1 year after the last full payment?   (26 full payments; 27th payment of $24.85)

6. A debt of $6500 is to be amortized with annual payments of $1000. How many full payments will there be and what will be the size of the concluding payment? The interest rate is $3\frac{1}{2}\%$.

7. Work Problem 5 using a rate of 5%.
                        (32 full payments; 33rd payment of $493.62)

8. A $10,000 mortgage is to be amortized with monthly payments of $125. If the rate is 5% converted monthly, how many full payments will there be and what will be the size of the concluding payment?

9. A widow inherits an estate of $12,000 on March 1, 1964. Instead of taking the cash she immediately invests the money at 3% converted monthly with the understanding that she will be paid $125 monthly, with the first payment to be made on April 1, 1964. How many $125 payments will she receive? Get the size and date of the concluding payment.
                        (109 full payments; $114.00 on May 1, 1973)

10. Work Problem 9 if the widow could get 4% converted monthly.

5.7   Sinking Funds

When a sum of money will be needed at some future date, it is good practice to accumulate systematically a fund that will equal the desired sum at the time it is needed. The money accumulated in this way is called a **sinking fund.** Sinking funds are used to redeem bond issues, pay off other debts, replace worn-out equipment, or provide money for the purchase of new equipment.

Sinking funds are used to retire some loans because the borrower is not allowed to make payments on the principal until the entire debt is due. The creditor may want it this way so that he will not have the problem of reinvesting a part of his capital every few months. Aside from the extra bother, there is also the possibility that he may have to make the new loan at a lower rate.

While the deposits to a sinking fund may be unequal and at unequal intervals of time, this is usually not done because the problem then must be worked sum by sum using the focal date procedure in Chapter 2. A much more common and systematic procedure is to accumulate the fund by equal deposits at equal intervals. Each periodic deposit is invested on the specified date and allowed to accumulate until the final maturity value is needed. This is the method we shall use.

Since the amount needed in the sinking fund, the time it is needed, and the interest rate which the fund will earn are known, a sinking fund becomes simply an ordinary annuity in which the size of the payment is to be determined. When a sinking fund is used to retire a debt, the borrower continues to owe the entire principal on which he pays interest as it falls due to the creditor. The sinking fund is an entirely separate account and the interest rate it earns will probably be different than the rate paid on the debt.

EXAMPLE: A man wants to have $2000 to purchase a new car in three years. How much must he deposit every 6 months in an account paying 3% converted semiannually?

SOLUTION: Substituting in Formula (14),

$$R = S_n \times \frac{1}{s_{\overline{n}|}} = 2000 \times \frac{1}{s_{\overline{6}|1\frac{1}{2}\%}} = \$321.05$$

It is sometimes desirable to have a schedule to show how much is in the sinking fund at any time. The following is a schedule for the above example.

Sinking Fund Schedule

Period	Amount in Fund at Start of Period	Interest Earned on Sinking Fund During Period	Deposit at End of Period	Amount in the Fund at End of Period
1	—	—	$ 321.05	$ 321.05
2	$ 321.05	$ 4.82	321.05	646.92
3	646.92	9.70	321.05	977.67
4	977.67	14.67	321.05	1313.39
5	1313.39	19.70	321.05	1654.14
6	1654.14	24.81	321.05	2000.00
		$73.70	$1926.30	

It is well to note the advantage of this systematic way of providing for some future purchase. First of all the buyer avoids the very high interest rates commonly charged on installment buying. Second he gets interest on his own savings. Third there is a good chance that he will be able to get a discount when he is in a position to pay cash for the item he wants.

5.8 Total Periodic Charge

In the above example we assumed a case in which a person was simply saving money for a future purchase. The most common use of sinking funds is to make provision for retiring a debt. In such cases the borrower must meet two charges — the interest when it is due and the periodic deposits to the sinking fund. Note that there is no relation between the interest on the debt and the interest earned on the sinking fund. The interest on the debt is not paid from the sinking fund. The two are entirely separate. However, for accounting purposes we can add the two to get the total periodic charge. This is illustrated by an example.

EXAMPLE: A man borrows $2000 for 3 years at 5% interest payable semi-annually. He makes periodic deposits into a sinking fund earning 3% converted semiannually. Get the total periodic payment and construct a schedule.

SOLUTION: The interest every 6 months will be $2\frac{1}{2}\%$ of $2000 or $50. From (14), the deposit every 6 months to the sinking fund is,

$$R = 2000 \times \frac{1}{s_{\overline{6}|1\frac{1}{2}\%}} = \$321.05$$

Thus the total cost to the borrower every 6 months will be the sum of these two or $371.05. Note again that the $50 and the $321.05 may be paid to different persons or institutions. However, when the amount in the sinking fund reaches $2000 it will be drawn out and paid to the lender, probably with the last interest payment.

Sinking Fund and Interest Schedule

Period	Amount in Fund at Start of Period	Interest Earned on Sinking Fund During Period	Deposit at End of Period	Amount in Fund at End of Period	Interest on Debt	Total Payment Periodic
1	—	—	$ 321.05	$ 321.05	$50.00	$371.05
2	$ 321.05	$ 4.82	321.05	646.92	50.00	371.05
3	646.92	9.70	321.05	977.67	50.00	371.05
4	977.67	14.67	321.05	1313.39	50.00	371.05
5	1313.39	19.70	321.05	1654.14	50.00	371.05
6	1654.14	24.81	321.05	2000.00	50.00	371.05
		$73.70	$1926.30			

Exercise 5c

(Round periodic deposits up to the cent)

1. A firm expects to need $50,000 on May 1, 1970, to replace some machine tools. To provide this amount the firm makes equal annual deposits into a fund that is invested at 4%. If the first deposit is made on May 1, 1965, and the last deposit on May 1, 1970, what will be the size of each deposit? Prepare a schedule for this problem.   (R = $7538.10)

2. A sinking fund of $6000 is to be accumulated with 5 equal annual deposits at the end of each year. If interest is earned at 3%, get the size of the deposit and prepare a schedule.

3. A couple would like to accumulate $4000 for a down payment on a home by August 1, 1967. They plan to make semiannual deposits in a building and loan with the first deposit to be made on August 1, 1963, and the last deposit on February 1, 1967. If the building and loan pays 4% compounded semiannually on February 1 and August 1, the couple should deposit how much every 6 months? (Payments of $456.91 will amount to $4000.08)

4. What would be the semiannual deposit in problem 3 if the rate is $4\frac{1}{2}$% compounded semiannually?

5. A company borrows $80,000 at 4% for 12 years. If they set up a sinking fund at 3% to repay the debt, what is the total annual cost of this obligation?   ($8836.97)

6. A man borrows $5500 for 6 years at 7%. To be sure that he will be able to repay the debt, he makes equal deposits at the end of each year in an investment paying 4% compounded annually. What is the total annual cost of this loan?

5.9 Sinking Fund with Specified Deposit

In some transactions the size of the payment to the sinking fund is specified, and the problem is to determine the number of payments. Usually in such cases an integral number of payments will not give the exact result desired. This means that an irregular deposit must be made either at the time of the last regular deposit or one period later. In this book we shall assume the latter procedure unless the problem specifies otherwise.

EXAMPLE: A man wants to accumulate $10,000 to start a business. If he can save $750 every six months, how long will it take him to accumulate $10,000? He is able to put his savings at the end of each 6 months in an investment paying 5% compounded semiannually.

SOLUTION: Substituting in Formula (12)

$$10,000 = 750 s_{\overline{n}|2\frac{1}{2}\%}$$

$$s_{\overline{n}|} = \frac{10,000}{750} = 13.33$$

From Table 2 we find that he will have to make 11 deposits of $750 plus a smaller 12th deposit. To get the size of the concluding deposit, the most direct procedure is to get the amount of an annuity due of 11 deposits and subtract this from the $10,000.

$$S_n = R(s_{\overline{n+1}|} - 1)$$
$$= 750(s_{\overline{11+1}|} - 1) = 750(13.79555 - 1)$$
$$= 750 \times 12.79555 = \$9,596.66$$
$$12\text{th payment} = 10,000 - 9,596.66 = \$403.34$$

The student should note that this or any similar problem can be worked by setting up a focal date and an equation of value.

Focal Date
Need $10,000
here

1   2   3   ...   10   11   12 Payments

$750 $750 $750 $750 $750 Have amount of annuity
                                 due of eleven $750 payments

Balance needed $= 10,000 -$
$$750(s_{\overline{11+1}|} - 1)$$

5.10 Comparison of Amortization and Sinking Funds

When a debt is amortized, each payment pays the outstanding interest at that time and the balance is used to reduce the principal. When a sinking fund is used, the entire principal remains unpaid until the due date of the debt. Each interest period, the debtor pays only the interest to the lender. Then he makes a separate deposit into a sinking fund which will accumulate to the principal of the debt.

The amortization method has the advantage of being more convenient as it requires only a single payment each period. Which method will be cheaper depends on the rates of interest. If the rate received on the sinking fund is the same as that charged on the debt the total periodic cost of the two methods will be the same. If the sinking fund earns a lower rate of interest than is charged on the debt, the periodic cost for the sinking fund method will be greater than for the amortization method. The reason is that the buyer will be paying one rate of interest on his debt while receiving a lower rate on his savings. Conversely, if the borrower can get more interest on the sinking fund than he is paying on the debt, he would be ahead to use a sinking fund. Since such a situation would be very unusual for most borrowers, it is usually better for a person to amortize a debt. The effect of different interest rates on the total periodic cost can be shown by an example.

EXAMPLE: A man borrows $1000 to be repaid in equal annual installments at the end of each year for 3 years. Find the total annual cost under the following conditions:

(a) The debt is amortized at 4%.

(b) Interest at 4% is paid on the debt and a sinking fund is set up at 3%.

(c) Interest at 4% is paid on the debt and a sinking fund is set up at 4%.

(d) Interest at 4% is paid on the debt and a sinking fund is set up at 5%.

SOLUTION:

a	b
$R = 1000 \dfrac{1}{a_{\overline{3}\vert 4\%}} = \$360.35$ This is the total annual cost as it includes both interest and principal.	Int. $= .04 \times 1000 \qquad = \$\ 40.00$ $R \quad = 1000 \times \dfrac{1}{s_{\overline{3}\vert 3\%}} = \ 323.53$ $\qquad\qquad\qquad$ Total $\quad \$363.53$
c	d
Interest $\qquad\qquad \$\ 40.00$ $R = 1000 \times \dfrac{1}{s_{\overline{3}\vert 4\%}} = \quad 320.35$ $\qquad\qquad\qquad\qquad \$360.35$ Note that this is the same as the amortization plan.	Interest $\qquad\qquad \$\ 40.00$ $R = 1000 \times \dfrac{1}{s_{\overline{3}\vert 5\%}} = \quad 317.21$ $\qquad\qquad\qquad\qquad \$357.21$

Note that all of the above plans result in the entire debt, principal and interest, being paid in 3 years. Besides simplifying the transaction and usually having a lower periodic cost, the amortization plan has another practical advantage for most borrowers. It literally forces the borrower to reduce the principal as he goes along. If most people tried to pay future debts by setting up sinking funds they would probably spend some of the periodic deposits instead of saving them. The result would be that when the debt comes due they would not have enough in the sinking fund to pay it. That is why most home mortgages today are paid off with amortization or direct reduction loans.

Because of the importance of a thorough understanding of the amortization and sinking fund methods, the two are sketched on page 156 for a debt of $1000 to be repaid with three annual payments.

Exercise 5d

(Round periodic payments up to the cent)

1. A debt of $4000 is due at the end of 5 years. To be certain that he will have this amount when it is due, the borrower decides to set up a sinking fund by making deposits at the end of each year into an account paying $3\frac{1}{2}\%$. Construct a schedule showing how this fund accumulates.   ($R = \$745.93$)

2. A sinking fund is set up to accumulate $8500 in 6 years. If the fund earns 4% converted annually, what is the size of the deposit at the end of each year. Construct a schedule.

Amortization of a Debt   Sinking Fund

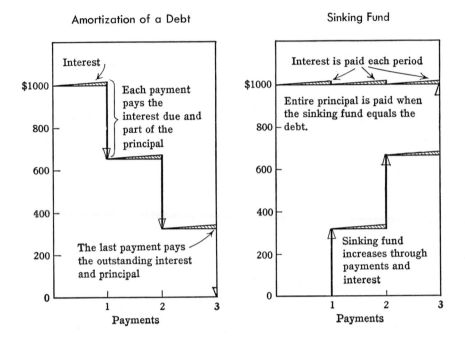

3. A man wants to accumulate $8000 to start a business. If he can save $800 every 6 months and can invest these savings at 3% compounded semi-annually, how long will it take him? What is the size of the concluding deposit?   (9 full deposits; 10th deposit of $237.82)

4. A couple wants to accumulate $2500 for a down payment on a home. If they can deposit $250 at the end of each 6 months in a building and loan paying 4% converted semiannually, how many full deposits must they make and what will be the size of the concluding deposit?

5. The management of a factory wants to set up a sinking fund to provide $40,000 for the replacement of a machine at the end of 6 years. If equal deposits are made at the end of each 6 months in a fund earning 4% converted semiannually, find the size of each deposit. If the machine has to be replaced at the end of 4 years, how much will be in the fund at that time?
                    ($R = 2982.39; At the end of 4 years fund contains $25,597.76)

6. Work Problem 5 for a rate of 3%.

7. A man borrows $5000 to be repaid in equal annual installments at the end of each year for 6 years. Find the total annual cost under the following conditions.
   (a) The debt is amortized at 5%.
   (b) Interest at 5% is paid on the debt and a sinking fund is set up at 3%.

(c) Interest at 5% is paid on the debt and a sinking fund is set up at 5%.

(d) Interest at 5% is paid on the debt and a sinking fund is set up at 6%.

[(a) $985.09; (b) $1022.99; (c) $985.09; (d) $966.82]

8. Get the total annual cost for a loan of $12,000 repaid in 4 equal annual payments under the following conditions.

(a) The debt is amortized at 3%.

(b) Interest at 3% is paid on the debt and a sinking fund is set up at $2\frac{1}{2}\%$.

(c) Interest at 3% is paid on the debt and a sinking fund is set up at 3%.

(d) Interest at 3% is paid on the debt and a sinking fund is set up at $3\frac{1}{2}\%$.

5.11 Aids to Computation

In most businesses, a calculator is available for doing the arithmetic in mathematics of finance problems. It is a good idea to get from the manufacturer's representative the instruction sheets pertaining to the types of problems encountered in the business. These instruction sheets describe the most efficient way to solve problems with the particular make of machine. In some cases, a valuable built-in check is included as a part of the suggested procedure. If a short amortization schedule using equal payments is prepared on a desk calculator, the work can be checked by noting if the last payment is within a few cents of the other payments. If a person is preparing a long schedule by line-by-line simple interest computations, an error early in the work will be serious if it is not discovered quickly. By using the method of Section 5.3, the outstanding principal can be computed for certain lines, such as every 12th one, before doing the detailed computations. Then an error will be discovered as soon as the simple interest computations do not agree with the previously computed principal for that line. Differences of a few cents due to rounding entries to the penny may occur, in which case the value to retain is the one resulting from the line-by-line computations.

Because of the labor required to prepare long amortization schedules, the work is often done today by specialists in the field such as the Financial Publishing Company. With modern electronic computing equipment, schedules can be prepared quickly at reasonable cost. A few lines from such a schedule are shown below. The final entry in each line (except in the last line) is the outstanding principal after the numbered payment has been made. The last entry in the schedule is the concluding payment. The schedule shows exactly how much of each payment goes to principal and how much to interest. This schedule is for a $10,000 loan at 6% converted monthly to be repaid with payments of $100 a month. The schedule shows that 138 full payments and a 139th payment of $97.63 will be required to amortize the loan.

Schedule of Direct Reduction Loan

RATE %   PAYMENT $ LOAN $ TERM: YEARS   MONTHS   PERIODS
  6.00   100.00   10,000.00   11   7   139

Prepared by Financial Publishing Company, Boston

Payment Number	Payment on Interest	Principal	Balance of Loan	Payment Number	Payment on Interest	Principal	Balance of Loan
1	50.00	50.00	9,950.00	61	32.56	67.44	6,444.09
2	49.75	50.25	9,899.75	62	32.22	67.78	6,376.31
3	49.50	50.50	9,849.25	63	31.88	68.12	6,308.19
4	49.25	50.75	9,798.50	64	31.54	68.46	6,239.73
5	48.99	51.01	9,747.49	65	31.20	68.80	6,170.93
56	34.22	65.78	6,777.96	135	2.45	97.55	392.73
57	33.89	66.11	6,711.85	136	1.96	98.04	294.69
58	33.56	66.44	6,645.41	137	1.47	98.53	196.16
59	33.23	66.77	6,578.64	138	.98	99.02	97.14
60	32.89	67.11	6,511.53	139	.49	97.14	97.63*

The final payment is usually somewhat different from the regular payment, and is shown starred on the last line.

5.12   Some Practical Points

Most students will in later life borrow several thousand dollars to buy a home. Here are a few rules that can save hundreds of dollars.

1. *Look for a Low Rate.* Throughout this text, many problems have been worked using different rates to show that a small difference in the rate may mean hundreds of dollars difference in interest. For example, on a $10,000 loan at 5% to be repaid monthly over 20 years, the total interest is $5839. On the same loan at $4\frac{1}{2}$% the total interest would be $5184. When a difference of only $\frac{1}{2}$% can save $655 on a typical loan, it is easy to see why a little time should be spent looking for the best available rate. If it is necessary to make a loan at a relatively high rate, do not overlook the possibility of having it refinanced later at a lower rate.

2. *Pay Off Quickly.* As long as you owe several thousand dollars, you will be paying a lot of interest every year even though you have a relatively low rate. The sooner a loan is paid off, the less the interest. A $10,000 loan paid off in 20 years at 6% will cost $7194 in interest. If the same loan is paid off in 10 years, the interest will drop to $3322, a difference of $3872. Interest charges for common rates and payment periods are shown on page 159.

Payment Period		Rate				
Years	Months	4%	4½%	5%	5½%	6%
10	120	$2149	$2437	$2728	$3023	$3322
15	180	3314	3770	4234	4708	5189
20	240	4544	5184	5839	6509	7194
25	300	5835	6675	7538	8423	9329
30	360	7187	8241	9326	10440	11584

3. *Keep Payments Within Your Means.* The preceding paragraph pointed out the savings that result from paying a loan off quickly. But be careful not to commit yourself to monthly payments that are beyond your means. A $10,000 loan paid off over 20 years at 5% costs $66.00 a month. Paying it off in 10 years increases the monthly payment to $106.07.

4. *Avoid Penalty Clauses.* Fortunately there is a way to keep the monthly payments within your means and yet be able to pay the loan off quickly if your income increases or you receive a sum of money from an inheritance or other source. Get a loan which has a monthly payment you can afford but which can be paid off more rapidly *without a penalty* if you are able at any time to make larger payments. The borrower who has prepaid a part of his loan may be helped later if sickness or temporary loss of income prevents him from making some of the regular monthly payments.

5. *Make a Large Down Payment.* The larger the down payment, the less you will have to borrow and the less you will pay in interest. However, don't make the mistake of putting all of your cash into the down payment. Moving expenses, needed equipment for a new home, and other expenses involved in getting settled may amount to several hundred dollars. If you have to get a small loan from a bank or loan company or buy on the installment plan, you may have to pay 12% or more interest a year as was pointed out in Chapter 3. Too many people try to buy a home with a minimum down payment. It is far better for them to save money so that they will be able to make a large down payment. Having a large down payment may also enable you to get a lower rate on the balance of the loan. Since there is less risk for the lender, he may offer better terms.

6. *Contact Several Lenders.* Mortgage loans are made by many types of lenders — banks, building and loan associations, insurance companies, private individuals, and others. Their lending practices, rates, appraisals, and down payment requirements vary so it will pay you to contact several lenders when you are in the market for a loan. Before you apply for a loan, as in all installment buying, read the application carefully. You may be required to pay a fee even if you decide to get the loan elsewhere. If you are interested in an

FHA or VA loan, remember that the money is still supplied by a private lender. If you get an FHA loan you pay a $\frac{1}{2}\%$ mortgage insurance premium each year on the balance due in addition to the rate on the loan. No matter where you get a loan, be sure that the principal is reduced as payments are made.

7. *Know What You Owe.* Always know how much you still owe and how much of your payments have gone to principal and how much to interest. One way to do this is to get periodic statements from the lender. Another way is to get an amortization schedule. A portion of a schedule is presented on page 161 to show how much valuable information is contained in a schedule of this type.

This schedule is for a Federal Housing Administration insured mortgage for $10,000 to be repaid in 30 years. The rate is $5\frac{1}{4}\%$, which was the legal maximum in January 1963. In addition to the interest, there is a mortgage insurance premium of $\frac{1}{2}\%$ a year on the average scheduled balance of loan principal outstanding during the year. FHA mortgage insurance protects the lender against loss on the loan. It does not protect the borrower against loss; but because of the insurance, lenders are able to make loans on terms that bring home ownership within the reach of many families who could not otherwise afford it.

Exercise 5e

1. Look up the complete Compound Interest and Annuity Tables in your school or public library and complete the following table for a loan specified by your instructor.

Monthly Payments for a Loan of $____

Payment Period		Rate				
Years	Months	4%	$4\frac{1}{2}\%$	5%	$5\frac{1}{2}\%$	6%
10						
12						
15						
18						
20						
25						
30						

AMORTIZATION SCHEDULE

Monthly Payment to Principal and Interest, $55.30   SERIAL OR PROJECT NO.

PAYMENT DATE (M / DAY / YR)	NO.	MORTGAGE INSURANCE PREMIUM ½ PERCENT	PAYMENT TO INTEREST 5¼ PERCENT	PAYMENT TO PRINCIPAL	TOTAL PERIODIC PAYMENT	BALANCE DUE	NO.	PAYMENT DATE (M / DAY / YR)
						10 000 00		
	1	4 14	43 75	11 55	59 44	9 988 45	1	
	2	4 14	43 70	11 60	59 44	9 976 85	2	
	3	4 14	43 65	11 65	59 44	9 965 20	3	
	4	4 14	43 60	11 70	59 44	9 953 50	4	
	5	4 14	43 55	11 75	59 44	9 941 75	5	
	6	4 14	43 50	11 80	59 44	9 929 95	6	
	7	4 14	43 44	11 86	59 44	9 918 09	7	
	8	4 14	43 39	11 91	59 44	9 906 18	8	
	9	4 14	43 34	11 96	59 44	9 894 22	9	
	10	4 14	43 29	12 01	59 44	9 882 21	10	
	11	4 14	43 23	12 07	59 44	9 870 14	11	
	12	4 14	43 18	12 12	59 44	9 858 02	12	
		49 68	521 62	141 98	713 28			

The schedule shows that during the first year $521.62 goes to interest leaving only $141.98 to reduce the debt. Below is a section of the schedule 15 years later. Although the borrower has been paying for 15 years and is beyond the half way point in time, it will be the middle of the 16th year before a third of the mortgage has been paid. Payments to interest are still greater than the amount going to principal.

NO.	MORTGAGE INSURANCE PREMIUM	PAYMENT TO INTEREST	PAYMENT TO PRINCIPAL	TOTAL PERIODIC PAYMENT	BALANCE DUE	NO.
181	2 79	29 96	25 34	58 09	6 822 26	181
182	2 79	29 85	25 45	58 09	6 796 81	182
183	2 79	29 74	25 56	58 09	6 771 25	183
184	2 79	29 62	25 68	58 09	6 745 57	184
185	2 79	29 51	25 79	58 09	6 719 78	185
186	2 79	29 40	25 90	58 09	6 693 88	186
187	2 79	29 29	26 01	58 09	6 667 87	187
188	2 79	29 17	26 13	58 09	6 641 74	188
189	2 79	29 06	26 24	58 09	6 615 50	189
190	2 79	28 94	26 36	58 09	6 589 14	190
191	2 79	28 83	26 47	58 09	6 562 67	191
192	2 79	28 71	26 59	58 09	6 536 08	192
	33 48	352 08	311 52	697 08		

The 30th year has finally arrived! The borrower has 348 payments behind him. He is almost a home owner. Because the payment was rounded from $55.23 up to $55.30, the loan is paid off with the 359th payment which is smaller than the regular payment. The last line gives the 30-year totals.

NO.	MORTGAGE INSURANCE PREMIUM	PAYMENT TO INTEREST	PAYMENT TO PRINCIPAL	TOTAL PERIODIC PAYMENT	BALANCE DUE	NO.
349	12	2 54	52 76	55 42	526 71	349
350	12	2 30	53 00	55 42	473 71	350
351	12	2 07	53 23	55 42	420 48	351
352	12	1 84	53 46	55 42	367 02	352
353	12	1 61	53 69	55 42	313 33	353
354	12	1 37	53 93	55 42	259 40	354
355	12	1 13	54 17	55 42	205 23	355
356	12	90	54 40	55 42	150 83	356
357	12	66	54 64	55 42	96 19	357
358	12	42	54 88	55 42	41 31	358
359	12	18	41 31	41 61		359
	1 32	15 02	579 47	595 81		
	936 72	9 838 89	10 000 00	20 775 61		

2. Determine the total interest for the loan in Problem 1. Values may be rounded to the nearest dollar.

Total Interest Paid on a Loan of $____

Payment Period		Rate				
Years	Months	4%	$4\frac{1}{2}\%$	5%	$5\frac{1}{2}\%$	6%
10						
12						
15						
18						
20						
25						
30						

6

BONDS

6.1 Bonds and Stocks

When a corporation or government needs money, the amount needed may be too large or the intended duration of the loan too long to obtain the money from a single bank or other lender. This situation can be met by issuing **bonds** which are purchased by individuals, insurance companies and other investors. Thus the buyer of a bond loans money to the organization that issued the bond. A stockholder, on the other hand, is a part owner of the corporation. Interest must be paid on bonds before dividends are declared on stocks. Both the **redemption price** of a bond and the **interest rate** are quoted in the bond itself. Therefore, we are able to use the compound interest and annuity formulas and tables to get the purchase price of a given bond at any time.

6.2 Kinds of Bonds

There are several ways in which bonds may be classified. A bond may be **registered** or **unregistered.** Registered bonds have the name of the owner on them and are valueless to anyone except the person whose name is registered with the issuing company or government. Bonds may be registered as to principal and interest or only as to principal. If interest payments are registered, they are sent by check to the registered owner. Unregistered bonds do not have the owner's name on them. Usually such bonds are printed with attached **coupons,** which are dated serially with the dates on which the interest will be due. All that the owner of an unregistered bond does to get his interest is to clip each coupon on or after the date printed on it and then present the coupon to his bank or broker for collection.

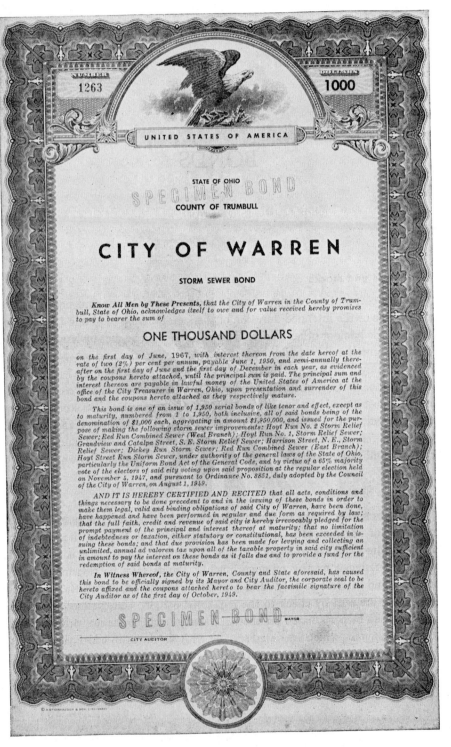

NUMBER 1263   1000

UNITED STATES OF AMERICA

STATE OF OHIO

COUNTY OF TRUMBULL

SPECIMEN BOND

CITY OF WARREN

STORM SEWER BOND

Know All Men by These Presents, that the City of Warren in the County of Trumbull, State of Ohio, acknowledges itself to owe and for value received hereby promises to pay to bearer the sum of

ONE THOUSAND DOLLARS

on the first day of June, 1967, with interest thereon from the date hereof at the rate of two (2%) per cent per annum, payable June 1, 1950, and semi-annually thereafter on the first day of June and the first day of December in each year, as evidenced by the coupons hereto attached, until the principal sum is paid. The principal sum and interest thereon are payable in lawful money of the United States of America at the office of the City Treasurer in Warren, Ohio, upon presentation and surrender of this bond and the coupons hereto attached as they respectively mature.

This bond is one of an issue of 1,950 serial bonds of like tenor and effect, except as to maturity, numbered from 1 to 1,950, both inclusive, all of said bonds being of the denomination of $1,000 each, aggregating in amount $1,950,000, and issued for the purpose of making the following storm sewer improvements: Hoyt Run No. 2 Storm Relief Sewer; Red Run Combined Sewer (West Branch); Hoyt Run No. 1, Storm Relief Sewer; Grandview and Catalpa Street, S. E. Storm Relief Sewer; Harrison Street, N. E., Storm Relief Sewer; Dickey Run Storm Sewer; Red Run Combined Sewer (East Branch); Hoyt Street Run Storm Sewer, under authority of the general laws of the State of Ohio, particularly the Uniform Bond Act of the General Code, and by virtue of a 65% majority vote of the electors of said city voting upon said proposition at the regular election held on November 4, 1947, and pursuant to Ordinance No. 3851, duly adopted by the Council of the City of Warren, on August 1, 1949.

AND IT IS HEREBY CERTIFIED AND RECITED that all acts, conditions and things necessary to be done precedent to and in the issuing of these bonds in order to make them legal, valid and binding obligations of said City of Warren, have been done, have happened and have been performed in regular and due form as required by law; that the full faith, credit and revenue of said city is hereby irrevocably pledged for the prompt payment of the principal and interest thereof at maturity; that no limitation of indebtedness or taxation, either statutory or constitutional, has been exceeded in issuing these bonds; and that due provision has been made for levying and collecting an unlimited, annual ad valorem tax upon all of the taxable property in said city sufficient in amount to pay the interest on these bonds as it falls due and to provide a fund for the redemption of said bonds at maturity.

In Witness Whereof, the City of Warren, County and State aforesaid, has caused this bond to be officially signed by its Mayor and City Auditor, the corporate seal to be hereto affixed and the coupons attached hereto to bear the facsimile signature of the City Auditor as of the first day of October, 1949.

SPECIMEN BOND   MAYOR

_____
CITY AUDITOR

A coupon bond consists of two parts:

1. The bond itself which is redeemable on the stated date (see illustration on page 164).

2. Coupons which can be cashed periodically (see below).

Bonds may also be subdivided according to the security back of them. A **mortgage bond** is secured by a mortgage issued against property of the corporation. A **debenture bond** is secured only by the general credit of the corporation, that is the reputation of the firm for meeting its obligations. Other types exist but we shall not go into them here because the computations involved in getting the value of a bond are not affected by the security behind it.

Interest on a bond may accumulate and be paid in one lump sum when the bond matures. Government savings bonds are the most common example of this type of bond. Since the value of government savings bonds at any time after issue is fixed and is printed on the bond, we shall not discuss them further. Our discussion will be limited to those bonds which have interest payments made periodically, usually semiannually.

The **face value** or **denomination** of a bond is usually some simple figure such as $100 or $1000. Most bonds are redeemable at **face value** or **par**. Occasionally a bond is redeemable at more than par. In such cases the redemption price will be a stated percentage of the face value. A $1000 bond redeemable at 102 would have a redemption price of $1020.

6.3   Finding the Purchase Price

One of the fundamental bond problems is determining the price an investor can pay for a certain bond to give him the yield he wants on his money. The student should note that in bond problems there are **two rates of interest**. One is the **interest** rate which the issuing organization pays on the face value of the bond. The other is the **yield** rate to maturity which the buyer of the bond gets on his investment. For example, suppose that several years ago a corporation issued a $1000 bond with interest at 5% payable semiannually. If this is a coupon bond, the owner will clip a $25 coupon every six months regardless of what he paid for the bond. Now suppose that today investors are glad to get $4\frac{1}{2}\%$ return on their money. This bond then would be quoted at more than $1000. The exact price, which we shall determine later, will be such that the buyer receives a $4\frac{1}{2}\%$ return on his invested capital.

Over the years a special terminology has grown up in connection with the buying and selling of bonds. We shall define these terms as we come to them. Since bond valuation is based on formulas already obtained for single sums and annuities, the main problem of students is to gain an understanding of bond terminology. The symbols and terms used in finding the purchase price of a bond are given below.

F = the face or par value of the bond.

C = the redemption price of the bond. This will be the same as the par value of the bond unless the problem states otherwise.

r = interest rate paid on the bond per period.

Fr = amount of each coupon or interest payment. From now on we use the word coupon for the periodic interest payments since the computations will be the same whether the interest is paid by check or coupon.

n = number of interest conversion periods from the given date to the maturity date of the bond.

i = yield rate per period. This is the rate of interest actually earned by the investor on his investment.

V = the purchase price of a bond.

P = premium.

D = discount.

We now get the purchase price of a bond on a coupon date. This is a day on which the organization that issued the bond pays interest. The seller will keep the coupon that is due on that date. The buyer pays for the present value of the redemption price of the bond and the present value of all future interest payments. These present values are to be *computed at the yield rate* because this is the return the investor wants on his investment. The bond rate is used only to get the periodic interest payment or coupon.

Adding the present value of the redemption price of the bond and the present value of the annuity formed by the coupons gives us the basic formula for the purchase price of a bond.

$$V = C(1+i)^{-n} + Fra_{\overline{n}|} \qquad (22)$$

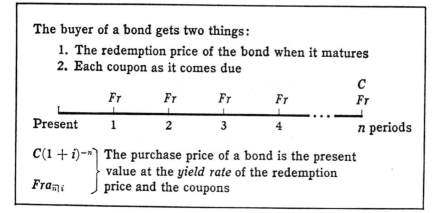

The buyer of a bond gets two things:
1. The redemption price of the bond when it matures
2. Each coupon as it comes due

$C(1+i)^{-n}$
$Fra_{\overline{n}|i}$ } The purchase price of a bond is the present value at the *yield rate* of the redemption price and the coupons

EXAMPLE 1: Find the purchase price of a $100 bond with interest at 4% payable semiannually, redeemable at par in 3 years, if the bond is bought to yield 3% on the investment. This is sometimes referred to as a 3% **basis.**

SOLUTION: The semiannual interest payments are 2% of $100 or $2. The buyer of this bond gets the present value at 3% of $100 due in 3 years, and the present value at 3% of the 6 interest payments of $2 each. We assume that the yield or investment rate is compounded at the same time as the interest is paid on the bond. This will make the yield rate per period $1\frac{1}{2}\%$ and the problem looks like this:

V or purchase price $= 100(1.015)^{-6} + 2a_{\overline{6}|1\frac{1}{2}\%}$

$$V = 100 \times .91454 + 2 \times 5.697$$
$$= 91.45 + 11.39 = \$102.84$$

In this case the bond is bought at a **premium** or for more than the par value because the buyer is willing to accept a yield rate that is lower than the interest rate on the bond. The buyer will get 3% converted semiannually on his investment of $102.84. The company that issued the bond will continue to pay 2% every 6 months on the $100 par value of the bond regardless of who buys it and what he pays.

EXAMPLE 2: A $1000, 3% bond is redeemable at 102 on April 1, 1976. Interest payments are made on April 1 and October 1 of each year. Find the purchase price of this bond on October 1, 1964, if the buyer wants a yield rate of $4\frac{1}{2}\%$.

SOLUTION: From October 1, 1964, to April 1, 1976, is $11\frac{1}{2}$ years so $n = 23$. The redemption price of the bond is 102% of $1000 or $1020. The interest payments are $1\frac{1}{2}\%$ of $1000 or $15. The yield rate per period is $\frac{1}{2}$ of $4\frac{1}{2}\%$ or $2\frac{1}{4}\%$. Sketching the problem and substituting these values in the purchase price formula, we have:

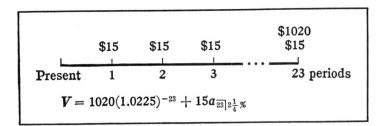

$$V = 1020 \times .599437 + 15 \times 17.8028$$
$$= \$611.43 + \$267.04 = \$878.47$$

In this case the bond is bought at a **discount** or less than the par value because the investor wants a greater return on his investment than the interest rate paid by the company on the par value of the bond. The owner of the bond, on the other hand, wants to convert it into cash. In this case he can do that only if he is willing to sell it for $878.47. In the investment market the price of a bond depends on the interest rate of the bond, the yield rate acceptable to investors, and the degree of safety associated with the particular bond.

Exercise 6a

Compute the purchase price of the bond in each of the following examples.

No.	Face Value	Time of Redemption	Bond Interest	Yield Rate	Compounded	Answer
1.	$ 500	10 yrs. at 102	$3\frac{1}{2}\%$, semiann.	4%	semiann.	$ 486.28
2.	100	4 yrs. at par	4%, semiann.	5%	semiann.	
3.	1000	10 yrs. at par	5%, semiann.	5%	semiann.	1000.00
4.	5000	30 yrs. at par	$4\frac{1}{2}\%$, annually	4%	annually	
5.	500	6 yrs. at par	$2\frac{1}{2}\%$, semiann.	3%	semiann.	486.38
6.	1000	$1\frac{1}{2}$ yrs. at par	4%, semiann.	3%	semiann.	
7.	1000	8 yrs. at 103	3%, semiann.	2%	semiann.	1099.18
8.	1000	26 yrs. at 103	5%, semiann.	6%	semiann.	
9.	100	3 yrs. at 102	4%, semiann.	5%	semiann.	98.97
10.	5000	17 yrs. at 102	3%, semiann.	$2\frac{1}{2}\%$	semiann.	
11.	500	20 yrs. at par	3%, annually	$2\frac{1}{2}\%$	annually	538.98
12.	1000	2 yrs. at $102\frac{1}{2}$	4%, semiann.	$3\frac{1}{2}\%$	semiann.	
13.	500	18 yrs. at par	4%, annually	$3\frac{1}{2}\%$	annually	532.97
14.	5000	$11\frac{1}{2}$ yrs. at 103	5%, semiann.	$3\frac{1}{2}\%$	semiann.	

15. Find the price of a $1000, 4% bond with semiannual coupons if it is bought to yield 5% compounded semiannually and is redeemable at par in: (a) 2 years; (b) 5 years; (c) 10 years. [(a) $981.19; (b) $956.24; (c) $922.05]

16. A $1000, 5% bond is redeemable at 103. Find the purchase price of this bond if it is bought to yield 4% at the following times: (a) 1 year before maturity; (b) 10 years before maturity; (c) 20 years before maturity. Coupons are payable semiannually.

17. Find the purchase price of a $500, 4% bond bearing semiannual coupons bought 15 years before maturity to yield 3% converted semiannually.

($560.04)

18. Work Problem 17 for a yield rate of 5%.

19. A $1000, 4% bond matures December 1, 1973. Coupons are payable on June 1 and December 1. The bond is purchased on June 1, 1964, to yield $3\frac{1}{2}\%$ compounded semiannually. What is the purchase price?   ($1040.11)

20. If the bond in Problem 19 is purchased on June 1, 1973, what would be the purchase price?

21. A $500, $3\frac{1}{2}\%$ bond with coupons payable on March 1 and September 1 is purchased on September 1, 1963. It is redeemable on September 1, 1975. What is the purchase price if it is bought to yield $4\frac{1}{2}\%$ compounded semiannually?   ($454.03)

22. What would be the purchase price of the bond in Problem 21, if the yield rate is $2\frac{1}{2}\%$?

23. A $1000, 5% bond, issued on April 1, 1960, is to be redeemed at 102 in 20 years. Coupon dates are April 1 and October 1. Find the price on October 1, 1966, to yield 4% converted semiannually.   ($1115.25)

24. What would be the purchase price of the bond in Problem 23 if the yield rate is 6%?

25. A $3\frac{1}{4}$% Florida Power Corporation $1000 bond with coupons payable on May 1 and November 1 is redeemable at par on November 1, 1978. At what price would this bond be sold on May 1, 1965, to yield $4\frac{1}{2}$% converted semiannually?   ($874.55)

26. A 5% Consolidated Natural Gas $1000 bond with coupons payable on March 1 and September 1 is redeemable at par on September 1, 1982. At what price would this bond be sold on March 1, 1966, to yield $4\frac{1}{2}$% converted semiannually?

6.4 Premium and Discount

Most bonds are **redeemable at par.** This makes possible a simplified method of computing the purchase price that covers most cases in actual practice. If the interest rate on the bond is greater than the yield rate on the purchase price, the buyer will pay more than the par value of the bond. This difference is called the premium and can be obtained easily as follows.

Since the redemption price equals the par value of the bond we can substitute F for C in the basic bond formula, giving

$$V = F(1 + i)^{-n} + Fra_{\overline{n}|}$$

Because the premium is the difference between the purchase price and the face value we can say

$$P = V - F$$

Substituting the value for V obtained above, we have

$$P = F(1 + i)^{-n} + Fra_{\overline{n}|} - F$$
$$= Fra_{\overline{n}|} - F + F(1 + i)^{-n}$$
$$= Fra_{\overline{n}|} - F[1 - (1 + i)^{-n}]$$

Multiplying the last term by $\dfrac{i}{i}$ will not change the value of the fraction and will enable us to replace $\dfrac{[1 - (1 + i)^{-n}]}{i}$ with $a_{\overline{n}|}$.

$$P = Fra_{\overline{n}|} - Fi\frac{[1 - (1 + i)^{-n}]}{i}$$

$$= Fra_{\overline{n}|} - Fia_{\overline{n}|}$$

$$P = (Fr - Fi)a_{\overline{n}|i} \qquad\qquad (23)$$

We now have to look up only one factor to get the value of a bond. Also, as the examples will show, the computations will be simplified. Note that in Formula (23), Fr is the coupon and Fi is the face value of bond times the *yield* rate.

EXAMPLE 1: Find the purchase price of a $1000, 5% bond redeemable at par on March 1, 1972, if it is bought on September 1, 1965, to yield 4% compounded semiannually.

SOLUTION: In this problem $Fr = 1000 \times .025 = 25$, $Fi = 1000 \times .02 = 20$, and $n = 13$. Substituting in Formula (23),

$$P = (25 - 20)a_{\overline{13}|2\%} = 5 \times 11.348 = \$56.74$$

From which the purchase price $= \$1056.74$

When the buyer of a bond wants a higher rate of return on his investment than the interest rate of the bond, he must get the bond at less than the par value or at a **discount.** This discount equals the par value minus the purchase price.

$$D = F - V$$

To get an equation for the discount we substitute the value of V from formula (22) and proceed as we did in getting the formula for the premium.

$$\begin{aligned}
D &= F - F(1+i)^{-n} - Fra_{\overline{n}|} \\
&= F[1 - (1+i)^{-n}] - Fra_{\overline{n}|} \\
&= Fi\frac{[1 - (1+i)^{-n}]}{i} - Fra_{\overline{n}|} \\
&= Fia_{\overline{n}|} - Fra_{\overline{n}|} \\
D &= (Fi - Fr)a_{\overline{n}|i}
\end{aligned}$$

$$(24)$$

EXAMPLE 2: Find the purchase price of a $1000, 3% bond redeemable at par on October 1, 1980, if it is bought on October 1, 1965, to yield $3\frac{1}{2}$% compounded semiannually.

SOLUTION: $Fi = 1000 \times .0175 = 17.50$, $Fr = 1000 \times .015 = 15$, and $n = 30$. Substituting in formula (24),

$$D = (17.50 - 15.00)a_{\overline{30}|1\frac{3}{4}\%} = 2.50 \times 23.186 = \$57.97$$

From which the purchase price $= \$942.03$

Exercise 6b

Find the purchase price of the following bonds. All are redeemable at par.

No.	Face Value	Time of Redemption	Bond Interest	Yield Rate	Compounded	Answer
1.	$1000	10 yrs.	4%, semiann.	3%	semiann.	$1085.85
2.	500	5 yrs.	3½%, semiann.	4%	semiann.	
3.	100	8 yrs.	5%, semiann.	4%	semiann.	106.79
4.	500	2 yrs.	3%, semiann.	5%	semiann.	
5.	100	6 yrs.	4%, semiann.	3½%	semiann.	102.69
6.	5000	9 yrs.	2%, semiann.	2½%	semiann.	
7.	1000	12 yrs.	5%, semiann.	4%	semiann.	1094.57
8.	10,000	15 yrs.	4%, semiann.	3%	semiann.	

9. A $500, 5% bond with interest payable on April 1 and October 1 is redeemable at par on October 1, 1967. What purchase price on April 1, 1964, would yield an investor 6% converted semiannually?   ($484.42)

10. A $10,000, 3% bond with interest payable on March 1 and September 1 is redeemable at par on September 1, 1973. What purchase price on September 1, 1964, will yield an investor 2½% converted semiannually?

11. On June 1, 1962, a company issued some $10,000, 3% bonds with coupons payable semiannually on June 1 and December 1. The bonds are redeemable at par on June 1, 1972. If a purchaser buys one of these bonds on December 1, 1966, to yield 4% converted semiannually, how much will the bond cost him?   ($9510.66)

12. An investor wishes to realize at least 4½% converted semiannually on some money he has to invest. To get this return, what is the most he could pay on June 15, 1965, for a $5000, 4% bond redeemable at par on June 15, 1978? The bond interest is payable semiannually on June 15 and December 15.

13. A $1000, 3% Cleveland Electric Illuminating Co. bond matures at par on December 1, 1982. Coupons are payable on June 1 and December 1. Find the price on June 1, 1967, to yield 4½% converted semiannually. ($833.90)

14. Work Problem 13 for a yield rate of 5%.

15. A 3½%, $1000 Chesapeake and Ohio bond is redeemable at par on May 1, 1996. Coupons are paid on May 1 and November 1. Find the price on November 1, 1966, to yield 4½%.   ($837.57)

16. What would be the quoted price for the bond in Problem 15 to yield 4%?

17. A $1000, 5½% Olin Mathieson Chemical Company bond is redeemable at par on November 1, 1982. Coupons are payable on May 1 and November 1. On May 1, 1965, this bond would cost how much if the yield is to be 4½% converted semiannually?   ($1120.23)

18. Find the cost of the bond in Problem 17 if the yield is to be 5% converted semiannually.

19. A $1000, $3\frac{1}{8}$% Commonwealth Edison Debenture is redeemable at par on October 1, 2004. Coupons are payable on October 1 and April 1. If this bond is bought to yield 4% converted semiannually the purchase price would be how much on: (a) October 1, 1974; (b) October 1, 1984; (c) October 1, 1994. [(a) $848.09; (b) $880.46; (c) $928.55]

20. Work Problem 19 for a yield rate of $3\frac{1}{2}$%.

6.5 Amortization of the Premium

When the purchase price of a bond is higher than the maturity value, the buyer's capital can be kept intact by setting aside enough from the interest payments to equal the premium when the bond is redeemed. A systematic way to do this is to compute the interest at the yield rate on the book value of the bond (the value at which the bond is carried on the books of the owner), subtract this from the bond interest, and apply this difference to periodically reducing the book value. Under this plan the bond will have a gradually decreasing book value that will equal the redemption price of the bond when it matures. This method insures that the investment always earns its yield rate and what remains from the bond coupon is used to amortize the premium. An example will show how this is done.

EXAMPLE: A $1000 5% bond maturing at par in two years is bought on June 1, 1965, to yield 4%. The interest is paid twice a year. Construct a schedule for the amortization of the premium.

SOLUTION: The premium $= (25 - 20)a_{\overline{4}|2\%} = 5 \times 3.808 = \$19.04$

Thus the purchase price of the bond is $1019.04. This is the initial investment on which the buyer wants to realize 4%. At the end of 6 months, he cashes a coupon worth $25. However, 2% of $1019.04 is only $20.38. Thus in effect the buyer has received from his coupon $20.38 in interest while the difference between this and the $25, which is $4.62, can be looked on as a partial return of his premium. This $4.62 is capital for reinvestment and is no longer considered part of the investment in the bond. These partial returns of the capital will equal the total premium when the bond is redeemed so that the buyer's capital remains intact. Each period then shows a decreased investment in the bond and an increased part of the bond interest applied to the amortization of the premium. The money invested in the bond at any time is the book value of the bond. The following schedule shows how the book value finally equals the redemption price of the bond. Long schedules of this type are often prepared on electronic computers.

Amortization of the Premium

Date	Interest on Book Value at Yield Rate	Interest on Bond	Amount for Amortization of Premium	Book Value
June 1, 1965	—	—	—	$1019.04
Dec. 1, 1965	$20.38	$25.00	$4.62	1014.42
June 1, 1966	20.29	25.00	4.71	1009.71
Dec. 1, 1966	20.19	25.00	4.81	1004.90
June 1, 1967	20.10	25.00	4.90	1000.00
			$19.04	

6.6 Accumulation of the Discount

If the bond is bought below par, the bond interest will not equal the desired return on the investment. This means that a portion of the desired interest will not be received with the bond payments but will be obtained when the bond is redeemed at more than the purchase price. Rather than picking up the increase in the value of the bond all at once, the deficit between the desired interest and the bond interest can be applied each period to raise the book value from the purchase price to the redemption price.

EXAMPLE: A $1000, 5% bond maturing at par in two years is bought on June 1, 1965, to yield 6%. The interest is paid twice a year. Construct a schedule for the accumulation of the discount.

SOLUTION: The discount $= (30 - 25)a_{\overline{4}|3\%}$
$$= 5 \times 3.717 = \$18.59$$

Thus the purchase price of the bond is $981.41. This is the investment on which the buyer wants to realize 6%. At the end of six months the owner cashes a coupon worth $25. However, 3% of $981.41 is $29.44. The $4.44 in excess of the bond interest must come from the increase in the book value of the bond. The following schedule shows how these periodic differences result in the book value of the bond finally equaling the redemption price.

Accumulation of the Discount

Date	Interest on Book Value at Yield Rate	Interest on Bond	Amount for Accumulation of Discount	Book Value
June 1, 1965	—	—	—	$ 981.41
Dec. 1, 1965	$29.44	$25.00	$4.44	985.85
June 1, 1966	29.58	25.00	4.58	990.43
Dec. 1, 1966	29.71	25.00	4.71	995.14
June 1, 1967	29.86	25.00	4.86	1000.00
			$18.59	

Exercise 6c

1. A $5000 bond with interest at 4%, payable January 1 and July 1, is to mature at par on July 1, 1968. Construct a schedule showing the amortization of the premium if the bond is bought on July 1, 1965, to yield 3% converted semiannually.   (Purchase price $5142.43)

2. A $500, 6% bond with coupons payable on March 1 and September 1 is to mature at par on March 1, 1968. Construct a schedule showing the amortization of the premium if the bond is bought on September 1, 1965, to yield 5%, compounded semiannually.

3. A $1000, 3% bond with semiannual coupons on April 1 and October 1, will mature on October 1, 1967. Construct a schedule showing the accumulation of the discount if the bond is bought on April 1, 1964, to yield 4%.

(Purchase price $967.64)

4. A $10,000 bond with interest at $2\frac{1}{2}\%$, payable annually on June 1, is to mature at par on June 1, 1974. It is bought on June 1, 1965, to yield 3%. Construct a schedule showing the accumulation of the discount.

6.7 Bonds Purchased Between Coupon Dates

In all of the problems worked so far to get the purchase price of a bond, the bond was purchased on a coupon date. The seller kept the coupon that was due on that date and the buyer had to hold the bond for a full period before he could cash his first coupon. In practice, of course, bonds are usually purchased between coupon dates. This means that the purchaser will get the full value of the next coupon even though he has not had his money invested during all of the interest period. The seller, on the other hand, has had his money tied up for part of a coupon period but he will not collect any of his interest from the company that issued the bond. The logical solution to this problem, and the one followed in practice, is for the buyer to pay the seller for the accrued portion of the current coupon.

The actual sale price of a bond between coupon dates is the sum of the value of the bond itself and the accrued portion of the current coupon. Thus bonds are sold at a quoted price "and interest." The price that is quoted on the bond market, sometimes called the **market** or **and interest** price, is the price of the bond itself to yield a certain return. To this is added the accrued interest to get the total purchase price paid for the bond.

EXAMPLE: A $5000, 6% bond with interest payable semiannually on June 1 and December 1 is redeemable at par on June 1, 1967. This bond is purchased on October 1, 1965, to yield 4% converted semiannually. What is the purchase price?

SOLUTION: To get the *quoted* or *and interest* price, we will first determine the value of the bond on the coupon dates immediately preceding and following the purchase date. Then we have to interpolate to get the *and interest* price on the purchase date.

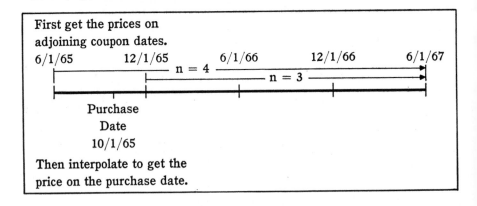

For June 1, 1965 the premium $= (150 - 100)a_{\overline{4}|2\%} = \$190.39$

For Dec. 1, 1965 the premium $= (150 - 100)a_{\overline{3}|2\%} = \$144.19$

Thus the price on a coupon date drops from $5190.39 on June 1, 1965 to $5144.19 on December 1, 1965. This is a decrease of $46.20. We now interpolate to find what part of this decrease has occurred on October 1. Since October 1 is ⅔ of the way from June 1 to December 1, we simply multiply $46.20 by this ratio giving us $30.80.

This makes the quoted price on October 1, $5190.39 − $30.80 = $5159.59. But on October 1, $\frac{4}{6}$ of a coupon has also accrued. This ratio applied to the total interest payment of $150 equals $100. Thus the actual selling price on October 1 would be $5159.59 + 100 = $5259.59. Note that the buyer on this date has to wait only 2 months until he gets a full coupon of $150. At this time he is reimbursed for the extra $100 he paid the seller.

The sketch uses the data from the preceding example to show the relationship between the various prices in bond problems. Note that the *quoted* or *and interest* price approaches the par value of the bond and finally equals it on the maturity date. The actual price equals the *and interest* price only on interest dates.

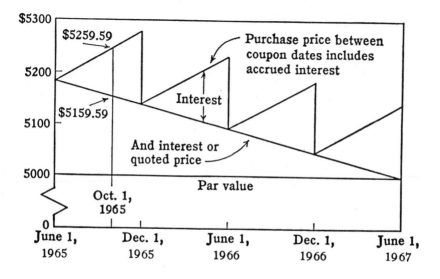

The sketch shows why the quoted price of a bond does not include the accrued interest. If the actual purchase price were quoted, there would be a big change in the price before and after an interest date that would be caused by the paying of the bond interest rather than to any change in the value of the bond itself.

Exercise 6d

In the following problems coupons are paid twice a year and the yield rate is compounded semiannually. Get the *and interest* and the total price for the indicated purchase date.

No.	Par Value	Coupon Rate	Coupon Dates	Maturity Date	Purchase Date	Yield Rate
1.	$1000	4%	Jan. 1, July 1	Jan. 1, 1970	June 1, 1965	3%
2.	500	5%	Mar. 1, Sept. 1	Sept. 1, 1966	July 1, 1964	3½%
3.	100	4%	May 1, Nov. 1	Nov. 1, 1996	Dec. 1, 1966	5%
4.	5000	3%	Feb. 1, Aug. 1	Feb. 1, 1977	Nov. 1, 1965	3½%

(Answers: Problem 1: *and interest* price $1042.53; total price $1059.20. Problem 3: *and interest* price $84.56; total price $84.89.)

5. A Michigan Consolidated Gas Company $1000, 3½% bond is redeemable at par on August 1, 1976. Coupons are payable on February 1 and August 1. Get the *and interest* and the total price if the bond is sold on June 1, 1965, to yield 4½% converted semiannually.   ($912.98, $924.65)

6. A 5% bond having a par value of $1000 is issued on April 1, 1966. It is to be redeemed at par in 10 years. Coupons are payable on April 1 and October 1. What is the quoted price on February 1, 1968, to yield 4½% converted semiannually? What would be the total price including the accrued interest on this date?

7. A New Jersey Bell Telephone $1000, 2¾% bond is redeemable at par on March 15, 1990. Coupon dates are March 15 and September 15. Get the *and interest* and the total price if this bond is sold on October 15, 1964, to yield 4%.   ($801.70; $803.99)

8. A $1000 bond, bearing interest at 4½% payable semiannually on March 1 and September 1 is to be redeemed at par on September 1, 1975. It is purchased on July 1, 1967, to yield 5% converted semiannually. What was the quoted or market price? What was the purchase price including accrued interest?

9. A 5%, $1000 bond is to be redeemed at par on April 1, 1975. Coupons are payable on April 1 and October 1. This bond is sold on August 1, 1964, at a price which will yield 4% converted semiannually. What was the quoted price? What was the total price including accrued interest?

($1086.14; $1102.81)

10. A 5% bond having a par value of $1000 was issued on April 1, 1962. It is to be redeemed at par in 20 years. Coupons are payable on April 1 and October 1. What is the quoted price on February 1, 1964, to yield 4½% converted semiannually? What would be the total price including accrued interest on this date?

11. A $1000, 2¾% Cincinnati Gas and Electric Company first mortgage bond is redeemable at par on October 1, 1975. Coupons are payable on April 1 and October 1. What would be the *and interest* and the actual purchase price of this bond on March 1, 1965, if the yield rate is to be 4% converted semiannually?   ($893.01; $904.47)

12. Work Problem 11 for a yield rate of $4\frac{1}{2}\%$ converted semiannually.

6.8   Finding the Yield Rate

Up to now we have been determining the purchase price of a bond to yield a certain rate of return on the investment. In practice, the quoted or the and interest price is often given without stating the yield rate. Since the purchaser is interested in the return he will get on his investment, it is necessary to determine the yield rate. The yield which we get is known as *yield to maturity* by investment dealers. It is the true overall rate of return which an investor gets on his invested capital. Another yield which is sometimes used is the *current yield* obtained by dividing the annual return in dollars by the current price. This is very simple to compute but is not a true measure of return on invested capital. For this reason, whenever yield rate is used in this text, it means yield to maturity. We get the yield rate in two ways. The first is the Bond Salesman's Method which is simple and usually leads to fairly accurate results.

EXAMPLE 1: A $1000, 5% bond redeemable at par in 10 years has interest payable semiannually. The quoted price is $1050. What is the yield rate?

SOLUTION: Here we have a bond which has a book value of $1050 now and $1000 in 10 years or 20 periods:

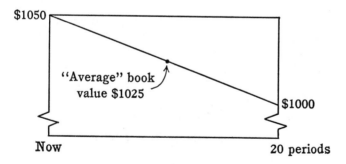

We add these two values and divide by 2 to get an "average" investment or book value.

$$\frac{1050 + 1000}{2} = \$1025$$

The periodic interest on this bond is $25. But it has been purchased at a premium of $50 which must be amortized over the 20 periods. The "average" amortization per period $= 50/20 = \$2.50$. This is deducted from the interest payments so that our return per period is $22.50 on an investment of $1025. This makes the approximate yield rate $22.50/1025 = 2.2\%$ per period or 4.4% nominal.

If a more accurate value for the yield rate is desired, we use trial and error until we find two adjacent yield rates which bracket the given price. We then find the yield rate by interpolation. The Bond Salesman's Method showed that the yield rate is close to 2.2% per period. We try the closest table value to this and compute the purchase price.

With our tables this is $4\frac{1}{2}\%$ a year or $2\frac{1}{4}\%$ a period. Using Formula (23) for bond premium, we get

$$P = (25 - 22.50)a_{\overline{20}|2\frac{1}{4}\%} = 2.50(15.964) = \$39.91$$

This would make the purchase price $1039.91. Since the actual purchase price was $1050, the yield rate must be less than $2\frac{1}{4}\%$. The closest table value lower than this is 2%, so we compute the purchase price at 2%.

$$P = (25 - 20)a_{\overline{20}|2\%} = 5(16.351) = \$81.76$$

and $\qquad V = \$1081.76$

We now have a purchase price below the quoted price and another one above. Since our tables do not permit any closer approximations, we interpolate,

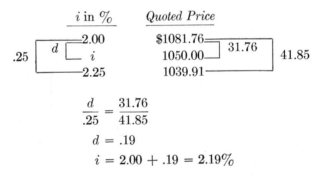

$$\frac{d}{.25} = \frac{31.76}{41.85}$$

$$d = .19$$

$$i = 2.00 + .19 = 2.19\%$$

Nominal annual yield $= 2i = 4.38\%$

What this method of determining the yield rate comes down to is finding two adjacent rates in the table such that the quoted price of the bond lies between the prices determined using the two tabular rates. In practical investment work it is usually possible to simplify computations by using bond tables which will be described later. We shall work one more example to show how the yield rate is determined if the bond is bought at a discount or between interest dates.

EXAMPLE: A \$1000, 4% bond with coupons payable semiannually on April 1 and October 1 is redeemable at par on April 1, 1980. On June 1, 1965, this bond is quoted at 94. What is the yield rate?

SOLUTION: First we use the approximate method to get an estimate of the yield rate assuming that the bond was quoted on the nearest interest date, in this case April 1, 1965. Averaging the quoted price and the redemption price gives

$$\frac{940 + 1000}{2} = \$970$$

The semiannual coupon is \$20. In addition to the interest there will be an increase of \$60 in the value of the bond. Averaged over 30 periods this amounts to \$2 per period. Therefore we have an average return of \$22 on an average investment of \$970. This makes the approximate yield rate

$$\frac{22}{970} = 2.3\% \text{ per period or } 4.6\% \text{ nominal}$$

If we want a more accurate answer, it is necessary to make trial computations using assumed yield rates. We use the value obtained above as a guide in selecting trial rates.

First we try $2\frac{1}{4}\%$ ($4\frac{1}{2}\%$ nominal).

Date	*Discount*	*Quoted Price*
April 1, 1965	$(22.50 - 20.00)a_{\overline{30}|} = \$54.11$	\$945.89
June 1, 1965		?
Oct. 1, 1965	$(22.50 - 20.00)a_{\overline{29}|} = 52.83$	947.17

$\left.\begin{array}{c} \$945.89 \\ ? \\ 947.17 \end{array}\right\}\;d\;\Big\}\;1.28$

Since June 1 is $\frac{2}{6}$ of the way from April 1 to October 1, the interpolation to get the June 1 price is

$$\frac{d}{1.28} = \frac{2}{6}$$
$$d = .43$$

And the June 1 price for a yield rate of $2\frac{1}{4}\%$ per period is

$$\$945.89 + .43 = \$946.32$$

This shows that the true yield rate must be more than $2\frac{1}{4}\%$ so we repeat the above procedure with a trial rate of $2\frac{1}{2}\%$.

Date	*Discount*	*Quoted Price*
April 1, 1965	$(25.00 - 20.00)a_{\overline{30}|} = \$104.65$	$895.35
June 1, 1965		?
Oct. 1, 1965	$(25.00 - 20.00)a_{\overline{29}|} = 102.27$	897.73

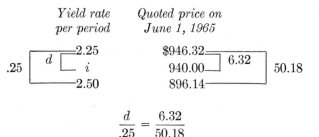

$$\frac{d}{2.38} = \frac{2}{6}$$

$$d = .79$$

From which the June 1, 1965, price for a yield rate of $2\frac{1}{2}\%$ per period is

$$\$895.35 + .79 = \$896.14$$

We can now summarize the results as follows:

	Yield rate per period	*Quoted price on June 1, 1965*
.25	2.25 / d / i / 2.50	\$946.32 / 940.00 / 896.14

$$\frac{d}{.25} = \frac{6.32}{50.18}$$

$$d = .03$$

From which $i = 2.25 + .03 = 2.28\%$ and the nominal yield rate is

$$2 \times 2.28 = 4.56\% \text{ converted semiannually}$$

Exercise 6e

(Answers should be based on interpolation)

1. A \$1000, 3% bond with semiannual coupons is redeemable at par in 10 years. If this bond is bought for \$970.00, what is the nominal yield rate, converted semiannually? $\qquad$ (3.36%)

2. A \$500, 4% bond with semiannual coupons is redeemable at par in 5 years. If this bond is bought for \$480, what is the nominal yield rate, converted semiannually.

3. A \$1000, 5% bond with semiannual coupons is redeemable at par in 10 years. If this bond is bought for \$1050, what is the nominal yield rate, converted semiannually? (4.38%)

4. A \$5000, 2½% bond with semiannual coupons is redeemable at par in 20 years. If this bond is bought for \$5300, what is the nominal yield rate, converted semiannually?

5. Get the nominal yield rate for a \$1000, 4% bond quoted at 98 on June 1, 1965, if the bond is to be redeemed at par on December 1, 1972. Coupons are payable on June 1 and December 1. (4.32%)

6. A \$1000, 6% bond with coupons payable semiannually on March 1 and September 1 is issued on March 1, 1956, to mature in 20 years. On September 1, 1964, this bond is quoted at 102. If purchased at this price what would be the nominal yield rate converted semiannually?

7. A \$1000, 5% bond issued on August 1, 1962, is to be redeemed at par on August 1, 1967. Coupons are payable semiannually on February 1 and August 1. If this bond is quoted at 95 on February 1, 1965, what is the nominal yield rate converted semiannually? (7.22%)

8. A \$1000, 4% Baltimore and Ohio RR bond is redeemable on September 1, 1980. Coupon dates are March 1 and September 1. If this bond is quoted at 70 on September 1, 1965, what is the nominal yield rate converted semiannually?

9. A \$500, 5% bond with coupons payable on January 1 and July 1 is redeemable at par on July 1, 1968. It is purchased on February 1, 1964 for \$530 plus accrued interest. What is the yield rate? (3.52%)

10. A \$1000, 4% bond with coupons payable on March 1 and September 1 is redeemable at par on March 1, 1970. It is purchased on May 1, 1965, for \$960 plus accrued interest. What is the yield rate?

6.9 Bond Tables

Companies that buy and sell bonds reduce the computations required to get the price of a bond or the yield rate by using bond tables that cover most of the cases that arise in practice. Bond tables are available in large volumes with answers to 4 or 6 decimal places and in pocket-size books with values to 2 decimal places. The tables give the *and interest* prices of bonds for a wide range of yield and coupon rates and lengths of time until the maturity date of the bond. A sample page from the 6-place tables of the Financial Publishing Company is shown on page 185, and a sample page from the pocket-size book is shown on page 186. The examples below are based on page 185 which is for a \$100, 2¾% bond with interest paid semiannually.

EXAMPLE 1: A $1000, $2\frac{3}{4}$% bond with interest payable semiannually is redeemable in 23 years. What is the purchase price for a yield rate of 1.5%?

SOLUTION: We simply go down the yield rate column to 1.50 and read the purchase price of $124.239 for a $100 bond. A $1000 bond will cost $1242.39.

EXAMPLE 2: A $1000, $2\frac{3}{4}$% bond with interest payable semiannually is redeemable in 23 years and 3 months. What is the purchase price for a yield rate of 5%?

SOLUTION: Since the bond is not being purchased on a coupon date, we must first obtain the *and interest* price and then add the accrued interest. Both of these can be obtained directly from the table. The *and interest* price is $692.70. From the bottom of the table we get $.6875 for the accrued interest for 3 months on $100. On $1000 it will be $6.88. Adding the two gives a purchase price of $699.58.

EXAMPLE 3: A $1000, $2\frac{3}{4}$% bond redeemable in 23 years is quoted at $1250. What is the nominal yield rate?

SOLUTION: The equivalent price for a $100 bond is $125. From the table we see that the yield rate is between 1.45 and 1.50%. If a more accurate answer is needed, we interpolate,

Yield Rate in %   *Quoted Price*

$$.05\% \begin{bmatrix} d \begin{bmatrix} 1.45 \\ \text{Rate} \end{bmatrix} \\ 1.50 \end{bmatrix} \qquad \begin{bmatrix} 125.35 \\ 125.00 \end{bmatrix} .35 \\ 124.24 \end{bmatrix} 1.11$$

$$\frac{d}{.05} = \frac{.35}{1.11}$$

$$d = .016$$

Yield rate = $1.45 + .016 = 1.466\%$ converted semiannually.

The following examples are based on the pocket-size tables.

EXAMPLE 4: Find the *and interest* price of a $100, $2\frac{3}{4}$% bond redeemable in 14 years and 6 months to yield 3% converted semiannually.

SOLUTION: Opposite 3% under 14–6 we find the answer to be $97.08.

2¾% COUPON   23 YEARS

Yield	Even	1 Month	2 Months	3 Months	4 Months	5 Months
.00	163.250000	163.479167	163.708333	163.937500	164.166667	164.395833
.05	161.736617	161.958989	162.181360	162.403732	162.626104	162.848477
.10	160.239532	160.455235	160.670938	160.886643	161.102349	161.318057
.15	158.758557	158.967716	159.176877	159.386041	159.595207	159.804376
.20	157.293510	157.496247	157.698989	157.901735	158.104486	158.307241
.25	155.844208	156.040644	156.237088	156.433538	156.629995	156.826459
.30	154.410472	154.600726	154.790990	154.981264	155.171547	155.361840
.35	152.992124	153.176312	153.360514	153.544729	153.728958	153.913199
.40	151.588989	151.767227	151.945482	152.123754	152.302043	152.480349
.45	150.200894	150.373294	150.545715	150.718158	150.890622	151.063107
.50	148.827667	148.994340	149.161039	149.327765	149.494516	149.661293
.55	147.469139	147.630195	147.791282	147.952400	148.113549	148.274729
.60	146.125144	146.280689	146.436271	146.591890	146.747546	146.903238
.65	144.795515	144.945656	145.095840	145.246066	145.396335	145.546646
.70	143.480091	143.624931	143.769820	143.914758	144.059745	144.204781
.75	142.178708	142.318349	142.458046	142.597799	142.737608	142.877472
.80	140.891208	141.025751	141.160357	141.295026	141.429758	141.564553
.85	139.617433	139.746977	139.876591	140.006276	140.136031	140.265856
.90	138.357228	138.481870	138.606590	138.731388	138.856264	138.981218
.95	137.110438	137.230273	137.350195	137.470202	137.590296	137.710476
1.00	135.876912	135.992035	136.107252	136.222564	136.337970	136.453472
1.05	134.656500	134.767002	134.877608	134.988317	135.099129	135.210045
1.10	133.449052	133.555024	133.661110	133.767308	133.873618	133.980041
1.15	132.254422	132.355954	132.457609	132.559386	132.661284	132.763304
1.20	131.072465	131.169645	131.266958	131.364401	131.461976	131.559682
1.25	129.903037	129.995952	130.089009	130.182206	130.275545	130.369025
1.30	128.745998	128.834732	128.923618	129.012655	129.101844	129.191183
1.35	127.601207	127.685844	127.770643	127.855603	127.940726	128.026010
1.40	126.468525	126.549147	126.629942	126.710908	126.792048	126.873359
1.45	125.347817	125.424504	125.501375	125.578429	125.655667	125.733087
1.50	124.238946	124.311779	124.384806	124.458027	124.531443	124.605052
1.55	123.141780	123.210636	123.280097	123.349564	123.419237	123.489114
1.60	122.056186	122.121542	122.187115	122.252904	122.318911	122.385134
1.65	120.982035	121.043765	121.105725	121.167914	121.230331	121.292976
1.70	119.919196	119.977376	120.035797	120.094459	120.153361	120.212504

Yield	Even	1 Month	2 Months	3 Months	4 Months	5 Months
5.00	69.451559	69.389843	69.329321	69.269989	69.211842	69.154874
5.05	58.918721	68.856348	68.795184	68.735224	68.676462	68.618895
5.10	68.391188	68.328179	68.266394	68.205828	68.146474	68.088329
5.15	67.868901	67.805279	67.742894	67.681742	67.621818	67.563116
5.20	67.351804	67.287588	67.224625	67.162909	67.102434	67.043196
5.25	66.839840	66.775052	66.711530	66.649270	66.588265	66.528511
5.30	66.332953	66.267612	66.203553	66.140768	66.079254	66.019004
5.35	65.831089	65.765215	65.700637	65.637348	65.575343	65.514617
5.40	65.334192	65.267805	65.202727	65.138953	65.076477	65.015293
5.45	64.842209	64.775327	64.709769	64.645529	64.582601	64.520976
5.50	64.355086	64.287729	64.221709	64.157021	64.093658	64.031616
5.55	63.872771	63.804956	63.738493	63.673375	63.609597	63.547152
5.60	63.395213	63.326957	63.260068	63.194538	63.130362	63.067532
5.65	62.922358	62.853680	62.786383	62.720458	62.655901	62.592704
5.70	62.454157	62.385074	62.317385	62.251083	62.186161	62.122614

Accrued Interest on $100	5 Months	4 Months	3 Months	2 Months	1 Month
	1.145833	.916667	.687500	.458333	.229167

FACSIMILE OF PORTION OF A PAGE OF BOND TABLES

Bond tables used by courtesy of the Financial Publishing Co., Boston, Mass.

2¾%			YEARS AND MONTHS					
Mat. Yield	14-1	14-2	14-3	14-4	14-5	14-6	14-7	14-8
.50	130.56	130.73	130.91	131.08	131.26	131.43	131.61	131.78
.60	128.99	129.16	129.32	129.49	129.65	129.81	129.98	130.14
.70	127.45	127.60	127.76	127.91	128.06	128.22	128.37	128.53
.75	126.68	126.83	126.98	127.13	127.28	127.43	127.58	127.73
.80	125.92	126.07	126.21	126.36	126.50	126.65	126.79	126.93
.85	125.17	125.31	125.45	125.59	125.73	125.87	126.01	126.15
.90	124.42	124.55	124.69	124.82	124.96	125.10	125.23	125.36
.95	123.67	123.81	123.94	124.07	124.20	124.33	124.46	124.59
1.00	122.94	123.06	123.19	123.31	123.44	123.57	123.69	123.82
1.05	122.20	122.32	122.44	122.57	122.69	122.81	122.93	123.05
1.10	121.47	121.59	121.71	121.82	121.94	122.06	122.17	122.29
1.15	120.75	120.86	120.97	121.09	121.20	121.31	121.42	121.54
1.20	120.03	120.14	120.25	120.35	120.46	120.57	120.68	120.79
1.25	119.31	119.42	119.52	119.63	119.73	119.84	119.94	120.04
1.30	118.60	118.70	118.80	118.91	119.01	119.11	119.21	119.30
1.35	117.90	118.00	118.09	118.19	118.28	118.38	118.48	118.57
1.40	117.20	117.29	117.38	117.48	117.57	117.66	117.75	117.84
1.45	116.51	116.59	116.68	116.77	116.86	116.95	117.03	117.12
1.50	115.82	115.90	115.98	116.07	116.15	116.23	116.32	116.40
1.55	115.13	115.21	115.29	115.37	115.45	115.53	115.61	115.69
1.60	114.45	114.52	114.60	114.68	114.75	114.83	114.90	114.98
1.65	113.77	113.84	113.92	113.99	114.06	114.13	114.21	114.28
1.70	113.10	113.17	113.24	113.31	113.37	113.44	113.51	113.58
1.75	112.43	112.50	112.56	112.63	112.69	112.76	112.82	112.88
1.80	111.77	111.83	111.89	111.95	112.01	112.06	112.14	112.20
1.85	111.11	111.17	111.23	111.28	111.34	111.40	111.46	111.51
1.90	110.46	110.51	110.57	110.62	110.67	110.73	110.78	110.83
1.95	109.81	109.86	109.91	109.96	110.01	110.06	110.11	110.16
2.00	109.16	109.21	109.26	109.30	109.35	109.40	109.45	109.49
2.05	108.52	108.57	108.61	108.65	108.70	108.74	108.78	108.83
2.10	107.89	107.93	107.97	108.01	108.05	108.09	108.13	108.17
2.15	107.26	107.29	107.33	107.37	107.40	107.44	107.48	107.51
2.20	106.63	106.66	106.69	106.73	106.76	106.80	106.83	106.86
2.25	106.01	106.03	106.06	106.10	106.13	106.16	106.19	106.21
2.30	105.39	105.41	105.44	105.47	105.45	105.52	105.55	105.57
2.35	104.77	104.79	104.82	104.84	104.87	104.89	104.91	104.94
2.40	104.16	104.18	104.20	104.22	104.24	104.26	104.28	104.30
2.45	103.55	103.57	103.59	103.61	103.62	103.64	103.66	103.68
2.50	102.95	102.97	102.98	102.99	103.01	103.03	103.04	103.05
2.55	102.35	102.36	102.37	102.39	102.40	102.41	102.42	102.43
2.60	101.76	101.77	101.77	101.78	101.79	101.80	101.81	101.82
2.65	101.17	101.17	101.18	101.18	101.19	101.20	101.20	101.21
2.70	100.58	100.58	100.59	100.59	100.59	100.60	100.60	100.60
2.75	100.00	100.00	100.00	100.00	100.00	100.00	100.00	100.00
2.80	99.42	99.42	99.41	99.41	99.41	99.41	99.40	99.40
2.85	98.85	98.84	98.83	98.83	98.82	98.82	98.81	98.81
2.90	98.27	98.27	98.26	98.25	98.24	98.23	98.23	98.22
2.95	97.71	97.70	97.68	97.67	97.66	97.65	97.64	97.63
3.00	97.14	97.13	97.12	97.10	97.09	97.08	97.06	97.05
3.05	96.58	96.57	96.55	96.54	96.52	96.51	96.49	96.47
3.10	96.03	96.01	95.99	95.97	95.95	95.94	95.92	95.90

472

Pocket-size Bond Tables

EXAMPLE 5: A $2\frac{3}{4}\%$ bond redeemable in 14 years and 3 months is quoted at 105. What is the yield rate?

SOLUTION: The table shows that the rate is between 2.30 and 2.35%. This narrow range is a satisfactory answer for many purposes. Interpolation could be used to get a closer approximation to the true yield rate.

EXAMPLE 6: A $1000, $2\frac{3}{4}\%$ bond matures in 14 years and 6 months. What should be the quoted price to yield 2%?

SOLUTION: The table value is 109.40 for a $100 bond. Therefore the value of a $1000 bond would be $1094.00.

Exercise 6f

(Use the sample bond table on page 185. All yield rates are converted semiannually.)

1. A \$1000, $2\frac{3}{4}\%$ bond with interest payable semiannually is redeemable at par in 23 years. What is the purchase price for a yield rate of 5%?

($694.52)

2. Work Problem 1 for a yield rate of 1.6%.

3. A \$1000, $2\frac{3}{4}\%$ bond with interest payable semiannually is redeemable at par in 23 years and 5 months. Get the *and interest* and the purchase price for a yield rate of 5%.   ($691.55; $693.84)

4. A \$500, $2\frac{3}{4}\%$ bond with semiannual coupons is redeemable at par in 23 years and 3 months. Get the *and interest* and the purchase price for a yield rate of 1.5%.

5. A \$1000, $2\frac{3}{4}\%$ bond redeemable at par in 23 years is sold for \$670. What is the nominal yield rate?   (5.23%)

6. A \$500, $2\frac{3}{4}\%$ bond is redeemable at par in 23 years. If a buyer pays \$630 for this bond, what rate of return will he get on his money?

7

DEPRECIATION AND
CAPITAL BUDGETING

7.1 Depreciation Is an Expense

The cost of a machine, building, or other tangible asset is an expense to be recovered out of revenue during the life of the asset. All machinery is headed for the junk heap, and its cost should be recovered before it gets there.

The earnings of a business are dependent on having adequate capital, materials, and labor. If the costs of assets are not recovered by the end of their useful lives, a company may find itself in serious financial trouble.

One cause of depreciation is wear and tear resulting from use of the asset. Another cause is obsolescence which means that the asset is out of date because of the development of a better machine, an increase in demand which the present asset cannot meet, or a big decrease in demand for the products which the asset has been producing. A change in the costs of the factors of production may cause obsolescence. For example, increased labor costs may result in the installation of more efficient machinery before the old is worn out.

The importance of allowing for depreciation can be illustrated by a simple example. A man buys a heavy-duty dump truck for $12,000. Contractors will pay $50 a day for his services and the use of the truck. From this $50 he must pay maintenance and operating expenses, his wages, and earn a reasonable return on his invested capital. And, if he hopes to remain in business, he should also recover the $12,000 by the end of the useful life of the truck. Eventually this truck, like any machine, will have to be replaced because it wears out or becomes obsolete. Regardless of the reason for replacement, the capital invested in an asset should be recovered from the income of the business. This replacement of invested capital is an expense, and it should be met from current income in the same way that labor, materials, interest, and other costs are recovered from the sale of the goods or services sold by a company.

The terms that will be used in depreciation problems are:

C = the **original cost** of the asset.

S = the **scrap, salvage, or residual value** of the asset at the end of its useful life.

n = the **useful life** of the asset in years.

W = the **wearing value** of the asset. It is the difference between cost and scrap value. $W = C - S$.

R = the **periodic depreciation charge.** This is usually an annual charge. It may or may not be equal from year to year depending on the method of depreciation.

Both the estimated life of an asset and its scrap value are estimates made by authorities who are familiar with the particular asset. The Internal Revenue Service publishes useful life guidelines which may be used in the preparation of income tax returns.

While money recovered through depreciation allowances may be put into securities or other investments to build up a fund which will be used to replace the asset, a much more common practice is to use recovered funds in the operation of the business. In the modern corporation, depreciation charges are a major source of funds for capital projects. Used to purchase currently needed assets, the recovered funds usually earn a higher rate of return than could be obtained from income on fixed investments.

The value at which an asset is shown on the accounting records of a company is called *carrying value* or *book value*. Initially the book value is the cost of the asset. After the first year it equals the amount of capital still invested in the property and which must be recovered in the future through depreciation charges and salvage value. As an asset depreciates, it is carried at a decreasing book value. The depreciation allowance each year offsets the decrease in book value. The sum of the depreciation allowances is called the total accumulated depreciation. At all times the book value plus the total accumulated depreciation should equal the cost of the asset.

In general, depreciation charges are on an annual basis. The amount of depreciation to be charged the first year on an asset purchased during that year can be determined in several ways. One way is to prorate the charge for the time remaining in the year. An asset purchased on March 1 would be depreciated an amount equal to a year's depreciation times 10/12. A second method is to depreciate all assets one half a year during the first year. A third system takes a full year's depreciation on assets purchased before July 1 and does not claim any depreciation for the first year on assets purchased from July 1 on. The second and third methods have the advantage of simplicity, and over the long run will average out to charges that are fair to both the business and the government. Whatever method is adopted by a company, it should be followed consistently. Unless stated otherwise, the problems in this text are based on the assumption that the asset was purchased before the middle of the year and a full year's depreciation is to be charged the first year. If another method is used in a firm, a simple arithmetic adjustment can be used to get the first year's depreciation.

Practices differ regarding the handling of scrap values. Some accountants claim that because salvage estimates often require forecasts many years into an uncertain future plus the fact that removal costs may offset recovery income, the best practice is to assume zero scrap value. If this is done and the fully depreciated asset is eventually sold, any receipts from salvage sales would then be reported as income and taxes paid at that time. Others claim that if salvage is likely to be material, the assumption of zero scrap value is not a sound practice. Since the student may in his later work encounter either or both practices, we assume in some problems that the company will get something for the asset when they dispose of it, and in other cases we depreciate on the assumption of zero scrap value.

There are several ways of allowing for depreciation which meet government regulations. We first discuss three methods based on time: *straight line*, *declining balance*, and *sum of the years digits*.

7.2 Straight Line Method

The simplest method of allowing for depreciation is the straight line method. This method spreads depreciation evenly over the useful life of the property. The periodic depreciation charge is obtained by simply dividing the wearing value by the useful life.

$$R = \frac{W}{n} \tag{25}$$

The book value at any time equals the original cost minus the periodic charge times the number of charges that have been made.

EXAMPLE: A machine costs \$5000 and has an estimated scrap value of \$500 at the end of 5 years. Find the annual depreciation charge and the book value at the end of 3 years.

SOLUTION: $W = C - S = 5000 - 500 = \$4500$

$$R = \frac{W}{n} = \frac{4500}{5} = \$900$$

Book value at the end of 3 years = 5000 − (3 × 900) = \$2300.

In many cases the scrap value is assumed to be zero, and a rate is determined from the estimated life of the asset. For an asset with a 5-year life, the rate would be 1/5 or 20% and the annual depreciation under the straight line method would be 20% of the cost.

7.3 Declining Balance Method

Under this method the depreciation allowance for each year is a constant per cent of the undepreciated or book value of the asset. Since the book value decreases each year, the depreciation charges are largest at first and then become progressively smaller.

New assets having a life of at least 3 years can be depreciated under this method at twice the straight line rate assuming no salvage value. If it is anticipated that a particular asset will have material scrap value, depreciation should stop when cost less this salvage has been recovered even though this occurs before the end of the useful life. A taxpayer using the 200% or double declining balance method can change to the straight line method at any time. If the asset has no salvage value, a shift will have to be made at some time to the straight line method since the declining balance method cannot depreciate an asset to zero.

If the declining balance method is applied to used tangible property acquired after 1953, the rate per year may not exceed 150% of the straight line method, and a change to the straight line method requires the consent of the Internal Revenue Service.

EXAMPLE: A new machine costs \$5000 and has an estimated scrap value of \$500 at the end of 5 years. Find the annual depreciation allowances if the double declining balance method is used for 3 years and the straight line method is used for the last 2 years.

SOLUTION: The double declining balance rate is 40% since it is twice the straight line rate of 20% based on a life of 5 years with no allowance for salvage.

First year's depreciation allowance = .40 × 5000 = \$2000

Book value at the beginning of the second year = 5000–2000 = \$3000

Second year's depreciation allowance = .40 × 3000 = \$1200

Book value at the beginning of the third year = 3000–1200 = \$1800

Third year's depreciation allowance = .40 × 1800 = \$ 720

Book value at the beginning of the fourth year = 1800– 720 = \$1080

Annual depreciation charge for the last two years under the straight line method $= \frac{1080-500}{2} = \$ 290$

7.4 Sum of the Years Digits

This is a simple method for making the depreciation allowances large during the early years of the useful life of the asset. The depreciation for each year is a fraction of the wearing value. The denominator of the fraction is obtained by numbering the years of useful life and adding. For example, if the estimated life is 4 years, the denominator $= 1 + 2 + 3 + 4 = 10$. The numerator for the first year is the estimated useful life. Each year the numerator is reduced by 1.

EXAMPLE 1: A machine costs $5000. It has an estimated scrap value of $500 at the end of 5 years. Get the annual depreciation allowances using the sum of the years digits.

SOLUTION: The sum of the digits is $1 + 2 + 3 + 4 + 5 = 15$. Depreciation allowances are:

Year	Depreciation Allowance
1	$4500 \times 5/15 = \$1500$
2	$4500 \times 4/15 = 1200$
3	$4500 \times 3/15 = 900$
4	$4500 \times 2/15 = 600$
5	$4500 \times 1/15 = 300$
	$\overline{\$4500}$

Note that most of the cost is recovered early in the life of the asset.

EXAMPLE 2: A store building costs $510,000 and has an estimated life of 50 years. Assume zero salvage value and use the sum of the years digits to get the first two year's and the last two year's depreciation allowances.

SOLUTION: Since the digits from 1 to 50 form an arithmetic progression, we can get their sum quickly and easily by using the formula developed in algebra for the sum of an arithmetic progression.

$$S = \frac{n}{2}\,(t_1 + t_n)$$

where $S =$ the sum
$n =$ number of terms
$t_1 =$ the first term
$t_n =$ the last term

Substituting the values in this problem, we have:

$$S = \frac{50}{2}(1 + 50) = 1275$$

Since the first term in the sum of the years digits is 1 and the last term is n, we can write the sum as:

$$S = \frac{n}{2}(1 + n) = \frac{n + n^2}{2} = \frac{(n \times n) + n}{2}$$

Because of its simplicity, many accountants prefer this formula. In our problem, we have:

$$S = \frac{(50 \times 50) + 50}{2} = \frac{2550}{2} = 1275$$

Year	Depreciation Allowance
1	510,000 × 50/1275 = $20,000
2	510,000 × 49/1275 = 19,600
⋮	
⋮	
49	510,000 × 2/1275 = 800
50	510,000 × 1/1275 = 400

Since the depreciation allowances form an arithmetic progression with a decrease of $400 each year, a simple way to get each year's depreciation is to subtract $400 from the preceding year's value.

7.5 Comparison of Different Methods

The tables and sketches below show how the depreciation is accumulated and the book value reduced under the three methods. All are for an asset costing $5000 with a scrap value of $500 at the end of 5 years.

Straight Line Method

Year	Periodic Depreciation Charge	Total Accumulated Depreciation	Book Value
0			$5000
1	$900	$ 900	4100
2	900	1800	3200
3	900	2700	2300
4	900	3600	1400
5	900	4500	500

Double Declining Balance
(40% a year for 3 years and then straight line)

Year	Periodic Depreciation Charge	Total Accumulated Depreciation	Book Value
0			$5000
1	$2000	$2000	3000
2	1200	3200	1800
3	720	3920	1080
4	290	4210	790
5	290	4500	500

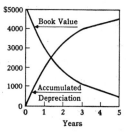

Sum of the Years Digits

Year	Periodic Depreciation Charge	Total Accumulated Depreciation	Book Value
0			$5000
1	$1500	$1500	3500
2	1200	2700	2300
3	900	3600	1400
4	600	4200	800
5	300	4500	500

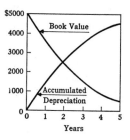

7.6   Determining the Best Method

The objective of all depreciation methods is the eventual recovery of the money invested in an asset, but there are differences in the rate of recovery. This is an important consideration because the value of a sum of money depends not only on the dollar amount but also on when it is received.

An advantage of the straight line method is its simplicity. There are times when the straight line method offers not only simplicity but also financial advantages. The taxes of an individual are dependent on his tax bracket. In a new business, the owners may be in a low tax bracket while the business is getting established. Large depreciation charges then may be less desirable than later when a person is in a higher bracket.

The declining balance and the sum of the years digits result in a quick recovery of a large part of the money invested in an asset. Since depreciation charges reduce the income reported for tax purposes, high depreciation during the early years means savings on income tax during these years. This decrease in tax liability results in more money available sooner for use in the business. A dollar now is worth more than a dollar in several years because it can be put to use sooner to repay debts, expand the business, or it can be invested at interest.

Accelerated depreciation methods result in large depreciation allowances when the asset is new and repair costs are low and smaller depreciation allowances later when maintenance costs are higher. The result is a better matching of revenues with expenses throughout the life of the asset.

In times of rising prices with resulting decreases in the purchasing power of the dollar, a rapid write-off may mean that dollars recovered early have more purchasing power than dollars recovered after additional price increases. In particular cases, this may be offset if the newer and more expensive machines are also more productive.

Different depreciation methods can be compared on a present value basis by discounting all the depreciation charges. This is done in the table below for the $5000 asset discussed in the preceding section. The comparison is based on the assumption that money will earn 8% for the company. The non-uniform payments of the declining balance and sum of the years digits must be discounted one by one using the *Present Worth of 1* factor. For comparison purposes, we have also used this factor for the straight line method although one would usually get the total present value with one computation using the *Present Worth of 1 per Period* factor. Factors taken to 3 decimal places result in answers that are adequate for comparison purposes.

Year	Present Worth of 1 at 8%	Annual Depreciation Charge			Present Worth of Annual Charge		
		Straight Line	Double Declining Balance	Sum of Years Digits	Straight Line	Double Declining Balance	Sum of Years Digits
1	.926	$900	$2000	$1500	$833	$1852	$1389
2	.857	900	1200	1200	771	1028	1028
3	.794	900	720	900	715	572	715
4	.735	900	290	600	662	213	441
5	.681	900	290	300	613	197	204
		500*	500*	500*	340**	340**	340**
		$5000	$5000	$5000	$3934	$4202	$4117

* Estimated salvage value.
** Present worth of estimated salvage value.

Both the double declining balance and the sum of the years digits always result in a greater present value than the straight line method. That the difference can be substantial is shown by this example.

People who are responsible for preparing income tax reports for a business should understand the various methods of depreciation and be familiar with current tax regulations. Using the most advantageous system of depreciation will result in timing depreciation charges so that they will be of greatest benefit to the business.

Exercise 7a

1. A truck costs $7000 and has an estimated scrap value of $1000 at the end of 5 years. Prepare depreciation schedules and graphs showing the total accumulated depreciation and book value for the straight line, double declining balance shifting to straight line at the end of 3 years, and sum of the years digits methods.

2. A taxi costs $2500 and has an estimated scrap value of $500 at the end of 3 years. Prepare depreciation schedules and graphs showing the total accumulated depreciation and book value for the straight line, double declining balance shifting to straight line at the end of 1 year, and sum of the years digits methods.

3. An electric generator costs $39,000. It has an estimated life of 12 years and negligible scrap value. Compute the first two years' depreciation allowances for the straight line, double declining balance, and sum of the years digits.

$$\begin{bmatrix} \text{Straight line: \$3250.00; \$3250.00} \\ \text{Double declining balance: \$6500.00; \$5416.67} \\ \text{Sum of the years digits: \$6000.00; \$5500.00} \end{bmatrix}$$

4. A sewing machine costs $400. It has an estimated life of 14 years and a salvage value of $50. Compute the first two years' depreciation allowances under straight line, double declining balance, and sum of the years digits methods.

5. An apartment building costs $82,000. Assume a life of 40 years and negligible scrap value and get the first two years' depreciation allowances under straight line, double declining balance, and sum of the years digits methods.

$$\begin{bmatrix} \text{Straight line: \$2050.00; \$2050.00} \\ \text{Double declining balance: \$4100.00; \$3895.00} \\ \text{Sum of the years digits: \$4000.00; \$3900.00} \end{bmatrix}$$

6. A warehouse cost $366,000. It has an estimated life of 60 years and negligible scrap value. Compute the first two years' depreciation under straight line, double declining balance, and sum of the years digits methods.

7. When a $13,000 machine was purchased, the estimated life was 8 years and the estimated salvage value was $1000. However, soon after the machine was put into operation, it became advisable to replace it with a greatly improved model. The replacement was made after the third annual depreciation charge. What was the total accumulated depreciation at this time if depreciation was handled using: (a) straight line; (b) double declining balance; (c) sum of the years digits?   [(a) $4500.00; (b) $7515.63; (c) $7000.00]

8. A machine which cost $7500 has an estimated scrap value of $300 at the end of 12 years. At the end of 5 years, the machine becomes obsolete because of the development of a better machine. What will be the total accumulated depreciation at this time if the depreciation was handled using: (a) straight line; (b) double declining balance; (c) sum of the digits?

9. A used truck was purchased for $3000. It has an estimated life of 4 years and a scrap value of $600. Find the first two years' depreciation allowances under: (a) straight line; (b) 150% declining balance; (c) sum of the years digits.

$$\begin{bmatrix} \text{Straight line: \$600.00; \$600.00} \\ \text{150\% declining balance: \$1125.00; \$703.12} \\ \text{Sum of the years digits: \$960.00; \$720.00} \end{bmatrix}$$

10. A farmer paid $2000 for a used tractor. It has an estimated life of 8 years and a scrap value of $200. Find the first two years' depreciation allowances under: (a) straight line; (b) 150% declining balance; (c) sum of the years digits.

7.7 Depreciation Based on Use

The depreciation methods discussed so far have been based on the asset having an assumed life in years. We now consider a method which is based on the hours an asset is used or the number of units it produces. This method allows for more depreciation during a busy period when a factory may be working two or three shifts as compared to one shift during normal times.

EXAMPLE 1: A machine costs $5000 and has an estimated scrap value of $200. Machines of this type have an estimated operating life of 20,000 hours. This machine has been run as follows: first year, 2200 hours; second year, 4000 hours; third year, 1800 hours; fourth year, 3000 hours; fifth year, 4000 hours. Prepare a table showing the depreciation for each year.

SOLUTION: The total wearing value is $4800. The depreciation charge for the first year is $4800 \times \dfrac{2200}{20,000} = \$528$. Continuing this for successive years, we have:

Year	Fraction of Useful Life	Periodic Depreciation Charge	Accumulated Depreciation	Book Value
0				$5000
1	2200/20,000	$528	$ 528	4472
2	4000/20,000	960	1488	3512
3	1800/20,000	432	1920	3080
4	3000/20,000	720	2640	2360
5	4000/20,000	960	3600	1400

EXAMPLE 2: A machine costs $5000 and has an estimated scrap value of $200. It is estimated that this machine will produce 50,000 units. The annual

production has been: first year 8000 units; second year 5000 units; third year 12,000 units; fourth year 10,000 units; fifth year 5000 units. Prepare a table showing the depreciation for each year.

SOLUTION: The total wearing value is $4800. The depreciation charge for the first year is $4800 \times \dfrac{8000}{50,000} = \$768.$ Continuing this for successive years, we have:

Year	Fraction of Estimated Production	Periodic Depreciation Charge	Accumulated Depreciation	Book Value
0				$5000
1	8,000/50,000	$ 768	$ 768	4232
2	5,000/50,000	480	1248	3752
3	12,000/50,000	1152	2400	2600
4	10,000/50,000	960	3360	1640
5	5,000/50,000	480	3840	1160

Exercise 7b

1. A piece of machinery cost $8000 and has an estimated scrap value of $2000. Machines of this type have an estimated working-hour life of 10,000 hours. This machine is used as follows: first year 3000 hours: second year 1200 hours; third year 1000 hours; fourth year 2000 hours. Prepare a depreciation schedule for the 4 years this machine has been in use.

2. A machine costs $30,000 and has an estimated scrap value of $4000. It is estimated that this machine will produce 120,000 units during its useful life. The machine produces the following outputs during the first 5 years it is in use: first year 20,000 units; second year 15,000 units; third year 25,000 units; fourth year 10,000 units; fifth year 18,000 units. Prepare a depreciation schedule.

7.8 Capital Budgeting

"Will it pay?" is an important and difficult question which the management of a business must face when planning for the future. It is particularly important to find the right answer when management is considering a capital expenditure, that is, a major replacement or addition to plant capacity. Since several years may be required to recover the large initial outlays involved in capital expenditures, errors in capital budgeting can have serious consequences for a company.

Combining the focal date techniques developed in earlier chapters with the depreciation methods discussed in this chapter results in useful methods for evaluating proposed capital expenditures. As is the case throughout the mathematics of finance, our analysis is based on the fact that money has a *time value*. A sum of money expected in the future must be discounted if it is to be compared with a cash outlay. This is usually done at a rate which is high enough to include both a reasonable return on the investment and an allowance for risk.

In capital budgeting, the comparison of expenses and income on a present value basis is called *discounted cash flow analysis*. Cash flows include some or all of the following:

Cash Outflows	*Cash Inflows*
Initial investment	Net income after taxes
Continuing costs in	Depreciation allowances
future years	Salvage value

Since some of the expenses and all of the revenues occur in the future, we discount future cash flows before we compare proposed projects or estimate the rate of return to be expected on an investment. Because the future contains many uncertainties, the returns from a proposed investment depend to a considerable extent on forecasting judgment relative to sales, prices, and other variables. Thus in discounted cash flow analysis we have estimates, not the mathematical certitude that we had in earlier chapters when dealing with fixed payments and annuities certain. Predicting cash flows is the most complex and difficult aspect of the capital budgeting process. Once these estimates have been made, it is relatively easy to use mathematics of finance to compare proposed projects and estimate rates of return.

In predicting the future, two types of risk are involved. One is that the asset may not perform as expected because of early breakdown, high maintenance costs, low productivity, or early obsolescence. The other risk is that demand for the product or future economic conditions may not develop as expected.

To help compensate for the uncertainties involved in estimating future cash flows, we use interest rates considerably larger than those used in the usual compound interest problems. This is reasonable since a firm that could get 5 or 6% on a bond or mortgage will expect a considerably higher return when putting money into a project that involves greater risks. When a reasonable allowance for risk-taking is added to the cost of capital, which may be 8 or 10% or more, a firm may feel that a rate of return of 10 or 15% or more is required to make a project attractive.

In discounted cash flow analysis, two discount factors are used: *Present Worth of* 1 for discounting single sums and *Present Worth of* 1 *per Period* for discounting a series of equal cash flows equally spaced. These factors are given in Table 4. Since cash flow analysis is based on estimates, the discount factors are given to 3 decimal places, sufficient for practical work with uncertain data.

7.9   Determining Net Cash Flows

After cash inflows and outflows have been estimated, we get the net cash flow for each year and then use the present value, focal date approach to bring all flows to the same point in time. Net cash flows depend on estimated revenue, expenses, depreciation allowances, taxes, and other factors. The examples in this book are based on a tax rate of 30% for firms having profits up to $25,000 a year and 52% for firms having profits above $25,000. These rates may be changed in the future. In some applications it may be necessary to allow for state and other taxes. However, the method applies regardless of rates. The effect of different methods of depreciation will be brought out in the examples.

EXAMPLE 1: A company is considering the purchase of a machine which costs $15,000 and has an estimated salvage value of $3000 at the end of its useful life of 3 years. Annual operating costs are expected to be about $1000 a year. Additional revenue expected from the machine is $7000 a year. Get the net cash flows for this machine assuming a 52% tax rate and (a) straight line depreciation; (b) double declining balance for the first year and straight line for the next two years; (c) sum of the years digits.

Straight Line

Net income before taxes and depreciation

= additional revenue − additional costs $\qquad$ 7000 − 1000 = $6000

Annual depreciation allowance $\qquad\qquad \dfrac{15,000 - 3000}{3} = 4000$

Taxable income = net income − depreciation $\qquad$ 6000 − 4000 = 2000

Income after taxes = .48 × taxable income $\qquad$ .48 × 2000 = 960

Net cash flow = income after taxes + depreciation $\qquad$ 960 + 4000 = 4960

The year-by-year determination of cash flows can be presented quite well in tabular form.

Year	Net Income before Taxes and Depreciation	Depreciation Allowance	Taxable Income	Income After Taxes	Net Cash Flow
0	− $15,000				− $15,000
1	6,000	$4,000	$2,000	$960	4,960
2	6,000	4,000	2,000	960	4,960
3	6,000	4,000	2,000	960	7,960*
		$12,000	$6,000	$2,880	$2,880

* Includes $3000 salvage value.

Double Declining Balance

The first year's depreciation is 2/3 of the purchase price, or $10,000. This is more than the net income for the year, resulting in a taxable income of − $4000. If this machine represented all of the company's operations, the excess depreciation could be transferred to a later year. If the company has other income, as will usually be the case, the excess depreciation on this machine can be used to reduce reported earnings by $4000. This will result in a tax shield or tax offset of $.52 \times 4000 = \$2080$. This means that the income after taxes from this asset will be − $1920. Since this is what we get from $.48(-4000)$, we can use the same procedure for getting income after taxes whether the taxable income is plus or minus.

Year	Net Income Before Taxes and Depreciation	Depreciation Allowance	Taxable Income	Income After Taxes	Net Cash Flow
0	− $15,000				− $15,000
1	6,000	$10,000	− $4000	− $1920	8,080
2	6,000	1,000	5000	2400	3,400
3	6,000	1,000	5000	2400	6,400*
		$12,000	$6000	$2880	$2,880

* Includes $3000 salvage value.

Straight Line		Declining Balance		Sum of the Digits	
	Inflows		Inflows		Inflows
Outflow		Outflow		Outflow	
$15,000 4960 4960 7960		$15,000 8080 3400 6400		$15,000 6000 4960 6920	
0 1 2 3		0 1 2 3		0 1 2 3	
Years		Years		Years	

Sum of the Years Digits

The denominator of the annual fraction $= 1 + 2 + 3 = 6$.

Year	Net Income Before Taxes and Depreciation	Depreciation Allowance	Taxable Income	Income After Taxes	Net Cash Flow
0	− $15,000				− $15,000
1	6,000	$6,000	$ 0	$ 0	6,000
2	6,000	4,000	2000	960	4,960
3	6,000	2,000	4000	1920	6,920*
		$12,000	$6000	$2880	$2,880

* Includes $3000 salvage value.

Note that the totals are the same for all methods of depreciation, but there are differences in the year-by-year net cash flows.

Time diagrams are quite helpful in presenting net cash flow problems in pictorial form.

Histograms can be used to give an overall picture of cash flow problems. Sometimes the various inflows and outflows are shaded differently so a busy reader can see at a glance the different expenses and sources of income.

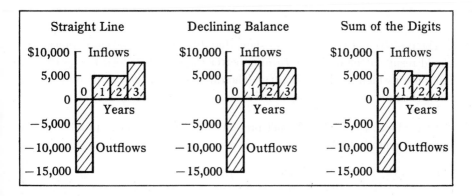

7.10 Present Value of Net Flows

Different proposals or different methods of depreciation result in greatly different cash flows. To compare one with another, we use the focal date approach which has been so useful throughout the mathematics of finance. While the focal date could be put anywhere, it is usually taken to be the point where the major expenditure of funds will be made. If relatively small planning expenditures are involved in the years preceding the installation of an asset, these are brought forward at compound interest. Estimated future net cash flows are discounted to the installation date.

The interest rate used in discounted cash flow analysis can be the estimated cost of capital to the company. If the present value of the inflows is less than the corresponding value of the outflows, the installation would not be profitable. Another way to choose a rate is to estimate what could be earned on alternative investments. A third approach to capital budgeting problems is to use the estimated cash flows to determine the rate of return. This method is described in the next section.

EXAMPLE 1: Determine the net present value of the proposal in Section 7.9 using an estimated cost of capital of 8% and the three methods of depreciation.

SOLUTION: We discount each net cash flow to the present using the *Present Worth of* 1 factors. The algebraic sum is the net present value of the project. A tabular arrangement systematizes the work and makes comparisons easy.

Year	Discount Factor at 8%	Straight Line		Double Dec. Balance		Sum of Digits	
		Net Cash Flow	Present Value	Net Cash Flow	Present Value	Net Cash Flow	Present Value
0	1.000	−$15,000	−$15,000	−$15,000	−$15,000	−$15,000	−$15,000
1	.926	4,960	4,593	8,080	7,482	6,000	5,556
2	.857	4,960	4,251	3,400	2,914	4,960	4,251
3	.794	7,960	6,320	6,400	5,082	6,920	5,494
			$ 164		$ 478		$ 301

The positive net present values show that all of the methods of depreciation would result in the project returning better than 8% provided the actual net flows are as high as the estimates. The differences in the net present values show the advantages of a rapid write-off.

EXAMPLE 2: Determine the net present values for the above problem using a cost of capital of 10%.

Year	Discount Factor at 10%	Straight Line		Double Dec. Balance		Sum of Digits	
		Net Cash Flow	Present Value	Net Cash Flow	Present Value	Net Cash Flow	Present Value
0	1.000	−$15,000	−$15,000	−$15,000	−$15,000	−$15,000	−$15,000
1	.909	4,960	4,509	8,080	7,345	6,000	5,454
2	.826	4,960	4,097	3,400	2,808	4,960	4,097
3	.751	7,960	5,978	6,400	4,806	6,920	5,197
			−$ 416		−$ 41		−$ 252

Regardless of the method of depreciation, a 10% return cannot be expected from this asset.

7.11 Rate of Return

The internal rate of return is the rate which will make cash inflows equal to outflows. This rate must be found by trial and error unless the cash flow happen to form an ordinary annuity as in the first example.

EXAMPLE 1: A company is considering the purchase of an asset which costs $6000 and has negligible scrap value at the end of its useful life of 3 years. Annual net income over operating expenses is expected to be $4000 a year. Find the internal rate of return assuming straight line depreciation and a tax rate of 52%.

SOLUTION: Annual depreciation allowance $= 6000/3 = \$2000$

Taxable income $4000 - 2000 = 2000$

Income after taxes $.48 \times 2000 = 960$

Annual net cash inflow $2000 + 960 = 2960$

Since the net cash inflows in this problem form an ordinary annuity, we find the rate following the method in Section 3.10. Substituting in Formula (13),

$$2960a_{\overline{3}|} = 6000$$

$$a_{\overline{3}|} = \frac{6000}{2960} = 2.027$$

According to the table, the rate is between 22 and 24%. If a more precise answer is required, we interpolate.

$$\begin{array}{ccc} i \text{ in } \% & & a_{\overline{3}|} \\ \end{array}$$

$$2 \quad d \left[\begin{array}{c} 22 \\ i \\ 24 \end{array} \right. \qquad \left. \begin{array}{c} 2.042 \\ 2.027 \\ 1.981 \end{array} \right] 15 \right] 61$$

$$\frac{d}{2} = \frac{15}{61}$$

$$d = \frac{2 \times 15}{61} = .5$$

$$i = 22.0 + .5 = 22.5\%$$

EXAMPLE 2: Work the example above using double declining balance for 2 years and straight line for the third year.

SOLUTION: The first year's depreciation is $6000 \times 2/3 = \$4000$. Continuing with the solution in tabular form, we have:

Year	Net Income Before Taxes and Depreciation	Depreciation Allowance	Taxable Income	Income After Taxes	Net Cash Flow
0	− $6000				− $6000
1	4000	$4000	$ 0	$ 0	4000
2	4000	1333	2667	1280	2613
3	4000	667	3333	1600	2267
				$2880	$2880

To get the rate of return when the cash inflows are different, we use trial and error until we find a rate which makes the total present value of the inflows equal to the present value of the outflows. By this process we find that the rate is between 25 and 30% because 25% results in a present value greater than $6000 and 30% a value below $6000. The work is summarized below.

Year	Cash Inflow	Present Value at 25%		Present Value at 30%	
		of $1	of Cash Inflows	of $1	of Cash Inflows
1	$4000	.800	$3200	.769	$3076
2	2613	.640	1672	.592	1547
3	2267	.512	1161	.455	1031
			$6033		$5654

If a more precise answer is required, we interpolate.

$$
\begin{array}{ccc}
 & i \text{ in } \% & \begin{array}{c}Present\ Value\\ of\ Inflows\end{array}
\end{array}
$$

$$
5 \left[d \left[\begin{array}{c} 25 \\ i \end{array} \right. \quad \begin{array}{c} 6033 \\ 6000 \end{array} \right] 33 \quad \right] 379
$$
$$
 30 \qquad 5654
$$

$$
\frac{d}{5} = \frac{33}{379}
$$

$$
d = \frac{5 \times 33}{379} = .4
$$

$$
i = 25.0 + .4 = 25.4\%
$$

Going to a more rapid write-off has increased the internal rate of return by almost 3 percentage points.

An advantage of the discounted cash flow method is that interest is computed only on the amount of unrecovered capital to date. The rate is not affected by what is done with the recovered capital. This enables us to check a computed rate by finding how long it would take to recover the invested capital if the project were financed at a capital rate equal to the rate of return. If the rate is correct, the period required to recover the investment and the life of the project will be the same.

EXAMPLE 3: A machine which costs $15,925 will produce estimated net cash inflows of $7560 a year for 3 years. Find the rate of return and check.

SOLUTION: Since this is an ordinary annuity with a present value of 15,925 and a periodic payment of 7560, we have

$$a_{\overline{3}|} = \frac{15,925}{7,560} = 2.106$$

This *Present Worth of 1 per Period* factor corresponds to a rate of 20%. The table below shows that we earn 20% on invested capital and in 3 years recover the investment. The amount of capital recovered equals net cash inflow minus return on unrecovered capital.

Year	Unrecovered Capital at Beginning of the Year	Net Cash Inflow	Return of 20% on Unrecovered Capital	Amount of Capital Recovered
1	$15,925	$7560	$3185	$4375
2	11,550	7560	2310	5250
3	6,300	7560	1260	6300
				$15,925

7.12 Comparison of Alternatives

Discounted cash flow analysis can be used to help management choose among proposed capital expenditures. One method is to get the rate of return for each proposal. Another method is to rank projects on the basis of net present values. If the proposals differ greatly as to costs and income streams, a method that is preferable to net present value comparisons is the use of a *profitability index* which is the ratio of present value of net cash inflows to present value of outlays. Different methods of comparing alternatives do not always lead to the same ranking as is shown in the example.

EXAMPLE: A company is considering two projects which have the following net cash flows after allowing for depreciation, taxes, and other expenses. Find the net present values and profitability indexes using a rate of 16%. Find the internal rates of return for the two proposals.

	Present	*Proposal A*		*Proposal B*	
Year	*Worth of 1 at 16%*	*Net Cash Inflow*	*Present Value*	*Net Cash Inflow*	*Present Value*
0	1.000	− $30,000	− $30,000	− $30,000	− $30,000
1	.862	0	0	0	0
2	.743	25,000	18,575	0	0
3	.641	25,000	16,025	0	0
4	.552	0	0	34,000	18,768
5	.476	0	0	34,000	16,184
			$ 4,600		$ 4,952
	Profitability Index		1.15		1.17

$$\text{The profitability index for Proposal } A = \frac{18,575 + 16,025}{30,000}$$

$$= \frac{34,600}{30,000} = 1.15$$

On the basis of either net present value or profitability index, *B* would be ranked first.

A trial and error determination of the internal rate of return puts *A* first with a rate of about 23% compared to 20% for *B*. Had the present value comparisons been at a rate close to these true rates of return, *A* would have also been first on a net present value basis.

Of the methods we have discussed for evaluating alternatives, the net present value and profitability index methods have the advantage of ease of computation as compared to the sometimes tedious calculations required to get the internal rate of return. Another advantage of the present value method is that an allowance for risk can be added to the estimated cost of capital. On the other hand, if the present value analysis is based on an incorrect rate, the ranking of projects may be wrong. When we use the internal rate of return, we can rank proposals in order of yield. Then we can see which will probably be most profitable and how far we can go down the list before reaching a point below the cost of capital where a proposal would be a losing proposition.

There are, of course, situations where nonmonetary considerations, such as employee morale and community relations, result in adopting proposals that are not financially attractive. In other cases expenses simply have to be made. Management has no choice about repairing or replacing a new roof and installing adequate safety devices.

Exercise 7c

1. A machine which costs $12,000 and which has negligible scrap value at the end of its life of 6 years will produce an estimated net cash inflow of $3000 a year for 6 years. Find the net present value of this investment at (a) 12%; (b) 14%.   [(a) $333; (b) − $333]

2. A machine which costs $38,000 and has no scrap value at the end of its life will produce an estimated net cash inflow of $10,000 a year for 6 years. Find the net present value at (a) 10%; (b) 12%.

3. Work Problem 1 assuming an estimated scrap value of $2000 at the end of its useful life.   [(a) $1347; (b) $579]

4. Work Problem 2 assuming an estimated scrap value of $5000 at the end of the machine's useful life.

5. A company is going to install a plastics molding press. Three presses are being considered. They have the following estimated cash flows. Get their net present values using a rate of 16%. Find the profitability indexes.

	Press A	*Press B*	*Press C*
Cost installed	$9000	$12,000	$10,500
Net cash inflows	$2000 a year for 12 years	$3000 a year for 10 years	$2500 a year for 7 years

(*Press A:* $1394; 1.15   *Press B:* $2499; 1.21   *Press C:* − $402; .96)

6. A manufacturer is going to install a drying oven. The choice has been narrowed to the following which meet his specifications. Get their net present values using a rate of 10%.

	Oven A	*Oven B*
Cost installed	$28,000	$35,000
Net cash inflows	$6000 a year for 8 years	$6000 a year for 10 years

Find the profitability index for the ovens.

7. A machine costs $25,000. It will result in estimated net cash inflows of $5000 a year for 10 years. Find the estimated internal rate of return to one decimal place when expressed as a per cent. The machine has no scrap value.   (15.1%)

8. A new machine which costs $36,000 and has no scrap value at the end of its life of 6 years is expected to produce net cash inflows of $10,000 a year. Find the estimated internal rate of return to 1 decimal place when expressed as a per cent.

9. A company is considering the installation of an asset which will involve a large cash expenditure. Cash flow projections have been made by the engineering department in cooperation with other departments. Find the rate of return for each project to the nearest per cent.

	Proposal A	Proposal B	Proposal C
Initial cost	$200,000	$250,000	$225,000
Net cash inflows	$40,000 a year for 10 years	$80,000 a year for 5 years	$45,000 a year for 8 years

$$(A: 15\%; B: 18\%; C: 12\%)$$

10. The management of a company is considering whether to install a high speed automatic punch press costing $20,000 or three hand-fed presses costing $9000 each. None of the presses will have any scrap value. Find the rate of return for each proposal to the nearest tenth of one per cent.

	Automatic Press	Three Hand-fed Presses
Initial cost	$20,000	$27,000
Net cash inflows	$5000 a year for 6 years	$5000 a year for 10 years

11. Find the rate of return for the following proposals to the nearest tenth of one per cent. (Work as deferred annuities.)

	Proposal A	Proposal B
Initial cost	$20,000	$12,500
Net cash inflows	Nothing for 3 years. $10,000 a year for next 5 years.	Nothing for 4 years. $10,000 a year for next 4 years.

$$(A: 17.0\%; B: 20.0\%)$$

12. Find the rate of return for the following proposals to the nearest tenth of one percent.

	Proposal A	Proposal B
Initial cost	$300,000	$425,000
Net cash inflows	Nothing for first 2 years. $80,000 a year for next 8 years.	Nothing for first 3 years. $150,000 a year for next 6 years.

13. A company is considering the purchase of materials handling equipment. The initial cost will be $36,000 and the annual outlay for maintenance, power, and other expenses will be an estimated $1000. It is expected that the equipment will reduce labor costs by $10,000 a year for 12 years. The estimated life of the asset is 12 years with no salvage value. Assume a tax rate of 52% and straight line depreciation and get the rate of return to the nearest percent.   (12%)

14. A tractor costs $14,000. It has an estimated life of 6 years and a salvage value of $2000. The annual outlay for maintenance will run about $500. It is expected that this tractor will result in an annual increase in revenue of $5000. Assume a tax rate of 52% and straight line depreciation and get the rate of return to the nearest percent.

15. A company is considering the purchase of an asset which costs $6000 and has negligible scrap value at the end of its useful life of 4 years. Annual net income over operating expenses is expected to be $3500 a year. The tax rate is 52%. Find the rate of return to the nearest tenth of one percent assuming (a) straight line depreciation; (b) double declining balance for 2 years and then straight line; (c) sum of the years digits.

[(a) 23.2%; (b) 25.8%; (c) 25.1%]

16. A small company is considering the purchase of a machine which costs $8000 and has an estimated scrap value of 10% of cost at the end of 4 years. It is estimated that this machine will increase the net income before taxes by $3000 a year. The tax rate is 30%. Find the rate of return to the nearest tenth of one percent using (a) straight line depreciation; (b) double declining balance for 2 years and then straight line; (c) sum of the years digits.

17. A company is considering the purchase of an asset which costs $15,000 and has an estimated scrap value of $3000 at the end of 5 years. It is estimated that this asset will reduce labor costs by $5000 a year. Assume a tax rate of 52% and find the rate of return assuming (a) straight line depreciation; (b) double declining balance for 3 years and then straight line; (c) sum of the years digits.   [(a) 11.6%; (b) 13.4%; (c) 12.5%]

18. A contractor can purchase a heavy-duty truck with a 12-cubic-yard dump body for $13,000. Its estimated life is 7 years and its estimated salvage value is $2000. Maintenance is estimated at $1100 per year. Daily operating expenses are expected to be $23 including the cost of the driver. The contractor can hire a similar unit and its driver for $53 a day. If the interest rate is taken at 8%, how many days per year must the services of a dump truck be required to justify the purchase of a truck? Use straight line depreciation. Assume that the daily savings resulting from owning a truck can be lumped together and considered as a single year-end savings. Make no allowance for taxes.

7.13 Depletion

Some natural resources, such as mines, oil wells, and sources of natural gas, produce an income for awhile and then become used up. This gradual using up of a resource which will not be replaced is called **depletion.** The income from an asset of this type should not only pay a return on the investment, but should also recover the cost of the asset less any resale value it may have when the natural resources are exhausted. Only in this way can the business operate in accordance with the fundamental principle of keeping the invested capital unimpaired.

EXAMPLE 1: A firm buys a mine for $200,000. An annual return of $30,000 over operating costs is expected for the next 15 years. At the end of this time it is estimated that the land can be sold for $10,000. This means that there will be a decrease in the value of the property of $190,000. In this case we shall assume that the invested capital will be recovered by making periodic deposits to a sinking fund paying 3%. What return can the firm expect on their investment?

SOLUTION: We must first find the size of the annual deposit to the sinking fund.

$$R = 190,000 \times \frac{1}{s_{\overline{15}|3\%}} = 190,000 \times .05376658 = \$10,215.65$$

This should be deducted from the $30,000 to replace the invested capital. This makes the net return

$$\$30,000.00 - 10,215.65 = \$19,784.35$$

The rate of return on the investment then becomes

$$\frac{19,784.35}{200,000} = .0989 \text{ or } 9.9\%$$

If C is the original cost, S the resale value when the natural resource is used up, i the yield rate on the investment, and r the rate earned on the sinking fund, we can write the following general formula:
Annual return = (Cost × the yield rate) + (Annual deposit into sinking fund)

Or using symbols: Annual return = $Ci + (C - S) \cdot \dfrac{1}{s_{\overline{n}|r}}$

In this formula we have added the subscript r to the $\dfrac{1}{s_{\overline{n}|}}$ factor to emphasize the fact that the sinking fund rate is to be used when getting the numerical value of this factor.

In some cases the investor knows what rate of return he wants on his investment, so the problem becomes one of determining a purchase price that will result in the desired yield.

EXAMPLE 2: A mining property is expected to yield an annual return of $40,000 over operating costs for the next 20 years when it will be exhausted and have a resale value of about $20,000. What could a firm pay for the mine if they want a return of 8% on their investment and can set up a sinking fund at 3%?

SOLUTION: $40,000 = C \times .08 + (C - 20,000) \cdot \dfrac{1}{s_{\overline{20}|3\%}}$

$$40,000 = .08C + .03721571C - 744.31$$

$$40,744.31 = .11721571C$$

$$C = \dfrac{40,744.31}{.11721571} = \$347,601$$

Exercise 7d

1. A sand and gravel company is considering the purchase of a piece of property for sale at $45,000. It is estimated that the property will produce a net annual return over operating costs of $7000 for 10 years at the end of which time the estimated resale value of the property is $5000. If the firm can build up a replacement fund for their capital at 3% converted annually, what is the estimated rate of return they could expect on this investment? (Give answer to the nearest .1%)   (7.8%)

2. A lumber company leases a tract of timber for 8 years for $60,000. They expect to get an annual return over operating costs of about $10,000. If they set up a sinking fund at 4% to recover their investment, what return can they expect on their investment?

3. A quarry is expected to yield a net income over operating costs of $20,000 a year for 15 years at which time it will have little or no resale value. What could a firm pay for this quarry if they want a yield of 8% on their investment and set up a sinking fund at $2\frac{1}{2}\%$ to replace their capital? Give answer to the nearest $100.   ($147,300)

4. A company is considering the purchase of some timber land. Company engineers estimate that the land will produce a net return of $30,000 a year over operating costs for 6 years at which time the land can be sold for about $40,000. How much can the company pay for the land if they want a return of 7% on their investment and they can set up a sinking fund at $3\frac{1}{2}\%$ to replace their capital?

5. A mine is expected to yield an annual return of $40,000 over operating costs for the next 20 years when it will be exhausted and have an estimated resale value of $2000. What could a firm pay for the mine if they want an annual return of 8% on their investment and can accumulate a sinking fund at 3%? Answer to the nearest $100.   ($341,900)

6. A gravel pit is expected to produce an average return over operating costs of $7000 a year for 8 years. If it will have little or no resale value, what can a firm pay for it if they want a 6% return on their investment and can accumulate a sinking fund at 3%?

7.14   Capitalized Cost

The **capitalized cost** of an asset is the original cost of an item plus the present value of an unlimited number of renewals. We shall first determine the formulas used for capitalized cost and then discuss their application. The quantities and symbols used in capitalized cost work are:

$$K = \text{the capitalized cost}$$
$$C = \text{the original cost}$$
$$S = \text{the scrap or salvage value}$$
$$W = \text{the wearing value.}\ \ W = C - S$$
$$n = \text{useful life in interest conversion periods.}$$

To find the present value of the unlimited number of renewals, we use perpetuity formula (21) substituting $\$W$ for the periodic payment. This is added to the first cost to give us the basic formula for capitalized cost:

$$K = C + \frac{W}{i} \times \frac{1}{s_{\overline{n}|}} \tag{26}$$

In many cases the item has little or no scrap value. In this case the replacement cost equals the first cost and a simpler formula can be derived as follows:

$$K = C + \frac{C}{i} \times \frac{1}{s_{\overline{n}|}}$$

Multiplying C by $\dfrac{i}{i}$ and factoring $\dfrac{C}{i}$, we have

$$K = \frac{C}{i}\left(i + \frac{1}{s_{\overline{n}|}}\right)$$

Replacing $\dfrac{1}{s_{\overline{n}|}}$ by its exponential from,

$$K = \frac{C}{i}\left(i + \frac{i}{(1+i)^n - 1}\right) = \frac{C}{i}\left(\frac{i(1+i)^n - i + i}{(1+i)^n - 1}\right)$$

Combining terms and multiplying numerator and denominator by $(1+i)^{-n}$,

$$K = \frac{C}{i}\left(\frac{i}{1 - (1+i)^{-n}}\right)$$

Substituting $\dfrac{1}{a_{\overline{n}|}}$ for the exponential expression,

$$K = \frac{C}{i} \times \frac{1}{a_{\overline{n}|}} \tag{27}$$

All of the factors in a capitalized cost problem are estimates: the useful life of the asset, its replacement cost, and the value of money in the future. In spite of these limitations capitalized cost can be a very useful tool. It can be used to arrive at an estimate of the endowment required for a specific purpose. A more frequent use is to determine which of two or more items would be more economical for a particular job. The capitalized cost formulas enable us to get two assets with different costs and different useful lives on a common basis. The asset with the lower capitalized cost will be the more economical. No actual fund will be set up in cases such as this.

EXAMPLE 1: What is the estimated endowment for the construction of a mess hall at a boys' camp if the building costs $12,000, and will need to be replaced about every 25 years at approximately the same cost? By how much will the endowment have to be increased to provide $300 at the end of each year for maintenance? Estimated return on the endowment fund is 3%.

SOLUTION: Since the replacement cost is assumed to be the same as the first cost, we can use (27):

$$K = \frac{12,000}{.03} \times \frac{1}{a_{\overline{25}|3\%}}$$

$$= 400,000 \times .05742787 = \$22,971.15$$

The annual maintenance costs form a perpetuity. The present value can be found from (20):

$$A_\infty = \frac{300}{.03} = \$10,000$$

Therefore, to provide for initial construction, replacement every 25 years, and annual maintenance, an endowment of about $33,000 would be needed.

EXAMPLE 2: A machine costs $4500, has an estimated life of 15 years, and an estimated scrap value of $700. Find the capitalized cost at 4%.

SOLUTION: Substituting in (26), we have

$$K = 4500 + \frac{3800}{.04} \times \frac{1}{s_{\overline{15}|4\%}}$$

$$= 4500 + (95,000 - .0499410) = 4500 + 4744.40$$

$$K = \$9244.40$$

EXAMPLE 3: One grade of floor covering for a store costs $750 installed and has an estimated life of 8 years. A better grade has an estimated life of 12 years. If money is worth 3%, the better grade would be worth how much?

SOLUTION: To solve this problem we shall assume that the two are equally desirable from an economic standpoint if their capitalized costs are equal. In either case an initial installation and an unlimited number of renewals would be provided for. If C is the unknown cost of the better grade we can use (27) and set the two capitalized costs equal to each other.

$$\frac{C}{.03} \times \frac{1}{a_{\overline{12}|3\%}} = \frac{750}{.03} \times \frac{1}{a_{\overline{8}|3\%}}$$

$$C = 750 \times a_{\overline{12}|} \times \frac{1}{a_{\overline{8}|}}$$

$$= 750 \times 9.954004 \times .142456 = \$1063.51$$

Therefore if the better grade can be installed for less than $1063.51 it will be more economical.

Exercise 7e

1. A memorial library for a town will cost $60,000. The estimated annual maintenance cost is $1800 and the estimated life is 60 years. If the replacement cost is assumed to be the same as the first cost, what endowment (to the nearest $1000) will build, replace and maintain this library in perpetuity? Assume that 4% will be earned on the endowment. ($111,000)

2. Work Problem 1 if the interest on the endowment will be $3\frac{1}{2}\%$.

3. A philanthropist wants to provide an endowment to construct a community building costing $350,000 and replace it every 50 years. If the estimated return on the endowment is $3\frac{1}{2}\%$, what size endowment will be needed? ($426,337)

4. The original cost of a shelter house for a park is $7000. It is estimated that it will have to be replaced every 12 years at the same cost. What donation will be needed to endow this shelter house in perpetuity if the money can be invested at 4%?

5. One type of roof costs $600 and has to be replaced every 10 years. Another type costs $1200 and will last 25 years. If money is worth 4%, which is the more economical? (The $600 roof)

6. A building can be painted for $1200 with a paint that will last 4 years. If a better paint is used, the cost will be $1500 and the job will last 6 years. If money is worth 3%, which job is more economical?

7. A machine costs $15,000, has an estimated life of 12 years, and a scrap value of $2000. Find the capitalized cost at 3%. ($45,533.57)

8. A machine costs $7500, has an estimated life of 6 years and a scrap value of $1200. What is the capitalized cost at 5%?

9. Timbers used in a certain type of construction work cost $700 and last 12 years. A preservative treatment is expected to increase the life to 18 years. If money is worth 4%, how much can be paid for the preservative treatment?

($244.21)

7.15 Composite Life

Usually the assets of a business have probable lives that vary widely. When a plant is to be used as security for a bond issue, it may be necessary to determine the *composite life* of the plant. This is the time necessary for the total annual depreciation charge to equal the total wearing value.

EXAMPLE: Find the composite life of the following plant if depreciation is based on the straight line method.

SOLUTION: The following table shows how the total annual charge and the total wearing value are obtained.

Item	Life in Years	Cost	Scrap Value	Wearing Value	Annual Charge
Building	60	$120,000	$ 0	$120,000	$2000
Machine tools	15	50,000	5000	45,000	3000
Other machinery	10	30,000	2000	28,000	2800
				$193,000	$7800

Composite life = 193,000 ÷ 7800 = 24.7 years.

This example shows that if this plant is to be used as security for a long-term loan or bond issue, the term of the loan should be less than 24 years. To have a reasonable margin of safety the term should probably be considerably less than the composite life.

Exercise 7f

1. A plant consists of the following: (a) a building worth $70,000 with a life of 50 years and no scrap value; (b) machine tools worth $25,000 with a life of 15 years and a scrap value of $3000; (c) equipment worth $20,000 with a life of 12 years and a scrap value of $1000. Find the composite life if depreciation is based on the straight line method.   (25− years)

2. If depreciation is based on the straight line method, find the composite life of the plant described below:

Item	Life in Years	Cost	Scrap Value
Building	40	$60,000	$ 0
Power plant	15	8,000	500
Machine tools	18	22,000	1000
Dies, jigs, fixtures, etc.	7	6,500	0

8

LIFE ANNUITIES

8.1 The Mortality Table

Up to now we have been dealing with single payments and with annuities that were certain to be paid. We shall now work problems which are contingent on how long a person lives.

Suppose some young 18-year old men want to set up a fund from which all who are living 20 years from now will receive $1000. How much should each one put into the fund now? To answer this question we need to be able to predict how many of the original group will be living 20 years from now. While no one can tell who will die during the next 20 years, it is possible to use past mortality data to predict approximately *how many* will die during a given period. Before we can work the problem, we must understand the basic tool of the life insurance actuary — the mortality table.

Insurance companies have kept careful records which show the number of people living and dying at each age of life. These records show that death rates are predictable with sufficient accuracy to estimate future deaths based on past experience. These statistics of the "march through life" are compiled into a table which is called a mortality table.

As life expectancy changes, a mortality table will become obsolete and must be replaced with more recent data. In this book we use the 1958 Commissioners Standard Ordinary (CSO) Mortality table. This is Table 5 in the back of the book. This table is being used by the majority of insurance companies and will be the mandatory non-forfeiture and valuation standard in most states by January 1, 1966. Note that values for 15-year old females and up are the same as the values for a male three years younger. Values for females age 0 to 14 are given in the complete tables of the Society of Actuaries. In practical applications, annuity and insurance contracts may be based on different mortality tables. Since the basic principles involved in life annuity and life insurance problems are the same regardless of the mortality table, all problems in this text are based on the 1958 CSO Table.

The CSO table starts with 10,000,000 people living at age 0. The l_x column gives the number living at age x. The d_x column gives the number that can be expected to die before reaching age $x + 1$. Thus 70,800 of the 10,000,000 living at age 0 can be expected to die before reaching age 1. The probability of dying within a year for a person age x is indicated by the symbol q_x. It is obtained by dividing the number dying at age x by the number living at age x. In symbols, $q_x = d_x/l_x$. An easier figure to work with is the death rate per 1000 which is given in the mortality table under the symbol 1000 q_x.

EXAMPLE 1: What is the probability that a 20-year old man will live to age 50? Of a group of 1000 20-year old men, what is the predicted number that will live to age 50?

SOLUTION: The probability that a 20-year old man will live to age 50 is simply the number still living at age 50 divided by the number living at age 20.

$$\frac{l_{50}}{l_{20}} = \frac{8\ 762\ 306}{9\ 664\ 994} = .9066$$

Out of 1000 20-year old men, the predicted number that will live to age 50 is $1000 \times .9066 = 907$.

EXAMPLE 2: What is the probability that a 20-year old man will die before reaching age 50? Of a group of 1000 20-year old men, what is the predicted number that will die before reaching age 50?

SOLUTION: The probability of a man dying between age 20 and age 50 is the number dying during this period divided by the number living at age 20.

$$\frac{l_{20} - l_{50}}{l_{20}} = \frac{9\ 664\ 994 - 8\ 762\ 306}{9\ 664\ 994} = .0934$$

Note that if we have the probability that a man will live to age 50, we can get the probability that he will die by age 50 by subtracting the probability of living from 1 since he will certainly do one or the other. Probability of dying by age $50 = 1.0000 - .9066 = .0934$.

Out of 1000 20-year old men, the predicted number that will die before reaching age 50 is $1000 \times .0934 = 93$.

EXAMPLE 3: Get the answers to Examples 1 and 2 for women.

Probability of living $= \dfrac{l_{50}}{l_{20}} = \dfrac{8\,948\,114}{9\,713\,967} = .9212$

Predicted number living to age 50 $= 1000 \times .9212 = 921$

Probability of dying $= \dfrac{l_{20} - l_{50}}{l_{20}} = \dfrac{9\,713\,967 - 8\,948\,114}{9\,713\,967} = .0788$

Predicted number dying before age 50 $= 1000 \times .0788 = 79$.

Note the considerably lower mortality predictions for women.

Exercise 8a

1. Use the CSO Mortality Table to find the values of: (a) l_{20}; (b) l_{40}; (c) l_{60} for men and for women.

$$\begin{bmatrix} \text{Men: (a) } 9\,664\,994; \text{ (b) } 9\,241\,359; \text{ (c) } 7\,698\,698 \\ \text{Women: (a) } 9\,713\,967; \text{ (b) } 9\,325\,594; \text{ (c) } 8\,106\,161 \end{bmatrix}$$

2. Use the CSO Mortality Table to find the values of: (a) l_{30}; (b) l_{50}; (c) l_{70} for men and for women.

3. Use the CSO Mortality Table to find the values of: (a) d_{20}; (b) d_{40}; (c) d_{60} for men and for women.

$$\begin{bmatrix} \text{Men: (a) } 17\,300; \text{ (b) } 32\,622; \text{ (c) } 156\,592 \\ \text{Women: (a) } 15\,737; \text{ (b) } 26\,112; \text{ (c) } 125\,970 \end{bmatrix}$$

4. Use the CSO Mortality Table to find the values of: (a) d_{30}; (b) d_{50}; (c) d_{70} for men and for women.

5. Find the death rates per 1000 for: (a) 20-year old; (b) 40-year old; and (c) 60-year old men and women.

$$\begin{bmatrix} \text{Men: (a) } 1.79; \text{ (b) } 3.53; \text{ (c) } 20.34 \\ \text{Women: (a) } 1.62; \text{ (b) } 2.80; \text{ (c) } 15.54 \end{bmatrix}$$

6. Find the death rates per 1000 for (a) 30-year old; (b) 50-year old, and (c) 70-year old men and women.

7. Of a group of 1000 25-year old men and 1000 25-year old women, what are the predicted numbers that will die before reaching the age of 45?
(Men 55; women 47)

8. Of a group of 1000 30-year old men and 1000 30-year old women, what are the predicted numbers that will die before reaching the age of 65?

9. A college graduating class has 300 21-year old men in it. What is the predicted number of living alumni from this group: (a) 25 years, (b) 50 years, and (c) 75 years after graduation? [(a) 280; (b) 165; (c) 2]

10. Work Problem 9 assuming a group of 300 21-year old women.

8.2 Interest and Loading

In determining the premium a policyholder should pay, an insurance company will make allowance for the interest that will be earned on the premiums when they are invested by the company. All computations in this book are based on a rate of $2\frac{1}{2}\%$ compounded annually.

Actual insurance premiums consist of two parts — the **net premium** and the **loading.** The net premium takes into account mortality and interest on invested premiums. The loading takes care of the insurance company's cost of doing business. Since each company has its own method of allowing for loading, we shall compute only net premiums. In all cases the present value of the net premiums will equal the present value of all future benefits. This means that, regardless of the type of policy, we derive the formula for net premiums from the basic equation of value:

$$\frac{\text{Net premiums discounted}}{\text{to date of issue}} = \frac{\text{Benefits discounted}}{\text{to date of issue}}$$

Actuarial symbols used in this book correspond to those used by the Society of Actuaries. Since many of the symbols require multiple subscripts, it is suggested that students use the verbal description of each problem when discussing it. Then the right formula can be obtained by simply referring to the discussion of that type of problem.

8.3 Pure Endowment

The problem at the beginning of this chapter was what is known as a **pure endowment,** that is, a *single* payment which will go to a person at a certain time *if he is living at that time.* To get a formula for a pure endowment we assume that the size of the payment is 1. Then to solve any problem all we need do is multiply by the size of the payment in the particular problem.

If l_x individuals aged x establish a fund to pay \$1 to each member living at age $x + n$, the number of dollars needed in n years will equal the l_{x+n} entry in the mortality table. Since the money is not needed until n years from now, we need set aside today only the present or discounted value of this amount. If the symbol $_nE_x$ is used to represent each person's contribution to the fund, the total original premiums will equal $l_x \cdot {_nE_x}$, and the problem can be sketched as shown.

Discounting the benefits and setting up an equation of value, we have

$$l_x \cdot {_nE_x} = (1 + i)^{-n} l_{x+n}$$

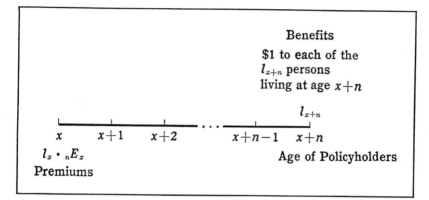

Following common actuarial practice, we substitute the single letter v for $(1 + i)^{-1}$. Then $v^n = [(1 + i)^{-1}]^n = (1 + i)^{-n}$. Substituting in the above formula and solving for $_nE_x$, we have the following expression for the net premium for a \$1 endowment in n years issued to a person aged x years:

$$_nE_x = \frac{v^n l_{x+n}}{l_x}$$

To reduce the numerical work required to solve life annuity and insurance problems, we now introduce the **commutation functions** which are used by life insurance actuaries. These functions simplify formulas and eliminate multiple and tedious computations. They are defined below.

Commutation functions; numerical values are in Table 6

$$D_x = v^x l_x$$
$$N_x = D_x + D_{x+1} + \cdots + D_{\omega-1}$$
$$C_x = v^{x+1} d_x$$
$$M_x = C_x + C_{x+1} + \cdots + C_{\omega-1}$$

Note that all of the commutation functions combine *Present Worth of 1* factors and values from the mortality table. This means that a different table of commutation functions is required for each combination of interest rate and mortality table. Commutation functions may involve 100 terms or more. They simplify actuarial formulas, and they are indispensable labor savers when calculations are done manually or with desk calculators.

The subscript x indicates the age at which a person gets an annuity or insurance policy. The Greek letter ω (omega) is the terminal age of a mortality table. It is the lowest age at which there are no survivors. For the 1958 CSO Table, $\omega = 100$ for males and 103 for females. Other mortality tables used by insurance companies have different terminal ages, but the formulas derived in this text are applicable regardless of the interest rate or mortality table.

The Commutation Columns in Table 6 were taken from Volume I of the Monetary Tables published by the Society of Actuaries. Examples and answers to problems are based on the complete factors. Because of the numerical work involved if a calculator is not available, some instructors have students substitute complete factors and then permit them to round the values to a specified number of significant figures before completing the problem using logarithms, slide rule, or arithmetic to get the final answer. Answers obtained in this way will usually differ slightly from the more precise answers in the text.

If we multiply the numerator and denominator of the equation for the present value of a pure endowment by v^x, we have

$$_nE_x = \frac{v^{x+n}l_{x+n}}{v^x l_x}$$

Substituting commutation functions, this can be written as follows:

$$_nE_x = \frac{D_{x+n}}{D_x} \tag{28}$$

In all formulas in this and the next chapter, x is the age of the person at the time the endowment, annuity, or life insurance is purchased. The meaning of n is defined for each formula. In this formula it means that the person will receive the endowment at the end of n years if he is then living. In some problems we are given the age at which the person is to get the endowment. In such cases, it is not necessary to get n since this age equals $x + n$.

EXAMPLE 1: What is the net single premium for an 18-year old man for a 20-year pure endowment of $1000?

SOLUTION: Formula (28) gives the cost of a pure endowment of $1. Therefore a $1000 pure endowment due in 20 years would cost an 18-year old man,

$$1000\,\frac{D_{38}}{D_{18}} = 1000\,\frac{3\,638\,747.1}{6\,218\,174.5} = \$585.18$$

EXAMPLE 2: Solve Example 1 for an 18-year old woman.

SOLUTION: $$1000\,\frac{D_{38}}{D_{18}} = 1000\,\frac{3\,949\,851.1}{6\,727\,326.8} = \$587.14$$

Note the higher cost to a woman because she has a higher expectation than a man of living to the end of the endowment period.

EXAMPLE 3: Find the net single premium for an 18-year old man for a pure endowment of $1000 at age 60.

SOLUTION: $1000 \dfrac{D_{60}}{D_{18}} = 1000 \dfrac{1\,749\,787.7}{6\,218\,174.5} = \$281.40$

This is less than the answer to Example 1 because the endowment period is much longer. Pure endowments are rarely sold separately. However, they are often a part of life insurance policies. The endowment feature can make such policies quite expensive unless the endowment period is a long one.

Pure endowments illustrate what it means to accumulate a fund with benefit of survivorship. In Example 3, the share of each individual who survives to age 60 is made up in part of the shares forfeited by those who die before reaching 60. Thus each survivor receives more than he would get from interest alone. At $2\frac{1}{2}\%$ compounded annually, the $281.40 in Example 3 would amount to $281.40(1.025)^{42} = \$793.83$. With interest and survivorship, those who live to the end of the endowment period get $1000.

Exercise 8b

1. Find the net cost to a 30-year old man of a pure endowment of $1000 in (a) 20 years, (b) 40 years.   [(a) $564.05; (b) $219.68]

2. Work Problem 1 for a woman.

3. What would be the cost to a 25-year old man of an endowment of $10,000 when he is 65 years of age?   ($2644.97)

4. Work Problem 3 for a woman.

8.4 Whole Life Annuities

Instead of a single payment, people often prefer to receive benefits from insurance policies and other investments in equal periodic payments. If these payments are to continue as long as the designated person or annuitant lives, the annuity is called a **whole life annuity.** While the payments can be made at any interval, we shall limit ourselves to annual payments. Also in all of our derivations the size of each payment will be $1. Then to solve any particular problem, all we have to do is multiply the appropriate formula by the size of the payment. As was the case with annuities certain, the first payment can be made one year hence, at once, or several years hence.

We first consider the *ordinary* or *immediate life* annuity which provides for annual payments starting in one year, if the annuitant is then living, and continuing throughout his lifetime. Our computations will be based on the assumption that l_x persons age x each deposit $\$a_x$. Thus the original amount in the fund, $l_x a_x$, plus interest must be adequate to pay each person $\$1$ at the end of each year throughout the rest of his life.

One year after the plan is started there will be l_{x+1} persons living and each of them must be paid out of the fund. Every year from then on each of the survivors will get $\$1$. This will continue as long as there are survivors, which is age 99 for men and 102 for women when the CSO table is used.

Since beginning students find derivations easier to follow when numerical values are used, the formulas in this chapter are derived assuming the CSO Table for males with l_{99} as the last entry in the table. Formulas derived in this way are completely general and are the same as we would get using the expression l_{w-1} for the final entry.

To get an equation of value, we discount all of these future payments to the present date. Thus the present value of the payment to be made in one year is vl_{x+1}; the present value of the payment to be made in two years is $v^2 l_{x+2}$ and so on. A time diagram of payments and premiums is shown below. The symbol a_x is used to represent the premium of each person.

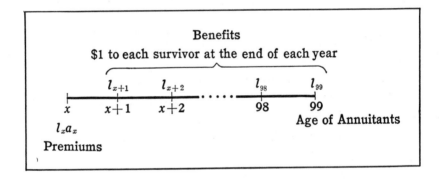

Bringing everything back to the present and setting up an equation of value, we have

$$l_x a_x = vl_{x+1} + v^2 l_{x+2} + \cdots + v^{98-x} l_{98} + v^{99-x} l_{99}$$

Therefore the cost per person is

$$a_x = \frac{vl_{x+1} + v^2 l_{x+2} + \cdots + v^{98-x} l_{98} + v^{99-x} l_{99}}{l_x}$$

To get the cost of this annuity for a man aged 20, we would have to discount all the annual payments from 21 to 99. To avoid this labor we first multiply numerator and denominator by v^x.

$$a_x = \frac{v^{x+1} l_{x+1} + v^{x+2} l_{x+2} + \cdots + v^{98} l_{98} + v^{99} l_{99}}{v^x l_x}$$

Then we simplify, using commutation symbols.

$$a_x = \frac{D_{x+1} + D_{x+2} + \cdots + D_{98} + D_{99}}{D_x}$$

$$a_x = \frac{N_{x+1}}{D_x} \tag{29}$$

8.5 Whole Life Annuity Due

If the first payment is made at once and payments are made throughout the lifetime of the annuitant, the annuity is called a **whole life annuity due.** The present value of a whole life annuity due of 1 per year is indicated by the symbol $\ddot{a}_x$. Since the only difference between this annuity and the immediate whole life annuity described in the preceding section is the payments made to the l_x individuals at the start, we can say

$$l_x \ddot{a}_x = l_x + v l_{x+1} + v^2 l_{x+2} + \cdots + v^{98-x} l_{98} + v^{99-x} l_{99}$$

Solving for $\ddot{a}_x$ and multiplying numerator and denominator by v^x,

$$\ddot{a}_x = \frac{v^x l_x + v^{x+1} l_{x+1} + v^{x+2} l_{x+2} + \cdots + v^{98} l_{98} + v^{99} l_{99}}{v^x l_x}$$

$$= \frac{D_x + D_{x+1} + D_{x+2} + \cdots + D_{98} + D_{99}}{D_x}$$

$$\ddot{a}_x = \frac{N_x}{D_x} \tag{30}$$

Because of its frequent use in annuity work, values of $\ddot{a}_x$ are given in Table 6 along with the commutation columns. By simply subtracting 1 from the values of $\ddot{a}_x$ we can get the present value of an immediate whole life annuity of 1 per year. Therefore

$$a_x = \ddot{a}_x - 1$$

EXAMPLE 1: Find the net single premium for a whole life annuity due of $1000 per year issued to a man aged 50.

SOLUTION: Formula (30) gives the net single premium for a whole life annuity due of $1 per year. For annual payments of $1000 the premium is

$$1000 \ddot{a}_{50} = 1000 \times 17.614151 = \$17,614.15$$

EXAMPLE 2: How much would an immediate life annuity of $500 a year cost a man aged 18?

SOLUTION: From (29) the value of an immediate life annuity of $500 a year is $500 a_{18}$. Since the immediate life annuity is the same as the life annuity due except that the first payment is made in one year, the value of a_{18} can be obtained by subtracting 1 from $\ddot{a}_{18}$. Therefore the cost is

$$500\,(\ddot{a}_{18} - 1) = 500\,(28.963722 - 1.0000) = \$13,981.86$$

EXAMPLE 3: A man dies and leaves his widow a $20,000 insurance policy. If she is 60 years old and elects to receive annual payments for life with the first payment to be made now, what is the size of each payment?

SOLUTION: In this problem the present value of the life annuity due is known and the size of the annual payment is to be determined. Letting R represent the size of each payment, we have

$$R\ddot{a}_{60} = 20,000$$

$$R = \frac{20,000}{\ddot{a}_{60}} = \frac{20,000}{14.502179} = \$1379.10$$

EXAMPLE 4: Find the size of the payment in Example 3 if the first payment is to be made in 1 year.

SOLUTION: This is an ordinary or immediate whole life annuity.

$$Ra_{60} = R\,(\ddot{a}_{60} - 1) = 20,000$$

$$R = \frac{20,000}{13.502179} = \$1481.24$$

Exercise 8c

1. Find the net single premium for a life annuity of $1000 per year for a 30-year old man if: (a) the first payment is to be made now; (b) the first payment is to be made in 1 year.   [(a) \$25,518.94; (b) \$24,518.94]

2. A man plans to retire at 65. At that time, a life annuity of $2000 a year would cost how much if: (a) the first payment is made at age 65; (b) the first payment is made at age 66?

3. A 50-year old widow wants to use part of her estate to purchase an immediate life annuity of $2500 a year. Find the net single premium.

($44,813.60)

4. A 50-year old man wants to buy an annuity which will pay him $1000 a year for life with the first payment to be made when he is age 51. Find the net single premium.

5. A man will retire at age 65 and start receiving social security benefits of $150 a month. Find the approximate present value of these payments. For this purpose, replace the 12 monthly payments with an approximately equivalent payment of $1800 at the end of each year.   ($18,066)

6. At age 62, a widow is to receive $100 a month in social security benefits. What is the approximate present value of her benefits?

7. A 20-year old man takes out a life insurance policy on which the premiums are $100 a year at the beginning of each year for life. Find the net present value of these premiums.   ($2845.36)

8. A 35-year old man takes out a life insurance policy on which the premiums are $250 a year at the beginning of each year for life. Find the net present value of the premiums.

9. A widow, who is the beneficiary of a $20,000 insurance policy, decides to take an annual income for life. If she is 48 years old, find the size of each payment if the first payment is to be made: (a) now, (b) in 1 year.

[(a) $1010.97 (b) $1064.79]

10. A 50-year old man invests $100,000 in a whole life annuity with the first payment to be made in 1 year. What is the size of each payment?

11. In his will, a man directs that each of his twin children, a boy and a girl, is to receive a life annuity due with a present value of $100,000. At his death, the children are 19 years of age. Find the lifetime income of each.

(Boy $3482.94; Girl $3394.99)

12. A man directs that $\frac{2}{3}$ of his estate is to be used to purchase an ordinary life annuity for his wife and the remaining $\frac{1}{3}$ an ordinary life annuity for his son. The estate amounts to $150,000. When the annuities are purchased, the widow is 62 and the son is 30. Find the annual income of each.

8.6   Deferred Whole Life Annuity

Another type of annuity is the n-year deferred immediate life annuity. This is the same as an immediate life annuity with the first n payments omitted. The first payment is made at age $x + n + 1$. The present value of an annuity of 1 per year is denoted by $_{n|}a_x$. The benefits and premiums are shown on the time diagram below.

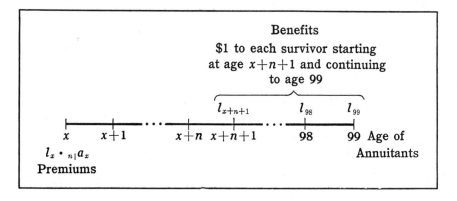

Discounting the benefits and setting up the equation of value, we have

$$l_x \cdot {}_{n|}a_x = v^{n+1}l_{x+n+1} + \cdots + v^{98-x}l_{98} + v^{99-x}l_{99}$$

Solving for the individual premium and multiplying numerator and denominator by v^x,

$$_{n|}a_x = \frac{v^{x+n+1}l_{x+n+1} + \cdots + v^{98}l_{98} + v^{99}l_{99}}{v^x l_x}$$

$$= \frac{D_{x+n+1} + \cdots + D_{98} + D_{99}}{D_x}$$

$$_{n|}a_x = \frac{N_{x+n+1}}{D_x} \tag{31}$$

In many deferred life annuity problems, we are given the age at which the first payment is to be made. Since this is equal to $x + n + 1$, we can simply substitute this value in the formula and need not determine n.

EXAMPLE 1: A man 40 years of age wants a life income of $2000 a year with the first annual payment to be made when he is 65. What is the net cost of this annuity?

SOLUTION: Since the first payment is to be made at age 65, $x + n + 1 = 65$. Substituting in Formula (31),

$$\text{Net cost} = 2000 \frac{N_{65}}{D_{40}} = 2000 \frac{15\ 077\ 832.8}{3\ 441\ 765.1} = \$8761.69$$

EXAMPLE 2: A 15-year old girl receives an inheritance of $30,000. If she is to get annual payments for life starting on her 21st birthday, what will be the size of each payment?

SOLUTION: If R represents the annual payment, we have

$$30,000 = R \frac{N_{21}}{D_{15}}$$

$$R = 30,000 \frac{D_{15}}{N_{21}} = 30,000 \frac{7\ 273\ 432.5}{180\ 101\ 480.3} = \$1211.56$$

Exercise 8d

1. What is the net cost of a whole life annuity of $1000 a year for a 50-year old man if the first payment is to be made 15 years hence?   ($5914.44)

2. Find the net single premium for an annuity of $1000 a year issued to a 55-year old man if the first payment is to be made at the age of 65.

3. Find the answer to Problem 1 if the annuitant is a woman.

($7003.19)

4. Find the answer to Problem 2 if the annuitant is a woman.

5. A 45-year old man receives an inheritance of $24,000. He uses this money to buy a whole life annuity the first payment of which is to be made when he is 60. What will be the size of the annual payment?   ($3229.85)

6. When his $10,000 endowment policy matures at age 50, a man decides to use this money to buy a life annuity starting at age 65 when his social security payments will begin. What annual payment will be provided by the proceeds of the insurance policy?

7. A man who is now 48 years old would like to have an annual income of $2400 starting when he is age 60. What is the net cost of this annuity?

($20,360.15)

8. A 58-year old man expects to get about $1500 a year from social security when he reaches age 65. He now has money with which he wants to buy a life annuity which will provide another $1500 a year for life with the first annual payment to be made when he reaches age 65. How much will this annuity cost him now?

9. A widow is 50 years old when her husband dies. One of his insurance policies is for $15,000. This policy is to provide the widow an income for life starting when she is 60. What annual payment will she receive?   ($1461.55)

10. A 45-year old widow is left $15,000 from an insurance policy. What annual income for life would she get from this policy if the first payment is made: (a) now; (b) in 1 year; (c) when she is age 65?

11. A 55-year old man pays $20,000 for a whole life annuity with the first payment to be made when he is 65. Find the size of the annual payment.

($2841.79)

12. Find the annual payment in Problem 11 if the first payment is to be made when the man is 62.

8.7   Temporary Immediate Life Annuity

A temporary life annuity is one which ends after a certain number of years or at the death of the annuitant, whichever occurs first. If the first payment is made one year hence and if the payments are made for n years, we have an **n-year temporary immediate life annuity.** Indicating the present value by $a_{x:\overline{n}|}$ and showing benefits and premiums on a time scale, we have

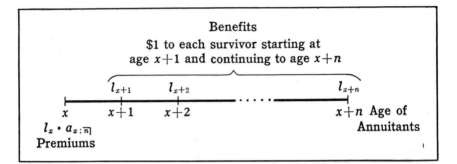

Note that this annuity ceases with the final payments to the l_{x+n} individuals living n years after the start of the program. The equation of value becomes

$$l_x \cdot a_{x:\overline{n}|} = vl_{x+1} + v^2 l_{x+2} + \cdots + v^n l_{x+n}$$

Solving for the individual premium, multiplying numerator and denominator by v^x and substituting commutation symbols, we have

$$a_{x:\overline{n}|} = \frac{D_{x+1} + D_{x+2} + \cdots + D_{x+n}}{D_x}$$

Since $N_{x+1} = D_{x+1} + D_{x+2} + \cdots + D_{x+n} + D_{x+n+1} + \cdots + D_{99}$

And $N_{x+n+1} = \qquad\qquad\qquad\qquad\qquad D_{x+n+1} + \cdots + D_{99}$

The numerator can be written as $N_{x+1} - N_{x+n+1}$

$$a_{x:\overline{n}|} = \frac{N_{x+1} - N_{x+n+1}}{D_x} \tag{32}$$

EXAMPLE: How much would a man aged 18 have to pay for a 5-year temporary life annuity of $1000 per year if the first payment is to be made when the man is aged 19?

SOLUTION:

$$1000 a_{18:\overline{5}|} = 1000 \frac{N_{18+1} - N_{18+5+1}}{D_{18}} = 1000 \frac{N_{19} - N_{24}}{D_{18}}$$

$$= 1000 \frac{173\ 883\ 305.8 - 145\ 143\ 761.6}{6\ 218\ 174.5} = \$4621.86$$

8.8   Temporary Life Annuity Due

If the first payment is made at once, we have a temporary life annuity due, the present value of which is indicated by $\ddot{a}_{x:\overline{n}|}$. Proceeding in the usual manner, we find that the present value is

$$\ddot{a}_{x:\overline{n}|} = \frac{N_x - N_{x+n}}{D_x} \tag{33}$$

EXAMPLE: How much would a 5-year temporary life annuity due of $1000 per year cost a man aged 18?

SOLUTION:

$$1000\ddot{a}_{18:\overline{5}|} = 1000\,\frac{N_{18} - N_{18+5}}{D_{18}} = 1000\,\frac{N_{18} - N_{23}}{D_{18}}$$

$$= 1000\,\frac{180\ 101\ 480.3 - 150\ 590\ 927.4}{6\ 218\ 174.5} = \$4745.85$$

8.9 Deferred Temporary Life Annuity

A series of annual payments which commences at age $x + n + 1$ and continues for m years if the annuitant survives is called an **n-year deferred m-year temporary immediate annuity.** The symbol for the present value of $1 per year is denoted by $_{n|m}a_x$. Proceeding in the usual manner, we get the following formula for the present value. Note that in this formula, which is given here as it appears in actuarial publications, n stands for the interval of deferment and m is the number of payments.

$$_{n|m}a_x = \frac{N_{x+n+1} - N_{x+n+m+1}}{D_x} \tag{34}$$

EXAMPLE 1: How much would a 5-year temporary life annuity of $1000 a year cost a man aged 18 if he is to receive the first payment when he is 28?

SOLUTION: In this problem x, the age of the annuitant, is 18; n, the interval of deferment, is 9; and m, the number of payments, is 5. Substituting in (34), we have

$$1000_{9|5}a_{18} = 1000\,\frac{N_{28} - N_{33}}{D_{18}}$$

$$= 1000\,\frac{124\ 748\ 159.0 - 102\ 134\ 645.1}{6\ 218\ 174.5} = \$3636.68$$

All temporary life annuity problems can be solved using the following general formula in which R is the size of the periodic payment.

$$\text{Net present value} = R\,\frac{N_{\text{age at first payment}} - N_{\text{age at first payment + number of payments}}}{D_{\text{age when annuity is purchased}}}$$

EXAMPLE 2: Find the net cost of a $2000 a year temporary life annuity for 10 years for a 50-year old woman if the first payment is to be made when she is: (a) 50; (b) 51; (c) 62.

SOLUTION:

(a) Net cost $= 2000 \dfrac{N_{50} - N_{60}}{D_{50}}$

$$= 2000 \frac{53\ 058\ 604.2 - 28\ 773\ 199.9}{2\ 803\ 559.9} = \$17{,}324.69$$

(b) Net cost $= 2000 \dfrac{N_{51} - N_{61}}{D_{50}}$

$$= 2000 \frac{50\ 255\ 044.3 - 26\ 789\ 139.5}{2\ 803\ 559.9} = \$16{,}740.08$$

(c) Net cost $= 2000 \dfrac{N_{62} - N_{72}}{D_{50}}$

$$= 2000 \frac{24\ 883\ 551.1 - 10\ 065\ 398.9}{2\ 803\ 559.9} = \$10{,}570.95$$

Exercise 8e

1. Find the net single premium of a temporary immediate life annuity of $1000 per year for 10 years if the annuitant is an 18-year old man.

($8668.66)

2. Find the net single premium of a temporary immediate life annuity of $1200 a year for 10 years if the annuitant is a 64-year old man.

3. How much would a 10-year temporary life annuity due of $1200 a year cost a 28-year old man?   ($10,664.73)

4. Find the net cost of a 15-year temporary life annuity due of $840 a year for a 65-year old man.

5. What is the net single premium for a temporary immediate life annuity of $3000 per year for 20 years if the annuitant is a 65-year old woman?

($31,767.12)

6. At age 55, a man buys an annuity which will provide him 15 annual payments of $800. If the first payment is to be made when the man is age 65, how much will the annuity cost?

7. What is the net single premium for a temporary life annuity due of $2500 a year for 10 years if the annuitant is a 62-year old woman?

($20,271.01)

8. How much money must be set aside to provide a 12-year old boy with $1000 a year for 4 years if he is to receive the first payment when he is 18?

9. A 50-year old woman inherits \$40,000. With \$20,000, she buys a 20-year temporary life annuity with the first payment to be made when she is 65. What will be the size of each payment? (\$3078.07)

10. What would be the size of the payment in Problem 9 if the woman was 64 years old when she purchased the annuity?

8.10 Joint Life Annuities

All of the annuities in this chapter were based on a single life. This means that when the annuitant dies the payments cease. Annuities may also be based on more than one life. For example, a joint life annuity continues in existence as long as all the lives survive, and stops upon the occurrence of the first death. A joint-and-survivor annuity continues as long as any member of the group survives. This type of annuity might be attractive to a retired couple who would want their income to continue as long as both or either of them is living. These other types of annuities are based on the principles given in this chapter. However, the mathematics involved is beyond the range of an elementary text. They are mentioned here to acquaint students with the fact that annuities are available to meet those practical situations that involve combinations of two or more lives.

8.11 Summary of Life Annuity Formulas

The six annuity formulas derived in this chapter can be divided into two general classes:

(1) Whole life annuities which provide equal periodic payments as long as the annuitant lives.

(2) Temporary life annuities in which the payments cease after a specified time or when the annuitant dies depending on which comes first.

Both of the general classes of annuities are divided into three types, depending on when the first payment is made relative to x, the age of the annuitant at the time the annuity is purchased. Immediate or ordinary life annuities have the first payment made at age $x + 1$. Life annuities due have the first payment made at age x. Deferred immediate life annuities have the first payment made at age $x + n + 1$ where n is the interval of deferment.

The formulas in this book are the same as those used by the Society of Actuaries. This will acquaint students with modern actuarial practice. It will also provide a sound foundation for those students who want to continue to more advanced work in insurance.

The annuity formulas are summarized below as derived in this chapter and in a second and more general form using verbal subscripts. All formulas are for periodic payments of \$1. For other periodic payments simply multiply by the size of the payment.

Whole Life Annuities

Immediate or ordinary (First payment at age $x + 1$)	$a_x = \dfrac{N_{x+1}}{D_x}$ $\qquad (a_x = \ddot{a}_x - 1)$ (29)
Due (First payment at age x)	$\ddot{a}_x = \dfrac{N_x}{D_x}$ (30)
Deferred (First payment at age $x + n + 1$)	$_{n|}a_x = \dfrac{N_{x+n+1}}{D_x}$ (31)

All of the whole life annuities can be solved using the following general formula. This is convenient when the time of the first payment is given in terms of the age of the annuitant.

$$\text{Value} = \frac{N_{\text{age at which the first payment is due}}}{D_{\text{age when annuity is purchased}}}$$

Temporary Life Annuities

Immediate or ordinary (First payment at age $x + 1$. Payments at the end of each year for n years.)	$a_{x:\overline{n}|} = \dfrac{N_{x+1} - N_{x+n+1}}{D_x}$ (32)
Due (First payment at age x. Payments at the beginning of each year for n years.)	$\ddot{a}_{x:\overline{n}|} = \dfrac{N_x - N_{x+n}}{D_x}$ (33)
Deferred (First payment at age $x + n + 1$. Payments for m years.)	$_{n|m}a_x = \dfrac{N_{x+n+1} - N_{x+n+m+1}}{D_x}$ (34)

All of the temporary life annuities can be solved using the following general formula. This is convenient when the time of the first payment is given in terms of the age of the annuitant.

$$\text{Value} = \frac{N_{\text{age at first payment}} - N_{\text{age at first payment + number of payments}}}{D_{\text{age when annuity is purchased}}}$$

9

LIFE INSURANCE

9.1 Life Insurance

Life insurance makes it possible for a man of moderate income to provide an income for his family if he should die. The fundamental principle of life insurance can be illustrated by a simple example.

Suppose that a group of 10,000 18-year old men in good health want to take out an insurance policy that would pay $1000 to the beneficiary of each of the young men who dies before reaching age 19. If we refer to the CSO Mortality Table, we find that the average death rate for 18-year old men is 1.69 per 1000. Therefore, our group would expect about 17 deaths during the coming year. If each of the 10,000 men pays a premium of $1.70 into a common fund, there would immediately be set up a fund of $17,000 from which the 17 death benefits would be paid.

In practical insurance plans interest is earned on invested funds. An interest rate of $2\frac{1}{2}\%$ will be used in all insurance problems in this book. Gross insurance premiums must be large enough to pay both death benefits and company expenses. We shall compute only net premiums making no allowance for loading for the four most common types of policies: term, straight life, limited payment life, and endowment.

Before we start computing net premiums, it is interesting to see how the cost of commercial insurance varies with the type of policy. While there is some variation in cost from one company to another, the following graphs are typical of costs from a representative company. The rates are annual rates per $1000 for a man taking out a $10,000 or larger policy. In general, the rates would be somewhat higher for smaller policies. A much larger policy, such as $25,000, would probably have a lower rate. Rates for women are likely to be lower because of their higher life expectancy.

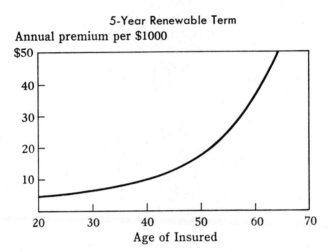

Term insurance has a premium which is based on expected death benefits for a limited period such as 5 or 10 years. Because mortality rates increase as people get older, the premium for a term policy increases with the age of the insured. Term insurance is quite expensive beyond middle age.

A level premium policy costs more initially than term insurance, but the premium does not increase. During the early years of the policy this excess premium is set aside as a reserve to help meet increased death benefits later on. The sketches in this section are for level premium policies issued to a man aged 20.

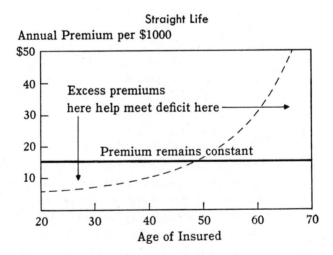

The most common type of level premium policy is straight life, also known as whole life or ordinary life. The cost of this policy is determined by the age

of the insured when he first takes out the policy. He can then carry it for the
rest of his life at the same premium.

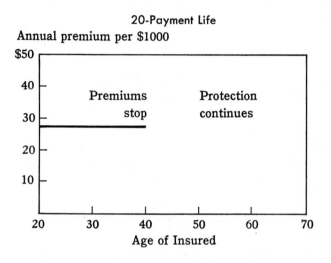

Limited pay life requires payments for a certain number of years at the end
of which time the policy becomes fully paid-up for the life of the insured.
This means that the premiums must be higher than for ordinary life because
the reserve must be built up in a shorter time. How much higher will depend
on the payment period.

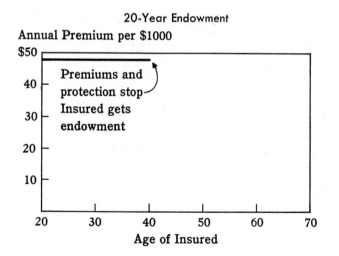

Endowment policies provide protection for a stated number of years at the
end of which time protection ceases and, if the insured is still living, the face

value of the policy is paid to him. The insurance company must set the premium large enough to take care of the *certainty* that they will have to pay someone, either the beneficiary or the insured, by the end of the endowment period. This makes endowment policies very expensive if the endowment period is short. From a representative company a ten thousand dollar 20-year endowment policy would cost a 20-year old man about $480 a year. If he purchased an endowment at age 65, the cost would drop to $191, because the endowment period is now much longer.

9.2 Determining the Premium

As an illustration of how insurance premiums are determined, let us see how we could get the premium for an ordinary life policy for an 18-year old man. We shall assume that the policy is for $1. Then to get the cost of any policy, all we need do is multiply our result by the size of the policy. Also we shall assume that the policy is to be purchased by a net single premium of A.

Referring to the mortality table we see that there are 9,698,230 men alive at age 18. If each of them took out a $1 whole life policy, and paid for it with a single premium, the total premiums plus interest would have to be sufficient to pay the $1 death benefits to the beneficiary of each insured person at the end of the year in which the insured dies. All of the formulas in this book are for payments made at the end of the year in which a person dies. (In practice insurance companies pay benefits upon proof of death rather than waiting until the end of the year. To take care of this practice insurance companies make a small adjustment in the net premiums.) Referring to the mortality table we see that the company would have to pay 16,390 death benefits one year after the policies were issued, 16,846 in two years, and so on to the end of the mortality table as shown below.

	16,390	16,846	17,300		12,916	6,415	Deaths
18	19	20	21	...	99	100	Age of insured

Thus the insurance company will need $16,390 in a year, $16,846 in two years, $12,916 in 81 years, $6415 in 82 years, and various other amounts for all of the intervening years. The total present value of all these future payments must now be determined by discounting each year's death benefits. Then dividing this total by 9,698,230 will give us the cost per person.

9.3 Straight Life Insurance

To avoid the work involved in discounting many payments, we now derive a formula for getting the premium for an ordinary or straight life policy using the commutation functions. The company issues $1 policies to l_x persons living at age x. At the end of the first year the company will have to pay $\$d_x$ in death benefits. Payments at the end of the second year will be $\$d_{x+1}$ and so on out to $\$d_{99}$. Each of the l_x persons will pay a net single premium, $\$A_x$, for his policy. Thus the number living at age x times the net single premium paid by each must equal the present value of all future death benefits.

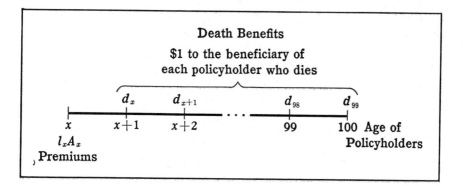

The equation of value is

$$l_x A_x = vd_x + v^2 d_{x+1} + \cdots + v^{99-x}d_{98} + v^{100-x}d_{99}$$

Solving for A_x and multiplying numerator and denominator by v^x,

$$A_x = \frac{v^{x+1}d_x + v^{x+2}d_{x+1} + \cdots + v^{99}d_{98} + v^{100}d_{99}}{v^x l_x}$$

We can now substitute the appropriate commutation functions defined on page 223 and simplify.

$$A_x = \frac{C_x + C_{x+1} + \cdots + C_{98} + C_{99}}{D_x}$$

$$A_x = \frac{M_x}{D_x} \tag{35}$$

Values of $1000A_x$ are given in Table 6.

EXAMPLE 1: Find the net single premium for a $10,000 whole life policy for an 18-year old man.

SOLUTION: $10,000A_{18} = 10 \times 293.5677 = \$2935.68$

By paying \$2935.68 (plus loading) the person would have a \$10,000 policy for the rest of his life.

Because of the large premium, most young people are not able to buy a whole life policy with a single premium. A man who has carried insurance for many years may find it advisable to use the cash value of his policy to buy a paid-up policy that will be in effect for the rest of his life without the payment of additional premiums. At the time a man retires, his children will probably be grown and self supporting, so he will need less insurance. At the same time his income may be less. By converting his insurance to a paid-up policy, he can get the protection he needs without having to use money needed to meet other expenses.

EXAMPLE 2: A man retires at age 65. He has been carrying a \$20,000 straight life policy which now has a cash value of \$11,400. How much paid-up insurance will this buy?

SOLUTION: According to Table 6, $1000A_{65} = 730.80721$

This means that the single premium for a \$1 straight life policy is .73080 721. Letting y represent the unknown amount of insurance this man can buy with \$11,400, we have,

$$.73080\ 721y = 11,400$$

$$y = \frac{11,400}{.73080\ 721} = \$15,599.19$$

If this is enough insurance to meet his present needs, it would be foolish to continue to pay premiums out of retirement income that is needed for other purposes.

Since the cost of a single premium policy is too large for most people, most insurance is paid for with annual or more frequent payments. We now determine how to get the annual premium for a straight life policy. The insurance company must take into account the fact that the money received from a policyholder will depend on how long he lives. Even though a policyholder dies after paying only one annual premium, his beneficiary will get the full value of the policy. The expected death benefits will be the same as in the preceding example. The expected total premium for any year will be the number living at that time multiplied by the net annual premium, which we designate by P_x. The present value of the death benefits must equal the present value of the expected premiums.

Since the premiums are equal and are paid at the beginning of each year, they form a whole life annuity due. The present value of a whole life annuity due of $1 is $\dfrac{N_x}{D_x}$ [Formula (30), page 227.] Therefore, the present value of the premiums is $P_x\dfrac{N_x}{D_x}$. This will equal the present value of the death benefits which are the same as for a single premium whole life or $\dfrac{M_x}{D_x}$ [Formula (35), page 241.] Setting the present value of the premiums equal to the present value of the death benefits, we have

$$P_x\frac{N_x}{D_x} = \frac{M_x}{D_x}$$

$$P_x = \frac{D_x}{N_x} \cdot \frac{M_x}{D_x}$$

$$P_x = \frac{M_x}{N_x} \tag{36}$$

EXAMPLE 3: Find the net annual premium for a $1000 straight life policy for an 18-year old man.

SOLUTION: $1000P_{18} = 1000\dfrac{M_{18}}{N_{18}} = 1000\dfrac{1\,825\,455.4}{180\,101\,480.3} = \$10.14$

Exercise 9a

1. Find the net single premiums for a $1000 straight life policy issued to: (a) a 22-year old man; (b) a 27-year old man; (c) a 32-year old man; and to a woman of the same ages. $\begin{bmatrix} \text{Man: (a) } \$318.99\text{; (b) } \$354.29\text{; (c) } \$394.03 \\ \text{Woman: (a) } \$299.72\text{; (b) } \$332.60\text{; (c) } \$369.64 \end{bmatrix}$

2. Find the net single premiums for a $1000 straight life policy issued to: (a) a 20-year old man; (b) a 40-year old man; (c) a 60-year old man; and to a woman of the same ages.

3. Find the net single premiums for a straight life policy of $5000 issued to: (a) a 20-year old man; (b) a 40-year old man; (c) a 60-year old man; and to a woman of the same ages. $\begin{bmatrix} \text{Man: (a) } \$1530.05\text{; (b) } \$2335.64\text{; (c) } \$3393.11 \\ \text{Woman: (a) } \$1437.62\text{; (b) } \$2192.23\text{; (c) } \$3231.44 \end{bmatrix}$

4. Find the net single premiums for a straight life policy of $10,000 issued to: (a) an 18-year old man; (b) a 28-year old man; (c) a 38-year old man; and to a woman of the same ages.

5. Find the net annual premiums for the policies in Problem 3.

$$\begin{bmatrix} \text{Man: (a) \$53.77; (b) \$106.91; (c) \$257.51} \\ \text{Woman: (a) \$49.21; (b) \$95.22; (c) \$222.82} \end{bmatrix}$$

6. Find the net annual premiums for the policies in Problem 4.

7. Find the net single premium and the net annual premium for a straight life policy of $2500 issued to a 25-year old man and woman.

(Man: $849.12, $31.36; Woman: $797.48, $28.56)

8. Get the net single premium and the net annual premium for a straight life policy of $5000 issued to (a) a 12-year old boy; (b) a 24-year old man.

9. A father takes out $2000 straight life policies for each of his three boys who are 9, 11, and 14 years of age. Get the net annual premium for each policy. ($15.65; $16.55; $18.04)

10. Get the annual premiums for the policies in Problem 9 if the boys are 19, 21, and 24 years of age.

9.4 Term Insurance

Term insurance, as we have seen, has an increasing premium as the insured gets older. Usually the premium is not changed every year, but only every 5, 10 or 20 years. Thus term insurance is usually described as 5-year term, and so on. We now derive a general formula for the net single premium, $A^1_{x:\overline{n}|}$, for a $1, n-year term policy, issued to l_x individuals age x. The deaths and premiums for the period from age x to age $x + n$ can be sketched as follows:

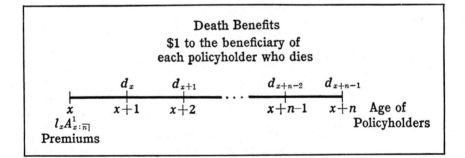

As in the preceding example, we bring everything back to age x and set up an equation of value:

$$l_x A^1_{x:\overline{n}|} = vd_x + v^2 d_{x+1} + \cdots + v^{n-1} d_{x+n-2} + v^n d_{x+n-1}$$

Multiplying through by v^x and substituting commutation functions, we have

$$A^1_{x:\overline{n}|} = \frac{C_x + C_{x+1} + \cdots + C_{x+n-2} + C_{x+n-1}}{D_x}$$

Since $\quad M_x = C_x + C_{x+1} + \cdots + C_{x+n-1} + C_{x+n} + \cdots + C_{99}$

and $\quad M_{x+n} = \qquad\qquad\qquad\qquad\qquad C_{x+n} + \cdots + C_{99}$

we can write the numerator as $M_x - M_{x+n}$ so that

$$A^1_{x:\overline{n}|} = \frac{M_x - M_{x+n}}{D_x} \tag{37}$$

If the policy is paid for with net annual premiums, $P^1_{x:\overline{n}|}$, the premiums form an n-year, temporary life annuity due. The present value of such an annuity of \$1 is $\dfrac{N_x - N_{x+n}}{D_x}$ [Formula (33), page 232]. Therefore, the present value of the premiums is $P^1_{x:\overline{n}|} \cdot \dfrac{N_x - N_{x+n}}{D_x}$. This will equal the present value of the death benefits which are the same as for a single premium, n-year term policy or $\dfrac{M_x - M_{x+n}}{D_x}$ [Formula (37), page 245.] Setting the present value of the premiums equal to the present value of the death benefits, we have

$$P^1_{x:\overline{n}|} \cdot \frac{N_x - N_{x+n}}{D_x} = \frac{M_x - M_{x+n}}{D_x}$$

$$P^1_{x:\overline{n}|} = \frac{D_x}{N_x - N_{x+n}} \cdot \frac{M_x - M_{x+n}}{D_x}$$

$$P^1_{x:\overline{n}|} = \frac{M_x - M_{x+n}}{N_x - N_{x+n}} \tag{38}$$

EXAMPLE: Find the net single premium and the net annual premium for a 5-year, \$1000 term policy for a man aged 18.

SOLUTION:

$$\text{Net single premium} = 1000 A^1_{18:\overline{5}|} = 1000 \frac{M_{18} - M_{23}}{D_{18}}$$

$$= 1000 \frac{1\ 825\ 455.4 - 1\ 774\ 216.4}{6\ 218\ 174.5} = \$8.24$$

$$\text{Net annual premium} = 1000 P^1_{18:\overline{5}|} = 1000 \frac{M_{18} - M_{23}}{N_{18} - N_{23}}$$

$$= 1000 \frac{1\ 825\ 455.4 - 1\ 774\ 216.4}{180\ 101\ 480.3 - 150\ 590\ 927.4} = \$1.74$$

Note that when the insured reaches age 23, this policy will have a higher premium.

Exercise 9b

1. Find the net single premium and the net annual premium for a 5-year, $5000 term policy issued to a 30-year old man and woman.

(Man: $52.14, $11.00; Woman: $48.16; $10.15)

2. Find the net single premium and the net annual premium for a 10-year, $5000 term policy issued to a 30-year old man and woman.

3. Find the net annual premium for a 5-year, $1000 term policy issued to: (a) a 20-year old man; (b) a 30-year old man; (c) a 40-year old man; (d) a 50-year old man; (e) a 60-year old man.

[(a) $1.81; (b) $2.20; (c) $4.08; (d) $9.73; (e) $23.70]

4. From a representative company get the actual premiums charged for the policies in Problem 3 and draw a graph to show the changing annual premium for term insurance. The age of the insured should be plotted on the horizontal axis.

5. Find the net single premiums for the following $1000 policies issued to a 22-year old man: (a) 5-year term; (b) 10-year term; (c) 20-year term.

[(a) $8.84; (b) $17.27; (c) $35.94]

6. Get the net single premiums for the following $1000 policies issued to a 22-year old woman: (a) 5-year term; (b) 10-year term; (c) 20-year term.

7. Find the net annual premiums for the policies in Problem 5.

[(a) $1.86; (b) $1.94; (c) $2.29]

8. Get the net annual premiums for the policies in Problem 6.

9.5 Limited Payment Life Insurance

A t-payment life policy is one which provides protection for the lifetime of the insured although premiums are paid for only t years. The present value of the benefits is the same as for an ordinary life policy, $\dfrac{M_x}{D_x}$. [Formula (35), page 241.] The net single premium for a limited payment life policy is the same as for a straight life policy since in both cases lifetime protection is provided. The net annual premiums form a t-year temporary life annuity due which has a present value of $\dfrac{N_x - N_{x+t}}{D_x}$ for payments of $1. [Formula (33), page 232.] If we designate the net annual premium for a t-payment life policy as ${}_tP_x$, the present value of the premiums will be ${}_tP_x \dfrac{N_x - N_{x+t}}{D_x}$. Setting the present value of the premiums equal to the present value of the benefits, we have

$$_tP_x \frac{N_x - N_{x+t}}{D_x} = \frac{M_x}{D_x}$$

$$_tP_x = \frac{D_x}{N_x - N_{x+t}} \cdot \frac{M_x}{D_x}$$

$$_tP_x = \frac{M_x}{N_x - N_{x+t}} \qquad (39)$$

Limited payment policies are frequently issued on the basis of being paid-up as of a certain age. Paid-up at age 65 means that when the insured reaches age 65, he will have paid-up protection for the rest of his life equal to the face value of the policy. His last premium is paid at age 64. A 20-year old man buying a paid-up policy at age 65 makes payments from age 20 to age 64 inclusive, a total of 45 payments. This means that $x + t$ in Formula (39) is 65 or the age at which the policy is paid-up. This makes it unnecessary to get t for policies which are paid-up as of a certain age. Simply replace $x + t$ with the age at which the policy is paid-up.

EXAMPLE 1: Find the net annual premium for a $1000, 20-payment life policy issued to an 18-year old man.

SOLUTION: The net annual premium is,

$$1000 \,_{20}P_{18} = 1000 \frac{M_{18}}{N_{18} - N_{18+20}}$$

$$= 1000 \frac{1\,825\,455.4}{180\,101\,480.3 - 82\,372\,958.6} = \$18.68$$

EXAMPLE 2: Find the net annual premium for a $1000 paid-up policy at age 65 issued to an 18-year old man.

SOLUTION: The net annual premium is,

$$1000 \frac{M_{18}}{N_{18} - N_{65}} = 1000 \frac{1\,825\,455.4}{180\,101\,480.3 - 15\,077\,832.8} = \$11.06$$

Note that this is not much higher than the annual premium of $10.14 for a straight life policy determined in Section 9.4.

Exercise 9c

1. Find the net annual premium for a $5000, 20-payment life policy issued to a 30-year old man and woman.   (Man $121.15; Woman $113.27)

2. Find the net annual premium for a $5000, 30-payment life policy issued to an 18-year old man.

3. Find the net annual premium for a $1000, 20-payment life policy issued to (a) a 20-year old man; (b) a 40-year old man; (c) a 60-year old man.

[(a) $19.48; (b) $30.84; (c) $56.66]

4. A 32-year old man takes out a $10,000 paid-up life policy at age 65. What is the annual premium?

5. Find the net annual premium for a $1000, 30-payment life policy issued to (a) a 20-year old man; (b) a 30-year old man.   [(a) $14.68; (b) $18.49]

6. A 24-year old man takes out a $5000, 20-payment life policy. What is the annual premium?

7. Find the net annual premium for a $10,000 paid-up policy at age 65 issued to a 25-year old man and woman.   (Man $140.61; Woman $130.67)

8. Find the net annual premium for a $10,000 paid-up policy at age 65 issued to a 35-year old man and woman.

9.6 Endowment Insurance

An endowment policy provides protection during the term of the policy and a pure endowment equal to the face value of the policy if the insured is still living when the policy matures. Therefore the net single premium for this policy would be the sum of the net single premium for an n-year term policy and a pure endowment due in n years. Using the symbol $A_{x:\overline{n}|}$ for the net single premium and combining Formulas (37) and (28), we have,

$$A_{x:\overline{n}|} = \frac{M_x - M_{x+n}}{D_x} + \frac{D_{x+n}}{D_x}$$

$$A_{x:\overline{n}|} = \frac{M_x - M_{x+n} + D_{x+n}}{D_x} \tag{40}$$

EXAMPLE 1: Find the net single premium for a $1000, 20-year endowment policy issued to a man aged 18.

SOLUTION: The net single premium is

$$1000 A_{18:\overline{20}|} = 1000 \frac{M_{18} - M_{18+20} + D_{18+20}}{D_{18}}$$

$$= 1000 \frac{1\ 825\ 455.4 - 1\ 629\ 650.6 + 3\ 638\ 747.1}{6\ 218\ 174.5}$$

$$= \$616.67$$

If an n-year endowment policy is purchased with net annual premiums, the premiums form an n-year temporary life annuity due. Using $P_{x:\overline{n}|}$ to designate the net annual premium and setting the present value of the annual premiums equal to the present value of the benefits, we have,

$$P_{x:\overline{n}|} \frac{N_x - N_{x+n}}{D_x} = \frac{M_x - M_{x+n} + D_{x+n}}{D_x}$$

$$P_{x:\overline{n}|} = \frac{D_x}{N_x - N_{x+n}} \cdot \frac{M_x - M_{x+n} + D_{x+n}}{D_x}$$

$$P_{x:\overline{n}|} = \frac{M_x - M_{x+n} + D_{x+n}}{N_x - N_{x+n}} \tag{41}$$

Endowment policies are frequently issued on the basis of the endowment being paid as of a certain age. Endowment at age 65 means that if the insured lives to age 65, he will receive the face amount of the policy. His last premium is paid at age 64. A 20-year old man buying an endowment at age 65 will make payments from age 20 to 64 inclusive, a total of 45 payments. This means that $x + n$ in Formula (41) is 65 or the age at which the endowment is paid. This makes it unnecessary to get n for endowment policies as of a certain age. Simply replace $x + n$ with the age at which the endowment is paid.

EXAMPLE 2: Find the net annual premium for a $1000, 20-year endowment policy issued to a man aged 18.

SOLUTION:

$$1000P_{18:\overline{20}|} = 1000 \frac{M_{18} - M_{18+20} + D_{18+20}}{N_{18} - N_{18+20}}$$

$$= 1000 \frac{1\ 825\ 455.4 - 1\ 629\ 650.6 + 3\ 638\ 747.1}{180\ 101\ 480.3 - 82\ 372\ 958.6} = \$39.24$$

EXAMPLE 3: Find the net annual premium for a $1000 endowment policy at age 65 issued to a 18-year old man.

SOLUTION: Substituting in (41) the net annual premium is,

$$1000P_{18:\overline{47}|} = 1000 \frac{M_{18} - M_{65} + D_{65}}{N_{18} - N_{65}}$$

$$= 1000 \frac{1\ 825\ 455.4 - 998\ 376.6 + 1\ 366\ 128.5}{180\ 101\ 480.3 - 15\ 077\ 832.8} = \$13.29$$

An interesting type of endowment occurs when a person with a straight life policy outlives the mortality table on which the policy is based. A mortality table has a terminal age ω as a matter of convenience for mathematical analysis. Actuaries know that some people will live beyond age ω. But to simplify

computations and formulas, it is necessary to assume a terminal age at which
there will be no survivors. Using the CSO Table for males, straight life premiums are based on the assumption that there will be no survivors at age 100.
The person who lives to 100 is then statistically dead. The time has come to
pay someone. Since the insured is still living, he becomes the beneficiary of
an endowment equal to the value of the policy.

Exercise 9d

1. Find the net single premium and the net annual premium for a $5000,
20-year endowment policy issued to a 30-year old man and to a 30-year old
woman.
$$\begin{bmatrix} \text{Man: } \$3099.55, \$198.90 \\ \text{Woman: } \$3092.75, \$197.75 \end{bmatrix}$$

2. Find the net single premium and the net annual premium for a $2500,
20-year endowment policy issued to a 28-year old man and to a 28-year old
woman.

3. Find the net annual premium for a $1000, 20-year endowment policy
issued to: (a) a 20-year old man; (b) a 40-year old man; (c) a 60-year old man.
[(a) $39.28; (b) $41.62; (c) $59.10]

4. Find the net single premium and the net annual premium for a $1000,
15-year endowment policy issued to a 6-year old boy.

5. A 25-year old man and a 25-year old woman take out a $5000 endow-
ment policy at age 65. Find the net single premium and the net annual
premium.
$$\begin{bmatrix} \text{Man: } \$2054.25, \$85.04 \\ \text{Woman: } \$2023.01, \$82.87 \end{bmatrix}$$

6. A 23-year old man takes out a $10,000 endowment policy at age 60.
Find the net single premium and the net annual premium.

9.7 Insurance Reserves

The net premium for a 1-year term policy is just sufficient to pay the death
claims at the end of that year. This is sometimes called the natural premium.
As people get older (beyond age 10) the probability of death increases and the
1-year term premium becomes greater. As was pointed out in the general
description of the various insurance policies, it is possible to avoid this increasing premium by writing level premium policies. These policies have a
higher premium than the 1-year term premium for the earlier years of the
policy. This excess plus accumulated interest is used to build up a **reserve fund**
which will be used to help pay death benefits when the level premium is smaller
than the 1-year term premium. In this book we shall compute **terminal
reserves** which are the reserves at the end of a policy year.

The following table shows the 1-year term premium for a $1000 policy for a person as his age increases from 20 to 70. Also shown is the level premium for a straight life policy issued to a person at age 20, and the difference in premiums between the natural premium and the level premium.

Age	1-Year Term Premium	Level Premium for Straight Life	Excess of Level Premium over 1-Year Term
20	$ 1.75	$10.75	$ 9.00
25	1.88		8.87
30	2.08		8.67
35	2.45		8.30
40	3.44		7.31
45	5.22		5.53
50	8.12		2.63
55	12.68		1.93 ⎫
60	19.84		9.09 ⎬ Deficit
65	30.98		20.23 ⎪
70	48.58		37.83 ⎭

The sketch below shows how the 1-year term premium and the level premium for straight life compare at different ages.

Net Annual Premium For a $1000 Policy

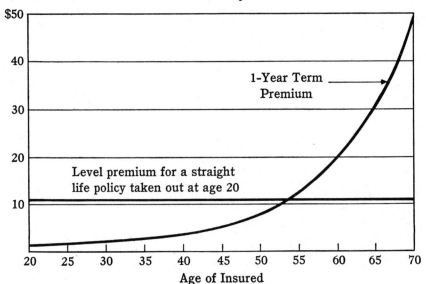

We shall now see how the reserve fund is built up when a person takes out a level premium policy. The best way to do this is to work out the financial details when a large group of persons of the same age are insured at the same time. So that the table will be complete and not too long, we work with a $1000, 10-year endowment policy issued to men age 20. The CSO Table shows that $l_{20} = 9\ 664\ 994$. From Formula (41), we get an annual premium of $87.98. We now compute the following for the first policy year.

Total premiums $\qquad\qquad\qquad$ $9,664,994 \times 87.98 = \$850,326,172.12$

Fund with interest at $2\frac{1}{2}\%$
at the end of the year $\qquad\qquad$ $850,326,172.12(1.025) = \$871,584,326.42$

From the Mortality Table
$d_{20} = 17,300$. Death claims
at the end of the first year
will be $\qquad\qquad\qquad\qquad\qquad\qquad$ $17,300 \times 1000 = \$17,300,000$

Fund at the end of the
year $\qquad\qquad$ $871,584,326.42 - 17,300,000.00 = \$854,284,326.42$

The survivors at the end of the first year is the same as the number living at the beginning of the second year or $l_{21} = 9,647,694$

This makes the fund per survivor $\dfrac{854,284,326.42}{9,647,694} = \$88.55$

The premiums at the beginning of the second year equal the number of survivors at the end of the first year times the annual premium:

$$9,647,694 \times 87.98 = \$848,804,118.12$$

The fund at the beginning of the second year is the sum of the fund at the end of the first year and the second years premiums:

$$854,284,326.42 + 848,804,118.12 = \$1,703,088,444.54$$

Values for the full 10 years of the policy are given below. The Fund per Survivor is given to the nearest cent; other entries are rounded to the dollar.

Policy Year	Premiums	Fund at Beginning of Year	Fund with Interest	Death Benefits	Fund at End of Year	Number of Survivors	Fund per Survivor
1	$850,326,172	$ 850,326,172	$ 871,584,326	$17,300,000	$ 854,284,326	9,647,694	$ 88.55
2	848,808,118	1,703,088,445	1,745,665,657	17,655,000	1,728,010,656	9,630,039	179.44
3	847,250,831	2,575,261,487	2,639,643,024	17,912,000	2,621,731,024	9,612,127	272.75
4	845,674,933	3,467,405,958	3,554,091,106	18,167,000	3,535,924,106	9,593,960	368.56
5	844,076,601	4,380,000,707	4,489,500,725	18,324,000	4,471,176,725	9,575,636	466.93
6	842,464,455	5,313,641,180	5,446,482,210	18,481,000	5,428,001,210	9,557,155	567.95
7	840,838,497	6,268,839,707	6,425,560,699	18,732,000	6,406,828,699	9,538,423	671.69
8	839,190,456	7,246,019,155	7,427,169,634	18,981,000	7,408,188,634	9,519,442	778.22
9	837,520,507	8,245,709,141	8,451,851,869	19,324,000	8,432,527,869	9,500,118	887.62
10	835,820,382	9,268,348,251	9,500,056,957	19,760,000	9,480,296,957	9,480,358	1000.00

9.8   The Prospective Method

In the preceding section the reserve was determined by accumulating premiums and deducting death benefits. This is called the **retrospective method** because it is based on past premiums and past benefits. Formulas can be derived to compute terminal reserves by the restrospective method without constructing a table. Another way to get reserves is to use the **prospective method** which is based on future benefits and premiums. The two methods give the same numerical result when dealing with net level premium policies. Advanced texts on insurance point out principles which will help the actuary to choose the method which will lead to the simpler formula for a particular problem.

The prospective method of computing reserves is based on the general definition of a reserve as the excess of the present value of future benefits over the present value of future premiums. At any time the reserve must be sufficient to make up the difference between the present value of the future benefits and the present value of the premiums. Expressing this as an equation of value, we have

$$\text{Reserve} = \left(\begin{array}{c}\text{Present value}\\ \text{of future benefits}\end{array}\right) - \left(\begin{array}{c}\text{Present value of}\\ \text{future premiums}\end{array}\right)$$

EXAMPLE 1: Get the reserve per survivor at the end of the 5th policy year for a \$1000, 10-year endowment policy issued to a person when he is aged 20.

SOLUTION: At the end of the 5th policy year the insured is aged 25. At that time the value of the future benefits is the net single premium for a 5-year, \$1000 endowment policy issued to a person aged 25. From (40) this is

$$1000A_{25:\overline{5}|} = 1000\,\frac{M_{25} - M_{30} + D_{30}}{D_{25}}$$

$$= 1000\,\frac{1\ 754\ 288.5 - 1\ 706\ 575.7 + 4\ 519\ 691.4}{5\ 165\ 008.0} = \$884.30$$

From (41) the value for the net annual premium for a 10-year endowment policy for \$1000 issued to a person aged 20 is

$$1000P_{20:\overline{10}|} = 1000\,\frac{M_{20} - M_{30} + D_{30}}{N_{20} - N_{30}}$$

$$= 1000\,\frac{1\ 804\ 922.4 - 1\ 706\ 575.7 + 4\ 519\ 691.4}{167\ 827\ 046.5 - 115\ 337\ 742.5} = \$87.98$$

Note that the net annual premium is based on the age of the insured when he takes out the policy regardless of his age at the time the reserve is to be determined. The 5 remaining payments of $87.98 form a temporary life annuity due. From (33) the present value of this annuity is

$$87.98\ddot{a}_{25:\overline{5}|} = 87.98\,\frac{N_{25} - N_{30}}{D_{25}}$$

$$= 87.98\,\frac{139\,839\,497.6 - 115\,337\,742.5}{5\,165\,008.0} = \$417.36$$

Using the symbol V for the terminal reserve, we have

$$V = 884.30 - 417.36 = \$466.94$$

The table for the retrospective method in the preceding section shows a terminal reserve of $466.93 at the end of the 5th policy year for the same policy. The difference is due to rounding values to the penny.

Exercise 9e

1. Complete the first 5 lines of a reserve fund schedule for a $1000 straight life policy issued to a group of 25-year old men.

2. Complete the first 5 lines of a reserve fund schedule for a $1000, 20-payment life policy issued to a group of 25-year old men.

3. Complete the first 5 lines of a reserve fund schedule for a $1000, 20-year endowment policy issued to a group of 25-year old men.

4. Complete the reserve fund schedule for a $1000, 5-year term policy issued to a group of 25-year old men.

5. Use the prospective method to get the reserve per survivor at the end of the 5th policy year for a $1000, 20-year endowment policy issued to a 30-year old man.   ($203.89)

6. Get the reserve for the policy in Problem 5 at the end of the 10th policy year.

7. Get the reserve per survivor at the end of the 10th policy year for a $10,000 straight life policy issued to a 20-year old man.   ($1031.31)

8. Get the reserve for the policy in Problem 7 at the end of the 20th policy year.

9.9 Buying Life Insurance

Most students will in later life buy life insurance. Since this insurance will mean a considerable expenditure year after year, a person's insurance program should be planned carefully. The experience gained computing net insurance premiums in a course in the mathematics of finance is ideal preparation for recognizing the advantages and disadvantages of the various commercial policies.

To begin with, the student should understand that his money can go entirely for protection if he buys term insurance, it can go largely for savings if he buys an annuity, or it can go for a combination of savings and protection if he gets a level premium policy which builds up a reserve as he goes along. With many types of policies to choose from, it is not surprising that people sometimes take out insurance that does not meet their particular needs. This can be tragic when a family finds that an inadequate and poorly planned insurance program does not begin to provide for their material well-being. The same expenditure on a different type of policy might have met family needs reasonably well. We now consider the four basic types of policies from a practical point of view.

Term insurance provides the most protection for the least cost. It may be the only way for a family of limited means to obtain adequate protection. For other families it can be very handy for special situations, such as additional protection when the children are young, or to cover the outstanding debt on a home. The disadvantages of term insurance are the increasing cost as the insured gets older, and the absence of a cash value. If a person gets term insurance with the idea of continuing it or converting it to a level premium plan, he should get a policy which can be renewed to age 60 or older, or converted to another type policy without a new physical examination. The chart on page 256 shows how the premium charged by a representative company for a term policy varies with the age of the insured.

The ordinary or straight life policy has at first a higher premium than term insurance but the cost will never increase. After the payment of a few premiums, there will be a reserve which can be used to keep the insurance in force if the insured is unable to keep up the premiums. Ordinary or straight life is probably the best all-around protection for most families if they can afford enough protection under this plan.

Limited payment policies, if the payment period is as short as 20 years, require high premiums so that the average family can carry such insurance only by reducing the amount of protection. Such policies are well suited to people like professional athletes who may have a relatively short period of high earning power and want to get their insurance paid for while their income is high.

Endowment policies are expensive because the premium must cover both protection and an endowment. Thus an endowment policy is essentially a term insurance policy plus a pure endowment. Very few people buy pure endowments and term insurance has a rather limited acceptance. Yet when

Cost of 5-Year Level Premium Term Insurance

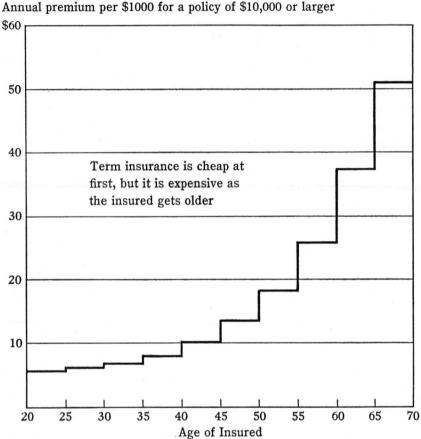

Annual premium per $1000 for a policy of $10,000 or larger

Term insurance is cheap at
first, but it is expensive as
the insured gets older

Age of Insured

the two are put in one package and sold as an endowment policy, it is quite attractive to many people. Short-term endowment policies are primarily savings. If a family man wants both savings and insurance, he should keep most of his savings separate from his insurance so that his family will get both if he dies.

Besides the basic policies discussed here, there are many combination policies. The buyer of insurance should analyze such policies carefully to see if a combination policy has any advantage for him over one or more of the four basic types.

9.10   Use of the Reserve

Earlier in this chapter we discussed the reserve which is accumulated as premiums are paid on level premium policies. The value of this reserve is not understood by many policyholders. This reserve can be used in several ways. A man can surrender the policy and take the cash. Before getting an expensive endowment policy to put a child through college, a couple should consider getting more straight life insurance on the father. Then the family will have more protection while the children are young. When the children reach college age, this straight life policy will have a substantial cash reserve. This reserve can be used if needed, or the policy can be kept in force to provide continued protection. It may eventually become a part of the couple's retirement income. If moderate income families understood the great flexibility of the straight life policy, there would be less buying of the more expensive plans with their limited protection.

Instead of taking the cash and dropping the policy, a family may borrow on the cash reserve at a rate which is usually far below the rate for small loans from commercial sources. Such loans should be repaid as soon as possible as the protection is reduced by the amount of the loan. The reserve may also be used as the single premium for a reduced amount of paid-up insurance. Another use of the reserve is extended term insurance which keeps the entire policy in force for a period which depends on the type of policy and the size of the reserve. If a man stops paying premiums on a level premium policy and does not take the cash, the company may automatically put into effect extended term insurance. Many people do not know this. As a result, there are probably policies thrown away or lying around in bureau drawers which are worth thousands of dollars, but which will never be collected because the survivors assume that the policy is worthless since the insured stopped paying premiums many years before his death.

Recently an insurance agent told us of a widow who received $10,000 from her husband's insurance when she had expected $5000. The man had carried two policies of $5000 in the same company. He paid on one until he died; the other he dropped years before. When the widow put in her claim, she did not mention the policy that had been dropped as she assumed that it was worthless. When settling her claim the insurance company found that death had occurred within the extended term period of the other policy, so the widow collected on both. In most cases there is no way for the insurance company to know that death came during the time of the extended term insurance unless a claim is made.

Insurance companies do what they can to prevent loss of benefits by notifying policyholders that extended term insurance is in effect if a policyholder stops paying premiums. Some companies indicate the exact date on which the coverage expires. The policyholder should file all such papers with the policy. Since papers may be lost or the company may lose contact with a policyholder, a check should be made on any policy that could possibly still be in effect.

The guaranteed values provided by the reserve in a particular policy can be found in the policy. To illustrate the great practical value of insurance reserves, the table on page 259 has been reprinted from the Veterans Administration bulletin for National Service Life Insurance. These guaranteed values are based on the American Experience Mortality Table with interest at 3%. Thus the values are somewhat different from those which would be obtained using the CSO Table with interest at $2\frac{1}{2}\%$ which is used in this text. All values are for a $1000 policy issued to a 25-year old person. Annual premiums for these policies are:

Policy	Annual Premium
Ordinary life	$16.22
20-payment life	25.10
20-year endowment	41.20

9.11 Summary of Insurance Formulas

The formulas used to determine life insurance premiums are summarized below for the convenience of the student.

Insurance Premiums

(All formulas are for a policy of $1)

Type of Policy	Net Single Premium	Net Annual Premium
Straight life	$A_x = \dfrac{M_x}{D_x} \qquad (35)$	$P_x = \dfrac{M_x}{N_x} \qquad (36)$
Term policy (for n years)	$A^1_{x:\overline{n}|} = \dfrac{M_x - M_{x+n}}{D_x} \quad (37)$	$P^1_{x:\overline{n}|} = \dfrac{M_x - M_{x+n}}{N_x - N_{x+n}} \quad (38)$
Limited payment life (payments for t years)	(Same as straight life)	$_tP_x = \dfrac{M_x}{N_x - N_{x+t}} \quad (39)$
Endowment policy (for n years)	$A_{x:\overline{n}|} = \dfrac{M_x - M_{x+n} + D_{x+n}}{D_x} \quad (40)$	$P_{x:\overline{n}|} = \dfrac{M_x - M_{x+n} + D_{x+n}}{N_x - N_{x+n}} \quad (41)$

Exercise 9f

1. A 28-year old man can afford to pay approximately $150 a year for life insurance. This will cover the net annual premium for what size policies of the following types? (Give answer to nearest $1000.)

(a) 5-year term.	($72,000)
(b) Straight life.	($11,000)
(c) Paid-up life policy at age 65.	($10,000)
(d) 20-payment life.	($6000)
(e) 20-year endowment.	($4000)

Guaranteed Values at Age 25 — $1,000

ORDINARY LIFE (PARTICIPATING)

End of policy year	Cash value	Paid-up insurance	Extension Years	Extension Days	End of policy year	Cash value	Paid-up insurance	Extension Years	Extension Days
1	$8.60	$23.78	1	34	13	$134.77	$304.26	15	355
2	17.47	47.55	2	87	14	147.39	326.76	16	297
3	26.61	71.28	3	158	15	160.36	349.05	17	190
4	36.04	94.99	4	249	16	173.67	371.09	18	41
5	45.76	118.66	5	354	17	187.34	392.91	18	215
6	55.77	142.24	7	111	18	201.37	414.49	18	352
7	66.09	165.75	8	240	19	215.77	435.81	19	91
8	76.72	189.16	10	6	20	230.50	456.82	19	165
9	87.67	212.47	11	133	25	309.14	556.79	19	197
10	98.94	235.64	12	244	30	394.11	646.17	18	220
11	110.55	258.68	13	325	35	482.33	723.44	17	52
12	122.49	281.56	14	364	40	570.12	788.29	15	145

20-PAYMENT LIFE (PARTICIPATING)

End of policy year	Cash value	Paid-up insurance	Extension Years	Extension Days	End of policy year	Cash value	Paid-up insurance	Extension Years	Extension Days
1	$17.81	$49.24	2	110	13	$287.07	$648.09	31	51
2	36.24	98.63	4	294	14	314.97	698.27	32	126
3	55.31	148.16	7	193	15	343.86	748.47	33	188
4	75.06	197.84	10	166	16	373.77	798.65	34	263
5	95.49	247.61	13	195	17	404.76	848.91	36	27
6	116.64	297.48	16	241	18	436.85	899.18	37	269
7	138.54	347.45	19	236	19	470.12	949.55	40	40
8	161.21	397.48	22	121	20	504.58	1,000.00	—	—
9	184.66	447.52	24	237	25	555.22		—	—
10	208.95	497.64	26	232	30	609.92		—	—
11	234.09	547.76	28	124	35	666.72		—	—
12	260.12	597.92	29	300	40	723.24		—	—

20-YEAR ENDOWMENT (PARTICIPATING)

End of policy year	Cash value	Paid-up insurance	Extension Years	Extension Days	Pure endowment	End of policy year	Cash value	Paid-up insurance	Extension Years	Extension Days	Pure endowment
1	$34.45	$57.51	4	219	———	11	$457.41	$590.47	9	—	$547.46
2	70.16	114.30	9	345	———	12	508.90	639.28	8	—	605.94
3	107.19	170.35	16	10	———	13	562.37	687.28	7	—	662.21
4	145.58	225.65	16	—	$68.76	14	617.88	734.43	6	—	716.35
5	185.39	280.18	15	—	145.19	15	675.54	780.75	5	—	768.40
6	226.67	333.91	14	—	218.78	16	735.46	826.23	4	—	818.47
7	269.49	386.85	13	—	289.63	17	797.73	870.88	3	—	866.59
8	313.91	438.99	12	—	357.82	18	862.49	914.73	2	—	912.85
9	359.98	490.30	11	—	423.46	19	929.87	957.77	1	—	957.31
10	407.79	540.79	10	—	486.65	20	1,000.00	1,000.00	—	—	———

Students who are interested in getting more information on life insurance can obtain practical and interesting publications from the Institute of Life Insurance, 488 Madison Ave., New York 22, New York.

2. Work Problem 1 for a 35-year old man.

3. Assume that the insured dies while the policies in Problem 1 are in force. The benefits are to be paid out in 120 payments certain with the first payment to be made 1 month after the insured dies. If the company allows 3% converted monthly on the proceeds left with them, what will be the size of the monthly payments for the five policies?

[(a) $695.24; (b) $106.22; (c) $96.56; (d) $57.94; (e) $38.62]

4. Get the size of the benefit payments for the policies in Problem 2 if the proceeds are paid out in 120 monthly payments and 3% converted monthly is earned on the balance left with the company.

10

STOCKS

10.1 The Element of Uncertainty

Mathematically there are no doubts about the results obtained for simple and compound interest problems and annuities certain. The times and amounts of all payments are specified definitely. While a death or business failure may result in unpredictable changes, no allowance is made for such possibilities when the problem is solved.

In the case of life annuities and life insurance, payments are contingent on a person's age, when he dies, and other factors. These uncertain events can be taken into account with a high degree of accuracy *on the average* if the actuary has reliable mortality data on which to base his calculations. While the company cannot make money on every policy, the actuary is able to set rates which are low enough to be competitive and high enough for the company probably to make a profit.

We now consider the application of the mathematics of finance to stocks, even though we can make neither certain calculations for individual problems nor even use actuarial data to make predictions that will be true on the average. In spite of the uncertainties, the mathematics of finance can be profitably applied to the buying of stocks.

Most students are interested in stocks, although not always for the right reason. Having heard of someone who made a killing by putting his money in a stock that went up like a rocket, they want to know how to do likewise with their first few paychecks. If we knew how, we would be busily doing it.

10.2 Kinds of Stocks

In the chapter on bonds, we saw that a person who buys a bond is lending money to a corporation or a government agency and is entitled to interest on his money and eventual return of his capital. A stockholder is a part owner of the company and must take his chances on the fortunes of the company. His place is at the end of the line after the workers, suppliers, and bondholders.

There are two basic types of stocks: *preferred* and *common*. Preferred stock has a stated return which is given on the stock certificate. Holders of preferred stock receive dividends only if declared by the board of directors. Preferred stock has a claim on earnings before payment may be made on the common stock, and preferred is usually entitled to priority over common stock if the company liquidates. However, owners of preferred rank below bondholders and other creditors. Most preferred is *cumulative* which means that if any dividends are omitted, they accumulate and must be paid before the common stockholders get anything. Some preferred stock is *convertible* which means that it may be converted into common. Generally, preferred stock has no voting privileges unless a stated number of dividends have not been declared on the preferred. Preferred stocks are usually redeemable at the company's option at fixed prices. This call feature, of no value to the investor, is important to the corporation because it enables the company to retire stock when the capital market is favorable.

At one time preferred stocks were used extensively by corporations to obtain capital. Today, aside from public utilities, preferred stocks are not much used for new financing. From the investor's standpoint, preferred stocks rank below bonds in safety and below common stocks in opportunities for growth and a share in the increasing profits of a successful corporation.

The venture capital which permits new firms to start and existing ones to expand is often obtained by selling common or capital stock. Common stockholders assume the risks of ownership and, in the event of a failure, may lose all or part of their investment. On the other hand, there is no ceiling on their possible profits. If their firm is successful, they may benefit from both increasing dividends and a rising value in the market price of their stock. As a rule, common stockholders may vote for the directors of a corporation and may suggest changes in corporate policy or practice. Dividends depend primarily on what a company earns in any given year and on anticipated return on reinvested earnings. The board of directors decides what dividends will be paid.

In the case of common stock, par value means the dollar amount assigned to the share by the company's charter. Par may also be used to compute the dollar amount of the common shares on the balance sheet. Many companies

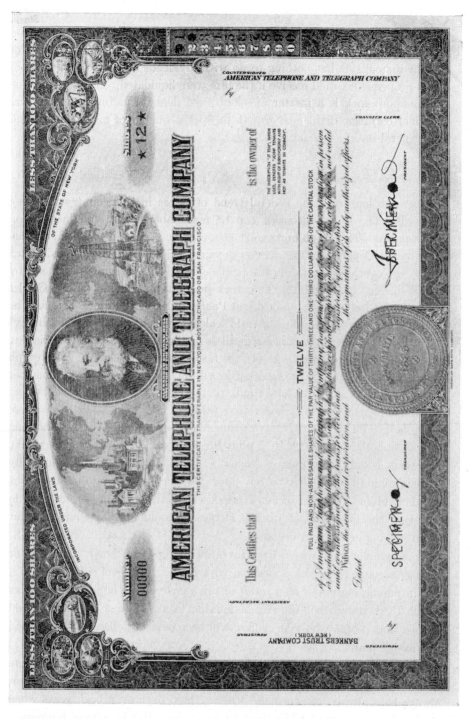

The actual piece of paper which is evidence of ownership of stock in a corporation is called a "stock certificate." Watermarked paper finely engraved with delicate etchings is used to discourage forgery.

today issue no-par stock. Par value is of little significance in the case of common stock. It has nothing to do with dividends and is no indication of what an investor would receive if the firm were liquidated. The market value of common stock is a matter of supply and demand as buyers and sellers consider earnings, dividends, growth prospects, quality of management, and the general business climate.

10.3 Price Trends

Over the long run, the general trend of prices in this country has been upwards. The same statement can be made about the trend in common stock prices. The graph on page 265 shows how prices have varied as measured by the Department of Labor's Consumer Price Index (CPI). This index shows the overall variation in the prices of goods and services purchased by middle-income city families. The stock price graph is based on the Cowles Commission Index and Standard and Poor's Index of 500 Stock Prices. The graphs are plotted on semilog or ratio scales on which equal per cent changes take the same vertical distance regardless of the magnitude of the variables. The steeper a line on such a graph, the faster the rate of change. This graph shows that from 1929 to 1932 stock prices dropped much faster than consumer prices. However, over the long trend, particularly from 1942 on, stock prices have, on the average, risen faster than prices of consumer goods. It is these rising long term trends that have made stock buying attractive for the long pull during the last 20 years. Wise investors recognize that money, like wampum, is only a medium of exchange. What really counts economically is maintaining their ability to buy goods. While there is no certainty that trends in either consumer or stock prices will be the same in the future as in the past, the likelihood of further increases should be taken into account when making investment decisions.

These graphs show why a fixed investment, such as a bond, mortgage, or savings account has a risk connected with it, the price-level risk or risk of a loss in purchasing power as a result of price increases. The history of prices in the U. S. shows that the risk of inflation is a real one. There is a good chance that people who loan money will be repaid in dollars of depreciated purchasing power.

Stocks over the years have provided a long-run hedge against inflation. We emphasize long-run because over shorter periods stock prices have not always kept abreast of consumer prices. There have even been years when stock prices went down while the CPI was rising. But in spite of temporary setbacks, investors with diversified portfolios of quality stocks are not only likely to preserve their purchasing power but to come out ahead in terms of

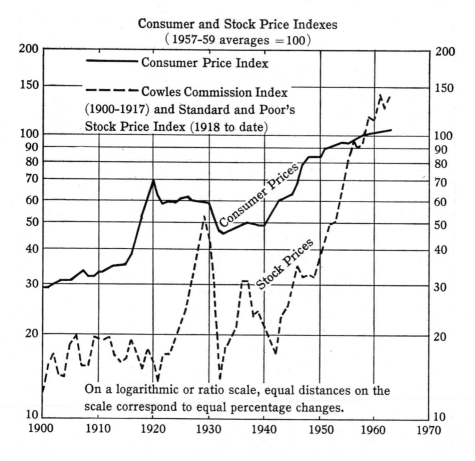

Consumer and Stock Price Indexes
(1957-59 averages = 100)

——— Consumer Price Index

— — — Cowles Commission Index
(1900-1917) and Standard and Poor's
Stock Price Index (1918 to date)

Consumer Prices

Stock Prices

On a logarithmic or ratio scale, equal distances on the
scale correspond to equal percentage changes.

real income over the years. This is what makes stocks attractive to the
investor who is interested in the long pull, not a quick profit.

To compare the real value of an investment at one time with its real value
at another time, we must multiply the number of dollars the investment is
worth by the value of the dollar which equals the reciprocal of the CPI.
When the CPI = 100 (actually 100%), the value of the dollar is $1/1.00 =$
$1.00. If the CPI is 125, the dollar is worth $1/1.25 = \$.80$. A CPI of 90
means a dollar worth $1/.90 = \$1.11$.

To compare the value of the dollar at one time with its value at another
time requires that all values be relative to the same base period. About
every 10 years the Bureau of Labor Statistics adopts a new base period for
the CPI and past index values are adjusted and spliced to the new series so
that a continuous picture of price changes is obtained. Because of their
importance for reference purposes and for solving problems in this chapter,
the value of the CPI and the corresponding value of the dollar are given
below. All values are relative to the latest base period, 1957–59 = 100.

Year	CPI 1957–59 = 100	Value of the Dollar	Year	CPI 1957–59 = 100	Value of the Dollar
1915	35.4	$2.82	1940	48.8	$2.05
1916	38.0	2.63	1941	51.3	1.95
1917	44.7	2.24	1942	56.8	1.76
1918	52.4	1.91	1943	60.3	1.66
1919	60.3	1.66	1944	61.3	1.63
1920	69.8	1.43	1945	62.7	1.59
1921	62.3	1.61	1946	68.0	1.47
1922	58.4	1.71	1947	77.8	1.29
1923	59.4	1.68	1948	83.8	1.19
1924	59.6	1.68	1949	83.0	1.20
1925	61.1	1.64	1950	83.8	1.19
1926	61.6	1.62	1951	90.5	1.10
1927	60.5	1.65	1952	92.5	1.08
1928	59.7	1.68	1953	93.2	1.07
1929	59.7	1.68	1954	93.6	1.07
1930	58.2	1.72	1955	93.3	1.07
1931	53.0	1.89	1956	94.7	1.06
1932	47.6	2.10	1957	98.0	1.02
1933	45.1	2.22	1958	100.7	.99
1934	46.6	2.15	1959	101.5	.99
1935	47.8	2.09	1960	103.1	.97
1936	48.3	2.07	1961	104.2	.96
1937	50.0	2.00	1962	105.4	.95
1938	49.1	2.04	1963	106.7	.94
1939	48.4	2.07	1964	108.1	.93

The graph on page 267 shows the long term trend in the purchasing power of the American dollar. This shows the risk in owning fixed-dollar investments. This graph also shows that there has been a marked decrease in the rate of depreciation of the dollar since 1952. From 1940 to 1952, the dollar dropped from $2.05 to $1.08, an annual compounded rate of depreciation of 5.2%. In the decade from 1952 to 1962, the rate of depreciation was 1.3% a year. Since 1952, many people have found themselves better off in terms of real income because their dollar incomes increased at a higher rate than the prices they paid.

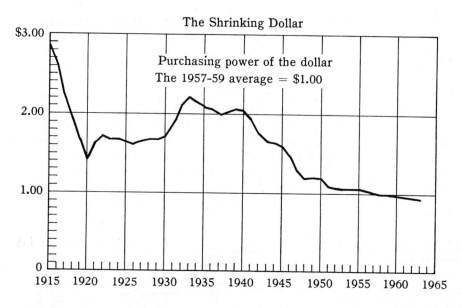

The Shrinking Dollar

Purchasing power of the dollar
The 1957–59 average = $1.00

10.4 Measurement of Growth and Decline

If a quantity has been changing over the years, we can determine the constant annual rate of change that would have produced this change. We simply solve for the rate on a compound interest basis using Formula (9) $S = P(1 + i)^n$. If time series data plot as approximately a straight line on a semilog or ratio graph, a rate based on past trends may be helpful in making predictions.

EXAMPLE 1: The Standard and Poor's Index of Industrial Stock Prices $(1941\text{–}43 = 10)$ was 18.33 in 1950 and 59.43 in 1960. Find the average annual rate of change.

SOLUTION:
$$18.33(1 + i)^{10} = 59.43$$

$$(1 + i)^{10} = \frac{59.43}{18.33} = 3.24$$

Since a factor this large is not in the compound interest tables, we use logs as in Example 4 on page 71.

$$10 \log(1 + i) = \log 59.43 - \log 18.33$$

$$\log(1 + i) = \frac{1.774006 - 1.263162}{10} = \frac{.510844}{10} = .051084$$

Looking up the antilog of .051084, we find that $1 + i = 1.12$. Therefore $i = .12$ or 12%.

How to Read Stock Tables

There are thousands of different stocks. Many of these are traded on the floor of the New York Stock Exchange, the American Stock Exchange, and various other exchanges throughout the country. Other stocks and bonds, called unlisted securities, are bought and sold in the "Over-the-counter" market. This is not a place but a method of doing business by private negotiation among dealers who use the telephone to buy and sell securities.

Many newspapers include tables of stock market information. Stocks are listed alphabetically under column headings that are easy to interpret. While symbols and abbreviations may vary somewhat with different newspapers, the table below from the June 5, 1963 issue of the Wall Street Journal is a good illustration of the type of information to be found in stock tables.

Highest and lowest prices during the indicated period.

Abbreviated name of the company. In this case Acme Steel Co.

Number following name shows indicated annual dividend, in this case $1.00. This is an estimate based on recent dividends. Letters following the dividend indicate other information which is usually given in footnotes at the end of the table.

"pf" indicates preferred stock.

The number of shares traded for the day expressed in hundreds. There were 7000 shares of this stock traded.

z before the number means actual number of shares traded, in this case 50.

x means ex dividend. This is shown on the day the stock goes ex dividend. If a person buys stock when it is selling ex dividend, he will not receive that dividend. It goes to the previous owner.

For this stock the opening price was 57½, the high for the day was 59.

The closing or last price of this stock was 20½. This was $.25 less than the closing for the previous day as indicated by the net change of −¼ point.

A

– 1963 –				Sales in					Net
High	Low	Stocks	Div.	100s	Open	High	Low	Close	Chg.
99½	72⅞	AbbottL	2.20	19	94¾	95¾	94¼	95¾	+ ¼
14⅝	12¼	ABCVen	.50b	181	13¾	14¼	13¾	14¼	+ ½
98¾	74¾	ACFInd	2.80	29	97¾	99½	96¾	99	+ ½
80	68¼	Acme M	2b	8	70¾	70¾	70	70	−1
19	13¾	Acme Stl	.60	37	19	19	18⅞	18⅞	− ⅛
27	25	Ad Exp	.30g	5	26⅜	26½	26⅜	26½	+ ⅛
13⅞	10	Ad Millis	.40	12	11⅛	11¼	10¾	10¾	− ⅜
54¾	43⅜	Addressog	1	241	53⅛	54¾	53⅛	54⅛	+ ⅞
18½	11¾	Admiral		102	18¼	18⅜	17¾	18⅛	− ⅛
26¾	22¼	Aeroqui	.40b	11	24¼	24¼	24	24	− ⅜
17¼	14⅛	Air Cont	.50	16	17⅛	17⅛	16¾	17	....
67¾	56	AirProd	.20b	40	67¾	67¾	65¾	66¾	−1
61¾	54⅛	Air Red	2.50	32	56⅛	56¼	55½	56	− ⅛
4⅛	3⅜	AJIndus	.21t	15	3⅝	3⅝	3⅝	3⅝	....
38¾	35	Ala Gas	1.70	9	37	37¼	36¾	37¼	− ¼
25¼	19	AicoProd	.40	23	24	24¼	23¾	23⅞	− ⅜
31¾	26⅞	Aldens	1b	x62	28¼	28¼	27⅜	27⅝	− 1/
13	9¾	AllegCp	.11g	15	10⅜	10⅜	10⅛	10⅛	− 1/
42½	31	Alleg 6pf	.60	4	32	32	31¼	31⅝	− 7/
38¾	32¾	Alleg Lud	2	x30	38⅛	38⅛	37½	37¾	....
52¾	47⅝	AllegPw	1.90	18	49	49⅛	49	49	− 1/
29	19¾	AllenInd	1.20	4	27⅞	27⅞	27¾	27¾	....
52	42¼	AlliedCh	1.80	70	49¾	49¾	49¼	49⅜	− 1/
15⅛	13⅛	AlliedKid	.60	1	13⅝	13⅝	13⅝	13⅝	− 1/
45¾	40	AlliedMills	2	2	45¼	45¼	45¼	45¼	....
9⅜	7	AlliedPd	.10g	6	8¼	8¼	8¼	8¼	....
57⅞	49⅝	Allied Str	3	51	52¼	52¾	51¼	51¼	−1
91	87	Allied St pf	4	z50	87	87	87	87	....
13⅞	11⅞	AlliedSup	.60	36	12⅞	13⅛	12⅞	13	+ 1/
20¼	14⅝	AllisChal	.50	144	19⅞	20⅜	19¾	20	....
19¼	16¼	Alpha PC	1	11	18¼	18¼	18¼	18¼	− 1/
34	24¾	Alside	.14p	86	33⅜	34⅞	33⅜	34	+1
27¾	20⅛	AlumLtd	.60	216	26½	27½	26½	27⅛	+ 3/
64⅞	51¼	Alcoa	1.20	155	64¼	65⅞	64	65¾	+15/
37	20¾	AmalSu	.80a	36	27	27	25¼	27	− 1/
26	22½	Amerac	.40a	12	25½	25½	25	25	− 1/
70¼	66⅝	Amerada Pet		75	68½	69¼	68½	69⅛	+ 7/
47⅜	22½	AmAg Ch	1	43	46⅞	47⅛	46⅞	46⅞	....
24⅝	17⅞	AmAirlin	1	111	23¾	24¼	23¾	24¼	+ 3/
26½	17⅞	Am Bak	1.80	5	25¼	25⅜	25⅛	25⅛	....
29¼	24¾	Am Bk N	.70	x1	26	26	26	26	+ 1
67	62	AmBkN pf	3	y40	63	63	62¾	62¾	+ 1
16¾	13½	ABosch	.50e	34	15⅛	15½	15	15½	+
58¾	48⅝	Am Brk	2.40	4	53½	53½	53½	53½	+ 1/
38¼	30¼	AmBdPar	1b	129	30⅛	30⅛	29½	29⅝	− 5/
47⅜	43⅝	Am Can	2	68	45⅝	45⅞	45½	45¾	....
42½	40½	ACan pf	1.75	15	41½	41⅞	41½	41½	− 1/
12½	10⅜	Am Cem	.50	4	12	12	11⅞	11⅞	....
55¾	47¼	AChain	2.50	3	52⅜	52⅜	52⅜	52⅜	− 3
25	20	ACBarg	1.20	10	24	24⅛	23⅞	24	+ 1/
28¼	22	AmC Ind	1b	1	22½	22½	22½	22½	+ 1/
74¾	41⅞	Am Cry S	2	24	57½	59	56	58½	...
59⅜	47¾	AmCyan	1.80	87	58⅞	59	58⅜	58⅝	− 1/
44⅞	36¾	AmDist	1.20	3	38½	38½	38⅜	38⅜	− 1/
37½	32⅜	A ElPw	1.08	77	35½	35⅞	35¼	35½	+ 1
36⅜	29½	Am Enka		72	34¼	34½	33	34½	+ 1
31⅜	17⅞	AExport	.50g	64	31	31¼	30⅝	31	− 3
13½	8⅞	AmFP	.64	74	12¾	12¾	12⅜	12½	− 1
45⅞	34¾	AHard	1.60a	8	44	44	43¾	44	− 3
58½	49⅜	AHome	1.44a	111	57⅝	58⅜	57⅝	58	+ 1
23	18⅝	Am Hosp	.30	62	20¾	20¾	20½	20½	− 1

EXAMPLE 2: The CPI was 83.8 in 1950 and 103.1 in 1960. Compute the average annual per cent change.

SOLUTION:
$$83.8(1 + i)^{10} = 103.1$$
$$(1 + i)^{10} = \frac{103.1}{83.8} = 1.23$$

In line 10 of the compound interest tables, we find that an *Amount of* 1 factor of 1.23 corresponds to a rate between 2 and $2\frac{1}{4}\%$. Interpolation gives an annual rate of 2.1%.

EXAMPLE 3: In 1950 the value of the dollar was $1.19 and in 1960 it was $.97. Get the average annual percent change.

SOLUTION:
$$1.19(1 + i)^{10} = .97$$

Since this will lead to a negative rate, which is not in the compound interest tables, we use logarithms as in Example 5 on page 71.

$$\log(1 + i) = \frac{(9.986772 - 10) - .075547}{10} = \frac{9.911225 - 10}{10}$$
$$= .991123 - 1$$

Looking up the antilog of .991123 − 1, we find that $1 + i = .9798$

Therefore
$$i = -.0202 = -2.0\%$$

Note that the annual per cent drop in the value of the dollar is not numerically equal to the annual per cent rise in the CPI. A larger change makes it easy to see why this is so. When the CPI goes from 100 to 200, there is a 100% rise in prices. There is a corresponding drop in the value of the dollar from $1.00 to $.50, a decrease of 50%, not 100%. The dollar may be shrinking, but it has not disappeared entirely.

10.5   Changes in Stock Values

Some buyers of stocks are interested primarily in receiving a liberal income. Others, who do not need the immediate income, look for stocks which they hope will increase greatly in market value over the years. One way to evaluate past price trends is to get the annual compounded rate of growth by substituting in Formula (9) and solving for i.

EXAMPLE 1: On December 31, 1957, Cincinnati Bell Telephone was 77 and on December 31, 1962, it was 98. What was the annual rate of growth in market value on a compound interest basis?

SOLUTION: Substituting $P = 77$, $S = 98$ and $n = 5$ in (9),

$$77(1 + i)^5 = 98$$
$$(1 + i)^5 = \frac{98}{77} = 1.27$$

Reference to line 5 in Table 2 under *Amount of* 1 shows that the annual rate of growth has been slightly under 5%. This is in addition to the annual dividend of \$4.50 which is almost 6% of \$77.

EXAMPLE 2: On December 31, 1958, Procter and Gamble was selling at 57. In 1960, it was split 2 for 1. On December 31, 1962, the stock was quoted at 70. What was the annual rate of growth over this period?

SOLUTION: Allowing for the split we have:

$$57(1 + i)^4 = 140$$

Since the rate is beyond the compound interest tables, we use logarithms.

$$\text{Log}(1 + i) = \frac{\log 140 - \log 57}{4} = \frac{2.146218 - 1.755875}{4} = .097563$$

Looking up the antilog of .097563, we find that $1 + i = 1.252$

Therefore $\qquad\qquad\qquad i = .252 = 25.2\%$

As long as an investor holds a security, a gain such as this is a paper profit which may be increased or decreased by changes in the market.

Stock prices can go down. In which case, the owner of a security has the unpleasant experience of watching his investment depreciate in value.

EXAMPLE 3: An investor bought Chesapeake and Ohio in 1959 at 67. Three years later the price was 52. What was the average annual rate of depreciation in the value of this stock?

SOLUTION: $\qquad 67(1 + i)^3 = 52$

$$\log(1 + i) = \frac{1.716003 - 1.826075}{3}$$

Practical work with logarithms requires that we have positive mantissas and integral characteristics. Therefore, we add 30 to the first log in the numerator and offset this addition by subtracting 30.

$$\log(1+i) = \frac{(31.716003 - 30) - 1.826075}{3} = \frac{29.889928 - 30}{3}$$

$$= 9.963309 - 10$$

Looking up the antilog of $9.963309 - 10$ we find that $1 + i = .919$

Therefore $\qquad i = .919 - 1 = -.081 = -8.1\%$

On the average, the market value of this stock dropped about 8% a year over the 3-year period. If this downward trend is reversed, the stock may in time recover this loss in market value. Careful investors maintain a cash reserve to avoid being forced to sell at a loss stocks which they would like to hold for anticipated future gains.

EXAMPLE 4: In 1940 a man purchased a savings bond for $75. He cashed it in 1950 for $100. Compare the purchasing power of the investment at the two times.

SOLUTION: The purchasing power of an investment depends on the number of dollars and the value of the dollar. Putting this investment at the two times on a comparable basis:

Year	Value of the Dollar (1957–59 = 100)	Value of Investment Current Dollars	Dollars of Constant Purchasing Power
1940	$2.05	$ 75	$154
1950	1.19	100	119

In spite of accumulated interest, the buying power of this investment dropped about 23% over the period. Rapidly rising prices are particularly hard on people who have their money in fixed dollar investments.

Exercise 10a

(Get annual compounded rates of change to the tenth of one per cent.)

1. What was the average annual per cent change in prices and in the value of the dollar from 1940 to 1960?

(Prices up 3.8% a year; value of dollar down 3.7% a year.)

2. Compare the average annual per cent increase in prices for the period 1915–19 with the period 1941–45.

3. Find the annual rate of change in prices and the value of the dollar from 1930 to 1933.

(Prices down 8.1% a year; value of dollar up 8.9% a year.)

4. Find the annual rate of change in prices and the value of the dollar from: (a) 1940 to 1950; (b) 1950 to 1963.

5. From 1950 to 1960, the Standard and Poor's Index of Industrial Stock Prices (1941–43 = 10) went from 18.33 to 59.43. Find the average annual rate of increase.   (12.5%)

6. From 1950 to 1960, the Standard and Poor's Index of Public Utilities Stocks went from 20.59 to 46.86. Find the average annual rate of increase.

7. Standard Oil of New Jersey was 50 at the end of 1959. At the end of 1962 it was $59\frac{1}{2}$. Find the average annual per cent increase in market value.   (6.0%)

8. At the end of 1960, General Motors was $40\frac{3}{4}$. Two years later the market price was 57. What was the annual rate of increase?

9. Westinghouse Electric was $57\frac{1}{4}$ in June of 1958. In 1960, the stock was split two for one. In June of 1962, the stock was quoted at $26\frac{1}{2}$. What was the annual per cent change?   (−1.9%)

10. Aluminum Limited was 34 in December of 1959. In December of 1962, the price had dropped to $20\frac{1}{4}$. Find the annual rate of depreciation over this period.

11. Standard and Poor's Composite Index of Stock Prices dropped from 26.02 in 1929 to 6.93 in 1932. What was the average annual rate of change over this period?   (−35.7%)

12. Standard and Poor's Composite Index of Stock Prices increased from 15.23 in 1949 to 62.38 in 1962. What was the average annual rate of increase over this period?

10.6 Commission Costs

When listed stocks are bought or sold through a broker, there is a commission which is added to the purchase price and subtracted from the sale price of the stock. State and federal taxes also add a small amount to the cost of selling stocks. The following are the minimum commission rates on the New York Stock Exchange which went into effect on March 30, 1959.

Size of Purchase	Round Lot of 100 Shares	Odd Lot 1 to 99 Shares*
Under $100	As mutually agreed (Usually 6%)	As mutually agreed (Usually 6%)
$ 100 to $ 399	2% plus $ 3	2% plus $ 1
$ 400 to $2399	1% plus $ 7	1% plus $ 5
$2400 to $4999	.5% plus $19	.5% plus $17
$5000 and over	.1% plus $39	.1% plus $37

* Transactions of less than 100 shares, called odd lots, are executed at $12\frac{1}{2}$¢ per share above the market price if the stock is selling at less than $40 per share and at 25¢ above the market price if the stock is selling at $40 or more. On sell transactions, the above amounts are deducted from the current price. Occasionally 10-share units are traded as round lots. These include stocks that are very high in price or inactive preferred stocks.

EXAMPLE 1: Find the total cost of 200 shares of General Electric selling at 79. What return does the investor get if the annual dividend is $2.00?

SOLUTION: Cost of 100 shares = 100 × 79 = $7900.00

.001 × 7900 = $ 7.90

Plus   39.00

Commission   46.90

Cost plus commission $7946.90

Total cost of 200 shares = 2 × 7946.90 = $15,893.80

Investor's rate of return = 400/15,893.80 = .0252 = 2.52%

EXAMPLE 2: Find the cost of 10 shares of General Electric selling at 79 and the rate of return.

SOLUTION: Since this is an odd lot, the sale will be executed at $79.25.

Cost of the stock = 10 × 79.25 = $792.50

Commission = .01 × 792.50 = $7.93

Plus   5.00

                              12.93

Total cost $805.43

Rate of return = 20/805.43 = 2.48%

It is also possible to buy stock by the dollar's worth in the same way that a motorist gets so many dollars' worth of gas regardless of the per-gallon cost. In 1954, the New York Stock Exchange initiated the monthly investment plan, commonly called MIP, under which it is possible to invest a set sum of money every month or three months acquiring full or fractional shares of any stock listed on the New York Stock Exchange.

With its constant monthly or quarterly payments, MIP puts stock buying on a regular budget basis for those who prefer to operate this way. While an investor may put as little as $40 a month or a quarter into stocks, the commission is high on small purchases. For this reason, some MIP customers let their monthly payments accumulate for three months and make a larger purchase every quarter. Others, introduced to stock buying through MIP, decide to accumulate money themselves and buy odd or round lots at lower commission costs.

The method of computing commissions for MIP purchases is best illustrated with an example.

EXAMPLE 3: A customer is buying Philadelphia Electric with an allotment of $50 a month. How much stock will he get, and what will be the yield if the stock is selling at 30 and the dividend is $1.20?

SOLUTION: On this small purchase, the commission will be 6% of the cost of the stock. However, the commission must come out of the $50. The size of the purchase, which we designate by P, can be determined by solving the equation:

$$P + .06P = 50$$

$$P = \frac{50}{1.06} = \$47.17$$

Since the odd-lot house which sells this stock collects its $\frac{1}{8}$ point over the market price, the person gets $47.17/30.125 = 1.5658$ shares. His proportionate dividend will be $1.20 \times 1.5658 = \$1.88$. The yield on his investment is $1.88/50 = .0376 = 3.76\%$.

It is interesting to compare buying costs, commission rates, and yield rates for purchases of different sizes. This is done below for Philadelphia Electric selling at 30 with a dividend of $1.20.

	Amount of Stock			
	$50 Worth	10 Shares	50 Shares	100 Shares
Market value per share	$30.00	$ 30.00	$ 30.00	$ 30.00
Market plus odd-lot add-on	$30.125	$ 30.125	$ 30.125	
Cost of stock	$47.17	$301.25	$1506.25	$3000.00
Commission	$ 2.83	$ 7.03	$ 20.06	$ 34.00
Total cost	$50.00	$308.28	$1526.31	$3034.00
Commission as a per cent of market value	6.00%	2.34%	1.34%	1.13%
Total dividend	$ 1.88	$ 12.00	$ 60.00	$ 120.00
Per cent yield	3.76%	3.89%	3.93%	3.96%

This table shows the wisdom of making fairly substantial purchases to reduce buying costs and raise yield rates.

Exercise 10b

1. An investor bought 100 shares of Westinghouse Electric at 36. What was the total cost? What yield rate will he get on his investment at the current dividend rate of $1.20?   ($3637; 3.3%)

2. Two hundred shares of General Electric were purchased at 75. Find the total cost and the yield rate if the dividend is $2.00.

3. Thirty-five shares of Boston Edison were purchased when the price was $36\frac{1}{4}$. Find the cost and yield rate if the annual dividend is $1.32.

($1290.86; 3.6%)

4. Ten shares of Sears Roebuck were purchased when the price was $79\frac{3}{4}$. Find the total cost and the rate of return if the annual dividend is $1.65.

5. Twenty shares of Kroger were purchased at $28\frac{3}{8}$. Find the cost and the rate of return if the dividend is $1.10.   ($580.70; 3.8%)

6. An investor bought Ford Motor when the price was 46. The annual dividend is $1.80. Find the total cost and the yield if he: (a) bought 10 shares; (b) bought 100 shares.

7. In 1958, forty shares of Westinghouse Electric were purchased when the price was 58. At that time the dividends were $2.00 a share. In 1959, the stock was split 2 for 1 and the dividend on the new shares set at $1.20. Find the cost of the stock and yield rate before and after the split.

($2358.30; 3.4%; 4.1%)

8. Bell and Howell was purchased when the price was 22 and the dividend $.40. Find the total cost and yield for: (a) 40 shares; (b) 1000 shares.

9. A MIP investor is buying Kroger with $40 a month payments. If the stock is selling at $24\frac{7}{8}$, how many shares will he get and what will be the rate of return if the dividend is $1.10?   (1.5096 shares; 4.15%)

10. A MIP investor puts $150 quarterly in Procter and Gamble. If the cost is 78 and the annual dividend $1.60, how many shares will he get each quarter and what will be the rate of return?

10.7 How Much Is a Stock Worth?

The price of a stock on a free market, such as the floor of a stock exchange, is determined by many factors: facts and rumors, hopes and fears, yields expected by investors, general business conditions, outlook for particular industries and companies, and many other things such as tax changes, presidential heart attacks, and what the dictators of distant countries are expected to do next. With so many unpredictable variables influencing stock prices, are there any objective mathematical standards by which the value of a stock can be judged? There are some useful standards of this type which can be used as guidelines in conjunction with other information in arriving at buy or sell decisions.

An important consideration for investors who depend on stocks for income is yield rates and consistent dividends. Many stocks have paid dividends every 3 months for 25 years or more. Some have even had an uninterrupted flow of dividends for a century or more. While this does not guarantee anything for the future, a history of payments over a long period including at

times adverse economic conditions is an indication of underlying strength in
a company's operations. Even with such stocks, there is an inherent risk
in using past results to predict an uncertain future. Present merits must also
be considered in evaluating the outlook for future dividends. Will they be
maintained, reduced, or increased?

While there is no guarantee that dividends and, therefore, yield rates will
continue into the future, a careful consideration of past performance may
result in conclusions that are at least quite probable. Suppose that a middle-
aged couple would like to invest some money now in a security which will
pay them a moderate yield at this time with a good prospect of increased
dividends in the future. They decide to invest in an electric utility because
they think that in most areas the utility will have an increasing business
regardless of general business fluctuations. Their broker suggests the following as representative companies that meet their needs. Since commission
costs cannot be determined until an order is placed, yield rates in material
supplied by brokers are determined by simply dividing the dividend by the
price. Actual net yields to the investor, determined as in the preceding
section, will be slightly lower than these published figures.

Company	*Closing Price March 29, 1963*	*Indicated Dividend*	*Indicated Yield*	*Dividend Increases 1953–63*
Duquesne Light Co.	$32\frac{3}{8}$	$1.28	4.0%	9
Indianapolis Power & Light	$31\frac{3}{4}$	1.04	3.3	9
Middle South Utilities	$38\frac{1}{2}$	1.10	2.9	9

While a fixed investment, such as a savings and loan account or an industrial bond, would pay a somewhat higher return now, the fact that these
companies have a past record of increasing dividends is attractive to this
couple because returns a few years from now are of greater importance than
present yields. This tabulation is, of course, only a preliminary guide for
further and more detailed study of these and other companies since past
dividend trends may not be continued and may even be reversed.

The *price-earnings ratio*, computed by dividing recent market price by
latest 12 months earnings, can be a useful guide in making investment decisions. On Wall Street there is considerable support for the idea that a
historic norm for this ratio is about 15. However, there is no absolute standard for deciding what the price-earnings ratio should be. It varies from
company to company, industry to industry, and as the economic outlook
changes. Unusually good or poor 12-months periods should be taken into
account in evaluating the significance of the ratio. The price-earnings ratio

for a growth company may be high and yet the stock will be quite attractive for certain investment objectives. Thus the price-earnings ratio is a relative matter and is useful only when used for comparison purposes. It is one of the tools which a wise investor uses in conjunction with other information.

For some investors, a liberal income is important. Consider a retired couple who need the income from their investments to meet current living expenses. They will be able to find many stocks which yield 4% or more. Typical of such stocks are the following.

Stock	Closing Price March 29, 1963	Earnings 1962	Indicated Dividend	Indicated Yield	P/E Ratio
Chesapeake and Ohio	56	$4.30	$4.00	7.1%	13.0
Columbia Gas	$28\frac{1}{8}$	1.63	1.16	4.1	17.3
Sunray DX Oil	$31\frac{1}{4}$	1.90	1.40	4.5	16.4
U. S. Playing Card	$26\frac{1}{8}$	1.45	1.30	5.0	18.0
Kroger	$25\frac{3}{4}$	1.62	1.10	4.3	15.9

We now consider an investor who is not dependent on present income from his stocks. For him, a price earnings ratio of 20, 30, or more may be acceptable if he thinks that the stock has a large growth potential. The following stocks will be of interest to him.

Stock	Closing Price March 29, 1963	Earnings 1962	Indicated Dividend	Indicated Yield	P/E Ratio
International Bus. Machines	$420\frac{3}{4}$	$8.72	$4.00	1.0%	48.3
Xerox Corp.	$160\frac{1}{2}$	3.60	1.00	.6	44.6
National Cash Register	$71\frac{1}{8}$	2.49	1.20	1.7	28.6
Polaroid	$136\frac{5}{8}$	2.52	.20	.1	54.2

An idea of whether or not the price-earnings ratio for a growth stock is reasonable might be obtained by using the past growth record of the company to predict the future. Suppose that the earnings of the company are now $10 a share and have been increasing at about 20% a year. This picture fits International Business Machines fairly well in 1963. If the approximately

20%-a-year increase continues for another 5 years, earnings will be about
$25. It is on prospects such as these that certain growth stocks are actively
traded at high P/E ratios.

Exercise 10c

1. An investor is interested in buying stock in an aerospace company.
His broker suggests the following stocks. Determine the yield and price
earnings ratios.

Company	Approximate Price March 29, 1963	Earnings per Share 1962	Indicated Dividend	Answers	
				Yield	P/E
Lockheed Aircraft	$52	$4.70	$1.20	2.3%	11.1
McDonnell Aircraft	53	4.02	1.00	1.9	13.2
N. American Av.	61	4.12	2.00	3.3	14.8
United Aircraft	47	2.60	2.00	4.3	18.1

2. Compute the yield and price earnings ratios for the following retailers.

Company	Approximate Price March 29, 1963	Earnings per Share 1962	Indicated Dividend
Fed. Dept. Stores	$46	$2.20	$1.20
Montgomery Ward	34	1.50	1.00
J. C. Penney	45	2.35	1.50
Sears Roebuck	78	3.10	1.65

3. Bring the data in Problem 1 up to date and note any significant changes.

4. Bring the data in Problem 2 up to date.

5. Compute the yield and price earnings ratio for the following banks:

Bank	Approximate Price March 29, 1963	Earnings per Share 1962	Indicated Dividend	Answers	
				Yield	P/E
Bank of America	$64	$2.92	$2.00	3.1%	21.9
Chase Manhattan	87	5.16	2.60	3.0	16.9
Mfg. Hanover Trust	59	3.36	2.00	3.4	17.6
Mellon Nat. Bank	82	3.91	2.00	2.4	21.0

6. Compute the yield and price earnings ratio for the following steel
companies:

Company	Approximate Price March 29, 1963	Earnings per Share 1962	Indicated Dividend
Bethlehem	$31	$1.80	$1.50
Inland	38	2.94	1.60
Jones and Laughlin	53	3.02	2.50
United States Steel	47	2.56	2.00

7. Bring the data in Problem 5 up to date.

8. Bring the data in Problem 6 up to date.

10.8 Sound Investment Principles

Stocks are an attractive investment if a person can afford them. This means more than just having a few dollars on hand. It costs money to buy stocks, and they can go down as well as up. A person should buy stocks only if he feels reasonably sure that he will not be forced to sell at a loss to get cash. He should be able to answer "Yes" to the following questions:

1. Do I have enough to cover living expenses comfortably? For the home buyer this includes a substantial equity in his house.

2. Do I have adequate life insurance to protect my family?

3. Do I have a cash reserve or savings account for emergencies?

How much for living expenses, how much insurance, how large a cash reserve, depend on the circumstances of the particular individual or family. When a person thinks that he has enough for his particular circumstances, he may reasonably start investing in stocks. Note that an honest appraisal of the situation would result in not buying stocks if there are consumer installment loans. We have seen in earlier chapters that these often mean interest charges of 12% or more. Since this is more than can be expected from stocks, such debts should be paid off before investing. Having satisfied himself that he can afford to buy stocks, a person should then decide on his investment objectives.

Common stocks may meet one or more of the following: safety of principal, liberal income, and growth. Some stocks may meet a couple of these objectives to an attractive degree. Thus a high degree of safety and a liberal dividend rate may be found in the same stock. Or a stock with good growth prospects may pay moderate dividends. However, do not expect to find an all-purpose stock that is very safe, pays large dividends, and is sure to go up.

Before buying, get facts. Do not buy on tips, or rumors, or on the recommendation of a high-pressure telephone salesman. Deal with a reputable broker who can suggest industries and particular companies that will meet your investment objectives. Consider the prospects of the various industries.

After deciding on an industry that meets your objectives, ask your broker to supply fact sheets on specific companies. Study these and then make your own decision. The more you know about various companies, the better equipped you will be to make a wise choice. Check on a company's profits, the future for its products, its price-earnings ratio, and the quality of its management. In any industry, some companies will be much better than others. It is management that makes the difference.

When a person is in a position to afford stock in several companies, there are advantages to diversification. Some industries will move ahead faster than others; some may even regress as their products are replaced by new inventions. Diversification protects the investor against the overall loss that would result from having all his money in a failing company. Having stocks in a reasonable number of industries and companies also improves a person's chances of making a profit as a result of one or more of his companies growing at a high rate.

While diversification reduces risk, there are investors who prefer not to diversify. They are willing to accept a higher degree of risk in the hope of having a larger-than-average gain. Even a person who diversifies should not own stocks in so many companies that he is unable to give a reasonable amount of supervision to each. As one authority has said, "Stocks are perishable." Only by keeping abreast of industry trends and the fortunes of particular companies can a person decide whether to buy more stock in a company, sell what he has, or simply hold. Also as a person gets older or his family situation changes, his investment objectives may change, indicating shifts from one type of security to another.

To keep commissions a small percentage of the value of stocks, a person can defer the purchase of stocks until he is able to invest three or four hundred dollars or more.

There is no system which will enable a person to consistently buy when the market is low and sell when it is high. A system which is recommended by some investment counselors is dollar averaging. A person who follows dollar averaging puts a certain amount into the stock of a particular company. At regular intervals, he continues to invest about the same amount in this company. When prices are low, his fixed amount buys more shares than when prices are high. Thus getting more shares when prices are low, less when they are high is the theory back of dollar cost averaging. When stock prices rise, a person's profit will be greater because of the larger number of shares purchased when prices were down. Dollar cost averaging means that a person must have the courage and the cash to keep right on buying in line with his plan to buy fixed-dollar amounts at regular intervals. The success of dollar cost averaging depends on the market value of a buyer's stocks having a generally upward trend in spite of inevitable reverses at times.

We have mentioned the advantages of a person diversifying his investment portfolio by getting stocks in different industries and companies. In this way, poor choices are likely to be offset by stocks that do well. Somewhat the same thing can be accomplished by investing in the shares of investment companies. An investment trust is a company that uses the capital supplied by individuals to buy a diversified group of securities. There are two principal types: closed-end and open-end. The capitalization of closed-end trusts is fixed. Their shares are bought and sold just like other stocks. Some closed-end trusts are listed on stock exchanges.

Open-end investment companies, usually called mutual funds, continue to offer new shares of stock for sale. The shares of mutual funds are bought and sold on the basis of their net asset value which is continually changing because the value of the fund's investments is continually changing. Such funds will redeem outstanding shares at any time at the current asset value per share.

The owner of a closed-end trust or mutual fund gets diversification and professional management. However, he pays for it. The buyer of shares in most mutual funds is required to pay a commission, which may be as much as 8%. This is more than the commission rates on common stocks and the shares of closed-end trusts. Shares of mutual funds can usually be sold without paying another commission, although there may be a small redemption fee.

In all investment trusts, both closed-end and open-end, the owner of shares must pay a management fee. This varies with the size of the fund but a typical figure is $\frac{1}{2}$ of 1% of net assets. This may seem small, but note that it is on assets. As a percentage of earnings, it may be as high as 15% or more. Mutual funds are usually sold by salesmen operating on a commission. Any investment should be *bought* only after the investor has made a thorough study and compared different investment possibilities. Only in this way can a person make a selection that is best from the standpoint of his resources, objectives, and temperament.

From the customer's standpoint, the buying of stocks is very simple. All he has to do is open an account with a broker and place verbal orders through him. But behind the scenes there is an amazingly complex and efficient system which is described in literature available from the exchanges and brokers. A visit to a broker's office will provide a student or potential investor an interesting overall picture of the operation of the stock market.

The government, the exchanges, and ethical brokers and investment firms help to protect the stock buyer from gyps and swindles. That gyps and swindles still exist is due in part to unwary and greedy buyers. They let themselves be taken by high pressure salesmen peddling questionable stocks.

By direct mail or long-distance calls, suckers learn that they are the lucky ones for whom some kind dealer has set aside a block of two or three hundred shares of low-priced stock at a special bargain price. Unless the buyer acts within a day or two, it will be too late. The chance of a lifetime to make a killing will be gone for good. What is really meant is that it will be gone for the salesman who may make a commission as high as 50%. "Investigate before you invest" should be the invariable rule of the buyer of stocks. Only in this way will he have a good chance to do well in the interesting and potentially profitable but uncertain stock market.

INDEX OF TABLES

Table 1

The Number of Each Day of the Year

Day of Month	Jan.	Feb.	Mar.	April	May	June	July	Aug.	Sept.	Oct.	Nov.	Dec.	Day of Month
1	1	32	60	91	121	152	182	213	244	274	305	335	1
2	2	33	61	92	122	153	183	214	245	275	306	336	2
3	3	34	62	93	123	154	184	215	246	276	307	337	3
4	4	35	63	94	124	155	185	216	247	277	308	338	4
5	5	36	64	95	125	156	186	217	248	278	309	339	5
6	6	37	65	96	126	157	187	218	249	279	310	340	6
7	7	38	66	97	127	158	188	219	250	280	311	341	7
8	8	39	67	98	128	159	189	220	251	281	312	342	8
9	9	40	68	99	129	160	190	221	252	282	313	343	9
10	10	41	69	100	130	161	191	222	253	283	314	344	10
11	11	42	70	101	131	162	192	223	254	284	315	345	11
12	12	43	71	102	132	163	193	224	255	285	316	346	12
13	13	44	72	103	133	164	194	225	256	286	317	347	13
14	14	45	73	104	134	165	195	226	257	287	318	348	14
15	15	46	74	105	135	166	196	227	258	288	319	349	15
16	16	47	75	106	136	167	197	228	259	289	320	350	16
17	17	48	76	107	137	168	198	229	260	290	321	351	17
18	18	49	77	108	138	169	199	230	261	291	322	352	18
19	19	50	78	109	139	170	200	231	262	292	323	353	19
20	20	51	79	110	140	171	201	232	263	293	324	354	20
21	21	52	80	111	141	172	202	233	264	294	325	355	21
22	22	53	81	112	142	173	203	234	265	295	326	356	22
23	23	54	82	113	143	174	204	235	266	296	327	357	23
24	24	55	83	114	144	175	205	236	267	297	328	358	24
25	25	56	84	115	145	176	206	237	268	298	329	359	25
26	26	57	85	116	146	177	207	238	269	299	330	360	26
27	27	58	86	117	147	178	208	239	270	300	331	361	27
28	28	59	87	118	148	179	209	240	271	301	332	362	28
29	29		88	119	149	180	210	241	272	302	333	363	29
30	30		89	120	150	181	211	242	273	303	334	364	30
31	31		90		151		212	243		304		365	31

For leap years the number of the day after
February 28 is one greater than that given in the table.

Table 2

Compound Interest and Annuity Tables

A Word about the Marginal Index

Down the side margin of each page runs an index designed to save much of the adjustment of rates which makes the ordinary table so confusing to the novice. It will help you.

All figures in the tables are calculated at some *rate per period*. This period may be anything from a day to 5 years or more, depending on how often the interest is calculated. You, however, usually have the *annual* rate quoted and that is what you can look up in the marginal index. Suppose a bank pays 2% per annum compounded *semiannually* (*i.e.*, adds interest each half year). Use the marginal index in the part where "SEMIANNUALLY" appears in capital letters, and find "2%" in that part. You have the table you want. Actually you realize that 2% per annum compounded semiannually means 1% per period where each period is a half year — but you do not need to make this adjustment in advance, simply use the index.

Caution: the number of periods in the table is not necessarily the number of years. It is the number of whatever unit you are using. When you use the "SEMIANNUALLY" index it is the number of half years. If you use the "MONTHLY" index it is the number of months.

The marginal index is there to help you. Use it.

What the Tables Are

In a Few Simple Words

(Not how to use them, but what they are)

1. Amount of 1. If you put a dollar in the bank and leave it there it grows, and this table (left-hand column on left-hand page) shows to what sum it does grow. If the rate is 2% to be figured each year, then at the end of 1 year you have $1.02 in the bank. The second year this grows to 1.02×1.02 or 1.0404. The third year this 1.0404 becomes 1.0404×1.02 or 1.061208. Observe that each result at the 2% rate can be obtained by multiplying the preceding result by 1.02 which is the ratio of increase at 2%. The table at any interest rate can be constructed by successive multiplication by its ratio of increase. There is nothing complicated to that.

2. Amount of 1 per Period. If you do not just put a dollar in the bank and leave it there, but at periodic intervals you go back and deposit another dollar each time, this table (middle column on left-hand page) shows what happens and how your money grows. Note that this table assumes that the deposit is made at the *end* of each period: the figure for 1 period is 1, meaning that 1 has just been deposited at the end of the period and has not had a chance to grow.

At the end of the second period this first dollar has grown (at 2%) to $1.02 and the second $1 has just been deposited, so the table shows $2.02.

Observe that this is just like the table for compound amount (left-hand column) in that the deposit of $1 is the basic event, and each $1 deposited starts to grow as shown in that table; but here we have a whole series of $1 deposits all growing at the same time, and each successively has been in the bank for one more period than the next deposit, right down to the latest deposit which has just been deposited. Therefore this table consists merely of adding all the items in the first table (left-hand column) down to the point desired. That feature of payment at the *end* of the period must be watched because it throws us out by one period: if you want to check the entry for 5 periods you could add up the first 4 entries in the left-hand column, then add 1 for the final deposit that has just been made, and you have the tabulated result.

This explanation is only here to show you that this table is just the combined total of a lot of $1 deposits, each growing for a different length of time in the manner shown in the left-hand column. Perhaps this is a little complicated, but there certainly is no dark mystery involved.

3. Sinking Fund. This table (right-hand column on left-hand page) shows how much money you must deposit each period in order to have $1 when you need it in the future. Each result is obtained merely by dividing 1 by the entry in the middle column beside it. For if $1 per period will grow to $25, then how much will be needed to grow to $1? Obviously $1 divided by $25, or 4c. You will not find any such simple unit figures in the tables but the reasoning is the same. It is entirely a matter of simple proportion. To put it concisely, each entry in this table is the *reciprocal* of the corresponding entry in the column to its left.

4. Present Worth of 1. If you want to have $1 in the bank at some time in the future this table (left-hand column of right-hand page) shows you how much you must deposit today. Obviously since the table for *Amount of 1* shows how money grows when left in the bank, this table is directly related to it. In other words, if $1 left in the bank will grow to $5, how much money will be needed to grow to $1? Obviously one-fifth of $1, or 20c. Again, you will not find such simple figures in even units in the table, but it is just a matter of simple proportion. To put it concisely, each entry in this table is the *reciprocal* of the corresponding entry in the table for the *Amount of 1*.

5. Present Worth of 1 per Period. We just saw that the preceding table showed us how much money we must put in the bank today in order to be able to draw out $1 at some specified date in the future. Now suppose we want to draw out $1, not on some one single occasion in the future, but $1 for each periodic interval for some length of time into the future. That is what is shown in this table.

Obviously since we are going to draw $1 at each date, we could use the preceding table for each of them, and add the entries. In fact, that is what the table is. If you will add the first five entries in the *Present Worth of 1* column you will get the result shown for 5 periods in the *Present Worth of 1 per Period* column. To express it concisely, each entry is the cumulative total of the figures in the column to the left of it.

4

6. *Partial Payment Table.* The preceding table shows what amount you must have today in order to get periodic payments of $1 in the future; but if you have $1 today, what size periodic payments will it get you in the future? Again, it is a matter of simple proportion. To put it concisely, each entry is the *reciprocal* of the corresponding entry in the column to the left of it. Usually, as the title indicates, this table will be used to show what you will have to pay at each period in the future if you borrow $1 today, but the explanation still stands.

Another basic relationship should be understood. In the *Sinking Fund* table we are concerned with the sum which must be set aside to grow to $1; but in this *Partial Payment* table we are concerned with paying off a loan of $1, which is the same thing as building up a sinking fund to pay the loan except that it includes the interest on the loan of $1. Therefore if you have the entry in the *Sinking Fund* table and add interest (always the i at the top of the page) you will get the corresponding entry in the *Partial Payment* table.

	P E R I O D S	AMOUNT OF 1 *How $1 left at compound interest will grow.*	AMOUNT OF 1 PER PERIOD *How $1 deposited periodically will grow.*	SINKING FUND *Periodic deposit that will grow to $1 at future date.*
	1	1.002 500 0000	1.000 000 0000	1.000 000 0000
	2	1.005 006 2500	2.002 500 0000	.499 375 7803
.0025	3	1.007 518 7656	3.007 506 2500	.332 501 3872
per period	4	1.010 037 5625	4.015 025 0156	.249 064 4507
	5	1.012 562 6564	5.025 062 5782	.199 002 4969
	6	1.015 094 0631	6.037 625 2346	.165 628 0344
	7	1.017 631 7982	7.052 719 2977	.141 789 2812
	8	1.020 175 8777	8.070 351 0959	.123 910 3464
	9	1.022 726 3174	9.090 526 9737	.110 004 6238
	10	1.025 283 1332	10.113 253 2911	.098 880 1498
	11	1.027 846 3411	11.138 536 4243	.089 778 4019
	12	1.030 415 9569	12.166 382 7654	.082 193 6988
	13	1.032 991 9968	13.196 798 7223	.075 775 9530
	14	1.035 574 4768	14.229 790 7191	.070 275 1024
	15	1.038 163 4130	15.265 365 1959	.065 507 7679
	16	1.040 758 8215	16.303 528 6089	.061 336 4152
	17	1.043 360 7186	17.344 287 4304	.057 655 8711
	18	1.045 969 1204	18.387 648 1490	.054 384 3341
	19	1.048 584 0432	19.433 617 2694	.051 457 2242
	20	1.051 205 5033	20.482 201 3126	.048 822 8772
ANNUALLY If compounded *annually* nominal annual rate is **1/4%**	21	1.053 833 5170	21.533 406 8158	.046 439 4700
	22	1.056 468 1008	22.587 240 3329	.044 272 7835
	23	1.059 109 2711	23.643 708 4337	.042 294 5496
	24	1.061 757 0443	24.702 817 7048	.040 481 2120
	25	1.064 411 4369	25.764 574 7491	.038 812 9829
	26	1.067 072 4655	26.828 986 1859	.037 273 1192
	27	1.069 740 1466	27.896 058 6514	.035 847 3580
	28	1.072 414 4970	28.965 798 7980	.034 523 4739
	29	1.075 095 5332	30.038 213 2950	.033 290 9281
	30	1.077 783 2721	31.113 308 8283	.032 140 5867
SEMIANNUALLY If compounded *semiannually* nominal annual rate is **1/2%**	31	1.080 477 7303	32.191 092 1003	.031 064 4944
	32	1.083 178 9246	33.271 569 8306	.030 055 6903
	33	1.085 886 8719	34.354 748 7551	.029 108 0574
	34	1.088 601 5891	35.440 635 6270	.028 216 1982
	35	1.091 323 0930	36.529 237 2161	.027 375 3321
	36	1.094 051 4008	37.620 560 3091	.026 581 2096
	37	1.096 786 5293	38.714 611 7099	.025 830 0408
	38	1.099 528 4956	39.811 398 2392	.025 118 4345
	39	1.102 277 3168	40.910 926 7348	.024 443 3475
	40	1.105 033 0101	42.013 204 0516	.023 802 0409
QUARTERLY If compounded *quarterly* nominal annual rate is **1%**	41	1.107 795 5927	43.118 237 0618	.023 192 0428
	42	1.110 565 0816	44.226 032 6544	.022 611 1170
	43	1.113 341 4943	45.336 597 7360	.022 057 2352
	44	1.116 124 8481	46.449 939 2304	.021 528 5535
	45	1.118 915 1602	47.566 064 0785	.021 023 3918
	46	1.121 712 4481	48.684 979 2387	.020 540 2162
	47	1.124 516 7292	49.806 691 6868	.020 077 6234
	48	1.127 328 0210	50.931 208 4160	.019 634 3270
	49	1.130 146 3411	52.058 536 4370	.019 209 1455
	50	1.132 971 7069	53.188 682 7781	.018 800 9920
MONTHLY If compounded *monthly* nominal annual rate is **3%**	51	1.135 804 1362	54.321 654 4851	.018 408 8649
	52	1.138 643 6466	55.457 458 6213	.018 031 8396
	53	1.141 490 2557	56.596 102 2678	.017 669 0613
	54	1.144 343 9813	57.737 592 5235	.017 319 7384
	55	1.147 204 8413	58.881 936 5048	.016 983 1371
	56	1.150 072 8534	60.029 141 3461	.016 658 5758
$i\ \ =.0025$	57	1.152 948 0355	61.179 214 1994	.016 345 4208
$j_{(2)}=.005$	58	1.155 830 4056	62.332 162 2349	.016 043 0822
$j_{(4)}=.01$	59	1.158 719 9816	63.487 992 6405	.015 751 0099
$j_{(12)}=.03$	60	1.161 616 7816	64.646 712 6221	.015 468 6907
	n	$s=(1+i)^n$	$s_{\overline{n}|}=\dfrac{(1+i)^n-1}{i}$	$\dfrac{1}{s_{\overline{n}|}}=\dfrac{i}{(1+i)^n-1}$

PRESENT WORTH OF 1	PRESENT WORTH OF 1 PER PERIOD	PARTIAL PAYMENT	P E R I O D S	RATE
What $1 due in the future is worth today.	*What $1 payable periodically is worth today.*	*Annuity worth $1 today.* *Periodic payment necessary to pay off a loan of $1.*		**1/4%**
.997 506 2344	.997 506 2344	1.002 500 0000	1	
.995 018 6877	1.992 524 9221	.501 875 7803	2	
.992 537 3443	2.985 062 2664	.335 001 3872	3	.0025
.990 062 1889	3.975 124 4553	.251 564 4507	4	*per period*
.987 593 2058	4.962 717 6612	.201 502 4969	5	
.985 130 3799	5.947 848 0410	.168 128 0344	6	
.982 673 6957	6.930 521 7367	.144 289 2812	7	
.980 223 1378	7.910 744 8745	.126 410 3464	8	
.977 778 6911	8.888 523 5656	.112 504 6238	9	
.975 340 3402	9.863 863 9058	.101 380 1498	10	
.972 908 0701	10.836 771 9759	.092 278 4019	11	
.970 481 8654	11.807 253 8413	.084 693 6988	12	
.968 061 7111	12.775 315 5524	.078 275 9530	13	
.965 647 5921	13.740 963 1446	.072 775 1024	14	
.963 239 4934	14.704 202 6380	.068 007 7679	15	
.960 837 3999	15.665 040 0379	.063 836 4152	16	
.958 441 2967	16.623 481 3345	.060 155 8711	17	
.956 051 1687	17.579 532 5033	.056 884 3341	18	
.953 667 0012	18.533 199 5045	.053 957 2242	19	
.951 288 7793	19.484 488 2838	.051 322 8772	20	
.948 916 4881	20.433 404 7719	.048 939 4700	21	ANNUALLY
.946 550 1128	21.379 954 8847	.046 772 7835	22	If compounded
.944 189 6387	22.324 144 5234	.044 794 5496	23	*annually*
.941 835 0511	23.265 979 5744	.042 981 2120	24	nominal annual rate is
.939 486 3352	24.205 465 9096	.041 312 9829	25	**1/4%**
.937 143 4765	25.142 609 3862	.039 773 1192	26	
.934 806 4604	26.077 415 8466	.038 347 3580	27	
.932 475 2722	27.009 891 1188	.037 023 4739	28	
.930 149 8975	27.940 041 0162	.035 790 9281	29	
.927 830 3217	28.867 871 3379	.034 640 5867	30	
.925 516 5303	29.793 387 8682	.033 564 4944	31	SEMIANNUALLY
.923 208 5091	30.716 596 3773	.032 555 6903	32	If compounded
.920 906 2434	31.637 502 6207	.031 608 0574	33	*semiannually*
.918 609 7192	32.556 112 3399	.030 716 1982	34	nominal annual rate is
.916 318 9218	33.472 431 2617	.029 875 3321	35	**1/2%**
.914 033 8373	34.386 465 0990	.029 081 2096	36	
.911 754 4511	35.298 219 5501	.028 330 0408	37	
.909 480 7493	36.207 700 2993	.027 618 4345	38	
.907 212 7175	37.114 913 0168	.026 943 3475	39	
.904 950 3416	38.019 863 3584	.026 302 0409	40	
.902 693 6076	38.922 556 9660	.025 692 0428	41	QUARTERLY
.900 442 5013	39.822 999 4673	.025 111 1170	42	If compounded
.898 197 0088	40.721 196 4761	.024 557 2352	43	*quarterly*
.895 957 1160	41.617 153 5921	.024 028 5535	44	nominal annual rate is
.893 722 8090	42.510 876 4011	.023 523 3918	45	**1%**
.891 494 0738	43.402 370 4750	.023 040 2162	46	
.889 270 8966	44.291 641 3715	.022 577 6234	47	
.887 053 2634	45.178 694 6349	.022 134 3270	48	
.884 841 1605	46.063 535 7955	.021 709 1455	49	
.882 634 5741	46.946 170 3695	.021 300 9920	50	
.880 433 4904	47.826 603 8599	.020 908 8649	51	MONTHLY
.878 237 8956	48.704 841 7555	.020 531 8396	52	If compounded
.876 047 7762	49.580 889 5317	.020 169 0613	53	*monthly*
.873 863 1184	50.454 752 6500	.019 819 7384	54	nominal annual rate is
.871 683 9086	51.326 436 5586	.019 483 1371	55	**3%**
.869 510 1333	52.195 946 6919	.019 158 5758	56	
.867 341 7788	53.063 288 4707	.018 845 4208	57	
.865 178 8317	53.928 467 3025	.018 543 0822	58	$i = .0025$
.863 021 2785	54.791 488 5810	.018 251 0099	59	$j_{(2)} = .005$
.860 869 1058	55.652 357 6868	.017 968 6907	60	$j_{(4)} = .01$ $j_{(12)} = .03$
$v^n = \dfrac{1}{(1+i)^n}$	$a_{\overline{n}|} = \dfrac{1-v^n}{i}$	$\dfrac{1}{a_{\overline{n}|}} = \dfrac{i}{1-v^n}$	n	

P E R I O D S	AMOUNT OF 1 *How $1 left at compound interest will grow.*	AMOUNT OF 1 PER PERIOD *How $1 deposited periodically will grow.*	SINKING FUND *Periodic deposit that will grow to $1 at future date.*
61	1.164 520 8235	65.808 329 4037	.015 195 6448
62	1.167 432 1256	66.972 850 2272	.014 931 4237
63	1.170 350 7059	68.140 282 3527	.014 675 6069
64	1.173 276 5826	69.310 633 0586	.014 427 8007
65	1.176 209 7741	70.483 909 6413	.014 187 6352
66	1.179 150 2985	71.660 119 4154	.013 954 7632
67	1.182 098 1743	72.839 269 7139	.013 728 8581
68	1.185 053 4197	74.021 367 8882	.013 509 6125
69	1.188 016 0533	75.206 421 3079	.013 296 7369
70	1.190 986 0934	76.394 437 3612	.013 089 9583
71	1.193 963 5586	77.585 423 4546	.012 889 0190
72	1.196 948 4675	78.779 387 0132	.012 693 6758
73	1.199 940 8387	79.976 335 4808	.012 503 6987
74	1.202 940 6908	81.176 276 3195	.012 318 8701
75	1.205 948 0425	82.379 217 0103	.012 138 9840
76	1.208 962 9126	83.585 165 0528	.011 963 8455
77	1.211 985 3199	84.794 127 9654	.011 793 2695
78	1.215 015 2832	86.006 113 2853	.011 627 0805
79	1.218 052 8214	87.221 128 5685	.011 465 1119
80	1.221 097 9535	88.439 181 3900	.011 307 2055
81	1.224 150 6984	89.660 279 3434	.011 153 2108
82	1.227 211 0751	90.884 430 0418	.011 002 9848
83	1.230 279 1028	92.111 641 1169	.010 856 3911
84	1.233 354 8005	93.341 920 2197	.010 713 3001
85	1.236 438 1876	94.575 275 0202	.010 573 5881
86	1.239 529 2830	95.811 713 2078	.010 437 1372
87	1.242 628 1062	97.051 242 4908	.010 303 8351
88	1.245 734 6765	98.293 870 5970	.010 173 5743
89	1.248 849 0132	99.539 605 2735	.010 046 2524
90	1.251 971 1357	100.788 454 2867	.009 921 7714
91	1.255 101 0636	102.040 425 4224	.009 800 0375
92	1.258 238 8162	103.295 526 4860	.009 680 9614
93	1.261 384 4133	104.553 765 3022	.009 564 4571
94	1.264 537 8743	105.815 149 7155	.009 450 4426
95	1.267 699 2190	107.079 687 5898	.009 338 8393
96	1.270 868 4670	108.347 386 8087	.009 229 5719
97	1.274 045 6382	109.618 255 2757	.009 122 5681
98	1.277 230 7523	110.892 300 9139	.009 017 7586
99	1.280 423 8292	112.169 531 6662	.008 915 0769
100	1.283 624 8887	113.449 955 4954	.008 814 4592
101	1.286 833 9510	114.733 580 3841	.008 715 8441
102	1.290 051 0358	116.020 414 3351	.008 619 1728
103	1.293 276 1634	117.310 465 3709	.008 524 3887
104	1.296 509 3538	118.603 741 5344	.008 431 4372
105	1.299 750 6272	119.900 250 8882	.008 340 2661
106	1.303 000 0038	121.200 001 5154	.008 250 8250
107	1.306 257 5038	122.503 001 5192	.008 163 0653
108	1.309 523 1476	123.809 259 0230	.008 076 9404
109	1.312 796 9554	125.118 782 1706	.007 992 4052
110	1.316 078 9478	126.431 579 1260	.007 909 4164
111	1.319 369 1452	127.747 658 0738	.007 827 9322
112	1.322 667 5680	129.067 027 2190	.007 747 9122
113	1.325 974 2370	130.389 694 7870	.007 669 3177
114	1.329 289 1726	131.715 669 0240	.007 592 1112
115	1.332 612 3955	133.044 958 1966	.007 516 2563
116	1.335 943 9265	134.377 570 5920	.007 441 7181
117	1.339 283 7863	135.713 514 5185	.007 368 4629
118	1.342 631 9958	137.052 798 3048	.007 296 4581
119	1.345 988 5758	138.395 430 3006	.007 225 6721
120	1.349 353 5472	139.741 418 8763	.007 156 0745
n	$s=(1+i)^n$	$s_{\overline{n}|}=\dfrac{(1+i)^n-1}{i}$	$\dfrac{1}{s_{\overline{n}|}}=\dfrac{i}{(1+i)^n-1}$

.0025

per period

ANNUALLY
If compounded
annually
nominal annual rate is

1/4%

SEMIANNUALLY
If compounded
semiannually
nominal annual rate is

1/2%

QUARTERLY
If compounded
quarterly
nominal annual rate is

1%

MONTHLY
If compounded
monthly
nominal annual rate is

3%

$i = .0025$
$j_{(2)} = .005$
$j_{(4)} = .01$
$j_{(12)} = .03$

8

PRESENT WORTH OF 1	PRESENT WORTH OF 1 PER PERIOD	PARTIAL PAYMENT	P E R I O D S	RATE
What $1 due in the future is worth today.	*What $1 payable periodically is worth today.*	*Annuity worth $1 today.* *Periodic payment necessary to pay off a loan of $1.*		$\frac{1}{4}\%$
.858 722 3000	56.511 079 9868	.017 695 6448	61	
.856 580 8479	57.367 660 8348	.017 431 4237	62	
.854 444 7361	58.222 105 5708	.017 175 6069	63	.0025
.852 313 9512	59.074 419 5220	.016 927 8007	64	
.850 188 4800	59.924 608 0020	.016 687 6352	65	*per period*
.848 068 3092	60.772 676 3112	.016 454 7632	66	
.845 953 4257	61.618 629 7369	.016 228 8581	67	
.843 843 8161	62.462 473 5530	.016 009 6125	68	
.841 739 4674	63.304 213 0205	.015 796 7369	69	
.839 640 3665	64.143 853 3870	.015 589 9583	70	
.837 546 5003	64.981 399 8873	.015 389 0190	71	
.835 457 8556	65.816 857 7429	.015 193 6758	72	
.833 374 4196	66.650 232 1625	.015 003 6987	73	
.831 296 1791	67.481 528 3417	.014 818 8701	74	
.829 223 1213	68.310 751 4630	.014 638 9840	75	
.827 155 2333	69.137 906 6963	.014 463 8455	76	
.825 092 5020	69.962 999 1983	.014 293 2695	77	
.823 034 9147	70.786 034 1130	.014 127 0805	78	
.820 982 4586	71.607 016 5716	.013 965 1119	79	
.818 935 1208	72.425 951 6923	.013 807 2055	80	
.816 892 8885	73.242 844 5809	.013 653 2108	81	ANNUALLY
.814 855 7492	74.057 700 3300	.013 502 9848	82	If compounded *annually*
.812 823 6900	74.870 524 0200	.013 356 3911	83	nominal annual rate is
.810 796 6982	75.681 320 7182	.013 213 3001	84	
.808 774 7613	76.490 095 4795	.013 073 5881	85	$\frac{1}{4}\%$
.806 757 8666	77.296 853 3461	.012 937 1372	86	
.804 746 0016	78.101 599 3478	.012 803 8351	87	
.802 739 1537	78.904 338 5015	.012 673 5743	88	
.800 737 3105	79.705 075 8120	.012 546 2524	89	
.798 740 4593	80.503 816 2713	.012 421 7714	90	
.796 748 5879	81.300 564 8592	.012 300 0375	91	SEMIANNUALLY
.794 761 6836	82.095 326 5428	.012 180 9614	92	If compounded *semiannually*
.792 779 7343	82.888 106 2771	.012 064 4571	93	nominal annual rate is
.790 802 7275	83.678 909 0046	.011 950 4426	94	
.788 830 6509	84.467 739 6555	.011 838 8393	95	$\frac{1}{2}\%$
.786 863 4921	85.254 603 1476	.011 729 5719	96	
.784 901 2390	86.039 504 3866	.011 622 5681	97	
.782 943 8793	86.822 448 2660	.011 517 7586	98	
.780 991 4008	87.603 439 6668	.011 415 0769	99	
.779 043 7914	88.382 483 4581	.011 314 4592	100	
.777 101 0388	89.159 584 4969	.011 215 8441	101	QUARTERLY
.775 163 1309	89.934 747 6278	.011 119 1728	102	If compounded *quarterly*
.773 230 0558	90.707 977 6836	.011 024 3887	103	nominal annual rate is
.771 301 8013	91.479 279 4849	.010 931 4372	104	
.769 378 3554	92.248 657 8403	.010 840 2661	105	1%
.767 459 7061	93.016 117 5464	.010 750 8250	106	
.765 545 8415	93.781 663 3880	.010 663 0653	107	
.763 636 7497	94.545 300 1376	.010 576 9404	108	
.761 732 4186	95.307 032 5562	.010 492 4052	109	
.759 832 8365	96.066 865 3928	.010 409 4164	110	MONTHLY
.757 937 9915	96.824 803 3843	.010 327 9322	111	If compounded *monthly*
.756 047 8719	97.580 851 2562	.010 247 9122	112	nominal annual rate is
.754 162 4657	98.335 013 7218	.010 169 3177	113	
.752 281 7613	99.087 295 4831	.010 092 1112	114	
.750 405 7469	99.837 701 2301	.010 016 2563	115	3%
.748 534 4109	100.586 235 6410	.009 941 7181	116	
.746 667 7415	101.332 903 3825	.009 868 4629	117	
.744 805 7272	102.077 709 1097	.009 796 4581	118	$i = .0025$
.742 948 3563	102.820 657 4661	.009 725 6721	119	$j_{(2)} = .005$
.741 095 6173	103.561 753 0834	.009 656 0745	120	$j_{(4)} = .01$
$v^n = \dfrac{1}{(1+i)^n}$	$a_{\overline{n}\|} = \dfrac{1-v^n}{i}$	$\dfrac{1}{a_{\overline{n}\|}} = \dfrac{i}{1-v^n}$	n	$j_{(12)} = .03$

9

P E R I O D S	AMOUNT OF 1 *How $1 left at compound interest will grow.*	AMOUNT OF 1 PER PERIOD *How $1 deposited periodically will grow.*	SINKING FUND *Periodic deposit that will grow to $1 at future date.*
121	1.352 726 9311	141.090 772 4235	.007 087 6357
122	1.356 108 7484	142.443 499 3546	.007 020 3274
123	1.359 499 0203	143.799 608 1030	.006 954 1219
124	1.362 897 7678	145.159 107 1232	.006 888 9925
125	1.366 305 0122	146.522 004 8910	.006 824 9134
126	1.369 720 7748	147.888 309 9033	.006 761 8597
127	1.373 145 0767	149.258 030 6780	.006 699 8070
128	1.376 577 9394	150.631 175 7547	.006 638 7320
129	1.380 019 3842	152.007 753 6941	.006 578 6118
130	1.383 469 4327	153.387 773 0783	.006 519 4245
131	1.386 928 1063	154.771 242 5110	.006 461 1486
132	1.390 395 4265	156.158 170 6173	.006 403 7635
133	1.393 871 4151	157.548 566 0439	.006 347 2491
134	1.397 356 0936	158.942 437 4590	.006 291 5859
135	1.400 849 4839	160.339 793 5526	.006 236 7549
136	1.404 351 6076	161.740 643 0365	.006 182 7379
137	1.407 862 4866	163.144 994 6441	.006 129 5169
138	1.411 382 1428	164.552 857 1307	.006 077 0747
139	1.414 910 5982	165.964 239 2735	.006 025 3944
140	1.418 447 8747	167.379 149 8717	.005 974 4598
141	1.421 993 9944	168.797 597 7464	.005 924 2549
142	1.425 548 9794	170.219 591 7408	.005 874 7644
143	1.429 112 8518	171.645 140 7201	.005 825 9733
144	1.432 685 6339	173.074 253 5719	.005 777 8669
145	1.436 267 3480	174.506 939 2058	.005 730 4311
146	1.439 858 0164	175.943 206 5538	.005 683 6522
147	1.443 457 6614	177.383 064 5702	.005 637 5168
148	1.447 066 3056	178.826 522 2317	.005 592 0117
149	1.450 683 9713	180.273 588 5372	.005 547 1243
150	1.454 310 6813	181.724 272 5086	.005 502 8422
151	1.457 946 4580	183.178 583 1899	.005 459 1535
152	1.461 591 3241	184.636 529 6478	.005 416 0463
153	1.465 245 3024	186.098 120 9719	.005 373 5094
154	1.468 908 4157	187.563 366 2744	.005 331 5315
155	1.472 580 6867	189.032 274 6901	.005 290 1019
156	1.476 262 1384	190.504 855 3768	.005 249 2100
157	1.479 952 7938	191.981 117 5152	.005 208 8456
158	1.483 652 6758	193.461 070 3090	.005 168 9986
159	1.487 361 8075	194.944 722 9848	.005 129 6592
160	1.491 080 2120	196.432 084 7923	.005 090 8180
161	1.494 807 9125	197.923 165 0042	.005 052 4657
162	1.498 544 9323	199.417 972 9167	.005 014 5931
163	1.502 291 2946	200.916 517 8490	.004 977 1916
164	1.506 047 0229	202.418 809 1437	.004 940 2524
165	1.509 812 1404	203.924 856 1665	.004 903 7671
166	1.513 586 6708	205.434 668 3069	.004 867 7276
167	1.517 370 6374	206.948 254 9777	.004 832 1258
168	1.521 164 0640	208.465 625 6151	.004 796 9539
169	1.524 966 9742	209.986 789 6792	.004 762 2043
170	1.528 779 3916	211.511 756 6534	.004 727 8696
171	1.532 601 3401	213.040 536 0450	.004 693 9424
172	1.536 432 8435	214.573 137 3851	.004 660 4156
173	1.540 273 9256	216.109 570 2286	.004 627 2824
174	1.544 124 6104	217.649 844 1542	.004 594 5358
175	1.547 984 9219	219.193 968 7645	.004 562 1693
176	1.551 854 8842	220.741 953 6865	.004 530 1764
177	1.555 734 5214	222.293 808 5707	.004 498 5508
178	1.559 623 8577	223.849 543 0921	.004 467 2863
179	1.563 522 9174	225.409 166 9498	.004 436 3768
180	1.567 431 7247	226.972 689 8672	.004 405 8164
n	$s=(1+i)^n$	$s_{\overline{n}|}=\dfrac{(1+i)^n-1}{i}$	$\dfrac{1}{s_{\overline{n}|}}=\dfrac{i}{(1+i)^n-1}$

.0025
per period

ANNUALLY
If compounded
annually
nominal annual rate is

1/4%

SEMIANNUALLY
If compounded
semiannually
nominal annual rate is

1/2%

QUARTERLY
If compounded
quarterly
nominal annual rate is

1%

MONTHLY
If compounded
monthly
nominal annual rate is

3%

$i = .0025$
$j_{(2)} = .005$
$j_{(4)} = .01$
$j_{(12)} = .03$

PRESENT WORTH OF 1	PRESENT WORTH OF 1 PER PERIOD	PARTIAL PAYMENT	P E R I O D S	RATE
What $1 due in the future is worth today.	*What $1 payable periodically is worth today.*	*Annuity worth $1 today.* *Periodic payment necessary to pay off a loan of $1.*		$1\!/\!4\%$

.739 247 4985	104.301 000 5819	.009 587 6357	121	
.737 403 9886	105.038 404 5705	.009 520 3274	122	.0025
.735 565 0759	105.773 969 6464	.009 454 1219	123	*per period*
.733 730 7490	106.507 700 3954	.009 388 9925	124	
.731 900 9965	107.239 601 3919	.009 324 9134	125	
.730 075 8070	107.969 677 1989	.009 261 8597	126	
.728 255 1691	108.697 932 3680	.009 199 8070	127	
.726 439 0714	109.424 371 4394	.009 138 7320	128	
.724 627 5026	110.148 998 9420	.009 078 6118	129	
.722 820 4515	110.871 819 3935	.009 019 4245	130	
.721 017 9067	111.592 837 3003	.008 961 1486	131	
.719 219 8571	112.312 057 1574	.008 903 7635	132	
.717 426 2914	113.029 483 4488	.008 847 2491	133	
.715 637 1984	113.745 120 6472	.008 791 5859	134	
.713 852 5670	114.458 973 2141	.008 736 7549	135	
.712 072 3860	115.171 045 6001	.008 682 7379	136	
.710 296 6444	115.881 342 2445	.008 629 5169	137	
.708 525 3311	116.589 867 5756	.008 577 0747	138	
.706 758 4350	117.296 626 0105	.008 525 3944	139	
.704 995 9451	118.001 621 9557	.008 474 4598	140	
.703 237 8505	118.704 859 8061	.008 424 2549	141	ANNUALLY
.701 484 1401	119.406 343 9463	.008 374 7644	142	If compounded
.699 734 8031	120.106 078 7494	.008 325 9733	143	*annually*
.697 989 8286	120.804 068 5780	.008 277 8669	144	nominal annual rate is
.696 249 2055	121.500 317 7835	.008 230 4311	145	$1\!/\!4\%$
.694 512 9232	122.194 830 7067	.008 183 6522	146	
.692 780 9708	122.887 611 6775	.008 137 5168	147	
.691 053 3375	123.578 665 0150	.008 092 0117	148	
.689 330 0124	124.267 995 0274	.008 047 1243	149	
.687 610 9850	124.955 606 0124	.008 002 8422	150	
.685 896 2444	125.641 502 2568	.007 959 1535	151	SEMIANNUALLY
.684 185 7799	126.325 688 0367	.007 916 0463	152	If compounded
.682 479 5810	127.008 167 6176	.007 873 5094	153	*semiannually*
.680 777 6369	127.688 945 2545	.007 831 5315	154	nominal annual rate is
.679 079 9370	128.368 025 1915	.007 790 1019	155	$1\!/\!2\%$
.677 386 4708	129.045 411 6624	.007 749 2100	156	
.675 697 2278	129.721 108 8901	.007 708 8456	157	
.674 012 1973	130.395 121 0874	.007 668 9986	158	
.672 331 3689	131.067 452 4563	.007 629 6592	159	
.670 654 7320	131.738 107 1883	.007 590 8180	160	
.668 982 2763	132.407 089 4646	.007 552 4657	161	QUARTERLY
.667 313 9914	133.074 403 4560	.007 514 5931	162	If compounded
.665 649 8667	133.740 053 3227	.007 477 1916	163	*quarterly*
.663 989 8920	134.404 043 2147	.007 440 2524	164	nominal annual rate is
.662 334 0568	135.066 377 2715	.007 403 7671	165	1%
.660 682 3509	135.727 059 6224	.007 367 7276	166	
.659 034 7640	136.386 094 3864	.007 332 1258	167	
.657 391 2858	137.043 485 6723	.007 296 9539	168	
.655 751 9061	137.699 237 5783	.007 262 2043	169	
.654 116 6145	138.353 354 1928	.007 227 8696	170	
.652 485 4010	139.005 839 5939	.007 193 9424	171	MONTHLY
.650 858 2554	139.656 697 8492	.007 160 4156	172	If compounded
.649 235 1675	140.305 933 0167	.007 127 2824	173	*monthly*
.647 616 1271	140.953 549 1438	.007 094 5358	174	nominal annual rate is
.646 001 1243	141.599 550 2682	.007 062 1693	175	3%
.644 390 1490	142.243 940 4171	.007 030 1764	176	
.642 783 1910	142.886 723 6081	.006 998 5508	177	
.641 180 2404	143.527 903 8485	.006 967 2863	178	$i\ \ =.0025$
.639 581 2872	144.167 485 1356	.006 936 3768	179	$j_{(2)}=.005$
.637 986 3214	144.805 471 4570	.006 905 8164	180	$j_{(4)}=.01$
				$j_{(12)}=.03$
$v^n=\dfrac{1}{(1+i)^n}$	$a_{\overline{n}\rvert}=\dfrac{1-v^n}{i}$	$\dfrac{1}{a_{\overline{n}\rvert}}=\dfrac{i}{1-v^n}$	**n**	

11

P E R I O D S	AMOUNT OF 1 *How $1 left at compound interest will grow.*	AMOUNT OF 1 PER PERIOD *How $1 deposited periodically will grow.*	SINKING FUND *Periodic deposit that will grow to $1 at future date.*
1	1.003 333 3333	1.000 000 0000	1.000 000 0000
2	1.006 677 7778	2.003 333 3333	.499 168 0532
3	1.010 033 3704	3.010 011 1111	.332 224 6872
4	1.013 400 1483	4.020 044 4815	.248 753 4664
5	1.016 778 1488	5.033 444 6298	.198 671 1037
6	1.020 167 4093	6.050 222 7785	.165 283 1700
7	1.023 567 9673	7.070 390 1878	.141 434 9100
8	1.026 979 8605	8.093 958 1551	.123 548 9461
9	1.030 403 1267	9.120 938 0156	.109 637 8463
10	1.033 837 8038	10.151 341 1423	.098 509 1513
11	1.037 283 9298	11.185 178 9461	.089 404 0234
12	1.040 741 5429	12.222 462 8759	.081 816 5709
13	1.044 210 6814	13.263 204 4189	.075 396 5609
14	1.047 691 3837	14.307 415 1003	.069 893 8273
15	1.051 183 6883	15.355 106 4839	.065 124 9147
16	1.054 687 6339	16.406 290 1722	.060 952 2317
17	1.058 203 2594	17.460 977 8061	.057 270 5613
18	1.061 730 6036	18.519 181 0655	.053 998 0681
19	1.065 269 7056	19.580 911 6690	.051 070 1451
20	1.068 820 6046	20.646 181 3746	.048 435 1068
21	1.072 383 3399	21.715 001 9792	.046 051 1125
22	1.075 957 9511	22.787 385 3191	.043 883 9290
23	1.079 544 4776	23.863 343 2702	.041 905 2766
24	1.083 142 9592	24.942 887 7477	.040 091 5888
25	1.086 753 4357	26.026 030 7069	.038 423 0700
26	1.090 375 9471	27.112 784 1426	.036 882 9698
27	1.094 010 5336	28.203 160 0897	.035 457 0196
28	1.097 657 2354	29.297 170 6233	.034 132 9889
29	1.101 316 0929	30.394 827 8588	.032 900 3344
30	1.104 987 1465	31.496 143 9516	.031 749 9184
31	1.108 670 4370	32.601 131 0981	.030 673 7824
32	1.112 366 0051	33.709 801 5351	.029 664 9625
33	1.116 073 8918	34.822 167 5402	.028 717 3393
34	1.119 794 1381	35.938 241 4320	.027 825 5129
35	1.123 526 7852	37.058 035 5701	.026 984 7007
36	1.127 271 8745	38.181 562 3554	.026 190 6517
37	1.131 029 4474	39.308 834 2299	.025 439 5741
38	1.134 799 5456	40.439 863 6773	.024 728 0754
39	1.138 582 2107	41.574 663 2229	.024 053 1113
40	1.142 377 4848	42.713 245 4337	.023 411 9414
41	1.146 185 4097	43.855 622 9184	.022 802 0932
42	1.150 006 0278	45.001 808 3282	.022 221 3293
43	1.153 839 3812	46.151 814 3559	.021 667 6205
44	1.157 685 5125	47.305 653 7371	.021 139 1223
45	1.161 544 4642	48.463 339 2496	.020 634 1539
46	1.165 416 2790	49.624 883 7137	.020 151 1807
47	1.169 301 0000	50.790 299 9928	.019 688 7988
48	1.173 198 6700	51.959 600 9928	.019 245 7213
49	1.177 109 3322	53.132 799 6627	.018 820 7662
50	1.181 033 0300	54.309 908 9949	.018 412 8462
51	1.184 969 8067	55.490 942 0249	.018 020 9592
52	1.188 919 7061	56.675 911 8317	.017 644 1802
53	1.192 882 7718	57.864 831 5378	.017 281 6540
54	1.196 859 0477	59.057 714 3096	.016 932 5889
55	1.200 848 5779	60.254 573 3573	.016 596 2506
56	1.204 851 4065	61.455 421 9351	.016 271 9573
57	1.208 867 5778	62.660 273 3416	.015 959 0750
58	1.212 897 1364	63.869 140 9194	.015 657 0135
59	1.216 940 1269	65.082 038 0558	.015 365 2226
60	1.220 996 5939	66.298 978 1826	.015 083 1887
n	$s=(1+i)^n$	$s_{\overline{n}\rceil}=\dfrac{(1+i)^n-1}{i}$	$\dfrac{1}{s_{\overline{n}\rceil}}=\dfrac{i}{(1+i)^n-1}$

.00333333

per period

ANNUALLY
If compounded
annually
nominal annual rate is

1/3%

SEMIANNUALLY
If compounded
semiannually
nominal annual rate is

2/3%

QUARTERLY
If compounded
quarterly
nominal annual rate is

1 1/3%

MONTHLY
If compounded
monthly
nominal annual rate is

4%

i = .00333333
$j_{(2)}$ = .00666666
$j_{(4)}$ = .01333333
$j_{(12)}$ = .04

12

PRESENT WORTH OF 1	PRESENT WORTH OF 1 PER PERIOD	PARTIAL PAYMENT	PERIODS	RATE
What $1 due in the future is worth today.	*What $1 payable periodically is worth today.*	*Annuity worth $1 today.* *Periodic payment necessary to pay off a loan of $1.*		$\frac{1}{3}\%$
.996 677 7409	.996 677 7409	1.003 333 3333	1	
.993 366 5191	1.990 044 2600	.502 501 3866	2	
.990 066 2981	2.980 110 5581	.335 558 0206	3	.00333333
.986 777 0413	3.966 887 5995	.252 086 7998	4	
.983 498 7123	4.950 386 3118	.202 004 4370	5	*per period*
.980 231 2747	5.930 617 5865	.168 616 5033	6	
.976 974 6924	6.907 592 2789	.144 768 2434	7	
.973 728 9293	7.881 321 2082	.126 882 2795	8	
.970 493 9495	8.851 815 1577	.112 971 1796	9	
.967 269 7171	9.819 084 8747	.101 842 4846	10	
.964 056 1964	10.783 141 0712	.092 737 3567	11	
.960 853 3519	11.743 994 4231	.085 149 9042	12	
.957 661 1481	12.701 655 5712	.078 729 8943	13	
.954 479 5496	13.656 135 1208	.073 227 1606	14	
.951 308 5212	14.607 443 6420	.068 458 2480	15	
.948 148 0278	15.555 591 6698	.064 285 5650	16	
.944 998 0343	16.500 589 7041	.060 603 8946	17	
.941 858 5060	17.442 448 2100	.057 331 4014	18	
.938 729 4079	18.381 177 6180	.054 403 4784	19	
.935 610 7056	19.316 788 3236	.051 768 4401	20	
.932 502 3644	20.249 290 6879	.049 384 4459	21	
.929 404 3499	21.178 695 0378	.047 217 2624	22	
.926 316 6278	22.105 011 6656	.045 238 6099	23	
.923 239 1639	23.028 250 8295	.043 424 9222	24	
.920 171 9242	23.948 422 7537	.041 756 4033	25	$\frac{1}{3}\%$
.917 114 8746	24.865 537 6282	.040 216 3032	26	
.914 067 9813	25.779 605 6095	.038 790 3529	27	
.911 031 2106	26.690 636 8201	.037 466 3222	28	
.908 004 5288	27.598 641 3490	.036 233 6677	29	
.904 987 9025	28.503 629 2515	.035 083 2517	30	**SEMIANNUALLY**
.901 981 2982	29.405 610 5496	.034 007 1157	31	If compounded
.898 984 6826	30.304 595 2322	.032 998 2959	32	*semiannually*
.895 998 0225	31.200 593 2547	.032 050 6726	33	nominal annual rate is
.893 021 2849	32.093 614 5395	.031 158 8462	34	
.890 054 4367	32.983 668 9763	.030 318 0341	35	$\frac{2}{3}\%$
.887 097 4453	33.870 766 4215	.029 523 9850	36	
.884 150 2777	34.754 916 6992	.028 772 9074	37	
.881 212 9013	35.636 129 6005	.028 061 4088	38	
.878 285 2837	36.514 414 8843	.027 386 4446	39	
.875 367 3924	37.389 782 2767	.026 745 2748	40	
.872 459 1951	38.262 241 4718	.026 135 4265	41	**QUARTERLY**
.869 560 6596	39.131 802 1313	.025 554 6626	42	If compounded
.866 671 7537	39.998 473 8850	.025 000 9539	43	*quarterly*
.863 792 4456	40.862 266 3306	.024 472 4556	44	nominal annual rate is
.860 922 7032	41.723 189 0338	.023 967 4872	45	$1\frac{1}{3}\%$
.858 062 4949	42.581 251 5287	.023 484 5141	46	
.855 211 7889	43.436 463 3177	.023 022 1322	47	
.852 370 5538	44.288 833 8714	.022 579 0546	48	
.849 538 7579	45.138 372 6293	.022 154 0995	49	
.846 716 3700	45.985 088 9993	.021 746 1795	50	
.843 903 3588	46.828 992 3582	.021 354 2925	51	**MONTHLY**
.841 099 6932	47.670 092 0513	.020 977 5135	52	If compounded
.838 305 3420	48.508 397 3933	.020 614 9874	53	*monthly*
.835 520 2744	49.343 917 6678	.020 265 9223	54	nominal annual rate is
.832 744 4596	50.176 662 1274	.019 929 5839	55	4%
.829 977 8667	51.006 639 9940	.019 605 2906	56	
.827 220 4651	51.833 860 4592	.019 292 4083	57	
.824 472 2244	52.658 332 6836	.018 990 3468	58	i = .00333333
.821 733 1140	53.480 065 7976	.018 698 5559	59	$j_{(2)}$ = .00666666
.819 003 1037	54.299 068 9012	.018 416 5221	60	$j_{(4)}$ = .01333333
$v^n = \dfrac{1}{(1+i)^n}$	$a_{\overline{n}|} = \dfrac{1-v^n}{i}$	$\dfrac{1}{a_{\overline{n}|}} = \dfrac{i}{1-v^n}$	n	$j_{(12)}$ = .04

ANNUALLY
If compounded
annually
nominal annual rate is

13

RATE **1/3%**	P E R I O D S	AMOUNT OF 1 *How $1 left at compound interest will grow.*	AMOUNT OF 1 PER PERIOD *How $1 deposited periodically will grow.*	SINKING FUND *Periodic deposit that will grow to $1 at future date.*
	61	1.225 066 5826	67.519 974 7766	.014 810 4321
	62	1.229 150 1379	68.745 041 3592	.014 546 5037
.00333333	63	1.233 247 3050	69.974 191 4970	.014 290 9833
per period	64	1.237 358 1293	71.207 438 8020	.014 043 4766
	65	1.241 482 6564	72.444 796 9314	.013 803 6138
	66	1.245 620 9320	73.686 279 5878	.013 571 0475
	67	1.249 773 0017	74.931 900 5198	.013 345 4509
	68	1.253 938 9117	76.181 673 5215	.013 126 5166
	69	1.258 118 7081	77.435 612 4332	.012 913 9548
	70	1.262 312 4371	78.693 731 1413	.012 707 4925
	71	1.266 520 1453	79.956 043 5785	.012 506 8720
	72	1.270 741 8791	81.222 563 7237	.012 311 8497
	73	1.274 977 6853	82.493 305 6028	.012 122 1958
	74	1.279 227 6110	83.768 283 2882	.011 937 6924
	75	1.283 491 7030	85.047 510 8991	.011 758 1337
	76	1.287 770 0087	86.331 002 6021	.011 583 3243
	77	1.292 062 5754	87.618 772 6108	.011 413 0793
	78	1.296 369 4506	88.910 835 1862	.011 247 2231
	79	1.300 690 6821	90.207 204 6368	.011 085 5891
	80	1.305 026 3177	91.507 895 3189	.010 928 0188
ANNUALLY *If compounded annually nominal annual rate is* **1/3%**	81	1.309 376 4055	92.812 921 6366	.010 774 3618
	82	1.313 740 9935	94.122 298 0421	.010 624 4750
	83	1.318 120 1301	95.436 039 0356	.010 478 2220
	84	1.322 513 8639	96.754 159 1657	.010 335 4730
	85	1.326 922 2434	98.076 673 0296	.010 196 1044
	86	1.331 345 3176	99.403 595 2730	.010 059 9983
	87	1.335 783 1353	100.734 940 5906	.009 927 0421
	88	1.340 235 7458	102.070 723 7259	.009 797 1285
	89	1.344 703 1982	103.410 959 4716	.009 670 1549
	90	1.349 185 5422	104.755 662 6699	.009 546 0233
SEMIANNUALLY *If compounded semiannually nominal annual rate is* **2/3%**	91	1.353 682 8274	106.104 848 2121	.009 424 6400
	92	1.358 195 1035	107.458 531 0395	.009 305 9154
	93	1.362 722 4205	108.816 726 1429	.009 189 7637
	94	1.367 264 8285	110.179 448 5634	.009 076 1028
	95	1.371 822 3780	111.546 713 3920	.008 964 8540
	96	1.376 395 1192	112.918 535 7699	.008 855 9420
	97	1.380 983 1030	114.294 930 8892	.008 749 2944
	98	1.385 586 3800	115.675 913 9921	.008 644 8420
	99	1.390 205 0012	117.061 500 3721	.008 542 5182
	100	1.394 839 0179	118.451 705 3733	.008 442 2592
QUARTERLY *If compounded quarterly nominal annual rate is* **1 1/3%**	101	1.399 488 4813	119.846 544 3913	.008 344 0036
	102	1.404 153 4429	121.246 032 8726	.008 247 6925
	103	1.408 833 9544	122.650 186 3155	.008 153 2693
	104	1.413 530 0676	124.059 020 2699	.008 060 6795
	105	1.418 241 8345	125.472 550 3374	.007 969 8707
	106	1.422 969 3072	126.890 792 1719	.007 880 7925
	107	1.427 712 5383	128.313 761 4791	.007 793 3963
	108	1.432 471 5801	129.741 474 0174	.007 707 6356
	109	1.437 246 4853	131.173 945 5974	.007 623 4651
	110	1.442 037 3069	132.611 192 0828	.007 540 8416
MONTHLY *If compounded monthly nominal annual rate is* **4%**	111	1.446 844 0980	134.053 229 3897	.007 459 7233
	112	1.451 666 9116	135.500 073 4877	.007 380 0698
	113	1.456 505 8013	136.951 740 3993	.007 301 8422
	114	1.461 360 8207	138.408 246 2006	.007 225 0030
	115	1.466 232 0234	139.869 607 0213	.007 149 5160
i = .00333333 $j_{(2)}$ = .00666666 $j_{(4)}$ = .01333333 $j_{(12)}$ = .04	116	1.471 119 4635	141.335 839 0447	.007 075 3463
	117	1.476 023 1950	142.806 958 5082	.007 002 4599
	118	1.480 943 2723	144.282 981 7032	.006 930 8243
	119	1.485 879 7499	145.763 924 9756	.006 860 4080
	120	1.490 832 6824	147.249 804 7255	.006 791 1805
	n	$s=(1+i)^n$	$s_{\overline{n}\rceil}=\dfrac{(1+i)^n-1}{i}$	$\dfrac{1}{s_{\overline{n}\rceil}}=\dfrac{i}{(1+i)^n-1}$

14

PRESENT WORTH OF 1 *What $1 due in the future is worth today.*	PRESENT WORTH OF 1 PER PERIOD *What $1 payable periodically is worth today.*	PARTIAL PAYMENT *Annuity worth $1 today.* *Periodic payment necessary to pay off a loan of $1.*	PERIODS	RATE $1/3\%$
.816 282 1631	55.115 351 0644	.018 143 7654	61	
.813 570 2622	55.928 921 3266	.017 879 8971	62	
.810 867 3710	56.739 788 6976	.017 624 3166	63	.00333333
.808 173 4595	57.547 962 1571	.017 376 8099	64	*per period*
.805 488 4978	58.353 450 6549	.017 136 9472	65	
.802 812 4563	59.156 263 1112	.016 904 3808	66	
.800 145 3053	59.956 408 4165	.016 678 7842	67	
.797 487 0152	60.753 895 4317	.016 459 8499	68	
.794 837 5567	61.548 732 9884	.016 247 2881	69	
.792 196 9004	62.340 929 8888	.016 040 8259	70	
.789 565 0170	63.130 494 9058	.015 840 2053	71	
.786 941 8774	63.917 436 7831	.015 645 1831	72	
.784 327 4525	64.701 764 2357	.015 455 5291	73	
.781 721 7135	65.483 485 9492	.015 271 0257	74	
.779 124 6314	66.262 610 5806	.015 091 4670	75	
.776 536 1775	67.039 146 7581	.014 916 6576	76	
.773 956 3231	67.813 103 0811	.014 746 4126	77	
.771 385 0396	68.584 488 1207	.014 580 5564	78	
.768 822 2986	69.353 310 4193	.014 418 9224	79	
.766 268 0717	70.119 578 4910	.014 261 3521	80	
.763 722 3306	70.883 300 8216	.014 107 6952	81	ANNUALLY If compounded *annually* nominal annual rate is
.761 185 0471	71.644 485 8687	.013 957 8083	82	
.758 656 1931	72.403 142 0619	.013 811 5553	83	
.756 135 7407	73.159 277 8025	.013 668 8063	84	
.753 623 6618	73.912 901 4643	.013 529 4378	85	$1/3\%$
.751 119 9287	74.664 021 3930	.013 393 3316	86	
.748 624 5136	75.412 645 9066	.013 260 3755	87	
.746 137 3890	76.158 783 2956	.013 130 4619	88	
.743 658 5273	76.902 441 8229	.013 003 4883	89	
.741 187 9009	77.643 629 7238	.012 879 3567	90	
.738 725 4826	78.382 355 2065	.012 757 9734	91	SEMIANNUALLY If compounded *semiannually* nominal annual rate is
.736 271 2452	79.118 626 4516	.012 639 2487	92	
.733 825 1613	79.852 451 6129	.012 523 0970	93	
.731 387 2039	80.583 838 8169	.012 409 4361	94	
.728 957 3461	81.312 796 1630	.012 298 1873	95	$2/3\%$
.726 535 5609	82.039 331 7239	.012 189 2753	96	
.724 121 8215	82.763 453 5454	.012 082 6277	97	
.721 716 1012	83.485 169 6466	.011 978 1753	98	
.719 318 3733	84.204 488 0199	.011 875 8516	99	
.716 928 6112	84.921 416 6311	.011 775 5925	100	
.714 546 7886	85.635 963 4197	.011 677 3370	101	QUARTERLY If compounded *quarterly* nominal annual rate is
.712 172 8790	86.348 136 2987	.011 581 0259	102	
.709 806 8562	87.057 943 1549	.011 486 6026	103	
.707 448 6938	87.765 391 8487	.011 394 0128	104	
.705 098 3660	88.470 490 2146	.011 303 2040	105	$1\frac{1}{3}\%$
.702 755 8465	89.173 246 0611	.011 214 1258	106	
.700 421 1094	89.873 667 1705	.011 126 7297	107	
.698 094 1290	90.571 761 2995	.011 040 9689	108	
.695 774 8794	91.267 536 1789	.010 956 7985	109	
.693 463 3350	91.960 999 5139	.010 874 1750	110	
.691 159 4701	92.652 158 9840	.010 793 0566	111	MONTHLY If compounded *monthly* nominal annual rate is
.688 863 2592	93.341 022 2431	.010 713 4031	112	
.686 574 6769	94.027 596 9201	.010 635 1756	113	
.684 293 6979	94.711 890 6180	.010 558 3364	114	
.682 020 2970	95.393 910 9150	.010 482 8494	115	4%
.679 754 4488	96.073 665 3638	.010 408 6796	116	
.677 496 1284	96.751 161 4921	.010 335 7932	117	
.675 245 3107	97.426 406 8028	.010 264 1577	118	$i = .00333333$
.673 001 9708	98.099 408 7735	.010 193 7414	119	$j_{(2)} = .00666666$ $j_{(4)} = .01333333$
.670 766 0838	98.770 174 8573	.010 124 5138	120	$j_{(12)} = .04$
$v^n = \dfrac{1}{(1+i)^n}$	$a_{\overline{n}} = \dfrac{1-v^n}{i}$	$\dfrac{1}{a_{\overline{n}}} = \dfrac{i}{1-v^n}$	n	

15

	P E R I O D S	AMOUNT OF 1 *How $1 left at compound interest will grow.*	AMOUNT OF 1 PER PERIOD *How $1 deposited periodically will grow.*	SINKING FUND *Periodic deposit that will grow to $1 at future date.*
	121	1.495 802 1247	148.740 637 4079	.006 723 1122
	122	1.500 788 1318	150.236 439 5326	.006 656 1748
.00333333	123	1.505 790 7589	151.737 227 6644	.006 590 3405
per period	124	1.510 810 0614	153.243 018 4232	.006 525 5828
	125	1.515 846 0949	154.753 828 4847	.006 461 8757
	126	1.520 898 9153	156.269 674 5796	.006 399 1942
	127	1.525 968 5783	157.790 573 4949	.006 337 5142
	128	1.531 055 1402	159.316 542 0732	.006 276 8121
	129	1.536 158 6574	160.847 597 2134	.006 217 0652
	130	1.541 279 1862	162.383 755 8708	.006 158 2514
	131	1.546 416 7835	163.925 035 0570	.006 100 3495
	132	1.551 571 5061	165.471 451 8406	.006 043 3385
	133	1.556 743 4112	167.023 023 3467	.005 987 1985
	134	1.561 932 5559	168.579 766 7579	.005 931 9100
	135	1.567 138 9977	170.141 699 3137	.005 877 4539
	136	1.572 362 7944	171.708 838 3114	.005 823 8120
	137	1.577 604 0037	173.281 201 1058	.005 770 9665
	138	1.582 862 6837	174.858 805 1095	.005 718 8999
	139	1.588 138 8926	176.441 667 7932	.005 667 5955
	140	1.593 432 6890	178.029 806 6858	.005 617 0369
ANNUALLY *If compounded annually* nominal annual rate is 1/3%	141	1.598 744 1312	179.623 239 3748	.005 567 2084
	142	1.604 073 2784	181.221 983 5060	.005 518 0943
	143	1.609 420 1893	182.826 056 7844	.005 469 6799
	144	1.614 784 9232	184.435 476 9737	.005 421 9504
	145	1.620 167 5397	186.050 261 8969	.005 374 8917
	146	1.625 568 0981	187.670 429 4366	.005 328 4900
	147	1.630 986 6584	189.295 997 5347	.005 282 7319
	148	1.636 423 2806	190.926 984 1931	.005 237 6043
	149	1.641 878 0249	192.563 407 4738	.005 193 0946
	150	1.647 350 9517	194.205 285 4987	.005 149 1904
SEMIANNUALLY *If compounded semiannually* nominal annual rate is 2/3%	151	1.652 842 1215	195.852 636 4504	.005 105 8797
	152	1.658 351 5952	197.505 478 5719	.005 063 1507
	153	1.663 879 4339	199.163 830 1671	.005 020 9920
	154	1.669 425 6987	200.827 709 6010	.004 979 3925
	155	1.674 990 4510	202.497 135 2997	.004 938 3415
	156	1.680 573 7525	204.172 125 7507	.004 897 8282
	157	1.686 175 6650	205.852 699 5032	.004 857 8425
	158	1.691 796 2506	207.538 875 1682	.004 818 3744
	159	1.697 435 5714	209.230 671 4187	.004 779 4140
	160	1.703 093 6900	210.928 106 9901	.004 740 9519
QUARTERLY *If compounded quarterly* nominal annual rate is 1 1/3%	161	1.708 770 6689	212.631 200 6801	.004 702 9787
	162	1.714 466 5712	214.339 971 3490	.004 665 4854
	163	1.720 181 4597	216.054 437 9202	.004 628 4631
	164	1.725 915 3979	217.774 619 3799	.004 591 9033
	165	1.731 668 4493	219.500 534 7779	.004 555 7976
	166	1.737 440 6774	221.232 203 2271	.004 520 1376
	167	1.743 232 1463	222.969 643 9045	.004 484 9154
	168	1.749 042 9202	224.712 876 0509	.004 450 1233
	169	1.754 873 0632	226.461 918 9711	.004 415 7535
	170	1.760 722 6401	228.216 792 0343	.004 381 7985
MONTHLY *If compounded monthly* nominal annual rate is 4%	171	1.766 591 7156	229.977 514 6744	.004 348 2512
	172	1.772 480 3546	231.744 106 3900	.004 315 1043
	173	1.778 388 6225	233.516 586 7446	.004 282 3510
	174	1.784 316 5846	235.294 975 3671	.004 249 9845
	175	1.790 264 3065	237.079 291 9517	.004 217 9981
	176	1.796 231 8542	238.869 556 2582	.004 186 3853
	177	1.802 219 2937	240.665 788 1124	.004 155 1398
i = .00333333 $j_{(2)}$ = .00666666 $j_{(4)}$ = .01333333 $j_{(12)}$ = .04	178	1.808 226 6914	242.468 007 4061	.004 124 2554
	179	1.814 254 1137	244.276 234 0974	.004 093 7261
	180	1.820 301 6274	246.090 488 2111	.004 063 5459
	n	$s=(1+i)^n$	$s_{\overline{n}|}=\dfrac{(1+i)^n-1}{i}$	$\dfrac{1}{s_{\overline{n}|}}=\dfrac{i}{(1+i)^n-1}$

PRESENT WORTH OF 1 What $1 due in the future is worth today.	PRESENT WORTH OF 1 PER PERIOD What $1 payable periodically is worth today.	PARTIAL PAYMENT Annuity worth $1 today. Periodic payment necessary to pay off a loan of $1.	PERIODS	RATE 1/3%
.668 537 6251	99.438 712 4824	.010 056 4456	121	
.666 316 5698	100.105 029 0522	.009 989 5081	122	
.664 102 8935	100.769 131 9457	.009 923 6739	123	.00333333
.661 896 5716	101.431 028 5173	.009 858 9161	124	*per period*
.659 697 5797	102.090 726 0970	.009 795 2090	125	
.657 505 8934	102.748 231 9904	.009 732 5276	126	
.655 321 4884	103.403 553 4788	.009 670 8475	127	
.653 144 3406	104.056 697 8194	.009 610 1454	128	
.650 974 4258	104.707 672 2452	.009 550 3985	129	
.648 811 7201	105.356 483 9654	.009 491 5848	130	
.646 656 1995	106.003 140 1648	.009 433 6828	131	
.644 507 8400	106.647 648 0048	.009 376 6719	132	
.642 366 6179	107.290 014 6227	.009 320 5319	133	
.640 232 5096	107.930 247 1323	.009 265 2433	134	
.638 105 4913	108.568 352 6235	.009 210 7873	135	
.635 985 5395	109.204 338 1630	.009 157 1454	136	
.633 872 6307	109.838 210 7937	.009 104 2998	137	
.631 766 7415	110.469 977 5352	.009 052 2332	138	
.629 667 8487	111.099 645 3839	.009 000 9288	139	
.627 575 9290	111.727 221 3129	.008 950 3703	140	
.625 490 9591	112.352 712 2720	.008 900 5417	141	ANNUALLY If compounded *annually* nominal annual rate is 1/3%
.623 412 9160	112.976 125 1880	.008 851 4277	142	
.621 341 7768	113.597 466 9648	.008 803 0132	143	
.619 277 5184	114.216 744 4832	.008 755 2837	144	
.617 220 1180	114.833 964 6012	.008 708 2250	145	
.615 169 5528	115.449 134 1540	.008 661 8233	146	
.613 125 8002	116.062 259 9542	.008 616 0652	147	
.611 088 8374	116.673 348 7915	.008 570 9377	148	
.609 058 6419	117.282 407 4334	.008 526 4280	149	
.607 035 1913	117.889 442 6247	.008 482 5238	150	
.605 018 4630	118.494 461 0877	.008 439 2130	151	SEMIANNUALLY If compounded *semiannually* nominal annual rate is 2/3%
.603 008 4349	119.097 469 5226	.008 396 4840	152	
.601 005 0846	119.698 474 6073	.008 354 3253	153	
.599 008 3900	120.297 482 9973	.008 312 7259	154	
.597 018 3289	120.894 501 3262	.008 271 6748	155	
.595 034 8793	121.489 536 2055	.008 231 1616	156	
.593 058 0193	122.082 594 2248	.008 191 1759	157	
.591 087 7268	122.673 681 9516	.008 151 7077	158	
.589 123 9802	123.262 805 9318	.008 112 7473	159	
.587 166 7577	123.849 972 6895	.008 074 2852	160	
.585 216 0376	124.435 188 7271	.008 036 3120	161	QUARTERLY If compounded *quarterly* nominal annual rate is 1 1/3%
.583 271 7982	125.018 460 5253	.007 998 8187	162	
.581 334 0182	125.599 794 5435	.007 961 7965	163	
.579 402 6759	126.179 197 2195	.007 925 2367	164	
.577 477 7501	126.756 674 9696	.007 889 1309	165	
.575 559 2194	127.332 234 1889	.007 853 4709	166	
.573 647 0625	127.905 881 2514	.007 818 2488	167	
.571 741 2583	128.477 622 5097	.007 783 4566	168	
.569 841 7857	129.047 464 2954	.007 749 0868	169	
.567 948 6236	129.615 412 9190	.007 715 1318	170	
.566 061 7511	130.181 474 6701	.007 681 5845	171	MONTHLY If compounded *monthly* nominal annual rate is 4%
.564 181 1473	130.745 655 8174	.007 648 4377	172	
.562 306 7913	131.307 962 6087	.007 615 6844	173	
.560 438 6624	131.868 401 2711	.007 583 3178	174	
.558 576 7400	132.426 978 0111	.007 551 3314	175	
.556 721 0033	132.983 699 0144	.007 519 7186	176	
.554 871 4318	133.538 570 4462	.007 488 4732	177	
.553 028 0052	134.091 598 4514	.007 457 5888	178	$i = .00333333$
.551 190 7028	134.642 789 1542	.007 427 0595	179	$j_{(2)} = .00666666$
.549 359 5045	135.192 148 6587	.007 396 8793	180	$j_{(4)} = .01333333$ $j_{(12)} = .04$
$v^n = \dfrac{1}{(1+i)^n}$	$a_{\overline{n}|} = \dfrac{1-v^n}{i}$	$\dfrac{1}{a_{\overline{n}|}} = \dfrac{i}{1-v^n}$	n	

P E R I O D S	AMOUNT OF 1 How $1 left at compound interest will grow.	AMOUNT OF 1 PER PERIOD How $1 deposited periodically will grow.	SINKING FUND Periodic deposit that will grow to $1 at future date.
1	1.004 166 6667	1.000 000 0000	1.000 000 0000
2	1.008 350 6944	2.004 166 6667	.498 960 4990
3	1.012 552 1557	3.012 517 3611	.331 948 2944
4	1.016 771 1230	4.025 069 5168	.248 442 9140
5	1.021 007 6693	5.041 840 6398	.198 340 2633
6	1.025 261 8680	6.062 848 3091	.164 938 9774
7	1.029 533 7924	7.088 110 1771	.141 081 3285
8	1.033 823 5165	8.117 643 9695	.123 188 4527
9	1.038 131 1145	9.151 467 4860	.109 272 0923
10	1.042 456 6608	10.189 598 6005	.098 139 2927
11	1.046 800 2303	11.232 055 2614	.089 030 9010
12	1.051 161 8979	12.278 855 4916	.081 440 8151
13	1.055 541 7391	13.330 017 3895	.075 018 6568
14	1.059 939 8297	14.385 559 1286	.069 514 1559
15	1.064 356 2457	15.445 498 9583	.064 743 7809
16	1.068 791 0633	16.509 855 2040	.060 569 8831
17	1.073 244 3594	17.578 646 2673	.056 887 2019
18	1.077 716 2109	18.651 890 6268	.053 613 8679
19	1.082 206 6952	19.729 606 8377	.050 685 2472
20	1.086 715 8897	20.811 813 5329	.048 049 6329
21	1.091 243 8726	21.898 529 4226	.045 665 1669
22	1.095 790 7221	22.989 773 2952	.043 497 6016
23	1.100 356 5167	24.085 564 0173	.041 518 6457
24	1.104 941 3356	25.185 920 5340	.039 704 7231
25	1.109 545 2578	26.290 861 8696	.038 036 0296
26	1.114 168 3630	27.400 407 1273	.036 495 8081
27	1.118 810 7312	28.514 575 4904	.035 069 7839
28	1.123 472 4426	29.633 386 2216	.033 745 7215
29	1.128 153 5778	30.756 858 6642	.032 513 0733
30	1.132 854 2177	31.885 012 2419	.031 362 6977
31	1.137 574 4436	33.017 866 4596	.030 286 6329
32	1.142 314 3371	34.155 440 9032	.029 277 9122
33	1.147 073 9802	35.297 755 2403	.028 330 4135
34	1.151 853 4551	36.444 829 2205	.027 438 7347
35	1.156 652 8445	37.596 682 6756	.026 598 0913
36	1.161 472 2313	38.753 335 5200	.025 804 2304
37	1.166 311 6990	39.914 807 7514	.025 053 3588
38	1.171 171 3310	41.081 119 4503	.024 342 0825
39	1.176 051 2116	42.252 290 7814	.023 667 3558
40	1.180 951 4250	43.428 341 9930	.023 026 4374
41	1.185 872 0559	44.609 293 4179	.022 416 8536
42	1.190 813 1895	45.795 165 4738	.021 836 3661
43	1.195 774 9111	46.985 978 6633	.021 282 9450
44	1.200 757 3066	48.181 753 5744	.020 754 7448
45	1.205 760 4620	49.382 510 8810	.020 250 0841
46	1.210 784 4639	50.588 271 3430	.019 767 4278
47	1.215 829 3992	51.799 055 8069	.019 305 3712
48	1.220 895 3550	53.014 885 2061	.018 862 6269
49	1.225 982 4190	54.235 780 5611	.018 438 0125
50	1.231 090 6791	55.461 762 9801	.018 030 4402
51	1.236 220 2236	56.692 853 6592	.017 638 9075
52	1.241 371 1412	57.929 073 8828	.017 262 4890
53	1.246 543 5209	59.170 445 0240	.016 900 3292
54	1.251 737 4523	60.416 988 5449	.016 551 6360
55	1.256 953 0250	61.668 725 9972	.016 215 6747
56	1.262 190 3293	62.925 679 0222	.015 891 7634
57	1.267 449 4556	64.187 869 3514	.015 579 2677
58	1.272 730 4950	65.455 318 8071	.015 277 5973
59	1.278 033 5388	66.728 049 3021	.014 986 2016
60	1.283 358 6785	68.006 082 8408	.014 704 5670
n	$s=(1+i)^n$	$s_{\overline{n}\rceil}=\dfrac{(1+i)^n-1}{i}$	$\dfrac{1}{s_{\overline{n}\rceil}}=\dfrac{i}{(1+i)^n-1}$

.00416666

per period

ANNUALLY
If compounded
annually
nominal annual rate is

5/12%

SEMIANNUALLY
If compounded
semiannually
nominal annual rate is

5/6%

QUARTERLY
If compounded
quarterly
nominal annual rate is

1 2/3%

MONTHLY
If compounded
monthly
nominal annual rate is

5%

i = .00416666
$j_{(2)}$ = .00833333
$j_{(4)}$ = .01666666
$j_{(12)}$ = .05

PRESENT WORTH OF 1	PRESENT WORTH OF 1 PER PERIOD	PARTIAL PAYMENT	P E R I O D S	RATE
What $1 due in the future is worth today.	*What $1 payable periodically is worth today.*	*Annuity worth $1 today.* *Periodic payment necessary to pay off a loan of $1.*		$5/12\%$

PRESENT WORTH OF 1	PRESENT WORTH OF 1 PER PERIOD	PARTIAL PAYMENT	PERIODS	
.995 850 6224	.995 850 6224	1.004 166 6667	1	
.991 718 4621	1.987 569 0846	.503 127 1656	2	
.987 603 4478	2.975 172 5323	.336 114 9611	3	.00416666
.983 505 5082	3.958 678 0405	.252 609 5807	4	*per period*
.979 424 5724	4.938 102 6129	.202 506 9300	5	
.975 360 5701	5.913 463 1830	.169 105 6440	6	
.971 313 4308	6.884 776 6138	.145 247 9951	7	
.967 283 0846	7.852 059 6984	.127 355 1193	8	
.963 269 4618	8.815 329 1602	.113 438 7590	9	
.959 272 4931	9.774 601 6533	.102 305 9594	10	
.955 292 1093	10.729 893 7626	.093 197 5677	11	
.951 328 2416	11.681 222 0043	.085 607 4818	12	
.947 380 8216	12.628 602 8259	.079 185 3235	13	
.943 449 7808	13.572 052 6067	.073 680 8226	14	
.939 535 0514	14.511 587 6581	.068 910 4475	15	
.935 636 5657	15.447 224 2238	.064 736 5498	16	
.931 754 2563	16.378 978 4802	.061 053 8686	17	
.927 888 0561	17.306 866 5363	.057 780 5346	18	
.924 037 8982	18.230 904 4344	.054 851 9139	19	
.920 203 7160	19.151 108 1505	.052 216 2996	20	
.916 385 4434	20.067 493 5938	.049 831 8335	21	ANNUALLY
.912 583 0141	20.980 076 6080	.047 664 2683	22	If compounded *annually* nominal annual rate is
.908 796 3626	21.888 872 9706	.045 685 3124	23	
.905 025 4234	22.793 898 3940	.043 871 3897	24	
.901 270 1311	23.695 168 5251	.042 202 6963	25	$5/12\%$
.897 530 4211	24.592 698 9462	.040 662 4748	26	
.893 806 2284	25.486 505 1746	.039 236 4506	27	
.890 097 4889	26.376 602 6635	.037 912 3882	28	
.886 404 1383	27.263 006 8018	.036 679 7400	29	
.882 726 1129	28.145 732 9147	.035 529 3644	30	
.879 063 3489	29.024 796 2636	.034 453 2995	31	SEMIANNUALLY
.875 415 7831	29.900 212 0467	.033 444 5789	32	If compounded *semiannually* nominal annual rate is
.871 783 3525	30.771 995 3992	.032 497 0801	33	
.868 165 9942	31.640 161 3934	.031 605 4014	34	
.864 563 6457	32.504 725 0391	.030 764 7580	35	$5/6\%$
.860 976 2447	33.365 701 2837	.029 970 8971	36	
.857 403 7291	34.223 105 0129	.029 220 0255	37	
.853 846 0373	35.076 951 0501	.028 508 7492	38	
.850 303 1077	35.927 254 1578	.027 834 0225	39	
.846 774 8790	36.774 029 0368	.027 193 1041	40	QUARTERLY
.843 261 2903	37.617 290 3271	.026 583 5203	41	If compounded *quarterly* nominal annual rate is
.839 762 2808	38.457 052 6079	.026 003 0328	42	
.836 277 7900	39.293 330 3979	.025 449 6117	43	
.832 807 7577	40.126 138 1556	.024 921 4115	44	
.829 352 1238	40.955 490 2795	.024 416 7508	45	$1 2/3\%$
.825 910 8287	41.781 401 1082	.023 934 0944	46	
.822 483 8128	42.603 884 9210	.023 472 0379	47	
.819 071 0169	43.422 955 9379	.023 029 2936	48	
.815 672 3820	44.238 628 3199	.022 604 6792	49	
.812 287 8493	45.050 916 1692	.022 197 1069	50	MONTHLY
.808 917 3603	45.859 833 5295	.021 805 5741	51	If compounded *monthly* nominal annual rate is
.805 560 8567	46.665 394 3862	.021 429 1557	52	
.802 218 2806	47.467 612 6668	.021 066 9959	53	
.798 889 5740	48.266 502 2408	.020 718 3026	54	
.795 574 6795	49.062 076 9203	.020 382 3414	55	5%
.792 273 5397	49.854 350 4600	.020 058 4300	56	
.788 986 0977	50.643 336 5577	.019 745 9344	57	
.785 712 2964	51.429 048 8542	.019 444 2639	58	$i = .00416666$
.782 452 0794	52.211 500 9336	.019 152 8683	59	$j^{(2)} = .00833333$
.779 205 3903	52.990 706 3239	.018 871 2336	60	$j^{(4)} = .01666666$
$v^n = \dfrac{1}{(1+i)^n}$	$a_{\overline{n}} = \dfrac{1-v^n}{i}$	$\dfrac{1}{a_{\overline{n}}} = \dfrac{i}{1-v^n}$	n	$j^{(12)} = .05$

P E R I O D S	AMOUNT OF 1 How $1 left at compound interest will grow.	AMOUNT OF 1 PER PERIOD How $1 deposited periodically will grow.	SINKING FUND Periodic deposit that will grow to $1 at future date.
61	1.288 706 0063	69.289 441 5193	.014 432 2133
62	1.294 075 6147	70.578 147 5257	.014 168 6915
63	1.299 467 5964	71.872 223 1404	.013 913 5810
64	1.304 882 0447	73.171 690 7368	.013 666 4875
65	1.310 319 0533	74.476 572 7815	.013 427 0410
66	1.315 778 7160	75.786 891 8348	.013 194 8939
67	1.321 261 1273	77.102 670 5508	.012 969 7194
68	1.326 766 3820	78.423 931 6781	.012 751 2097
69	1.332 294 5753	79.750 698 0600	.012 539 0752
70	1.337 845 8026	81.082 992 6353	.012 333 0426
71	1.343 420 1602	82.420 838 4379	.012 132 8540
72	1.349 017 7442	83.764 258 5981	.011 938 2660
73	1.354 638 6514	85.113 276 3423	.011 749 0484
74	1.360 282 9791	86.467 914 9937	.011 564 9834
75	1.365 950 8249	87.828 197 9728	.011 385 8649
76	1.371 642 2867	89.194 148 7977	.011 211 4978
77	1.377 357 4629	90.565 791 0844	.011 041 6967
78	1.383 096 4523	91.943 148 5472	.010 876 2862
79	1.388 859 3542	93.326 244 9995	.010 715 0995
80	1.394 646 2681	94.715 104 3537	.010 557 9781
81	1.400 457 2943	96.109 750 6218	.010 404 7716
82	1.406 292 5330	97.510 207 9161	.010 255 3366
83	1.412 152 0852	98.916 500 4490	.010 109 5368
84	1.418 036 0522	100.328 652 5342	.009 967 2424
85	1.423 944 5358	101.746 688 5865	.009 828 3297
86	1.429 877 6380	103.170 633 1223	.009 692 6807
87	1.435 835 4615	104.600 510 7603	.009 560 1828
88	1.441 818 1093	106.036 346 2218	.009 430 7286
89	1.447 825 6847	107.478 164 3310	.009 304 2155
90	1.453 858 2917	108.925 990 0157	.009 180 5454
91	1.459 916 0346	110.379 848 3075	.009 059 6247
92	1.465 999 0181	111.839 764 3421	.008 941 3636
93	1.472 107 3473	113.305 763 3602	.008 825 6764
94	1.478 241 1279	114.777 870 7075	.008 712 4808
95	1.484 400 4660	116.256 111 8355	.008 601 6983
96	1.490 585 4679	117.740 512 3014	.008 493 2533
97	1.496 796 2407	119.231 097 7694	.008 387 0737
98	1.503 032 8917	120.727 894 0101	.008 283 0899
99	1.509 295 5288	122.230 926 9018	.008 181 2355
100	1.515 584 2601	123.740 222 4305	.008 081 4466
101	1.521 899 1945	125.255 806 6907	.007 983 6618
102	1.528 240 4412	126.777 705 8852	.007 887 8222
103	1.534 608 1097	128.305 946 3264	.007 793 8710
104	1.541 002 3102	129.840 554 4361	.007 701 7539
105	1.547 423 1531	131.381 556 7462	.007 611 4184
106	1.553 870 7496	132.928 979 8993	.007 522 8141
107	1.560 345 2110	134.482 850 6489	.007 435 8923
108	1.566 846 6494	136.043 195 8600	.007 350 6065
109	1.573 375 1771	137.610 042 5094	.007 266 9115
110	1.579 930 9070	139.183 417 6865	.007 184 7639
111	1.586 513 9525	140.763 348 5935	.007 104 1220
112	1.593 124 4273	142.349 862 5460	.007 024 9453
113	1.599 762 4457	143.942 986 9733	.006 947 1950
114	1.606 428 1226	145.542 749 4190	.006 870 8335
115	1.613 121 5731	147.149 177 5416	.006 795 8246
116	1.619 842 9130	148.762 299 1147	.006 722 1333
117	1.626 592 2584	150.382 142 0276	.006 649 7257
118	1.633 369 7262	152.008 734 2861	.006 578 5693
119	1.640 175 4334	153.642 104 0123	.006 508 6326
120	1.647 009 4977	155.282 279 4457	.006 439 8849
n	$s=(1+i)^n$	$s_{\overline{n}|}=\dfrac{(1+i)^n-1}{i}$	$\dfrac{1}{s_{\overline{n}|}}=\dfrac{i}{(1+i)^n-1}$

.00416666

per period

ANNUALLY
If compounded
annually
nominal annual rate is

5/12%

SEMIANNUALLY
If compounded
semiannually
nominal annual rate is

5/6%

QUARTERLY
If compounded
quarterly
nominal annual rate is

1 2/3%

MONTHLY
If compounded
monthly
nominal annual rate is

5%

i = .00416666
$j_{(2)}$ = .00833333
$j_{(4)}$ = .01666666
$j_{(12)}$ = .05

PRESENT WORTH OF 1 *What $1 due in the future is worth today.*	PRESENT WORTH OF 1 PER PERIOD *What $1 payable periodically is worth today.*	PARTIAL PAYMENT *Annuity worth $1 today.* *Periodic payment necessary to pay off a loan of $1.*	PERIODS	RATE **5/12%**
.775 972 1729	53.766 678 4969	.018 598 8800	61	
.772 752 3714	54.539 430 8682	.018 335 3582	62	
.769 545 9300	55.308 976 7982	.018 080 2477	63	.00416666
.766 352 7934	56.075 329 5916	.017 833 1542	64	*per period*
.763 172 9063	56.838 502 4979	.017 593 7077	65	
.760 006 2137	57.598 508 7116	.017 361 5606	66	
.756 852 6609	58.355 361 3725	.017 136 3860	67	
.753 712 1935	59.109 073 5660	.016 917 8764	68	
.750 584 7570	59.859 658 3230	.016 705 7419	69	
.747 470 2974	60.607 128 6204	.016 499 7092	70	
.744 368 7609	61.351 497 3813	.016 299 5207	71	
.741 280 0939	62.092 777 4752	.016 104 9327	72	
.738 204 2428	62.830 981 7180	.015 915 7150	73	
.735 141 1547	63.566 122 8727	.015 731 6500	74	
.732 090 7765	64.298 213 6492	.015 552 5316	75	
.729 053 0554	65.027 266 7046	.015 378 1644	76	
.726 027 9390	65.753 294 6435	.015 208 3634	77	
.723 015 3749	66.476 310 0185	.015 042 9529	78	
.720 015 3111	67.196 325 3296	.014 881 7662	79	
.717 027 6957	67.913 353 0253	.014 724 6448	80	
.714 052 4771	68.627 405 5024	.014 571 4382	81	ANNUALLY If compounded *annually* nominal annual rate is
.711 089 6037	69.338 495 1061	.014 422 0032	82	
.708 139 0245	70.046 634 1306	.014 276 2035	83	
.705 200 6883	70.751 834 8188	.014 133 9091	84	
.702 274 5443	71.454 109 3632	.013 994 9964	85	**5/12%**
.699 360 5421	72.153 469 9052	.013 859 3473	86	
.696 458 6311	72.849 928 5363	.013 726 8494	87	
.693 568 7613	73.543 497 2976	.013 597 3952	88	
.690 690 8826	74.234 188 1802	.013 470 8821	89	
.687 824 9453	74.922 013 1255	.013 347 2121	90	
.684 970 8999	75.606 984 0254	.013 226 2914	91	SEMIANNUALLY If compounded *semiannually* nominal annual rate is
.682 128 6970	76.289 112 7224	.013 108 0303	92	
.679 298 2875	76.968 411 0098	.012 992 3431	93	
.676 479 6224	77.644 890 6322	.012 879 1475	94	
.673 672 6530	78.318 563 2852	.012 768 3650	95	**5/6%**
.670 877 3308	78.989 440 6159	.012 659 9200	96	
.668 093 6074	79.657 534 2233	.012 553 7403	97	
.665 321 4348	80.322 855 6581	.012 449 7566	98	
.662 560 7649	80.985 416 4230	.012 347 9022	99	
.659 811 5501	81.645 227 9731	.012 248 1133	100	QUARTERLY If compounded *quarterly* nominal annual rate is
.657 073 7429	82.302 301 7160	.012 150 3285	101	
.654 347 2958	82.956 649 0117	.012 054 4888	102	
.651 632 1618	83.608 281 1735	.011 960 5377	103	
.648 928 2939	84.257 209 4674	.011 868 4206	104	
.646 235 6454	84.903 445 1128	.011 778 0851	105	**1 2/3%**
.643 554 1697	85.546 999 2824	.011 689 4807	106	
.640 883 8204	86.187 883 1028	.011 602 5590	107	
.638 224 5514	86.826 107 6543	.011 517 2732	108	
.635 576 3168	87.461 683 9711	.011 433 5782	109	
.632 939 0707	88.094 623 0417	.011 351 4306	110	
.630 312 7675	88.724 935 8092	.011 270 7887	111	MONTHLY If compounded *monthly* nominal annual rate is
.627 697 3618	89.352 633 1710	.011 191 6120	112	
.625 092 8084	89.977 725 9794	.011 113 8617	113	
.622 499 0623	90.600 225 0417	.011 037 5002	114	
.619 916 0787	91.220 141 1204	.010 962 4913	115	**5%**
.617 343 8128	91.837 484 9331	.010 888 7999	116	
.614 782 2202	92.452 267 1533	.010 816 3924	117	
.612 231 2566	93.064 498 4100	.010 745 2360	118	i = .00416666
.609 690 8780	93.674 189 2879	.010 675 2992	119	$j_{(2)}$ = .00833333
.607 161 0403	94.281 350 3282	.010 606 5515	120	$j_{(4)}$ = .01666666
$v^n = \dfrac{1}{(1+i)^n}$	$a_{\overline{n}\rvert} = \dfrac{1-v^n}{i}$	$\dfrac{1}{a_{\overline{n}\rvert}} = \dfrac{i}{1-v^n}$	**n**	$j_{(12)}$ = .05

21

P E R I O D S	AMOUNT OF 1 *How $1 left at compound interest will grow.*	AMOUNT OF 1 PER PERIOD *How $1 deposited periodically will grow.*	SINKING FUND *Periodic deposit that will grow to $1 at future date.*
121	1.653 872 0373	156.929 288 9434	.006 372 2968
122	1.660 763 1708	158.583 160 9806	.006 305 8397
123	1.667 683 0173	160.243 924 1514	.006 240 4862
124	1.674 631 6965	161.911 607 1687	.006 176 2095
125	1.681 609 3286	163.586 238 8652	.006 112 9836
126	1.688 616 0341	165.267 848 1938	.006 050 7837
127	1.695 651 9343	166.956 464 2280	.005 989 5854
128	1.702 717 1507	168.652 116 1622	.005 929 3653
129	1.709 811 8055	170.354 833 3129	.005 870 1005
130	1.716 936 0213	172.064 645 1184	.005 811 7692
131	1.724 089 9214	173.781 581 1397	.005 754 3498
132	1.731 273 6294	175.505 671 0611	.005 697 8216
133	1.738 487 2695	177.236 944 6905	.005 642 1645
134	1.745 730 9665	178.975 431 9601	.005 587 3591
135	1.753 004 8455	180.721 162 9266	.005 533 3863
136	1.760 309 0324	182.474 167 7721	.005 480 2278
137	1.767 643 6534	184.234 476 8045	.005 427 8657
138	1.775 008 8352	186.002 120 4579	.005 376 2828
139	1.782 404 7054	187.777 129 2931	.005 325 4622
140	1.789 831 3917	189.559 533 9985	.005 275 3875
141	1.797 289 0225	191.349 365 3901	.005 226 0429
142	1.804 777 7267	193.146 654 4126	.005 177 4130
143	1.812 297 6339	194.951 432 1393	.005 129 4827
144	1.819 848 8741	196.763 729 7732	.005 082 2375
145	1.827 431 5777	198.583 578 6473	.005 035 6631
146	1.835 045 8759	200.411 010 2250	.004 989 7458
147	1.842 691 9004	202.246 056 1009	.004 944 4722
148	1.850 369 7833	204.088 748 0013	.004 899 8292
149	1.858 079 6574	205.939 117 7847	.004 855 8040
150	1.865 821 6560	207.797 197 4421	.004 812 3844
151	1.873 595 9129	209.663 019 0981	.004 769 5583
152	1.881 402 5625	211.536 615 0110	.004 727 3140
153	1.889 241 7399	213.418 017 5736	.004 685 6400
154	1.897 113 5805	215.307 259 3135	.004 644 5252
155	1.905 018 2204	217.204 372 8939	.004 603 9589
156	1.912 955 7963	219.109 391 1143	.004 563 9303
157	1.920 926 4455	221.022 346 9106	.004 524 4294
158	1.928 930 3057	222.943 273 3561	.004 485 4459
159	1.936 967 5153	224.872 203 6618	.004 446 9703
160	1.945 038 2132	226.809 171 1770	.004 408 9928
161	1.953 142 5391	228.754 209 3903	.004 371 5043
162	1.961 280 6330	230.707 351 9294	.004 334 4956
163	1.969 452 6357	232.668 632 5624	.004 297 9580
164	1.977 658 6883	234.638 085 1981	.004 261 8827
165	1.985 898 9329	236.615 743 8864	.004 226 2615
166	1.994 173 5117	238.601 642 8193	.004 191 0860
167	2.002 482 5680	240.595 816 3310	.004 156 3482
168	2.010 826 2454	242.598 298 8991	.004 122 0404
169	2.019 204 6881	244.609 125 1445	.004 088 1549
170	2.027 618 0410	246.628 329 8326	.004 054 6842
171	2.036 066 4495	248.655 947 8736	.004 021 6211
172	2.044 550 0597	250.692 014 3230	.003 988 9583
173	2.053 069 0183	252.736 564 3827	.003 956 6891
174	2.061 623 4725	254.789 633 4010	.003 924 8065
175	2.070 213 5703	256.851 256 8735	.003 893 3039
176	2.078 839 4602	258.921 470 4438	.003 862 1749
177	2.087 501 2913	261.000 309 9040	.003 831 4131
178	2.096 199 2133	263.087 811 1952	.003 801 0123
179	2.104 933 3767	265.184 010 4085	.003 770 9664
180	2.113 703 9324	267.288 943 7852	.003 741 2696
n	$s=(1+i)^n$	$s_{\overline{n}|}=\dfrac{(1+i)^n-1}{i}$	$\dfrac{1}{s_{\overline{n}|}}=\dfrac{i}{(1+i)^n-1}$

.00416666
per period

ANNUALLY
If compounded
annually
nominal annual rate is
5/12%

SEMIANNUALLY
If compounded
semiannually
nominal annual rate is
5/6%

QUARTERLY
If compounded
quarterly
nominal annual rate is
1 2/3%

MONTHLY
If compounded
monthly
nominal annual rate is
5%

$i = .00416666$
$j_{(2)} = .00833333$
$j_{(4)} = .01666666$
$j_{(12)} = .05$

22

PRESENT WORTH OF 1	PRESENT WORTH OF 1 PER PERIOD	PARTIAL PAYMENT	P E R I O D S	RATE
What $1 due in the future is worth today.	What $1 payable periodically is worth today.	Annuity worth $1 today. Periodic payment necessary to pay off a loan of $1.		5/12%
.604 641 6999	94.885 992 0281	.010 538 9634	121	
.602 132 8132	95.488 124 8413	.010 472 5064	122	
.599 634 3368	96.087 759 1780	.010 407 1529	123	.00416666
.597 146 2275	96.684 905 4055	.010 342 8761	124	per period
.594 668 4423	97.279 573 8478	.010 279 6503	125	
.592 200 9384	97.871 774 7862	.010 217 4504	126	
.589 743 6731	98.461 518 4593	.010 156 2521	127	
.587 296 6039	99.048 815 0632	.010 096 0319	128	
.584 859 6885	99.633 674 7517	.010 036 7672	129	
.582 432 8848	100.216 107 6366	.009 978 4358	130	
.580 016 1509	100.796 123 7875	.009 921 0164	131	
.577 609 4449	101.373 733 2323	.009 864 4882	132	
.575 212 7252	101.948 945 9575	.009 808 8312	133	
.572 825 9504	102.521 771 9079	.009 754 0257	134	
.570 449 0792	103.092 220 9871	.009 700 0529	135	
.568 082 0706	103.660 303 0577	.009 646 8944	136	
.565 724 8836	104.226 027 9413	.009 594 5324	137	
.563 377 4774	104.789 405 4187	.009 542 9495	138	
.561 039 8115	105.350 445 2302	.009 492 1288	139	
.558 711 8455	105.909 157 0758	.009 442 0542	140	
.556 393 5391	106.465 550 6149	.009 392 7096	141	ANNUALLY
.554 084 8522	107.019 635 4671	.009 344 0797	142	If compounded
.551 785 7449	107.571 421 2120	.009 296 1494	143	annually
.549 496 1775	108.120 917 3896	.009 248 9041	144	nominal annual rate is
.547 216 1104	108.668 133 5000	.009 202 3298	145	5/12%
.544 945 5041	109.213 079 0041	.009 156 4125	146	
.542 684 3195	109.755 763 3236	.009 111 1389	147	
.540 432 5173	110.296 195 8410	.009 066 4958	148	
.538 190 0588	110.834 385 8997	.009 022 4707	149	
.535 956 9050	111.370 342 8047	.008 979 0511	150	
.533 733 0174	111.904 075 8221	.008 936 2250	151	SEMIANNUALLY
.531 518 3576	112.435 594 1797	.008 893 9807	152	If compounded
.529 312 8872	112.964 907 0669	.008 852 3067	153	semiannually
.527 116 5682	113.492 023 6351	.008 811 1919	154	nominal annual rate is
.524 929 3625	114.016 952 9976	.008 770 6255	155	5/6%
.522 751 2324	114.539 704 2300	.008 730 5970	156	
.520 582 1401	115.060 286 3701	.008 691 0960	157	
.518 422 0483	115.578 708 4184	.008 652 1126	158	
.516 270 9194	116.094 979 3378	.008 613 6369	159	
.514 128 7164	116.609 108 0542	.008 575 6595	160	
.511 995 4023	117.121 103 4565	.008 538 1709	161	QUARTERLY
.509 870 9400	117.630 974 3965	.008 501 1623	162	If compounded
.507 755 2930	118.138 729 6895	.008 464 6246	163	quarterly
.505 648 4245	118.644 378 1140	.008 428 5494	164	nominal annual rate is
.503 550 2983	119.147 928 4123	.008 392 9281	165	1 2/3%
.501 460 8780	119.649 389 2902	.008 357 7526	166	
.499 380 1274	120.148 769 4177	.008 323 0149	167	
.497 308 0107	120.646 077 4284	.008 288 7071	168	
.495 244 4920	121.141 321 9204	.008 254 8216	169	
.493 189 5356	121.634 511 4560	.008 221 3509	170	
.491 143 1060	122.125 654 5620	.008 188 2877	171	MONTHLY
.489 105 1678	122.614 759 7298	.008 155 6250	172	If compounded
.487 075 6858	123.101 835 4155	.008 123 3557	173	monthly
.485 054 6248	123.586 890 0404	.008 091 4731	174	nominal annual rate is
.483 041 9500	124.069 931 9904	.008 059 9706	175	5%
.481 037 6266	124.550 969 6170	.008 028 8416	176	
.479 041 6198	125.030 011 2368	.007 998 0797	177	
.477 053 8953	125.507 065 1321	.007 967 6789	178	i = .00416666
.475 074 4185	125.982 139 5507	.007 937 6331	179	$j_{(2)}$ = .00833333
.473 103 1554	126.455 242 7061	.007 907 9363	180	$j_{(4)}$ = .01666666
$v^n = \dfrac{1}{(1+i)^n}$	$a_{\overline{n}} = \dfrac{1-v^n}{i}$	$\dfrac{1}{a_{\overline{n}}} = \dfrac{i}{1-v^n}$	n	$j_{(12)}$ = .05

23

P E R I O D S	AMOUNT OF 1 *How $1 left at compound interest will grow.*	AMOUNT OF 1 PER PERIOD *How $1 deposited periodically will grow.*	SINKING FUND *Periodic deposit that will grow to $1 at future date.*
1	1.005 000 0000	1.000 000 0000	1.000 000 0000
2	1.010 025 0000	2.005 000 0000	.498 753 1172
3	1.015 075 1250	3.015 025 0000	.331 672 2084
4	1.020 150 5006	4.030 100 1250	.248 132 7930
5	1.025 251 2531	5.050 250 6256	.198 009 9750
6	1.030 377 5094	6.075 501 8788	.164 595 4556
7	1.035 529 3969	7.105 879 3881	.140 728 5355
8	1.040 707 0439	8.141 408 7851	.122 828 8649
9	1.045 910 5791	9.182 115 8290	.108 907 3606
10	1.051 140 1320	10.228 026 4082	.097 770 5727
11	1.056 395 8327	11.279 166 5402	.088 659 0331
12	1.061 677 8119	12.335 562 3729	.081 066 4297
13	1.066 986 2009	13.397 240 1848	.074 642 2387
14	1.072 321 1319	14.464 226 3857	.069 136 0860
15	1.077 682 7376	15.536 547 5176	.064 364 3640
16	1.083 071 1513	16.614 230 2552	.060 189 3669
17	1.088 486 5070	17.697 301 4065	.056 505 7902
18	1.093 928 9396	18.785 787 9135	.053 231 7305
19	1.099 398 5843	19.879 716 8531	.050 302 5273
20	1.104 895 5772	20.979 115 4373	.047 666 4520
21	1.110 420 0551	22.084 011 0145	.045 281 6293
22	1.115 972 1553	23.194 431 0696	.043 113 7973
23	1.121 552 0161	24.310 403 2250	.041 134 6530
24	1.127 159 7762	25.431 955 2411	.039 320 6103
25	1.132 795 5751	26.559 115 0173	.037 651 8570
26	1.138 459 5530	27.691 910 5924	.036 111 6289
27	1.144 151 8507	28.830 370 1453	.034 685 6456
28	1.149 872 6100	29.974 521 9961	.033 361 6663
29	1.155 621 9730	31.124 394 6060	.032 129 1390
30	1.161 400 0829	32.280 016 5791	.030 978 9184
31	1.167 207 0833	33.441 416 6620	.029 903 0394
32	1.173 043 1187	34.608 623 7453	.028 894 5324
33	1.178 908 3343	35.781 666 8640	.027 947 2727
34	1.184 802 8760	36.960 575 1983	.027 055 8560
35	1.190 726 8904	38.145 378 0743	.026 215 4958
36	1.196 680 5248	39.336 104 9647	.025 421 9375
37	1.202 663 9274	40.532 785 4895	.024 671 3861
38	1.208 677 2471	41.735 449 4170	.023 960 4464
39	1.214 720 6333	42.944 126 6640	.023 286 0714
40	1.220 794 2365	44.158 847 2974	.022 645 5186
41	1.226 898 2077	45.379 641 5338	.022 036 3133
42	1.233 032 6987	46.606 539 7415	.021 456 2163
43	1.239 197 8622	47.839 572 4402	.020 903 1969
44	1.245 393 8515	49.078 770 3024	.020 375 4086
45	1.251 620 8208	50.324 164 1539	.019 871 1696
46	1.257 878 9249	51.575 784 9747	.019 388 9439
47	1.264 168 3195	52.833 663 8996	.018 927 3264
48	1.270 489 1611	54.097 832 2191	.018 485 0290
49	1.276 841 6069	55.368 321 3802	.018 060 8690
50	1.283 225 8149	56.645 162 9871	.017 653 7580
51	1.289 641 9440	57.928 388 8020	.017 262 6931
52	1.296 090 1537	59.218 030 7460	.016 886 7486
53	1.302 570 6045	60.514 120 8997	.016 525 0686
54	1.309 083 4575	61.816 691 5042	.016 176 8606
55	1.315 628 8748	63.125 774 9618	.015 841 3897
56	1.322 207 0192	64.441 403 8366	.015 517 9735
57	1.328 818 0543	65.763 610 8558	.015 205 9777
58	1.335 462 1446	67.092 428 9100	.014 904 8114
59	1.342 139 4553	68.427 891 0546	.014 613 9240
60	1.348 850 1525	69.770 030 5099	.014 332 8015
n	$s=(1+i)^n$	$s_{\overline{n}|}=\dfrac{(1+i)^n-1}{i}$	$\dfrac{1}{s_{\overline{n}|}}=\dfrac{i}{(1+i)^n-1}$

.005
per period

ANNUALLY
If compounded
annually
nominal annual rate is

1/2%

SEMIANNUALLY
If compounded
semiannually
nominal annual rate is

1%

QUARTERLY
If compounded
quarterly
nominal annual rate is

2%

MONTHLY
If compounded
monthly
nominal annual rate is

6%

$i = .005$
$j_{(2)} = .01$
$j_{(4)} = .02$
$j_{(12)} = .06$

24

PRESENT WORTH OF 1	PRESENT WORTH OF 1 PER PERIOD	PARTIAL PAYMENT	PERIODS	RATE
What $1 due in the future is worth today.	*What $1 payable periodically is worth today.*	*Annuity worth $1 today.* *Periodic payment necessary to pay off a loan of $1.*		1/2%
.995 024 8756	.995 024 8756	1.005 000 0000	1	
.990 074 5031	1.985 099 3787	.503 753 1172	2	
.985 148 7593	2.970 248 1380	.336 672 2084	3	.005
.980 247 5217	3.950 495 6597	.253 132 7930	4	*per period*
.975 370 6684	4.925 866 3281	.203 009 9750	5	
.970 518 0780	5.896 384 4061	.169 595 4556	6	
.965 689 6298	6.862 074 0359	.145 728 5355	7	
.960 885 2038	7.822 959 2397	.127 828 8649	8	
.956 104 6804	8.779 063 9201	.113 907 3606	9	
.951 347 9407	9.730 411 8608	.102 770 5727	10	
.946 614 8664	10.677 026 7272	.093 659 0331	11	
.941 905 3397	11.618 932 0668	.086 066 4297	12	
.937 219 2434	12.556 151 3103	.079 642 2387	13	
.932 556 4611	13.488 707 7714	.074 136 0860	14	
.927 916 8768	14.416 624 6482	.069 364 3640	15	
.923 300 3749	15.339 925 0231	.065 189 3669	16	
.918 706 8407	16.258 631 8637	.061 505 7902	17	
.914 136 1599	17.172 768 0236	.058 231 7305	18	
.909 588 2188	18.082 356 2424	.055 302 5273	19	
.905 062 9043	18.987 419 1467	.052 666 4520	20	
.900 560 1037	19.887 979 2504	.050 281 6293	21	ANNUALLY
.896 079 7052	20.784 058 9556	.048 113 7973	22	If compounded
.891 621 5972	21.675 680 5529	.046 134 6530	23	*annually*
.887 185 6689	22.562 866 2218	.044 320 6103	24	nominal annual rate is
.882 771 8098	23.445 638 0316	.042 651 8570	25	1/2%
.878 379 9103	24.324 017 9419	.041 111 6289	26	
.874 009 8610	25.198 027 8029	.039 685 6456	27	
.869 661 5532	26.067 689 3561	.038 361 6663	28	
.865 334 8788	26.933 024 2349	.037 129 1390	29	
.861 029 7302	27.794 053 9651	.035 978 9184	30	
.856 746 0002	28.650 799 9653	.034 903 0394	31	SEMIANNUALLY
.852 483 5823	29.503 283 5475	.033 894 5324	32	If compounded
.848 242 3704	30.351 525 9179	.032 947 2727	33	*semiannually*
.844 022 2591	31.195 548 1771	.032 055 8560	34	nominal annual rate is
.839 823 1434	32.035 371 3205	.031 215 4958	35	1%
.835 644 9188	32.871 016 2393	.030 421 9375	36	
.831 487 4814	33.702 503 7207	.029 671 3861	37	
.827 350 7278	34.529 854 4484	.028 960 4464	38	
.823 234 5550	35.353 089 0034	.028 286 0714	39	
.819 138 8607	36.172 227 8641	.027 645 5186	40	
.815 063 5430	36.987 291 4070	.027 036 3133	41	QUARTERLY
.811 008 5005	37.798 299 9075	.026 456 2163	42	If compounded
.806 973 6323	38.605 273 5398	.025 903 1969	43	*quarterly*
.802 958 8381	39.408 232 3779	.025 375 4086	44	nominal annual rate is
.798 964 0180	40.207 196 3959	.024 871 1696	45	2%
.794 989 0727	41.002 185 4686	.024 388 9439	46	
.791 033 9031	41.793 219 3717	.023 927 3264	47	
.787 098 4111	42.580 317 7828	.023 485 0290	48	
.783 182 4986	43.363 500 2814	.023 060 8690	49	
.779 286 0683	44.142 786 3497	.022 653 7580	50	
.775 409 0231	44.918 195 3728	.022 262 6931	51	MONTHLY
.771 551 2668	45.689 746 6396	.021 886 7486	52	If compounded
.767 712 7033	46.457 459 3429	.021 525 0686	53	*monthly*
.763 893 2371	47.221 352 5800	.021 176 8606	54	nominal annual rate is
.760 092 7732	47.981 445 3532	.020 841 3897	55	6%
.756 311 2171	48.737 756 5704	.020 517 9735	56	
.752 548 4748	49.490 305 0452	.020 205 9777	57	
.748 804 4525	50.239 109 4977	.019 904 8114	58	$i\ \ =.005$
.745 079 0572	50.984 188 5549	.019 613 9240	59	$j_{(2)}=.01$
.741 372 1962	51.725 560 7511	.019 332 8015	60	$j_{(4)}=.02$ $j_{(12)}=.06$
$v^n=\dfrac{1}{(1+i)^n}$	$a_{\overline{n}|}=\dfrac{1-v^n}{i}$	$\dfrac{1}{a_{\overline{n}|}}=\dfrac{i}{1-v^n}$	n	

25

P E R I O D S	AMOUNT OF 1 *How $1 left at compound interest will grow.*	AMOUNT OF 1 PER PERIOD *How $1 deposited periodically will grow.*	SINKING FUND *Periodic deposit that will grow to $1 at future date.*
61	1.355 594 4033	71.118 880 6624	.014 060 9637
62	1.362 372 3753	72.474 475 0657	.013 797 9613
63	1.369 184 2372	73.836 847 4411	.013 543 3735
64	1.376 030 1584	75.206 031 6783	.013 296 8058
65	1.382 910 3092	76.582 061 8366	.013 057 8882
66	1.389 824 8607	77.964 972 1458	.012 826 2728
67	1.396 773 9850	79.354 797 0066	.012 601 6326
68	1.403 757 8550	80.751 570 9916	.012 383 6600
69	1.410 776 6442	82.155 328 8466	.012 172 0650
70	1.417 830 5275	83.566 105 4908	.011 966 5742
71	1.424 919 6801	84.983 936 0182	.011 766 9297
72	1.432 044 2785	86.408 855 6983	.011 572 8879
73	1.439 204 4999	87.840 899 9768	.011 384 2185
74	1.446 400 5224	89.280 104 4767	.011 200 7037
75	1.453 632 5250	90.726 504 9991	.011 022 1374
76	1.460 900 6876	92.180 137 5241	.010 848 3240
77	1.468 205 1911	93.641 038 2117	.010 679 0785
78	1.475 546 2170	95.109 243 4028	.010 514 2252
79	1.482 923 9481	96.584 789 6198	.010 353 5971
80	1.490 338 5678	98.067 713 5679	.010 197 0359
81	1.497 790 2607	99.558 052 1357	.010 044 3910
82	1.505 279 2120	101.055 842 3964	.009 895 5189
83	1.512 805 6080	102.561 121 6084	.009 750 2834
84	1.520 369 6361	104.073 927 2164	.009 608 5545
85	1.527 971 4843	105.594 296 8525	.009 470 2084
86	1.535 611 3417	107.122 268 3368	.009 335 1272
87	1.543 289 3984	108.657 879 6784	.009 203 1982
88	1.551 005 8454	110.201 169 0768	.009 074 3139
89	1.558 760 8746	111.752 174 9222	.008 948 3717
90	1.566 554 6790	113.310 935 7968	.008 825 2735
91	1.574 387 4524	114.877 490 4758	.008 704 9255
92	1.582 259 3896	116.451 877 9282	.008 587 2381
93	1.590 170 6866	118.034 137 3178	.008 472 1253
94	1.598 121 5400	119.624 308 0044	.008 359 5050
95	1.606 112 1477	121.222 429 5445	.008 249 2984
96	1.614 142 7085	122.828 541 6922	.008 141 4302
97	1.622 213 4220	124.442 684 4006	.008 035 8279
98	1.630 324 4891	126.064 897 8226	.007 932 4222
99	1.638 476 1116	127.695 222 3118	.007 831 1466
100	1.646 668 4921	129.333 698 4233	.007 731 9369
101	1.654 901 8346	130.980 366 9154	.007 634 7320
102	1.663 176 3438	132.635 268 7500	.007 539 4728
103	1.671 492 2255	134.298 445 0938	.007 446 1026
104	1.679 849 6866	135.969 937 3192	.007 354 5669
105	1.688 248 9350	137.649 787 0058	.007 264 8133
106	1.696 690 1797	139.338 035 9408	.007 176 7913
107	1.705 173 6306	141.034 726 1206	.007 090 4523
108	1.713 699 4988	142.739 899 7512	.007 005 7496
109	1.722 267 9962	144.453 599 2499	.006 922 6382
110	1.730 879 3362	146.175 867 2462	.006 841 0745
111	1.739 533 7329	147.906 746 5824	.006 761 0168
112	1.748 231 4016	149.646 280 3153	.006 682 4247
113	1.756 972 5586	151.394 511 7169	.006 605 2593
114	1.765 757 4214	153.151 484 2755	.006 529 4829
115	1.774 586 2085	154.917 241 6968	.006 455 0594
116	1.783 459 1395	156.691 827 9053	.006 381 9538
117	1.792 376 4352	158.475 287 0449	.006 310 1321
118	1.801 338 3174	160.267 663 4801	.006 239 5619
119	1.810 345 0090	162.069 001 7975	.006 170 2114
120	1.819 396 7340	163.879 346 8065	.006 102 0502
n	$s=(1+i)^n$	$s_{\overline{n}\rceil}=\dfrac{(1+i)^n-1}{i}$	$\dfrac{1}{s_{\overline{n}\rceil}}=\dfrac{i}{(1+i)^n-1}$

.005
per period

ANNUALLY
If compounded
annually
nominal annual rate is
1/2%

SEMIANNUALLY
If compounded
semiannually
nominal annual rate is
1%

QUARTERLY
If compounded
quarterly
nominal annual rate is
2%

MONTHLY
If compounded
monthly
nominal annual rate is
6%

$i\ =.005$
$j^{(2)}=.01$
$j^{(4)}=.02$
$j^{(12)}=.06$

26

PRESENT WORTH OF 1 — What $1 due in the future is worth today.	PRESENT WORTH OF 1 PER PERIOD — What $1 payable periodically is worth today.	PARTIAL PAYMENT — Annuity worth $1 today. Periodic payment necessary to pay off a loan of $1.	PERIODS
.737 683 7774	52.463 244 5285	.019 060 9637	61
.734 013 7088	53.197 258 2373	.018 797 9613	62
.730 361 8993	53.927 620 1366	.018 543 3735	63
.726 728 2580	54.654 348 3946	.018 296 8058	64
.723 112 6946	55.377 461 0892	.018 057 8882	65
.719 515 1190	56.096 976 2082	.017 826 2728	66
.715 935 4418	56.812 911 6499	.017 601 6326	67
.712 373 5739	57.525 285 2238	.017 383 6600	68
.708 829 4267	58.234 114 6505	.017 172 0650	69
.705 302 9122	58.939 417 5627	.016 966 5742	70
.701 793 9425	59.641 211 5052	.016 766 9297	71
.698 302 4303	60.339 513 9355	.016 572 8879	72
.694 828 2889	61.034 342 2244	.016 384 2185	73
.691 371 4317	61.725 713 6561	.016 200 7037	74
.687 931 7729	62.413 645 4290	.016 022 1374	75
.684 509 2267	63.098 154 6557	.015 848 3240	76
.681 103 7082	63.779 258 3639	.015 679 0785	77
.677 715 1325	64.456 973 4964	.015 514 2252	78
.674 343 4154	65.131 316 9118	.015 353 5971	79
.670 988 4731	65.802 305 3849	.015 197 0359	80
.667 650 2220	66.469 955 6069	.015 044 3910	81
.664 328 5791	67.134 284 1859	.014 895 5189	82
.661 023 4618	67.795 307 6477	.014 750 2834	83
.657 734 7878	68.453 042 4355	.014 608 5545	84
.654 462 4754	69.107 504 9110	.014 470 2084	85
.651 206 4432	69.758 711 3542	.014 335 1272	86
.647 966 6102	70.406 677 9644	.014 203 1982	87
.644 742 8957	71.051 420 8601	.014 074 3139	88
.641 535 2196	71.692 956 0797	.013 948 3717	89
.638 343 5021	72.331 299 5818	.013 825 2735	90
.635 167 6638	72.966 467 2455	.013 704 9255	91
.632 007 6256	73.598 474 8712	.013 587 2381	92
.628 863 3091	74.227 338 1803	.013 472 1253	93
.625 734 6359	74.853 072 8162	.013 359 5050	94
.622 621 5283	75.475 694 3445	.013 249 2984	95
.619 523 9087	76.095 218 2532	.013 141 4302	96
.616 441 7002	76.711 659 9535	.013 035 8279	97
.613 374 8261	77.325 034 7796	.012 932 4222	98
.610 323 2101	77.935 357 9896	.012 831 1466	99
.607 286 7762	78.542 644 7658	.012 731 9369	100
.604 265 4489	79.146 910 2147	.012 634 7320	101
.601 259 1532	79.748 169 3679	.012 539 4728	102
.598 267 8141	80.346 437 1820	.012 446 1026	103
.595 291 3573	80.941 728 5393	.012 354 5669	104
.592 329 7088	81.534 058 2480	.012 264 8133	105
.589 382 7948	82.123 441 0428	.012 176 7913	106
.586 450 5421	82.709 891 5849	.012 090 4523	107
.583 532 8777	83.293 424 4626	.012 005 7496	108
.580 629 7290	83.874 054 1916	.011 922 6382	109
.577 741 0239	84.451 795 2155	.011 841 0745	110
.574 866 6905	85.026 661 9060	.011 761 0168	111
.572 006 6572	85.598 668 5632	.011 682 4247	112
.569 160 8529	86.167 829 4161	.011 605 2593	113
.566 329 2069	86.734 158 6230	.011 529 4829	114
.563 511 6486	87.297 670 2716	.011 455 0594	115
.560 708 1081	87.858 378 3797	.011 381 9538	116
.557 918 5155	88.416 296 8953	.011 310 1321	117
.555 142 8015	88.971 439 6968	.011 239 5619	118
.552 380 8970	89.523 820 5938	.011 170 2114	119
.549 632 7334	90.073 453 3272	.011 102 0502	120

$$v^n = \frac{1}{(1+i)^n} \qquad a_{\overline{n}|} = \frac{1-v^n}{i} \qquad \frac{1}{a_{\overline{n}|}} = \frac{i}{1-v^n} \qquad n$$

.005

per period

ANNUALLY
If compounded
annually
nominal annual rate is

1/2%

SEMIANNUALLY
If compounded
semiannually
nominal annual rate is

1%

QUARTERLY
If compounded
quarterly
nominal annual rate is

2%

MONTHLY
If compounded
monthly
nominal annual rate is

6%

$i = .005$
$j_{(2)} = .01$
$j_{(4)} = .02$
$j_{(12)} = .06$

P E R I O D S	AMOUNT OF 1 *How $1 left at compound interest will grow.*	AMOUNT OF 1 PER PERIOD *How $1 deposited periodically will grow.*	SINKING FUND *Periodic deposit that will grow to $1 at future date.*
121	1.828 493 7177	165.698 743 5405	.006 035 0488
122	1.837 636 1863	167.527 237 2582	.005 969 1786
123	1.846 824 3672	169.364 873 4445	.005 904 4121
124	1.856 058 4891	171.211 697 8117	.005 840 7224
125	1.865 338 7815	173.067 756 3008	.005 778 0838
126	1.874 665 4754	174.933 095 0823	.005 716 4712
127	1.884 038 8028	176.807 760 5577	.005 655 8603
128	1.893 458 9968	178.691 799 3605	.005 596 2277
129	1.902 926 2918	180.585 258 3573	.005 537 5506
130	1.912 440 9232	182.488 184 6491	.005 479 8068
131	1.922 003 1279	184.400 625 5723	.005 422 9751
132	1.931 613 1435	186.322 628 7002	.005 367 0346
133	1.941 271 2092	188.254 241 8437	.005 311 9653
134	1.950 977 5653	190.195 513 0529	.005 257 7476
135	1.960 732 4531	192.146 490 6182	.005 204 3626
136	1.970 536 1154	194.107 223 0712	.005 151 7918
137	1.980 388 7959	196.077 759 1866	.005 100 0175
138	1.990 290 7399	198.058 147 9825	.005 049 0223
139	2.000 242 1936	200.048 438 7224	.004 998 7893
140	2.010 243 4046	202.048 680 9161	.004 949 3023
141	2.020 294 6216	204.058 924 3206	.004 900 5453
142	2.030 396 0947	206.079 218 9422	.004 852 5029
143	2.040 548 0752	208.109 615 0370	.004 805 1600
144	2.050 750 8156	210.150 163 1121	.004 758 5021
145	2.061 004 5696	212.200 913 9277	.004 712 5150
146	2.071 309 5925	214.261 918 4973	.004 667 1849
147	2.081 666 1404	216.333 228 0898	.004 622 4984
148	2.092 074 4712	218.414 894 2303	.004 578 4423
149	2.102 534 8435	220.506 968 7014	.004 535 0041
150	2.113 047 5177	222.609 503 5449	.004 492 1712
151	2.123 612 7553	224.722 551 0627	.004 449 9317
152	2.134 230 8191	226.846 163 8180	.004 408 2738
153	2.144 901 9732	228.980 394 6371	.004 367 1861
154	2.155 626 4831	231.125 296 6102	.004 326 6575
155	2.166 404 6155	233.280 923 0933	.004 286 6771
156	2.177 236 6385	235.447 327 7088	.004 247 2344
157	2.188 122 8217	237.624 564 3473	.004 208 3191
158	2.199 063 4358	239.812 687 1690	.004 169 9212
159	2.210 058 7530	242.011 750 6049	.004 132 0308
160	2.221 109 0468	244.221 809 3579	.004 094 6384
161	2.232 214 5920	246.442 918 4047	.004 057 7348
162	2.243 375 6650	248.675 132 9967	.004 021 3108
163	2.254 592 5433	250.918 508 6617	.003 985 3577
164	2.265 865 5060	253.173 101 2050	.003 949 8667
165	2.277 194 8336	255.438 966 7110	.003 914 8295
166	2.288 580 8077	257.716 161 5446	.003 880 2378
167	2.300 023 7118	260.004 742 3523	.003 846 0837
168	2.311 523 8303	262.304 766 0641	.003 812 3592
169	2.323 081 4495	264.616 289 8944	.003 779 0568
170	2.334 696 8567	266.939 371 3439	.003 746 1690
171	2.346 370 3410	269.274 068 2006	.003 713 6885
172	2.358 102 1927	271.620 438 5416	.003 681 6081
173	2.369 892 7037	273.978 540 7343	.003 649 9209
174	2.381 742 1672	276.348 433 4380	.003 618 6201
175	2.393 650 8780	278.730 175 6052	.003 587 6991
176	2.405 619 1324	281.123 826 4832	.003 557 1514
177	2.417 647 2281	283.529 445 6156	.003 526 9705
178	2.429 735 4642	285.947 092 8437	.003 497 1504
179	2.441 884 1415	288.376 828 3079	.003 467 6850
180	2.454 093 5622	290.818 712 4494	.003 438 5683
n	$s=(1+i)^n$	$s_{\overline{n}\|}=\dfrac{(1+i)^n-1}{i}$	$\dfrac{1}{s_{\overline{n}\|}}=\dfrac{i}{(1+i)^n-1}$

.005

per period

ANNUALLY
If compounded
annually
nominal annual rate is

1/2%

SEMIANNUALLY
If compounded
semiannually
nominal annual rate is

1%

QUARTERLY
If compounded
quarterly
nominal annual rate is

2%

MONTHLY
If compounded
monthly
nominal annual rate is

6%

$i = .005$
$j_{(2)} = .01$
$j_{(4)} = .02$
$j_{(12)} = .06$

PRESENT WORTH OF 1 _What $1 due in the future is worth today._	PRESENT WORTH OF 1 PER PERIOD _What $1 payable periodically is worth today._	PARTIAL PAYMENT _Annuity worth $1 today._ _Periodic payment necessary to pay off a loan of $1._	P E R I O D S	RATE $\frac{1}{2}\%$
.546 898 2422	90.620 351 5693	.011 035 0488	121	
.544 177 3554	91.164 528 9247	.010 969 1786	122	
.541 470 0053	91.705 998 9300	.010 904 4121	123	.005
.538 776 1247	92.244 775 0548	.010 840 7224	124	
.536 095 6465	92.780 870 7013	.010 778 0838	125	_per period_
.533 428 5040	93.314 299 2052	.010 716 4712	126	
.530 774 6308	93.845 073 8361	.010 655 8603	127	
.528 133 9610	94.373 207 7971	.010 596 2277	128	
.525 506 4289	94.898 714 2259	.010 537 5506	129	
.522 891 9690	95.421 606 1950	.010 479 8068	130	
.520 290 5164	95.941 896 7114	.010 422 9751	131	
.517 702 0064	96.459 598 7178	.010 367 0346	132	
.515 126 3745	96.974 725 0924	.010 311 9653	133	
.512 563 5568	97.487 288 6491	.010 257 7476	134	
.510 013 4893	97.997 302 1384	.010 204 3626	135	
.507 476 1088	98.504 778 2472	.010 151 7918	136	
.504 951 3520	99.009 729 5992	.010 100 0175	137	
.502 439 1562	99.512 168 7554	.010 049 0223	138	
.499 939 4589	100.012 108 2143	.009 998 7893	139	
.497 452 1979	100.509 560 4123	.009 949 3023	140	
.494 977 3114	101.004 537 7237	.009 900 5453	141	ANNUALLY
.492 514 7377	101.497 052 4614	.009 852 5029	142	If compounded
.490 064 4156	101.987 116 8770	.009 805 1600	143	_annually_
.487 626 2842	102.474 743 1612	.009 758 5021	144	nominal annual rate is
.485 200 2828	102.959 943 4439	.009 712 5150	145	$\frac{1}{2}\%$
.482 786 3510	103.442 729 7950	.009 667 1849	146	
.480 384 4289	103.923 114 2239	.009 622 4984	147	
.477 994 4566	104.401 108 6805	.009 578 4423	148	
.475 616 3747	104.876 725 0552	.009 535 0041	149	
.473 250 1241	105.349 975 1793	.009 492 1712	150	
.470 895 6459	105.820 870 8252	.009 449 9317	151	SEMIANNUALLY
.468 552 8815	106.289 423 7066	.009 408 2738	152	If compounded
.466 221 7726	106.755 645 4792	.009 367 1861	153	_semiannually_
.463 902 2613	107.219 547 7405	.009 326 6575	154	nominal annual rate is
.461 594 2898	107.681 142 0304	.009 286 6771	155	1%
.459 297 8008	108.140 439 8312	.009 247 2344	156	
.457 012 7372	108.597 452 5684	.009 208 3191	157	
.454 739 0419	109.052 191 6103	.009 169 9212	158	
.452 476 6587	109.504 668 2690	.009 132 0308	159	
.450 225 5310	109.954 893 8000	.009 094 6384	160	
.447 985 6030	110.402 879 4030	.009 057 7348	161	QUARTERLY
.445 756 8189	110.848 636 2219	.009 021 3108	162	If compounded
.443 539 1233	111.292 175 3451	.008 985 3577	163	_quarterly_
.441 332 4610	111.733 507 8061	.008 949 8667	164	nominal annual rate is
.439 136 7771	112.172 644 5832	.008 914 8295	165	2%
.436 952 0170	112.609 596 6002	.008 880 2378	166	
.434 778 1264	113.044 374 7265	.008 846 0837	167	
.432 615 0511	113.476 989 7777	.008 812 3592	168	
.430 462 7374	113.907 452 5151	.008 779 0568	169	
.428 321 1318	114.335 773 6468	.008 746 1690	170	
.426 190 1809	114.761 963 8277	.008 713 6885	171	MONTHLY
.424 069 8317	115.186 033 6594	.008 681 6081	172	If compounded
.421 960 0315	115.607 993 6910	.008 649 9209	173	_monthly_
.419 860 7279	116.027 854 4189	.008 618 6201	174	nominal annual rate is
.417 771 8686	116.445 626 2874	.008 587 6991	175	6%
.415 693 4016	116.861 319 6890	.008 557 1514	176	
.413 625 2752	117.274 944 9642	.008 526 9705	177	
.411 567 4380	117.686 512 4021	.008 497 1504	178	$i \quad = .005$
.409 519 8388	118.096 032 2409	.008 467 6850	179	$j_{(2)} = .01$
.407 482 4267	118.503 514 6676	.008 438 5683	180	$j_{(4)} = .02$ $j_{(12)} = .06$
$v^n=\dfrac{1}{(1+i)^n}$	$a_{\overline{n}|}=\dfrac{1-v^n}{i}$	$\dfrac{1}{a_{\overline{n}|}}=\dfrac{i}{1-v^n}$	n	

29

P E R I O D S	AMOUNT OF 1 *How $1 left at compound interest will grow.*	AMOUNT OF 1 PER PERIOD *How $1 deposited periodically will grow.*	SINKING FUND *Periodic deposit that will grow to $1 at future date.*
1	1.007 500 0000	1.000 000 0000	1.000 000 0000
2	1.015 056 2500	2.007 500 0000	.498 132 0050
3	1.022 669 1719	3.022 556 2500	.330 845 7866
4	1.030 339 1907	4.045 225 4219	.247 205 0123
5	1.038 066 7346	5.075 564 6125	.197 022 4155
6	1.045 852 2351	6.113 631 3471	.163 568 9074
7	1.053 696 1269	7.159 483 5822	.139 674 8786
8	1.061 598 8478	8.213 179 7091	.121 755 5241
9	1.069 560 8392	9.274 778 5569	.107 819 2858
10	1.077 582 5455	10.344 339 3961	.096 671 2287
11	1.085 664 4146	11.421 921 9416	.087 550 9398
12	1.093 806 8977	12.507 586 3561	.079 951 4768
13	1.102 010 4494	13.601 393 2538	.073 521 8798
14	1.110 275 5278	14.703 403 7032	.068 011 4632
15	1.118 602 5942	15.813 679 2310	.063 236 3908
16	1.126 992 1137	16.932 281 8252	.059 058 7855
17	1.135 444 5545	18.059 273 9389	.055 373 2118
18	1.143 960 3887	19.194 718 4934	.052 097 6643
19	1.152 540 0916	20.338 678 8821	.049 167 4020
20	1.161 184 1423	21.491 218 9738	.046 530 6319
21	1.169 893 0234	22.652 403 1161	.044 145 4266
22	1.178 667 2210	23.822 296 1394	.041 977 4817
23	1.187 507 2252	25.000 963 3605	.039 998 4587
24	1.196 413 5294	26.188 470 5857	.038 184 7423
25	1.205 386 6309	27.384 884 1151	.036 516 4956
26	1.214 427 0306	28.590 270 7459	.034 976 9335
27	1.223 535 2333	29.804 697 7765	.033 551 7578
28	1.232 711 7476	31.028 233 0099	.032 228 7125
29	1.241 957 0857	32.260 944 7574	.030 997 2323
30	1.251 271 7638	33.502 901 8431	.029 848 1608
31	1.260 656 3021	34.754 173 6069	.028 773 5226
32	1.270 111 2243	36.014 829 9090	.027 766 3397
33	1.279 637 0585	37.284 941 1333	.026 820 4795
34	1.289 234 3364	38.564 578 1918	.025 930 5313
35	1.298 903 5940	39.853 812 5282	.025 091 7023
36	1.308 645 3709	41.152 716 1222	.024 299 7327
37	1.318 460 2112	42.461 361 4931	.023 550 8228
38	1.328 348 6628	43.779 821 7043	.022 841 5732
39	1.338 311 2778	45.108 170 3671	.022 168 9329
40	1.348 348 6123	46.446 481 6449	.021 530 1561
41	1.358 461 2269	47.794 830 2572	.020 922 7650
42	1.368 649 6861	49.153 291 4841	.020 344 5175
43	1.378 914 5588	50.521 941 1703	.019 793 3804
44	1.389 256 4180	51.900 855 7290	.019 267 5051
45	1.399 675 8411	53.290 112 1470	.018 765 2073
46	1.410 173 4099	54.689 787 9881	.018 284 9493
47	1.420 749 7105	56.099 961 3980	.017 825 3242
48	1.431 405 3333	57.520 711 1085	.017 385 0424
49	1.442 140 8733	58.952 116 4418	.016 962 9194
50	1.452 956 9299	60.394 257 3151	.016 557 8657
51	1.463 854 1068	61.847 214 2450	.016 168 8770
52	1.474 833 0126	63.311 068 3518	.015 795 0265
53	1.485 894 2602	64.785 901 3645	.015 435 4571
54	1.497 038 4672	66.271 795 6247	.015 089 3754
55	1.508 266 2557	67.768 834 0919	.014 756 0455
56	1.519 578 2526	69.277 100 3476	.014 434 7843
57	1.530 975 0895	70.796 678 6002	.014 124 9564
58	1.542 457 4027	72.327 653 6897	.013 825 9704
59	1.554 025 8332	73.870 111 0923	.013 537 2749
60	1.565 681 0269	75.424 136 9255	.013 258 3552
n	$s=(1+i)^n$	$s_{\overline{n}|}=\dfrac{(1+i)^n-1}{i}$	$\dfrac{1}{s_{\overline{n}|}}=\dfrac{i}{(1+i)^n-1}$

.0075

per period

ANNUALLY
If compounded
annually
nominal annual rate is

3/4%

SEMIANNUALLY
If compounded
semiannually
nominal annual rate is

1½%

QUARTERLY
If compounded
quarterly
nominal annual rate is

3%

MONTHLY
If compounded
monthly
nominal annual rate is

9%

$i = .0075$
$j_{(2)} = .015$
$j_{(4)} = .03$
$j_{(12)} = .09$

PRESENT WORTH OF 1 *What $1 due in the future is worth today.*	PRESENT WORTH OF 1 PER PERIOD *What $1 payable periodically is worth today.*	PARTIAL PAYMENT *Annuity worth $1 today.* *Periodic payment necessary to pay off a loan of $1.*	P E R I O D S	RATE $\frac{3}{4}\%$
.992 555 8313	.992 555 8313	1.007 500 0000	1	
.985 167 0782	1.977 722 9094	.505 632 0050	2	
.977 833 3282	2.955 556 2377	.338 345 7866	3	.0075
.970 554 1719	3.926 110 4096	.254 705 0123	4	
.963 329 2029	4.889 439 6125	.204 522 4155	5	*per period*
.956 158 0178	5.845 597 6303	.171 068 9074	6	
.949 040 2162	6.794 637 8464	.147 174 8786	7	
.941 975 4006	7.736 613 2471	.129 255 5241	8	
.934 963 1768	8.671 576 4239	.115 319 2858	9	
.928 003 1532	9.599 579 5771	.104 171 2287	10	
.921 094 9411	10.520 674 5182	.095 050 9398	11	
.914 238 1550	11.434 912 6731	.087 451 4768	12	
.907 432 4119	12.342 345 0850	.081 021 8798	13	
.900 677 3319	13.243 022 4169	.075 511 4632	14	
.893 972 5378	14.136 994 9547	.070 736 3908	15	
.887 317 6554	15.024 312 6101	.066 558 7855	16	
.880 712 3131	15.905 024 9232	.062 873 2118	17	
.874 156 1420	16.779 181 0652	.059 597 6643	18	
.867 648 7762	17.646 829 8414	.056 667 4020	19	
.861 189 8523	18.508 019 6937	.054 030 6319	20	
.854 779 0097	19.362 798 7034	.051 645 4266	21	ANNUALLY If compounded *annually* nominal annual rate is
.848 415 8905	20.211 214 5940	.049 477 4817	22	
.842 100 1395	21.053 314 7335	.047 498 4587	23	
.835 831 4040	21.889 146 1374	.045 684 7423	24	
.829 609 3340	22.718 755 4714	.044 016 4956	25	$\frac{3}{4}\%$
.823 433 5821	23.542 189 0535	.042 476 9335	26	
.817 303 8036	24.359 492 8571	.041 051 7578	27	
.811 219 6562	25.170 712 5132	.039 728 7125	28	
.805 180 8001	25.975 893 3134	.038 497 2323	29	
.799 186 8984	26.775 080 2118	.037 348 1608	30	
.793 237 6163	27.568 317 8281	.036 273 5226	31	SEMIANNUALLY If compounded *semiannually* nominal annual rate is
.787 332 6216	28.355 650 4497	.035 266 3397	32	
.781 471 5847	29.137 122 0344	.034 320 4795	33	
.775 654 1784	29.912 776 2128	.033 430 5313	34	
.769 880 0778	30.682 656 2907	.032 591 7023	35	$1\frac{1}{2}\%$
.764 148 9606	31.446 805 2513	.031 799 7327	36	
.758 460 5068	32.205 265 7581	.031 050 8228	37	
.752 814 3988	32.958 080 1569	.030 341 5732	38	
.747 210 3214	33.705 290 4783	.029 668 9329	39	
.741 647 9617	34.446 938 4400	.029 030 1561	40	
.736 127 0091	35.183 065 4492	.028 422 7650	41	QUARTERLY If compounded *quarterly* nominal annual rate is
.730 647 1555	35.913 712 6046	.027 844 5175	42	
.725 208 0948	36.638 920 6994	.027 293 3804	43	
.719 809 5233	37.358 730 2227	.026 767 5051	44	
.714 451 1398	38.073 181 3625	.026 265 2073	45	3%
.709 132 6449	38.782 314 0074	.025 784 9493	46	
.703 853 7419	39.486 167 7493	.025 325 3242	47	
.698 614 1359	40.184 781 8852	.024 885 0424	48	
.693 413 5344	40.878 195 4195	.024 462 9194	49	
.688 251 6470	41.566 447 0665	.024 057 8657	50	
.683 128 1856	42.249 575 2521	.023 668 8770	51	MONTHLY If compounded *monthly* nominal annual rate is
.678 042 8641	42.927 618 1163	.023 295 0265	52	
.672 995 3986	43.600 613 5149	.022 935 4571	53	
.667 985 5073	44.268 599 0222	.022 589 3754	54	
.663 012 9105	44.931 611 9327	.022 256 0455	55	9%
.658 077 3305	45.589 689 2633	.021 934 7843	56	
.653 178 4918	46.242 867 7551	.021 624 9564	57	
.648 316 1209	46.891 183 8760	.021 325 9704	58	$i = .0075$
.643 489 9463	47.534 673 8224	.021 037 2749	59	$j_{(2)} = .015$
.638 699 6986	48.173 373 5210	.020 758 3552	60	$j_{(4)} = .03$ $j_{(12)} = .09$
$v^n = \dfrac{1}{(1+i)^n}$	$a_{\overline{n}\rceil} = \dfrac{1-v^n}{i}$	$\dfrac{1}{a_{\overline{n}\rceil}} = \dfrac{i}{1-v^n}$	n	

31

RATE 1%	P E R I O D S	AMOUNT OF 1 *How $1 left at compound interest will grow.*	AMOUNT OF 1 PER PERIOD *How $1 deposited periodically will grow.*	SINKING FUND *Periodic deposit that will grow to $1 at future date.*
.01 *per period*	1 2 3 4 5	1.010 000 0000 1.020 100 0000 1.030 301 0000 1.040 604 0100 1.051 010 0501	1.000 000 0000 2.010 000 0000 3.030 100 0000 4.060 401 0000 5.101 005 0100	1.000 000 0000 .497 512 4378 .330 022 1115 .246 281 0939 .196 039 7996
	6 7 8 9 10	1.061 520 1506 1.072 135 3521 1.082 856 7056 1.093 685 2727 1.104 622 1254	6.152 015 0601 7.213 535 2107 8.285 670 5628 9.368 527 2684 10.462 212 5411	.162 548 3667 .138 628 2829 .120 690 2920 .106 740 3628 .095 582 0766
	11 12 13 14 15	1.115 668 3467 1.126 825 0301 1.138 093 2804 1.149 474 2132 1.160 968 9554	11.566 834 6665 12.682 503 0132 13.809 328 0433 14.947 421 3238 16.096 895 5370	.086 454 0757 .078 848 7887 .072 414 8197 .066 901 1717 .062 123 7802
	16 17 18 19 20	1.172 578 6449 1.184 304 4314 1.196 147 4757 1.208 108 9504 1.220 190 0399	17.257 864 4924 18.430 443 1373 19.614 747 5687 20.810 895 0444 22.019 003 9948	.057 944 5968 .054 258 0551 .050 982 0479 .048 051 7536 .045 415 3149
ANNUALLY If compounded *annually* nominal annual rate is **1%**	21 22 23 24 25	1.232 391 9403 1.244 715 8598 1.257 163 0183 1.269 734 6485 1.282 431 9950	23.239 194 0347 24.471 585 9751 25.716 301 8348 26.973 464 8532 28.243 199 5017	.043 030 7522 .040 863 7185 .038 885 8401 .037 073 4722 .035 406 7534
	26 27 28 29 30	1.295 256 3150 1.308 208 8781 1.321 290 9669 1.334 503 8766 1.347 848 9153	29.525 631 4967 30.820 887 8117 32.129 096 6898 33.450 387 6567 34.784 891 5333	.033 868 8776 .032 445 5287 .031 124 4356 .029 895 0198 .028 748 1132
SEMIANNUALLY If compounded *semiannually* nominal annual rate is **2%**	31 32 33 34 35	1.361 327 4045 1.374 940 6785 1.388 690 0853 1.402 576 9862 1.416 602 7560	36.132 740 4486 37.494 067 8531 38.869 008 5316 40.257 698 6170 41.660 275 6031	.027 675 7309 .026 670 8857 .025 727 4378 .024 839 9694 .024 003 6818
	36 37 38 39 40	1.430 768 7836 1.445 076 4714 1.459 527 2361 1.474 122 5085 1.488 863 7336	43.076 878 3592 44.507 647 1427 45.952 723 6142 47.412 250 8503 48.886 373 3588	.023 214 3098 .022 468 0491 .021 761 4958 .021 091 5951 .020 455 5980
QUARTERLY If compounded *quarterly* nominal annual rate is **4%**	41 42 43 44 45	1.503 752 3709 1.518 789 8946 1.533 977 7936 1.549 317 5715 1.564 810 7472	50.375 237 0924 51.878 989 4633 53.397 779 3580 54.931 757 1515 56.481 074 7231	.019 851 0232 .019 275 6260 .018 727 3705 .018 204 4058 .017 705 0455
	46 47 48 49 50	1.580 458 8547 1.596 263 4432 1.612 226 0777 1.628 348 3385 1.644 631 8218	58.045 885 4703 59.626 344 3250 61.222 607 7682 62.834 833 8459 64.463 182 1844	.017 227 7499 .016 771 1103 .016 333 8354 .015 914 7393 .015 512 7309
MONTHLY If compounded *monthly* nominal annual rate is **12%**	51 52 53 54 55	1.661 078 1401 1.677 688 9215 1.694 465 8107 1.711 410 4688 1.728 524 5735	66.107 814 0062 67.768 892 1463 69.446 581 0678 71.141 046 8784 72.852 457 3472	.015 126 8048 .014 756 0329 .014 399 5570 .014 056 5826 .013 726 3730
$i = .01$ $j_{(2)} = .02$ $j_{(4)} = .04$ $j_{(12)} = .12$	56 57 58 59 60	1.745 809 8192 1.763 267 9174 1.780 900 5966 1.798 709 6025 1.816 696 6986	74.580 981 9207 76.326 791 7399 78.090 059 6573 79.870 960 2539 81.669 669 8564	.013 408 2440 .013 101 5595 .012 805 7272 .012 520 1950 .012 244 4477
	n	$s=(1+i)^n$	$s_{\overline{n}\rvert}=\dfrac{(1+i)^n-1}{i}$	$\dfrac{1}{s_{\overline{n}\rvert}}=\dfrac{i}{(1+i)^n-1}$

32

PRESENT WORTH OF 1 *What $1 due in the future is worth today.*	PRESENT WORTH OF 1 PER PERIOD *What $1 payable periodically is worth today.*	PARTIAL PAYMENT *Annuity worth $1 today.* Periodic payment necessary to pay off a loan of $1.	PERIODS	RATE 1%
.990 099 0099	.990 099 0099	1.010 000 0000	1	
.980 296 0494	1.970 395 0593	.507 512 4378	2	
.970 590 1479	2.940 985 2072	.340 022 1115	3	.01
.960 980 3445	3.901 965 5517	.256 281 0939	4	*per period*
.951 465 6876	4.853 431 2393	.206 039 7996	5	
.942 045 2353	5.795 476 4746	.172 548 3667	6	
.932 718 0547	6.728 194 5293	.148 628 2829	7	
.923 483 2225	7.651 677 7518	.130 690 2920	8	
.914 339 8242	8.566 017 5760	.116 740 3628	9	
.905 286 9547	9.471 304 5307	.105 582 0766	10	
.896 323 7175	10.367 628 2482	.096 454 0757	11	
.887 449 2253	11.255 077 4735	.088 848 7887	12	
.878 662 5993	12.133 740 0728	.082 414 8197	13	
.869 962 9696	13.003 703 0423	.076 901 1717	14	
.861 349 4748	13.865 052 5172	.072 123 7802	15	
.852 821 2622	14.717 873 7794	.067 944 5968	16	
.844 377 4873	15.562 251 2667	.064 258 0551	17	
.836 017 3142	16.398 268 5809	.060 982 0479	18	
.827 739 9150	17.226 008 4959	.058 051 7536	19	
.819 544 4703	18.045 552 9663	.055 415 3149	20	
.811 430 1687	18.856 983 1349	.053 030 7522	21	ANNUALLY *If compounded annually* nominal annual rate is
.803 396 2066	19.660 379 3415	.050 863 7185	22	
.795 441 7887	20.455 821 1302	.048 885 8401	23	
.787 566 1274	21.243 387 2576	.047 073 4722	24	
.779 768 4430	22.023 155 7006	.045 406 7534	25	1%
.772 047 9634	22.795 203 6640	.043 868 8776	26	
.764 403 9241	23.559 607 5881	.042 445 5287	27	
.756 835 5684	24.316 443 1565	.041 124 4356	28	
.749 342 1470	25.065 785 3035	.039 895 0198	29	
.741 922 9178	25.807 708 2213	.038 748 1132	30	
.734 577 1463	26.542 285 3676	.037 675 7309	31	SEMIANNUALLY *If compounded semiannually* nominal annual rate is
.727 304 1053	27.269 589 4729	.036 670 8857	32	
.720 103 0745	27.989 692 5474	.035 727 4378	33	
.712 973 3411	28.702 665 8885	.034 839 9694	34	
.705 914 1991	29.408 580 0876	.034 003 6818	35	2%
.698 924 9496	30.107 505 0373	.033 214 3098	36	
.692 004 9006	30.799 509 9379	.032 468 0491	37	
.685 153 3670	31.484 663 3048	.031 761 4958	38	
.678 369 6702	32.163 032 9751	.031 091 5951	39	
.671 653 1389	32.834 686 1140	.030 455 5980	40	
.665 003 1078	33.499 689 2217	.029 851 0232	41	QUARTERLY *If compounded quarterly* nominal annual rate is
.658 418 9186	34.158 108 1403	.029 275 6260	42	
.651 899 9194	34.810 008 0597	.028 727 3705	43	
.645 445 4648	35.455 453 5245	.028 204 4058	44	
.639 054 9156	36.094 508 4401	.027 705 0455	45	4%
.632 727 6392	36.727 236 0793	.027 227 7499	46	
.626 463 0091	37.353 699 0884	.026 771 1103	47	
.620 260 4051	37.973 959 4935	.026 333 8354	48	
.614 119 2129	38.588 078 7064	.025 914 7393	49	
.608 038 8247	39.196 117 5311	.025 512 7309	50	
.602 018 6383	39.798 136 1694	.025 126 8048	51	MONTHLY *If compounded monthly* nominal annual rate is
.596 058 0577	40.394 194 2271	.024 756 0329	52	
.590 156 4928	40.984 350 7199	.024 399 5570	53	
.584 313 3592	41.568 664 0791	.024 056 5826	54	
.578 528 0784	42.147 192 1576	.023 726 3730	55	12%
.572 800 0776	42.719 992 2352	.023 408 2440	56	
.567 128 7898	43.287 121 0250	.023 101 5595	57	
.561 513 6532	43.848 634 6782	.022 805 7272	58	$i = .01$
.555 954 1121	44.404 588 7903	.022 520 1950	59	$j_{(2)} = .02$ $j_{(4)} = .04$
.550 449 6159	44.955 038 4062	.022 244 4477	60	$j_{(12)} = .12$
$v^n = \dfrac{1}{(1+i)^n}$	$a_{\overline{n}\rceil} = \dfrac{1-v^n}{i}$	$\dfrac{1}{a_{\overline{n}\rceil}} = \dfrac{i}{1-v^n}$	n	

	P E R I O D S	AMOUNT OF 1 *How $1 left at compound interest will grow.*	AMOUNT OF 1 PER PERIOD *How $1 deposited periodically will grow.*	SINKING FUND *Periodic deposit that will grow to $1 at future date.*
.0125 *per period*	1 2 3 4 5	1.012 500 0000 1.025 156 2500 1.037 970 7031 1.050 945 3369 1.064 082 1536	1.000 000 0000 2.012 500 0000 3.037 656 2500 4.075 626 9531 5.126 572 2900	1.000 000 0000 .496 894 4099 .329 201 1728 .245 361 0233 .195 062 1084
	6 7 8 9 10	1.077 383 1805 1.090 850 4703 1.104 486 1012 1.118 292 1774 1.132 270 8297	6.190 654 4437 7.268 037 6242 8.358 888 0945 9.463 374 1957 10.581 666 3731	.161 533 8102 .137 588 7209 .119 633 1365 .105 670 5546 .094 503 0740
	11 12 13 14 15	1.146 424 2150 1.160 754 5177 1.175 263 9492 1.189 954 7486 1.204 829 1829	11.713 937 2028 12.860 361 4178 14.021 115 9356 15.196 379 8848 16.386 334 6333	.085 368 3935 .077 758 3123 .071 320 9993 .065 805 1462 .061 026 4603
	16 17 18 19 20	1.219 889 5477 1.235 138 1670 1.250 577 3941 1.266 209 6116 1.282 037 2317	17.591 163 8162 18.811 053 3639 20.046 191 5310 21.296 768 9251 22.562 978 5367	.056 846 7221 .053 160 2341 .049 884 7873 .046 955 4797 .044 320 3896
ANNUALLY If compounded *annually* nominal annual rate is **1¼%**	21 22 23 24 25	1.298 062 6971 1.314 288 4808 1.330 717 0868 1.347 351 0504 1.364 192 9385	23.845 015 7684 25.143 078 4655 26.457 366 9463 27.788 084 0331 29.135 435 0836	.041 937 4854 .039 772 3772 .037 796 6561 .035 986 6480 .034 322 4667
	26 27 28 29 30	1.381 245 3503 1.398 510 9172 1.415 992 3036 1.433 692 2074 1.451 613 3600	30.499 628 0221 31.880 873 3724 33.279 384 2895 34.695 376 5932 36.129 068 8006	.032 787 2851 .031 366 7693 .030 048 6329 .028 822 2841 .027 678 5434
SEMIANNUALLY If compounded *semiannually* nominal annual rate is **2½%**	31 32 33 34 35	1.469 758 5270 1.488 130 5086 1.506 732 1400 1.525 566 2917 1.544 635 8703	37.580 682 1606 39.050 440 6876 40.538 571 1962 42.045 303 3361 43.570 869 6278	.026 609 4159 .025 607 9056 .024 667 8650 .023 783 8693 .022 951 1141
	36 37 38 39 40	1.563 943 8187 1.583 493 1165 1.603 286 7804 1.623 327 8652 1.643 619 4635	45.115 505 4982 46.679 449 3169 48.262 942 4334 49.866 229 2138 51.489 557 0790	.022 165 3285 .021 422 7035 .020 719 8308 .020 053 6519 .019 421 4139
QUARTERLY If compounded *quarterly* nominal annual rate is **5%**	41 42 43 44 45	1.664 164 7068 1.684 966 7656 1.706 028 8502 1.727 354 2108 1.748 946 1384	53.133 176 5424 54.797 341 2492 56.482 308 0148 58.188 336 8650 59.915 691 0758	.018 820 6327 .018 249 0606 .017 704 6589 .017 185 5745 .016 690 1188
	46 47 48 49 50	1.770 807 9652 1.792 943 0647 1.815 354 8531 1.838 046 7887 1.861 022 3736	61.664 637 2143 63.435 445 1795 65.228 388 2442 67.043 743 0973 68.881 789 8860	.016 216 7499 .015 764 0574 .015 330 7483 .014 915 6350 .014 517 6251
MONTHLY If compounded *monthly* nominal annual rate is **15%**	51 52 53 54 55	1.884 285 1532 1.907 838 7177 1.931 686 7016 1.955 832 7854 1.980 280 6952	70.742 812 2596 72.627 097 4128 74.534 936 1305 76.466 622 8321 78.422 455 6175	.014 135 7117 .013 768 9655 .013 416 5272 .013 077 6012 .012 751 4497
i = .0125 *j*(2) = .025 *j*(4) = .05 *j*(12) = .15	56 57 58 59 60	2.005 034 2039 2.030 097 1315 2.055 473 3456 2.081 166 7624 2.107 181 3470	80.402 736 3127 82.407 770 5166 84.437 867 6481 86.493 340 9937 88.574 507 7561	.012 437 3877 .012 134 7780 .011 843 0276 .011 561 5837 .011 289 9301
	n	$s=(1+i)^n$	$s_{\overline{n}\rceil}=\dfrac{(1+i)^n-1}{i}$	$\dfrac{1}{s_{\overline{n}\rceil}}=\dfrac{i}{(1+i)^n-1}$

PRESENT WORTH OF 1	PRESENT WORTH OF 1 PER PERIOD	PARTIAL PAYMENT	P E R I O D S	RATE
What $1 due in the future is worth today.	*What $1 payable periodically is worth today.*	*Annuity worth $1 today.* *Periodic payment necessary to pay off a loan of $1.*		$1\frac{1}{4}\%$

.987 654 3210	.987 654 3210	1.012 500 0000	1	
.975 461 0578	1.963 115 3788	.509 394 4099	2	
.963 418 3287	2.926 533 7074	.341 701 1728	3	.0125
.951 524 2752	3.878 057 9826	.257 861 0233	4	
.939 777 0619	4.817 835 0446	.207 562 1084	5	*per period*
.928 174 8760	5.746 009 9206	.174 033 8102	6	
.916 715 9269	6.662 725 8475	.150 088 7209	7	
.905 398 4463	7.568 124 2938	.132 133 1365	8	
.894 220 6877	8.462 344 9815	.118 170 5546	9	
.883 180 9262	9.345 525 9077	.107 003 0740	10	
.872 277 4579	10.217 803 3656	.097 868 3935	11	
.861 508 6004	11.079 311 9660	.090 258 3123	12	
.850 872 6918	11.930 184 6578	.083 820 9993	13	
.840 368 0906	12.770 552 7485	.078 305 1462	14	
.829 993 1759	13.600 545 9244	.073 526 4603	15	
.819 746 3466	14.420 292 2710	.069 346 7221	16	
.809 626 0213	15.229 918 2924	.065 660 2341	17	
.799 630 6384	16.029 548 9307	.062 384 7873	18	
.789 758 6552	16.819 307 5859	.059 455 4797	19	
.780 008 5483	17.599 316 1342	.056 820 3896	20	
.770 378 8132	18.369 694 9474	.054 437 4854	21	ANNUALLY
.760 867 9636	19.130 562 9110	.052 272 3772	22	If compounded
.751 474 5320	19.882 037 4430	.050 296 6561	23	*annually*
.742 197 0686	20.624 234 5116	.048 486 6480	24	nominal annual rate is
.733 034 1418	21.357 268 6534	.046 822 4667	25	$1\frac{1}{4}\%$
.723 984 3376	22.081 252 9910	.045 287 2851	26	
.715 046 2594	22.796 299 2504	.043 866 7693	27	
.706 218 5278	23.502 517 7782	.042 548 6329	28	
.697 499 7805	24.200 017 5587	.041 322 2841	29	
.688 888 6721	24.888 906 2308	.040 178 5434	30	
.680 383 8737	25.569 290 1045	.039 109 4159	31	SEMIANNUALLY
.671 984 0728	26.241 274 1773	.038 107 9056	32	If compounded
.663 687 9731	26.904 962 1504	.037 167 8650	33	*semiannually*
.655 494 2944	27.560 456 4448	.036 283 8693	34	nominal annual rate is
.647 401 7723	28.207 858 2171	.035 451 1141	35	$2\frac{1}{2}\%$
.639 409 1578	28.847 267 3749	.034 665 3285	36	
.631 515 2176	29.478 782 5925	.033 922 7035	37	
.623 718 7334	30.102 501 3259	.033 219 8308	38	
.616 018 5021	30.718 519 8281	.032 553 6519	39	
.608 413 3355	31.326 933 1635	.031 921 4139	40	
.600 902 0597	31.927 835 2233	.031 320 6327	41	QUARTERLY
.593 483 5158	32.521 318 7390	.030 749 0606	42	If compounded
.586 156 5588	33.107 475 2978	.030 204 6589	43	*quarterly*
.578 920 0581	33.686 395 3558	.029 685 5745	44	nominal annual rate is
.571 772 8968	34.258 168 2527	.029 190 1188	45	5%
.564 713 9722	34.822 882 2249	.028 716 7499	46	
.557 742 1948	35.380 624 4196	.028 264 0574	47	
.550 856 4886	35.931 480 9083	.027 830 7483	48	
.544 055 7913	36.475 536 6995	.027 415 6350	49	
.537 339 0531	37.012 875 7526	.027 017 6251	50	
.530 705 2376	37.543 580 9902	.026 635 7117	51	MONTHLY
.524 153 3211	38.067 734 3114	.026 268 9655	52	If compounded
.517 682 2925	38.585 416 6038	.025 916 5272	53	*monthly*
.511 291 1530	39.096 707 7568	.025 577 6012	54	nominal annual rate is
.504 978 9166	39.601 686 6734	.025 251 4497	55	15%
.498 744 6090	40.100 431 2824	.024 937 3877	56	
.492 587 2681	40.593 018 5505	.024 634 7780	57	
.486 505 9438	41.079 524 4943	.024 343 0276	58	$i = .0125$
.480 499 6976	41.560 024 1919	.024 061 5837	59	$j_{(2)} = .025$
.474 567 6026	42.034 591 7945	.023 789 9301	60	$j_{(4)} = .05$
				$j_{(12)} = .15$
$v^n = \dfrac{1}{(1+i)^n}$	$a_{\overline{n}|} = \dfrac{1-v^n}{i}$	$\dfrac{1}{a_{\overline{n}|}} = \dfrac{i}{1-v^n}$	n	

35

	P E R I O D S	AMOUNT OF 1 *How $1 left at compound interest will grow.*	AMOUNT OF 1 PER PERIOD *How $1 deposited periodically will grow.*	SINKING FUND *Periodic deposit that will grow to $1 at future date.*
	1	1.015 000 0000	1.000 000 0000	1.000 000 0000
.015 *per period*	2	1.030 225 0000	2.015 000 0000	.496 277 9156
	3	1.045 678 3750	3.045 225 0000	.328 382 9602
	4	1.061 363 5506	4.090 903 3750	.244 444 7860
	5	1.077 284 0039	5.152 266 9256	.194 089 3231
	6	1.093 443 2639	6.229 550 9295	.160 525 2146
	7	1.109 844 9129	7.322 994 1935	.136 556 1645
	8	1.126 492 5866	8.432 839 1064	.118 584 0246
	9	1.143 389 9754	9.559 331 6929	.104 609 8234
	10	1.160 540 8250	10.702 721 6683	.093 434 1779
	11	1.177 948 9374	11.863 262 4934	.084 293 8442
	12	1.195 618 1715	13.041 211 4308	.076 679 9929
	13	1.213 552 4440	14.236 829 6022	.070 240 3574
	14	1.231 755 7307	15.450 382 0463	.064 723 3186
	15	1.250 232 0667	16.682 137 7770	.059 944 3557
	16	1.268 985 5477	17.932 369 8436	.055 765 0778
	17	1.288 020 3309	19.201 355 3913	.052 079 6569
	18	1.307 340 6358	20.489 375 7221	.048 805 7818
	19	1.326 950 7454	21.796 716 3580	.045 878 4701
	20	1.346 855 0066	23.123 667 1033	.043 245 7359
ANNUALLY If compounded *annually* nominal annual rate is **1½%**	21	1.367 057 8316	24.470 522 1099	.040 865 4950
	22	1.387 563 6991	25.837 579 9415	.038 703 3152
	23	1.408 377 1546	27.225 143 6407	.036 730 7520
	24	1.429 502 8119	28.633 520 7953	.034 924 1020
	25	1.450 945 3541	30.063 023 6072	.033 263 4539
	26	1.472 709 5344	31.513 968 9613	.031 731 9599
	27	1.494 800 1774	32.986 678 4957	.030 315 2680
	28	1.517 222 1801	34.481 478 6732	.029 001 0765
	29	1.539 980 5128	35.998 700 8533	.027 778 7802
	30	1.563 080 2205	37.538 681 3661	.026 639 1883
SEMIANNUALLY If compounded *semiannually* nominal annual rate is **3%**	31	1.586 526 4238	39.101 761 5865	.025 574 2954
	32	1.610 324 3202	40.688 288 0103	.024 577 0970
	33	1.634 479 1850	42.298 612 3305	.023 641 4375
	34	1.658 996 3727	43.933 091 5155	.022 761 8855
	35	1.683 881 3183	45.592 087 8882	.021 933 6303
	36	1.709 139 5381	47.275 969 2065	.021 152 3955
	37	1.734 776 6312	48.985 108 7446	.020 414 3673
	38	1.760 798 2806	50.719 885 3758	.019 716 1329
	39	1.787 210 2548	52.480 683 6564	.019 054 6298
	40	1.814 018 4087	54.267 893 9113	.018 427 1017
QUARTERLY If compounded *quarterly* nominal annual rate is **6%**	41	1.841 228 6848	56.081 912 3199	.017 831 0610
	42	1.868 847 1151	57.923 141 0047	.017 264 2571
	43	1.896 879 8218	59.791 988 1198	.016 724 6488
	44	1.925 333 0191	61.688 867 9416	.016 210 3801
	45	1.954 213 0144	63.614 200 9607	.015 719 7604
	46	1.983 526 2096	65.568 413 9751	.015 251 2458
	47	2.013 279 1028	67.551 940 1848	.014 803 4238
	48	2.043 478 2893	69.565 219 2875	.014 374 9996
	49	2.074 130 4637	71.608 697 5768	.013 964 7841
	50	2.105 242 4206	73.682 828 0405	.013 571 6832
MONTHLY If compounded *monthly* nominal annual rate is **18%**	51	2.136 821 0569	75.788 070 4611	.013 194 6887
	52	2.168 873 3728	77.924 891 5180	.012 832 8700
	53	2.201 406 4734	80.093 764 8908	.012 485 3664
	54	2.234 427 5705	82.295 171 3642	.012 151 3812
	55	2.267 943 9840	84.529 598 9346	.011 830 1756
	56	2.301 963 1438	86.797 542 9186	.011 521 0635
$i = .015$ $j_{(2)} = .03$ $j_{(4)} = .06$ $j_{(12)} = .18$	57	2.336 492 5909	89.099 506 0624	.011 223 4068
	58	2.371 539 9798	91.435 998 6534	.010 936 6116
	59	2.407 113 0795	93.807 538 6332	.010 660 1241
	60	2.443 219 7757	96.214 651 7126	.010 393 4274
	n	$s=(1+i)^n$	$s_{\overline{n}|}=\dfrac{(1+i)^n-1}{i}$	$\dfrac{1}{s_{\overline{n}|}}=\dfrac{i}{(1+i)^n-1}$

PRESENT WORTH OF 1 *What $1 due in the future is worth today.*	PRESENT WORTH OF 1 PER PERIOD *What $1 payable periodically is worth today.*	PARTIAL PAYMENT *Annuity worth $1 today.* *Periodic payment necessary to pay off a loan of $1.*	PERIODS	RATE
.985 221 6749	.985 221 6749	1.015 000 0000	1	
.970 661 7486	1.955 883 4235	.511 277 9156	2	
.956 316 9937	2.912 200 4173	.343 382 9602	3	.015
.942 184 2303	3.854 384 6476	.259 444 7860	4	
.928 260 3254	4.782 644 9730	.209 089 3231	5	*per period*
.914 542 1925	5.697 187 1655	.175 525 2146	6	
.901 026 7907	6.598 213 9561	.151 556 1645	7	
.887 711 1238	7.485 925 0799	.133 584 0246	8	
.874 592 2402	8.360 517 3201	.119 609 8234	9	
.861 667 2317	9.222 184 5519	.108 434 1779	10	
.848 933 2332	10.071 117 7851	.099 293 8442	11	
.836 387 4219	10.907 505 2070	.091 679 9929	12	
.824 027 0166	11.731 532 2236	.085 240 3574	13	
.811 849 2775	12.543 381 5011	.079 723 3186	14	
.799 851 5049	13.343 233 0060	.074 944 3557	15	
.788 031 0393	14.131 264 0453	.070 765 0778	16	
.776 385 2604	14.907 649 3057	.067 079 6569	17	
.764 911 5866	15.672 560 8924	.063 805 7818	18	
.753 607 4745	16.426 168 3669	.060 878 4701	19	
.742 470 4182	17.168 638 7851	.058 245 7359	20	
.731 497 9490	17.900 136 7341	.055 865 4950	21	ANNUALLY *If compounded annually* nominal annual rate is
.720 687 6345	18.620 824 3685	.053 703 3152	22	
.710 037 0783	19.330 861 4468	.051 730 7520	23	
.699 543 9195	20.030 405 3663	.049 924 1020	24	
.689 205 8320	20.719 611 1984	.048 263 4539	25	$1\frac{1}{2}\%$
.679 020 5242	21.398 631 7225	.046 731 9599	26	
.668 985 7381	22.067 617 4606	.045 315 2680	27	
.659 099 2494	22.726 716 7100	.044 001 0765	28	
.649 358 8664	23.376 075 5763	.042 778 7802	29	
.639 762 4299	24.015 838 0062	.041 639 1883	30	
.630 307 8127	24.646 145 8189	.040 574 2954	31	SEMIANNUALLY *If compounded semiannually* nominal annual rate is
.620 992 9189	25.267 138 7379	.039 577 0970	32	
.611 815 6837	25.878 954 4216	.038 641 4375	33	
.602 774 0726	26.481 728 4941	.037 761 8855	34	
.593 866 0814	27.075 594 5755	.036 933 6303	35	3%
.585 089 7353	27.660 684 3109	.036 152 3955	36	
.576 443 0890	28.237 127 3999	.035 414 3673	37	
.567 924 2256	28.805 051 6255	.034 716 1329	38	
.559 531 2568	29.364 582 8822	.034 054 6298	39	
.551 262 3219	29.915 845 2042	.033 427 1017	40	
.543 115 5881	30.458 960 7923	.032 831 0610	41	QUARTERLY *If compounded quarterly* nominal annual rate is
.535 089 2494	30.994 050 0417	.032 264 2571	42	
.527 181 5265	31.521 231 5681	.031 724 6488	43	
.519 390 6665	32.040 622 2346	.031 210 3804	44	
.511 714 9423	32.552 337 1770	.030 719 7604	45	6%
.504 152 6526	33.056 489 8295	.030 251 2458	46	
.496 702 1207	33.553 191 9503	.029 803 4238	47	
.489 361 6953	34.042 553 6456	.029 374 9996	48	
.482 129 7491	34.524 683 3947	.028 964 7841	49	
.475 004 6789	34.999 688 0736	.028 571 6832	50	
.467 984 9053	35.467 672 9789	.028 194 6887	51	MONTHLY *If compounded monthly* nominal annual rate is
.461 068 8722	35.928 741 8511	.027 832 8700	52	
.454 255 0465	36.382 996 8977	.027 485 3664	53	
.447 541 9178	36.830 538 8154	.027 151 3812	54	
.440 927 9978	37.271 466 8132	.026 830 1756	55	18%
.434 411 8205	37.705 878 6337	.026 521 0635	56	
.427 991 9414	38.133 870 5751	.026 223 4068	57	
.421 666 9373	38.555 537 5124	.025 936 6116	58	$i \quad = .015$
.415 435 4062	38.970 972 9186	.025 660 1241	59	$j_{(2)} = .03$ $j_{(4)} = .06$
.409 295 9667	39.380 268 8853	.025 393 4274	60	$j_{(12)} = .18$
$v^n = \dfrac{1}{(1+i)^n}$	$a_{\overline{n}} = \dfrac{1-v^n}{i}$	$\dfrac{1}{a_{\overline{n}}} = \dfrac{i}{1-v^n}$	n	

	P E R I O D S	AMOUNT OF 1 *How $1 left at compound interest will grow.*	AMOUNT OF 1 PER PERIOD *How $1 deposited periodically will grow.*	SINKING FUND *Periodic deposit that will grow to $1 at future date.*
.0175 *per period*	1	1.017 500 0000	1.000 000 0000	1.000 000 0000
	2	1.035 306 2500	2.017 500 0000	.495 662 9492
	3	1.053 424 1094	3.052 806 2500	.327 567 4635
	4	1.071 859 0313	4.106 230 3594	.243 532 3673
	5	1.090 616 5643	5.178 089 3907	.193 121 4246
	6	1.109 702 3542	6.268 705 9550	.159 522 5565
	7	1.129 122 1454	7.378 408 3092	.135 530 5857
	8	1.148 881 7830	8.507 530 4546	.117 542 9233
	9	1.168 987 2142	9.656 412 2376	.103 558 1306
	10	1.189 444 4904	10.825 399 4517	.092 375 3442
	11	1.210 259 7690	12.014 843 9421	.083 230 3778
	12	1.231 439 3149	13.225 103 7111	.075 613 7738
	13	1.252 989 5030	14.456 543 0261	.069 172 8305
	14	1.274 916 8193	15.709 532 5290	.063 655 6179
	15	1.297 227 8636	16.984 449 3483	.058 877 3872
	16	1.319 929 3512	18.281 677 2119	.054 699 5764
	17	1.343 028 1149	19.601 606 5631	.051 016 2265
	18	1.366 531 1069	20.944 634 6779	.047 744 9244
	19	1.390 445 4012	22.311 165 7848	.044 820 6073
	20	1.414 778 1958	23.701 611 1860	.042 191 2246
ANNUALLY If compounded *annually* nominal annual rate is ## 1¾%	21	1.439 536 8142	25.116 389 3818	.039 814 6399
	22	1.464 728 7084	26.555 926 1960	.037 656 3782
	23	1.490 361 4608	28.020 654 9044	.035 687 9596
	24	1.516 442 7864	29.511 016 3652	.033 885 6510
	25	1.542 980 5352	31.027 459 1516	.032 229 5163
	26	1.569 982 6945	32.570 439 6868	.030 702 6865
	27	1.597 457 3917	34.140 422 3813	.029 290 7917
	28	1.625 412 8960	35.737 879 7730	.027 981 5145
	29	1.653 857 6217	37.363 292 6690	.026 764 2365
	30	1.682 800 1301	39.017 150 2907	.025 629 7549
SEMIANNUALLY If compounded *semiannually* nominal annual rate is ## 3½%	31	1.712 249 1324	40.699 950 4208	.024 570 0545
	32	1.742 213 4922	42.412 199 5532	.023 578 1216
	33	1.772 702 2283	44.154 413 0453	.022 647 7928
	34	1.803 724 5173	45.927 115 2736	.021 773 6297
	35	1.835 289 6963	47.730 839 7909	.020 950 8151
	36	1.867 407 2660	49.566 129 4873	.020 175 0673
	37	1.900 086 8932	51.433 536 7533	.019 442 5673
	38	1.933 338 4138	53.333 623 6465	.018 749 8979
	39	1.967 171 8361	55.266 962 0603	.018 093 9926
	40	2.001 597 3432	57.234 133 8963	.017 472 0911
QUARTERLY If compounded *quarterly* nominal annual rate is ## 7%	41	2.036 625 2967	59.235 731 2395	.016 881 7026
	42	2.072 266 2394	61.272 356 5362	.016 320 5735
	43	2.108 530 8986	63.344 622 7756	.015 786 6596
	44	2.145 430 1893	65.453 153 6742	.015 278 1026
	45	2.182 975 2176	67.598 583 8635	.014 793 2093
	46	2.221 177 2839	69.781 559 0811	.014 330 4336
	47	2.260 047 8864	72.002 736 3650	.013 888 3611
	48	2.299 598 7244	74.262 784 2514	.013 465 6950
	49	2.339 841 7021	76.562 382 9758	.013 061 2445
	50	2.380 788 9319	78.902 224 6779	.012 673 9139
MONTHLY If compounded *monthly* nominal annual rate is ## 21%	51	2.422 452 7382	81.283 013 6097	.012 302 6935
	52	2.464 845 6611	83.705 466 3479	.011 946 6511
	53	2.507 980 4602	86.170 312 0090	.011 604 9249
	54	2.551 870 1182	88.678 292 4691	.011 276 7169
	55	2.596 527 8453	91.230 162 5874	.010 961 2871
i = .0175 $j_{(2)}$ = .035 $j_{(4)}$ = .07 $j_{(12)}$ = .21	56	2.641 967 0826	93.826 690 4326	.010 657 9481
	57	2.688 201 5065	96.468 657 5152	.010 366 0611
	58	2.735 245 0329	99.156 859 0217	.010 085 0310
	59	2.783 111 8210	101.892 104 0546	.009 814 3032
	60	2.831 816 2778	104.675 215 8756	.009 553 3598
	n	$s=(1+i)^n$	$s_{\overline{n}} = \dfrac{(1+i)^n-1}{i}$	$\dfrac{1}{s_{\overline{n}}} = \dfrac{i}{(1+i)^n-1}$

PRESENT WORTH OF 1	PRESENT WORTH OF 1 PER PERIOD	PARTIAL PAYMENT	P E R I O D S	RATE
What $1 due in the future is worth today.	*What $1 payable periodically is worth today.*	*Annuity worth $1 today.* *Periodic payment necessary to pay off a loan of $1.*		1¾%
.982 800 9828	.982 800 9828	1.017 500 0000	1	
.965 897 7718	1.948 698 7546	.513 162 9492	2	
.949 285 2794	2.897 984 0340	.345 067 4635	3	.0175
.932 958 5056	3.830 942 5396	.261 032 3673	4	
.916 912 5362	4.747 855 0757	.210 621 4246	5	*per period*
.901 142 5417	5.648 997 6174	.177 022 5565	6	
.885 643 7756	6.534 641 3930	.153 030 5857	7	
.870 411 5731	7.405 052 9661	.135 042 9233	8	
.855 441 3495	8.260 494 3156	.121 058 1306	9	
.840 728 5990	9.101 222 9146	.109 875 3442	10	
.826 268 8934	9.927 491 8080	.100 730 3778	11	
.812 057 8805	10.739 549 6884	.095 113 7738	12	
.798 091 2830	11.537 640 9714	.086 672 8305	13	
.784 364 8973	12.322 005 8687	.081 155 6179	14	
.770 874 5919	13.092 880 4607	.076 377 3872	15	
.757 616 3066	13.850 496 7672	.072 199 5764	16	
.744 586 0507	14.595 082 8179	.068 516 2265	17	
.731 779 9024	15.326 862 7203	.065 244 9244	18	
.719 194 0073	16.046 056 7276	.062 320 6073	19	
.706 824 5772	16.752 881 3048	.059 691 2246	20	
.694 667 8891	17.447 549 1939	.057 314 6399	21	ANNUALLY
.682 720 2841	18.130 269 4780	.055 156 3782	22	If compounded *annually*
.670 978 1662	18.801 247 6442	.053 187 9596	23	nominal annual rate is
.659 438 0012	19.460 685 6454	.051 385 6510	24	
.648 096 3157	20.108 781 9611	.049 729 5163	25	1¾%
.636 949 6960	20.745 731 6571	.048 202 6865	26	
.625 994 7872	21.371 726 4443	.046 790 7917	27	
.615 228 2921	21.986 954 7364	.045 481 5145	28	
.604 646 9701	22.591 601 7066	.044 264 2365	29	
.594 247 6365	23.185 849 3431	.043 129 7549	30	SEMIANNUALLY
.584 027 1612	23.769 876 5042	.042 070 0545	31	If compounded *semiannually*
.573 982 4680	24.343 858 9722	.041 078 1216	32	nominal annual rate is
.564 110 5336	24.907 969 5059	.040 147 7928	33	
.554 408 3869	25.462 377 8928	.039 273 6297	34	
.544 873 1075	26.007 251 0003	.038 450 8151	35	3½%
.535 501 8255	26.542 752 8258	.037 675 0673	36	
.526 291 7204	27.069 044 5462	.036 942 5673	37	
.517 240 0201	27.586 284 5663	.036 249 8979	38	
.508 344 0001	28.094 628 5664	.035 593 9926	39	
.499 600 9829	28.594 229 5493	.034 972 0911	40	QUARTERLY
.491 008 3370	29.085 237 8863	.034 381 7026	41	If compounded *quarterly*
.482 563 4762	29.567 801 3625	.033 820 5735	42	nominal annual rate is
.474 263 8586	30.042 065 2211	.033 286 6596	43	
.466 106 9864	30.508 172 2075	.032 778 1026	44	
.458 090 4043	30.966 262 6117	.032 293 2093	45	7%
.450 211 6996	31.416 474 3113	.031 830 4336	46	
.442 468 5008	31.858 942 8121	.031 388 3611	47	
.434 858 4774	32.293 801 2895	.030 965 6950	48	
.427 379 3390	32.721 180 6285	.030 561 2445	49	
.420 028 8344	33.141 209 4629	.030 173 9139	50	MONTHLY
.412 804 7513	33.554 014 2142	.029 802 6935	51	If compounded *monthly*
.405 704 9152	33.959 719 1294	.029 446 6511	52	nominal annual rate is
.398 727 1894	34.358 446 3188	.029 104 9249	53	
.391 869 4736	34.750 315 7925	.028 776 7169	54	
.385 129 7038	35.135 445 4963	.028 461 2871	55	21%
.378 505 8514	35.513 951 3477	.028 157 9481	56	
.371 995 9228	35.885 947 2705	.027 866 0611	57	
.365 597 9585	36.251 545 2290	.027 585 0310	58	$i = .0175$
.359 310 0329	36.610 855 2619	.027 314 3032	59	$j_{(2)} = .035$
.353 130 2535	36.963 985 5154	.027 053 3598	60	$j_{(4)} = .07$
$v^n = \dfrac{1}{(1+i)^n}$	$a_{\overline{n}} = \dfrac{1-v^n}{i}$	$\dfrac{1}{a_{\overline{n}}} = \dfrac{i}{1-v^n}$	n	$j_{(12)} = .21$

39

P E R I O D S	AMOUNT OF 1 *How $1 left at compound interest will grow.*	AMOUNT OF 1 PER PERIOD *How $1 deposited periodically will grow.*	SINKING FUND *Periodic deposit that will grow to $1 at future date.*
1	1.020 000 0000	1.000 000 0000	1.000 000 0000
2	1.040 400 0000	2.020 000 0000	.495 049 5050
3	1.061 208 0000	3.060 400 0000	.326 754 6726
4	1.082 432 1600	4.121 608 0000	.242 623 7527
5	1.104 080 8032	5.204 040 1600	.192 158 3941
6	1.126 162 4193	6.308 120 9632	.158 525 8123
7	1.148 685 6676	7.434 283 3825	.134 511 9561
8	1.171 659 3810	8.582 969 0501	.116 509 7991
9	1.195 092 5686	9.754 628 4311	.102 515 4374
10	1.218 994 4200	10.949 720 9997	.091 326 5279
11	1.243 374 3084	12.168 715 4197	.082 177 9428
12	1.268 241 7946	13.412 089 7281	.074 559 5966
13	1.293 606 6305	14.680 331 5227	.068 118 3527
14	1.319 478 7631	15.973 938 1531	.062 601 9702
15	1.345 868 3383	17.293 416 9162	.057 825 4723
16	1.372 785 7051	18.639 285 2545	.053 650 1259
17	1.400 241 4192	20.012 070 9596	.049 969 8408
18	1.428 246 2476	21.412 312 3788	.046 702 1022
19	1.456 811 1725	22.840 558 6264	.043 781 7663
20	1.485 947 3960	24.297 369 7989	.041 156 7181
21	1.515 666 3439	25.783 317 1949	.038 784 7689
22	1.545 979 6708	27.298 983 5388	.036 631 4005
23	1.576 899 2642	28.844 963 2096	.034 668 0976
24	1.608 437 2495	30.421 862 4738	.032 871 0973
25	1.640 605 9945	32.030 299 7232	.031 220 4384
26	1.673 418 1144	33.670 905 7177	.029 699 2308
27	1.706 886 4766	35.344 323 8321	.028 293 0862
28	1.741 024 2062	37.051 210 3087	.026 989 6716
29	1.775 844 6903	38.792 234 5149	.025 778 3552
30	1.811 361 5841	40.568 079 2052	.024 649 9223
31	1.847 588 8158	42.379 440 7893	.023 596 3472
32	1.884 540 5921	44.227 029 6051	.022 610 6073
33	1.922 231 4039	46.111 570 1972	.021 686 5311
34	1.960 676 0320	48.033 801 6011	.020 818 6728
35	1.999 889 5527	49.994 477 6331	.020 002 2092
36	2.039 887 3437	51.994 367 1858	.019 232 8526
37	2.080 685 0906	54.034 254 5295	.018 506 7789
38	2.122 298 7924	56.114 939 6201	.017 820 5663
39	2.164 744 7682	58.237 238 4125	.017 171 1439
40	2.208 039 6636	60.401 983 1807	.016 555 7478
41	2.252 200 4569	62.610 022 8444	.015 971 8836
42	2.297 244 4660	64.862 223 3012	.015 417 2945
43	2.343 189 3553	67.159 467 7673	.014 889 9334
44	2.390 053 1425	69.502 657 1226	.014 387 9391
45	2.437 854 2053	71.892 710 2651	.013 909 6161
46	2.486 611 2894	74.330 564 4704	.013 453 4159
47	2.536 343 5152	76.817 175 7598	.013 017 9220
48	2.587 070 3855	79.353 519 2750	.012 601 8355
49	2.638 811 7932	81.940 589 6605	.012 203 9639
50	2.691 588 0291	84.579 401 4537	.011 823 2097
51	2.745 419 7897	87.270 989 4828	.011 458 5615
52	2.800 328 1854	90.016 409 2724	.011 109 0856
53	2.856 334 7492	92.816 737 4579	.010 773 9189
54	2.913 461 4441	95.673 072 2070	.010 452 2618
55	2.971 730 6730	98.586 533 6512	.010 143 3732
56	3.031 165 2865	101.558 264 3242	.009 846 5645
57	3.091 788 5922	104.589 429 6107	.009 561 1957
58	3.153 624 3641	107.681 218 2029	.009 286 6706
59	3.216 696 8513	110.834 842 5669	.009 022 4335
60	3.281 030 7884	114.051 539 4183	.008 767 9658
n	$s=(1+i)^n$	$s_{\overline{n}\|}=\dfrac{(1+i)^n-1}{i}$	$\dfrac{1}{s_{\overline{n}\|}}=\dfrac{i}{(1+i)^n-1}$

.02
per period

ANNUALLY
If compounded *annually* nominal annual rate is
2%

SEMIANNUALLY
If compounded *semiannually* nominal annual rate is
4%

QUARTERLY
If compounded *quarterly* nominal annual rate is
8%

MONTHLY
If compounded *monthly* nominal annual rate is
24%

$i = .02$
$j_{(2)} = .04$
$j_{(4)} = .08$
$j_{(12)} = .24$

PRESENT WORTH OF 1	PRESENT WORTH OF 1 PER PERIOD	PARTIAL PAYMENT	P E R I O D S	RATE
What $1 due in the future is worth today.	*What $1 payable periodically is worth today.*	*Annuity worth $1 today.* *Periodic payment necessary to pay off a loan of $1.*		**2%**
.980 392 1569	.980 392 1569	1.020 000 0000	1	
.961 168 7812	1.941 560 9381	.515 049 5050	2	.02
.942 322 3345	2.883 883 2726	.346 754 6726	3	
.923 845 4260	3.807 728 6987	.262 623 7527	4	*per period*
.905 730 8098	4.713 459 5085	.212 158 3941	5	
.887 971 3822	5.601 430 8907	.178 525 8123	6	
.870 560 1786	6.471 991 0693	.154 511 9561	7	
.853 490 3712	7.325 481 4405	.136 509 7991	8	
.836 755 2659	8.162 236 7064	.122 515 4374	9	
.820 348 2999	8.982 585 0062	.111 326 5279	10	
.804 263 0391	9.786 848 0453	.102 177 9428	11	
.788 493 1756	10.575 341 2209	.094 559 5966	12	
.773 032 5251	11.348 373 7460	.088 118 3527	13	
.757 875 0246	12.106 248 7706	.082 601 9702	14	
.743 014 7300	12.849 263 5006	.077 825 4723	15	
.728 445 8137	13.577 709 3143	.073 650 1259	16	
.714 162 5625	14.291 871 8768	.069 969 8408	17	
.700 159 3750	14.992 031 2517	.066 702 1022	18	
.686 430 7598	15.678 462 0115	.063 781 7663	19	
.672 971 3331	16.351 433 3446	.061 156 7181	20	
.659 775 8168	17.011 209 1614	.058 784 7689	21	ANNUALLY If compounded *annually* nominal annual rate is
.646 839 0361	17.658 048 1974	.056 631 4005	22	
.634 155 9177	18.292 204 1151	.054 668 0976	23	
.621 721 4879	18.913 925 6031	.052 871 0973	24	
.609 530 8705	19.523 456 4736	.051 220 4384	25	**2%**
.597 579 2848	20.121 035 7584	.049 699 2308	26	
.585 862 0440	20.706 897 8024	.048 293 0862	27	
.574 374 5529	21.281 272 3553	.046 989 6716	28	
.563 112 3068	21.844 384 6620	.045 778 3552	29	
.552 070 8890	22.396 455 5510	.044 649 9223	30	
.541 245 9696	22.937 701 5206	.043 596 3472	31	SEMIANNUALLY If compounded *semiannually* nominal annual rate is
.530 633 3035	23.468 334 8241	.042 610 6073	32	
.520 228 7289	23.988 563 5530	.041 686 5311	33	
.510 028 1656	24.498 591 7187	.040 818 6728	34	
.500 027 6134	24.998 619 3320	.040 002 2092	35	**4%**
.490 223 1504	25.488 842 4824	.039 232 8526	36	
.480 610 9317	25.969 453 4141	.038 506 7789	37	
.471 187 1880	26.440 640 6021	.037 820 5663	38	
.461 948 2235	26.902 588 8256	.037 171 1439	39	
.452 890 4152	27.355 479 2407	.036 555 7478	40	
.444 010 2110	27.799 489 4517	.035 971 8836	41	QUARTERLY If compounded *quarterly* nominal annual rate is
.435 304 1284	28.234 793 5801	.035 417 2945	42	
.426 768 7533	28.661 562 3334	.034 889 9334	43	
.418 400 7386	29.079 963 0720	.034 387 9391	44	
.410 196 8025	29.490 159 8745	.033 909 6161	45	**8%**
.402 153 7280	29.892 313 6025	.033 453 4159	46	
.394 268 3607	30.286 581 9632	.033 017 9220	47	
.386 537 6086	30.673 119 5718	.032 601 8355	48	
.378 958 4398	31.052 078 0115	.032 203 9639	49	
.371 527 8821	31.423 605 8937	.031 823 2097	50	
.364 243 0217	31.787 848 9153	.031 458 5615	51	MONTHLY If compounded *monthly* nominal annual rate is
.357 101 0017	32.144 949 9170	.031 109 0856	52	
.350 099 0212	32.495 048 9382	.030 773 9189	53	
.343 234 3345	32.838 283 2728	.030 452 2618	54	
.336 504 2496	33.174 787 5223	.030 143 3732	55	**24%**
.329 906 1270	33.504 693 6494	.029 846 5645	56	
.323 437 3794	33.828 131 0288	.029 561 1957	57	
.317 095 4700	34.145 226 4988	.029 286 6706	58	$i = .02$
.310 877 9118	34.456 104 4106	.029 022 4335	59	$j_{(2)} = .04$
.304 782 2665	34.760 886 6770	.028 767 9658	60	$j_{(4)} = .08$ $j_{(12)} = .24$
$v^n = \dfrac{1}{(1+i)^n}$	$a_{\overline{n}|} = \dfrac{1-v^n}{i}$	$\dfrac{1}{a_{\overline{n}|}} = \dfrac{i}{1-v^n}$	n	

41

RATE 2¼%	P E R I O D S	AMOUNT OF 1 *How $1 left at compound interest will grow.*	AMOUNT OF 1 PER PERIOD *How $1 deposited periodically will grow.*	SINKING FUND *Periodic deposit that will grow to $1 at future date.*
	1	1.022 500 0000	1.000 000 0000	1.000 000 0000
	2	1.045 506 2500	2.022 500 0000	.494 437 5773
.0225	3	1.069 030 1406	3.068 006 2500	.325 944 5772
	4	1.093 083 3188	4.137 036 3906	.241 718 9277
per period	5	1.117 677 6935	5.230 119 7094	.191 200 2125
	6	1.142 825 4416	6.347 797 4029	.157 534 9584
	7	1.168 539 0140	7.490 622 8444	.133 500 2470
	8	1.194 831 1418	8.659 161 8584	.115 484 6181
	9	1.221 714 8425	9.853 993 0003	.101 481 7039
	10	1.249 203 4265	11.075 707 8428	.090 287 6831
	11	1.277 310 5036	12.324 911 2692	.081 136 4868
	12	1.306 049 9899	13.602 221 7728	.073 517 4015
	13	1.335 436 1147	14.908 271 7627	.067 076 8561
	14	1.365 483 4272	16.243 707 8773	.061 562 2989
	15	1.396 206 8044	17.609 191 3046	.056 788 5250
	16	1.427 621 4575	19.005 398 1089	.052 616 6300
	17	1.459 742 9402	20.433 019 5664	.048 940 3926
	18	1.492 587 1564	21.892 762 5066	.045 677 1958
	19	1.526 170 3674	23.385 349 6630	.042 761 8152
	20	1.560 509 2007	24.911 520 0304	.040 142 0708
ANNUALLY *If compounded annually nominal annual rate is* 2¼%	21	1.595 620 6577	26.472 029 2311	.037 775 7214
	22	1.631 522 1225	28.067 649 8888	.035 628 2056
	23	1.668 231 3703	29.699 172 0113	.033 670 9724
	24	1.705 766 5761	31.367 403 3816	.031 880 2289
	25	1.744 146 3240	33.073 169 9577	.030 235 9889
	26	1.783 389 6163	34.817 316 2817	.028 721 3406
	27	1.823 515 8827	36.600 705 8980	.027 321 8774
	28	1.864 544 9901	38.424 221 7807	.026 025 2506
	29	1.906 497 2523	40.288 766 7708	.024 820 8143
	30	1.949 393 4405	42.195 264 0232	.023 699 3422
SEMIANNUALLY *If compounded semiannually nominal annual rate is* 4½%	31	1.993 254 7929	44.144 657 4637	.022 652 7978
	32	2.038 103 0258	46.137 912 2566	.021 674 1493
	33	2.083 960 3439	48.176 015 2824	.020 757 2169
	34	2.130 849 4516	50.259 975 6262	.019 896 5477
	35	2.178 793 5643	52.390 825 0778	.019 087 3115
	36	2.227 816 4194	54.569 618 6421	.018 325 2151
	37	2.277 942 2889	56.797 435 0615	.017 606 4289
	38	2.329 195 9904	59.075 377 3504	.016 927 5262
	39	2.381 602 9002	61.404 573 3408	.016 285 4319
	40	2.435 188 9654	63.786 176 2410	.015 677 3781
QUARTERLY *If compounded quarterly nominal annual rate is* 9%	41	2.489 980 7171	66.221 365 2064	.015 100 8666
	42	2.546 005 2833	68.711 345 9235	.014 553 6372
	43	2.603 290 4022	71.257 351 2068	.014 033 6398
	44	2.661 864 4362	73.860 641 6090	.013 539 0105
	45	2.721 756 3860	76.522 506 0452	.013 068 0508
	46	2.782 995 9047	79.244 262 4312	.012 619 2101
	47	2.845 613 3126	82.027 258 3359	.012 191 0694
	48	2.909 639 6121	84.872 871 6484	.011 782 3279
	49	2.975 106 5034	87.782 511 2605	.011 391 7908
	50	3.042 046 3997	90.757 617 7639	.011 018 3588
MONTHLY *If compounded monthly nominal annual rate is* 27%	51	3.110 492 4437	93.799 664 1636	.010 661 0190
	52	3.180 478 5237	96.910 156 6073	.010 318 8359
	53	3.252 039 2904	100.090 635 1309	.009 990 9447
	54	3.325 210 1745	103.342 674 4214	.009 676 5446
	55	3.400 027 4034	106.667 884 5958	.009 374 8930
	56	3.476 528 0200	110.067 911 9993	.009 085 3000
i = .0225 *j*(2) = .045 *j*(4) = .09 *j*(12) = .27	57	3.554 749 9004	113.544 440 0192	.008 807 1243
	58	3.634 731 7732	117.099 189 9197	.008 539 7687
	59	3.716 513 2381	120.733 921 6929	.008 282 6764
	60	3.800 134 7859	124.450 434 9310	.008 035 3275
	n	$s=(1+i)^n$	$s_{\overline{n}|}=\dfrac{(1+i)^n-1}{i}$	$\dfrac{1}{s_{\overline{n}|}}=\dfrac{i}{(1+i)^n-1}$

42

PRESENT WORTH OF 1	PRESENT WORTH OF 1 PER PERIOD	PARTIAL PAYMENT	P E R I O D S	RATE
What $1 due in the future is worth today.	What $1 payable periodically is worth today.	Annuity worth $1 today. Periodic payment necessary to pay off a loan of $1.		2¼%
.977 995 1100	.977 995 1100	1.022 500 0000	1	
.956 474 4352	1.934 469 5453	.516 937 5773	2	
.935 427 3205	2.869 896 8658	.348 444 5772	3	.0225
.914 843 3453	3.784 740 2110	.264 218 9277	4	
.894 712 3181	4.679 452 5291	.213 700 2125	5	per period
.875 024 2720	5.554 476 8011	.180 034 9584	6	
.855 769 4591	6.410 246 2602	.156 000 2470	7	
.836 938 3464	7.247 184 6066	.137 984 6181	8	
.818 521 6101	8.065 706 2167	.123 981 7039	9	
.800 510 1322	8.866 216 3489	.112 787 6831	10	
.782 894 9948	9.649 111 3436	.103 636 4868	11	
.765 667 4765	10.414 778 8202	.096 017 4015	12	
.748 819 0480	11.163 597 8681	.089 576 8561	13	
.732 341 3672	11.895 939 2354	.084 062 2989	14	
.716 226 2760	12.612 165 5113	.079 288 5250	15	
.700 465 7956	13.312 631 3069	.075 116 6300	16	
.685 052 1228	13.997 683 4298	.071 440 3926	17	
.669 977 6262	14.667 661 0560	.068 177 1958	18	
.655 234 8423	15.322 895 8983	.065 261 8152	19	
.640 816 4717	15.963 712 3700	.062 642 0708	20	
.626 715 3757	16.590 427 7457	.060 275 7214	21	ANNUALLY
.612 924 5728	17.203 352 3185	.058 128 2056	22	If compounded
.599 437 2350	17.802 789 5536	.056 170 9724	23	*annually*
.586 246 6846	18.389 036 2382	.054 380 2289	24	nominal annual rate is
.573 346 3908	18.962 382 6291	.052 735 9889	25	2¼%
.560 729 9666	19.523 112 5957	.051 221 3406	26	
.548 391 1654	20.071 503 7610	.049 821 8774	27	
.536 323 8781	20.607 827 6392	.048 525 2506	28	
.524 522 1302	21.192 349 7693	.047 320 8143	29	
.512 980 0784	21.645 329 8478	.046 199 3422	30	
.501 692 0082	22.147 021 8560	.045 152 7978	31	SEMIANNUALLY
.490 652 3308	22.637 674 1868	.044 174 1493	32	If compounded
.479 855 5802	23.117 529 7670	.043 257 2169	33	*semiannually*
.469 296 4110	23.586 826 1780	.042 396 5477	34	nominal annual rate is
.458 969 5951	24.045 795 7731	.041 587 3115	35	4½%
.448 870 0197	24.494 665 7928	.040 825 2151	36	
.438 992 6843	24.933 658 4771	.040 106 4289	37	
.429 332 6985	25.362 991 1756	.039 427 5262	38	
.419 885 2798	25.782 876 4554	.038 785 4319	39	
.410 645 7504	26.193 522 2057	.038 177 3781	40	QUARTERLY
.401 609 5358	26.595 131 7416	.037 600 8666	41	If compounded
.392 772 1622	26.987 903 9037	.037 053 6372	42	*quarterly*
.384 129 2540	27.372 033 1577	.036 533 6398	43	nominal annual rate is
.375 676 5320	27.747 709 6897	.036 039 0105	44	
.367 409 8112	28.115 119 5009	.035 568 0508	45	9%
.359 324 9988	28.474 444 4997	.035 119 2101	46	
.351 418 0917	28.825 862 5913	.034 691 0694	47	
.343 685 1753	29.169 547 7666	.034 282 3279	48	
.336 122 4208	29.505 670 1874	.033 891 7908	49	
.328 726 0839	29.834 396 2713	.033 518 3588	50	MONTHLY
.321 492 5026	30.155 888 7739	.033 161 0190	51	If compounded
.314 418 0954	30.470 306 8693	.032 818 8359	52	*monthly*
.307 499 3598	30.777 806 2291	.032 490 9447	53	nominal annual rate is
.300 732 8703	31.078 539 0994	.032 176 5446	54	
.294 115 2765	31.372 654 3760	.031 874 8930	55	27%
.287 643 3022	31.660 297 6782	.031 585 3000	56	
.281 313 7430	31.941 611 4212	.031 307 1243	57	
.275 123 4651	32.216 734 8863	.031 039 7687	58	i = .0225
.269 069 4035	32.485 804 2898	.030 782 6764	59	$j^{(2)}$ = .045
.263 148 5609	32.748 952 8506	.030 535 3275	60	$j^{(4)}$ = .09
				$j^{(12)}$ = .27
$v^n = \dfrac{1}{(1+i)^n}$	$a_{\overline{n}|} = \dfrac{1-v^n}{i}$	$\dfrac{1}{a_{\overline{n}|}} = \dfrac{i}{1-v^n}$	n	

P E R I O D S	AMOUNT OF 1 *How $1 left at compound interest will grow.*	AMOUNT OF 1 PER PERIOD *How $1 deposited periodically will grow.*	SINKING FUND *Periodic deposit that will grow to $1 at future date.*
1	1.025 000 0000	1.000 000 0000	1.000 000 0000
2	1.050 625 0000	2.025 000 0000	.493 827 1605
3	1.076 890 6250	3.075 625 0000	.325 137 1672
4	1.103 812 8906	4.152 515 6250	.240 817 8777
5	1.131 408 2129	5.256 328 5156	.190 246 8609
6	1.159 693 4182	6.387 736 7285	.156 549 9711
7	1.188 685 7537	7.547 430 1467	.132 495 4296
8	1.218 402 8975	8.736 115 9004	.114 467 3458
9	1.248 862 9699	9.954 518 7979	.100 456 8900
10	1.280 084 5442	11.203 381 7679	.089 258 7632
11	1.312 086 6578	12.483 466 3121	.080 105 9558
12	1.344 888 8242	13.795 552 9699	.072 487 1270
13	1.378 511 0449	15.140 441 7941	.066 048 2708
14	1.412 973 8210	16.518 952 8390	.060 536 5249
15	1.448 298 1665	17.931 926 6599	.055 766 4561
16	1.484 505 6207	19.380 224 8264	.051 598 9886
17	1.521 618 2612	20.864 730 4471	.047 927 7699
18	1.559 658 7177	22.386 348 7083	.044 670 0805
19	1.598 650 1856	23.946 007 4260	.041 760 6151
20	1.638 616 4403	25.544 657 6116	.039 147 1287
21	1.679 581 8513	27.183 274 0519	.036 787 3273
22	1.721 571 3976	28.862 855 9032	.034 646 6061
23	1.764 610 6825	30.584 427 3008	.032 696 3781
24	1.808 725 9496	32.349 037 9833	.030 912 8204
25	1.853 944 0983	34.157 763 9329	.029 275 9210
26	1.900 292 7008	36.011 708 0312	.027 768 7467
27	1.947 800 0183	37.912 000 7320	.026 376 8722
28	1.996 495 0188	39.859 800 7503	.025 087 9327
29	2.046 407 3942	41.856 295 7690	.023 891 2685
30	2.097 567 5791	43.902 703 1633	.022 777 6407
31	2.150 006 7686	46.000 270 7424	.021 739 0025
32	2.203 756 9378	48.150 277 5109	.020 768 3123
33	2.258 850 8612	50.354 034 4487	.019 859 3819
34	2.315 322 1327	52.612 885 3099	.019 006 7508
35	2.373 205 1861	54.928 207 4426	.018 205 5823
36	2.432 535 3157	57.301 412 6287	.017 451 5767
37	2.493 348 6986	59.733 947 9444	.016 740 8992
38	2.555 682 4161	62.227 296 6430	.016 070 1180
39	2.619 574 4765	64.782 979 0591	.015 436 1534
40	2.685 063 8384	67.402 553 5356	.014 836 2332
41	2.752 190 4343	70.087 617 3740	.014 267 8555
42	2.820 995 1952	72.839 807 8083	.013 728 7567
43	2.891 520 0751	75.660 803 0035	.013 216 8833
44	2.963 808 0770	78.552 323 0786	.012 730 3683
45	3.037 903 2789	81.516 131 1556	.012 267 5106
46	3.113 850 8609	84.554 034 4345	.011 826 7568
47	3.191 697 1324	87.667 885 2954	.011 406 6855
48	3.271 489 5607	90.859 582 4277	.011 005 9938
49	3.353 276 7997	94.131 071 9884	.010 623 4847
50	3.437 108 7197	97.484 348 7881	.010 258 0569
51	3.523 036 4377	100.921 457 5078	.009 908 6956
52	3.611 112 3486	104.444 493 9455	.009 574 4635
53	3.701 390 1574	108.055 606 2942	.009 254 4944
54	3.793 924 9113	111.756 996 4515	.008 947 9856
55	3.888 773 0341	115.550 921 3628	.008 654 1932
56	3.985 992 3599	119.439 694 3969	.008 372 4260
57	4.085 642 1689	123.425 686 7568	.008 102 0412
58	4.187 783 2231	127.511 328 9257	.007 842 4404
59	4.292 477 8037	131.699 112 1489	.007 593 0656
60	4.399 789 7488	135.991 589 9526	.007 353 3959
n	$s=(1+i)^n$	$s_{\overline{n}|}=\dfrac{(1+i)^n-1}{i}$	$\dfrac{1}{s_{\overline{n}|}}=\dfrac{i}{(1+i)^n-1}$

.025

per period

ANNUALLY
If compounded
annually
nominal annual rate is

2¹/₂%

SEMIANNUALLY
If compounded
semiannually
nominal annual rate is

5%

QUARTERLY
If compounded
quarterly
nominal annual rate is

10%

MONTHLY
If compounded
monthly
nominal annual rate is

30%

$i = .025$
$j_{(2)} = .05$
$j_{(4)} = .1$
$j_{(12)} = .3$

PRESENT WORTH OF 1 *What $1 due in the future is worth today.*	PRESENT WORTH OF 1 PER PERIOD *What $1 payable periodically is worth today.*	PARTIAL PAYMENT *Annuity worth $1 today.* *Periodic payment necessary to pay off a loan of $1.*	PERIODS	RATE $2\frac{1}{2}\%$
.975 609 7561	.975 609 7561	1.025 000 0000	1	
.951 814 3962	1.927 424 1523	.518 827 1605	2	
.928 599 4109	2.856 023 5632	.350 137 1672	3	.025
.905 950 6448	3.761 974 2080	.265 817 8777	4	
.883 854 2876	4.645 828 4956	.215 246 8609	5	*per period*
.862 296 8660	5.508 125 3616	.181 549 9711	6	
.841 265 2351	6.349 390 5967	.157 495 4296	7	
.820 746 5708	7.170 137 1675	.139 467 3458	8	
.800 728 3618	7.970 865 5292	.125 456 8900	9	
.781 198 4017	8.752 063 9310	.114 258 7632	10	
.762 144 7822	9.514 208 7131	.105 105 9558	11	
.743 555 8850	10.257 764 5982	.097 487 1270	12	
.725 420 3757	10.983 184 9738	.091 048 2708	13	
.707 727 1958	11.690 912 1696	.085 536 5249	14	
.690 465 5568	12.381 377 7264	.080 766 4561	15	
.673 624 9335	13.055 002 6599	.076 598 9886	16	
.657 195 0571	13.712 197 7170	.072 927 7699	17	
.641 165 9093	14.353 363 6264	.069 670 0805	18	
.625 527 7164	14.978 891 3428	.066 760 6151	19	
.610 270 9429	15.589 162 2856	.064 147 1287	20	
.595 386 2857	16.184 548 5714	.061 787 3273	21	ANNUALLY If compounded *annually* nominal annual rate is
.580 864 6690	16.765 413 2404	.059 646 6061	22	
.566 697 2380	17.332 110 4784	.057 696 3781	23	
.552 875 3542	17.884 985 8326	.055 912 8204	24	
.539 390 5894	18.424 376 4220	.054 275 9210	25	$2\frac{1}{2}\%$
.526 234 7214	18.950 611 1434	.052 768 7467	26	
.513 399 7282	19.464 010 8717	.051 376 8722	27	
.500 877 7836	19.964 888 6553	.050 087 9327	28	
.488 661 2523	20.453 549 9076	.048 891 2685	29	
.476 742 6852	20.930 292 5928	.047 777 6407	30	
.465 114 8148	21.395 407 4076	.046 739 0025	31	SEMIANNUALLY If compounded *semiannually* nominal annual rate is
.453 770 5510	21.849 177 9586	.045 768 3123	32	
.442 702 9766	22.291 880 9352	.044 859 3819	33	
.431 905 3430	22.723 786 2783	.044 006 7508	34	
.421 371 0664	23.145 157 3447	.043 205 5823	35	5%
.411 093 7233	23.556 251 0680	.042 451 5767	36	
.401 067 0471	23.957 318 1151	.041 740 8992	37	
.391 284 9240	24.348 603 0391	.041 070 1180	38	
.381 741 3893	24.730 344 4284	.040 436 1534	39	
.372 430 6237	25.102 775 0521	.039 836 2332	40	
.363 346 9499	25.466 122 0020	.039 267 8555	41	QUARTERLY If compounded *quarterly* nominal annual rate is
.354 484 8292	25.820 606 8313	.038 728 7567	42	
.345 838 8578	26.166 445 6890	.038 216 8833	43	
.337 403 7637	26.503 849 4527	.037 730 3683	44	
.329 174 4036	26.833 023 8563	.037 267 5106	45	10%
.321 145 7596	27.154 169 6159	.036 826 7568	46	
.313 312 9362	27.467 482 5521	.036 406 6855	47	
.305 671 1573	27.773 153 7094	.036 005 9938	48	
.298 215 7632	28.071 369 4726	.035 623 4847	49	
.290 942 2080	28.362 311 6805	.035 258 0569	50	
.283 846 0566	28.646 157 7371	.034 908 6956	51	MONTHLY If compounded *monthly* nominal annual rate is
.276 922 9820	28.923 080 7191	.034 574 4635	52	
.270 168 7629	29.193 249 4821	.034 254 4944	53	
.263 579 2809	29.456 828 7630	.033 947 9856	54	
.257 150 5180	29.713 979 2810	.033 654 1932	55	30%
.250 878 5541	29.964 857 8351	.033 372 4260	56	
.244 759 5650	30.209 617 4001	.033 102 0412	57	
.238 789 8195	30.448 407 2196	.032 842 4404	58	$i \quad = .025$
.232 965 6776	30.681 372 8972	.032 593 0656	59	$j_{(2)} = .05$ $j_{(4)} = .1$
.227 283 5879	30.908 656 4851	.032 353 3959	60	$j_{(12)} = .3$
$v^n = \dfrac{1}{(1+i)^n}$	$a_{\overline{n}} = \dfrac{1-v^n}{i}$	$\dfrac{1}{a_{\overline{n}}} = \dfrac{i}{1-v^n}$	n	

	P E R I O D S	AMOUNT OF 1 How $1 left at compound interest will grow.	AMOUNT OF 1 PER PERIOD How $1 deposited periodically will grow.	SINKING FUND Periodic deposit that will grow to $1 at future date.
	1	1.030 000 0000	1.000 000 0000	1.000 000 0000
	2	1.060 900 0000	2.030 000 0000	.492 610 8374
.03	3	1.092 727 0000	3.090 900 0000	.323 530 3633
per period	4	1.125 508 8100	4.183 627 0000	.239 027 0452
	5	1.159 274 0743	5.309 135 8100	.188 354 5714
	6	1.194 052 2965	6.468 409 8843	.154 597 5005
	7	1.229 873 8654	7.662 462 1808	.130 506 3538
	8	1.266 770 0814	8.892 336 0463	.112 456 3888
	9	1.304 773 1838	10.159 106 1276	.098 433 8570
	10	1.343 916 3793	11.463 879 3115	.087 230 5066
	11	1.384 233 8707	12.807 795 6908	.078 077 4478
	12	1.425 760 8868	14.192 029 5615	.070 462 0855
	13	1.468 533 7135	15.617 790 4484	.064 029 5440
	14	1.512 589 7249	17.086 324 1618	.058 526 3390
	15	1.557 967 4166	18.598 913 8867	.053 766 5805
	16	1.604 706 4391	20.156 881 3033	.049 610 8493
	17	1.652 847 6323	21.761 587 7424	.045 952 5294
	18	1.702 433 0612	23.414 435 3747	.042 708 6959
	19	1.753 506 0531	25.116 868 4359	.039 813 8806
	20	1.806 111 2347	26.870 374 4890	.037 215 7076
ANNUALLY If compounded *annually* nominal annual rate is	21	1.860 294 5717	28.676 485 7236	.034 871 7765
	22	1.916 103 4089	30.536 780 2954	.032 747 3948
	23	1.973 586 5111	32.452 883 7042	.030 813 9027
	24	2.032 794 1065	34.426 470 2153	.029 047 4159
3%	25	2.093 777 9297	36.459 264 3218	.027 427 8710
	26	2.156 591 2675	38.553 042 2515	.025 938 2903
	27	2.221 289 0056	40.709 633 5190	.024 564 2103
	28	2.287 927 6757	42.930 922 5246	.023 293 2334
	29	2.356 565 5060	45.218 850 2003	.022 114 6711
	30	2.427 262 4712	47.575 415 7063	.021 019 2593
SEMIANNUALLY If compounded *semiannually* nominal annual rate is	31	2.500 080 3453	50.002 678 1775	.019 998 9288
	32	2.575 082 7557	52.502 758 5228	.019 046 6183
	33	2.652 335 2384	55.077 841 2785	.018 156 1219
	34	2.731 905 2955	57.730 176 5169	.017 321 9633
6%	35	2.813 862 4544	60.462 081 8124	.016 539 2916
	36	2.898 278 3280	63.275 944 2668	.015 803 7942
	37	2.985 226 6778	66.174 222 5948	.015 111 6244
	38	3.074 783 4782	69.159 449 2726	.014 459 3401
	39	3.167 026 9825	72.234 232 7508	.013 843 8516
	40	3.262 037 7920	75.401 259 7333	.013 262 3779
QUARTERLY If compounded *quarterly* nominal annual rate is	41	3.359 898 9258	78.663 297 5253	.012 712 4089
	42	3.460 695 8935	82.023 196 4511	.012 191 6731
	43	3.564 516 7703	85.483 892 3446	.011 698 1103
	44	3.671 452 2734	89.048 409 1149	.011 229 8469
12%	45	3.781 595 8417	92.719 861 3884	.010 785 1757
	46	3.895 043 7169	96.501 457 2300	.010 362 5378
	47	4.011 895 0284	100.396 500 9469	.009 960 5065
	48	4.132 251 8793	104.408 395 9753	.009 577 7738
	49	4.256 219 4356	108.540 647 8546	.009 213 1383
	50	4.383 906 0187	112.796 867 2902	.008 865 4944
MONTHLY If compounded *monthly* nominal annual rate is	51	4.515 423 1993	117.180 773 3089	.008 533 8232
	52	4.650 885 8952	121.696 196 5082	.008 217 1837
	53	4.790 412 4721	126.347 082 4035	.007 914 7059
	54	4.934 124 8463	131.137 494 8756	.007 625 5841
36%	55	5.082 148 5917	136.071 619 7218	.007 349 0710
	56	5.234 613 0494	141.153 768 3135	.007 084 4726
	57	5.391 651 4409	146.388 381 3629	.006 831 1432
$i\ =.03$	58	5.553 400 9841	151.780 032 8038	.006 588 4819
$j_{(2)}=.06$ $j_{(4)}=.12$	59	5.720 003 0136	157.333 433 7879	.006 355 9281
$j_{(12)}=.36$	60	5.891 603 1040	163.053 436 8015	.006 132 9587
	n	$s=(1+i)^n$	$s_{\overline{n}\rceil}=\dfrac{(1+i)^n-1}{i}$	$\dfrac{1}{s_{\overline{n}\rceil}}=\dfrac{i}{(1+i)^n-1}$

PRESENT WORTH OF 1	PRESENT WORTH OF 1 PER PERIOD	PARTIAL PAYMENT	P E R I O D S	RATE
What $1 due in the future is worth today.	What $1 payable periodically is worth today.	Annuity worth $1 today. Periodic payment necessary to pay off a loan of $1.		3%
.970 873 7864	.970 873 7864	1.030 000 0000	1	
.942 595 9091	1.913 469 6955	.522 610 8374	2	
.915 141 6594	2.828 611 3549	.353 530 3633	3	.03
.888 487 0479	3.717 098 4028	.269 027 0452	4	
.862 608 7844	4.579 707 1872	.218 354 5714	5	per period
.837 484 2567	5.417 191 4439	.184 597 5005	6	
.813 091 5113	6.230 282 9552	.160 506 3538	7	
.789 409 2343	7.019 692 1895	.142 456 3888	8	
.766 416 7323	7.786 108 9219	.128 433 8570	9	
.744 093 9149	8.530 202 8368	.117 230 5066	10	
.722 421 2766	9.252 624 1134	.108 077 4478	11	
.701 379 8802	9.954 003 9936	.100 462 0855	12	
.680 951 3400	10.634 955 3336	.094 029 5440	13	
.661 117 8058	11.296 073 1394	.088 526 3390	14	
.641 861 9474	11.937 935 0868	.083 766 5805	15	
.623 166 9392	12.561 102 0260	.079 610 8493	16	
.605 016 4458	13.166 118 4718	.075 952 5294	17	
.587 394 6076	13.753 513 0795	.072 708 6959	18	
.570 286 0268	14.323 799 1063	.069 813 8806	19	
.553 675 7542	14.877 474 8605	.067 215 7076	20	
.537 549 2759	15.415 024 1364	.064 871 7765	21	ANNUALLY
.521 892 5009	15.936 916 6372	.062 747 3948	22	If compounded annually nominal annual rate is
.506 691 7484	16.443 608 3857	.060 813 9027	23	
.491 933 7363	16.935 542 1220	.059 047 4159	24	
.477 605 5693	17.413 147 6913	.057 427 8710	25	3%
.463 694 7274	17.876 842 4187	.055 938 2903	26	
.450 189 0558	18.327 031 4745	.054 564 2103	27	
.437 076 7532	18.764 108 2277	.053 293 2334	28	
.424 346 3623	19.188 454 5900	.052 114 6711	29	
.411 986 7595	19.600 441 3495	.051 019 2593	30	
.399 987 1452	20.000 428 4946	.049 998 9288	31	SEMIANNUALLY
.388 337 0341	20.388 765 5288	.049 046 6183	32	If compounded semiannually nominal annual rate is.
.377 026 2467	20.765 791 7755	.048 156 1219	33	
.366 044 8997	21.131 836 6752	.047 321 9633	34	
.355 383 3978	21.487 220 0731	.046 539 2916	35	6%
.345 032 4251	21.832 252 4981	.045 803 7942	36	
.334 982 9369	22.167 235 4351	.045 111 6244	37	
.325 226 1524	22.492 461 5874	.044 459 3401	38	
.315 753 5460	22.808 215 1334	.043 843 8516	39	
.306 556 8408	23.114 771 9742	.043 262 3779	40	
.297 628 0008	23.412 399 9750	.042 712 4089	41	QUARTERLY
.288 959 2240	23.701 359 1990	.042 191 6731	42	If compounded quarterly nominal annual rate is
.280 542 9360	23.981 902 1349	.041 698 1103	43	
.272 371 7825	24.254 273 9174	.041 229 8469	44	
.264 438 6238	24.518 712 5412	.040 785 1757	45	12%
.256 736 5279	24.775 449 0691	.040 362 5378	46	
.249 258 7650	25.024 707 8341	.039 960 5065	47	
.241 998 8009	25.266 706 6350	.039 577 7738	48	
.234 950 2922	25.501 656 9272	.039 213 1383	49	
.228 107 0798	25.729 764 0070	.038 865 4944	50	
.221 463 1843	25.951 227 1913	.038 533 8232	51	MONTHLY
.215 012 8003	26.166 239 9915	.038 217 1837	52	If compounded monthly nominal annual rate is
.208 750 2915	26.374 990 2830	.037 914 7059	53	
.202 670 1859	26.577 660 4690	.037 625 5841	54	
.196 767 1708	26.774 427 6398	.037 349 0710	55	36%
.191 036 0882	26.965 463 7279	.037 084 4726	56	
.185 471 9303	27.150 935 6582	.036 831 1432	57	
.180 069 8352	27.331 005 4934	.036 588 4819	58	$i = .03$
.174 825 0827	27.505 830 5761	.036 355 9281	59	$j_{(2)} = .06$
.169 733 0900	27.675 563 6661	.036 132 9587	60	$j_{(4)} = .12$ $j_{(12)} = .36$
$v^n = \dfrac{1}{(1+i)^n}$	$a_{\overline{n}|} = \dfrac{1-v^n}{i}$	$\dfrac{1}{a_{\overline{n}|}} = \dfrac{i}{1-v^n}$	n	

47

	P E R I O D S	AMOUNT OF 1 *How $1 left at compound interest will grow.*	AMOUNT OF 1 PER PERIOD *How $1 deposited periodically will grow.*	SINKING FUND *Periodic deposit that will grow to $1 at future date.*
	1	1.035 000 0000	1.000 000 0000	1.000 000 0000
.035	2	1.071 225 0000	2.035 000 0000	.491 400 4914
	3	1.108 717 8750	3.106 225 0000	.321 934 1806
per period	4	1.147 523 0006	4.214 942 8750	.237 251 1395
	5	1.187 686 3056	5.362 465 8756	.186 481 3732
	6	1.229 255 3263	6.550 152 1813	.152 668 2087
	7	1.272 279 2628	7.779 407 5076	.128 544 4938
	8	1.316 809 0370	9.051 686 7704	.110 476 6465
	9	1.362 897 3533	10.368 495 8073	.096 446 0051
	10	1.410 598 7606	11.731 393 1606	.085 241 3679
	11	1.459 969 7172	13.141 991 9212	.076 091 9658
	12	1.511 068 6573	14.601 961 6385	.068 483 9493
	13	1.563 956 0604	16.113 030 2958	.062 061 5726
	14	1.618 694 5225	17.676 986 3562	.056 570 7287
	15	1.675 348 8308	19.295 680 8786	.051 825 0694
	16	1.733 986 0398	20.971 029 7094	.047 684 8306
	17	1.794 675 5512	22.705 015 7492	.044 043 1317
	18	1.857 489 1955	24.499 691 3004	.040 816 8408
	19	1.922 501 3174	26.357 180 4960	.037 940 3252
	20	1.989 788 8635	28.279 681 8133	.035 361 0768
ANNUALLY If compounded *annually* nominal annual rate is **3½%**	21	2.059 431 4737	30.269 470 6768	.033 036 5870
	22	2.131 511 5753	32.328 902 1505	.030 932 0742
	23	2.206 114 4804	34.460 413 7257	.029 018 8042
	24	2.283 328 4872	36.666 528 2061	.027 272 8303
	25	2.363 244 9843	38.949 856 6933	.025 674 0354
	26	2.445 958 5587	41.313 101 6776	.024 205 3963
	27	2.531 567 1083	43.759 060 2363	.022 852 4103
	28	2.620 171 9571	46.290 627 3446	.021 602 6452
	29	2.711 877 9756	48.910 799 3017	.020 445 3825
	30	2.806 793 7047	51.622 677 2772	.019 371 3316
SEMIANNUALLY If compounded *semiannually* nominal annual rate is **7%**	31	2.905 031 4844	54.429 470 9819	.018 372 3998
	32	3.006 707 5863	57.334 502 4663	.017 441 5048
	33	3.111 942 3518	60.341 210 0526	.016 572 4221
	34	3.220 860 3342	63.453 152 4044	.015 759 6583
	35	3.333 590 4459	66.674 012 7386	.014 998 3473
	36	3.450 266 1115	70.007 603 1845	.014 284 1628
	37	3.571 025 4254	73.457 869 2959	.013 613 2454
	38	3.696 011 3152	77.028 894 7213	.012 982 1414
	39	3.825 371 7113	80.724 906 0365	.012 387 7506
	40	3.959 259 7212	84.550 277 7478	.011 827 2823
QUARTERLY If compounded *quarterly* nominal annual rate is **14%**	41	4.097 833 8114	88.509 537 4690	.011 298 2174
	42	4.241 257 9948	92.607 371 2804	.010 798 2765
	43	4.389 702 0246	96.848 629 2752	.010 325 3914
	44	4.543 341 5955	101.238 331 2998	.009 877 6816
	45	4.702 358 5513	105.781 672 8953	.009 453 4334
	46	4.866 941 1006	110.484 031 4467	.009 051 0817
	47	5.037 284 0392	115.350 972 5473	.008 669 1944
	48	5.213 588 9805	120.388 256 5864	.008 306 4580
	49	5.396 064 5948	125.601 845 5670	.007 961 6665
	50	5.584 926 8557	130.997 910 1618	.007 633 7096
MONTHLY If compounded *monthly* nominal annual rate is **42%**	51	5.780 399 2956	136.582 837 0175	.007 321 5641
	52	5.982 713 2710	142.363 236 3131	.007 024 2854
	53	6.192 108 2354	148.345 949 5840	.006 740 9997
	54	6.408 832 0237	154.538 057 8195	.006 470 8979
	55	6.633 141 1445	160.946 889 8432	.006 213 2297
	56	6.865 301 0846	167.580 030 9877	.005 967 2981
	57	7.105 586 6225	174.445 332 0722	.005 732 4549
	58	7.354 282 1543	181.550 918 6948	.005 508 0966
	59	7.611 682 0297	188.905 200 8491	.005 293 6605
	60	7.878 090 9008	196.516 882 8788	.005 088 6213

$i = .035$
$j_{(2)} = .07$
$j_{(4)} = .14$
$j_{(12)} = .42$

n	$s=(1+i)^n$	$s_{\overline{n}|}=\dfrac{(1+i)^n-1}{i}$	$\dfrac{1}{s_{\overline{n}|}}=\dfrac{i}{(1+i)^n-1}$

PRESENT WORTH OF 1 *What $1 due in the future is worth today.*	PRESENT WORTH OF 1 PER PERIOD *What $1 payable periodically is worth today.*	PARTIAL PAYMENT *Annuity worth $1 today.* *Periodic payment necessary to pay off a loan of $1.*	P E R I O D S	RATE **3½%**
.966 183 5749	.966 183 5749	1.035 000 0000	1	
.933 510 7004	1.899 694 2752	.526 400 4914	2	
.901 942 7057	2.801 636 9809	.356 934 1806	3	.035
.871 442 2277	3.673 079 2086	.272 251 1395	4	*per period*
.841 973 1669	4.515 052 3755	.221 481 3732	5	
.813 500 6443	5.328 553 0198	.187 668 2087	6	
.785 990 9607	6.114 543 9805	.163 544 4938	7	
.759 411 5562	6.873 955 5367	.145 476 6465	8	
.733 730 9722	7.607 686 5089	.131 446 0051	9	
.708 918 8137	8.316 605 3226	.120 241 3679	10	
.684 945 7137	9.001 551 0363	.111 091 9658	11	
.661 783 2983	9.663 334 3346	.103 483 9493	12	
.639 404 1529	10.302 738 4875	.097 061 5726	13	
.617 781 7903	10.920 520 2778	.091 570 7287	14	
.596 890 6186	11.517 410 8964	.086 825 0694	15	
.576 705 9117	12.094 116 8081	.082 684 8306	16	
.557 203 7794	12.651 320 5876	.079 043 1317	17	
.538 361 1396	13.189 681 7271	.075 816 8408	18	
.520 155 6904	13.709 837 4175	.072 940 3252	19	
.502 565 8844	14.212 403 3020	.070 361 0768	20	
.485 570 9028	14.697 974 2048	.068 036 5870	21	ANNUALLY
.469 150 6308	15.167 124 8355	.065 932 0742	22	If compounded
.453 285 6336	15.620 410 4691	.064 018 8042	23	*annually*
.437 957 1339	16.058 367 6030	.062 272 8303	24	nominal annual rate is
.423 146 9893	16.481 514 5923	.060 674 0354	25	**3½%**
.408 837 6708	16.890 352 2631	.059 205 3963	26	
.395 012 2423	17.285 364 5054	.057 852 4103	27	
.381 654 3404	17.667 018 8458	.056 602 6452	28	
.368 748 1550	18.035 767 0008	.055 445 3825	29	
.356 278 4106	18.392 045 4114	.054 371 3316	30	
.344 230 3484	18.736 275 7598	.053 372 3998	31	SEMIANNUALLY
.332 589 7086	19.068 865 4684	.052 441 5048	32	If compounded
.321 342 7136	19.390 208 1820	.051 572 4221	33	*semiannually*
.310 476 0518	19.700 684 2338	.050 759 6583	34	nominal annual rate is
.299 976 8617	20.000 661 0955	.049 998 3473	35	**7%**
.289 832 7166	20.290 493 8121	.049 284 1628	36	
.280 031 6102	20.570 525 4223	.048 613 2454	37	
.270 561 9422	20.841 087 3645	.047 982 1414	38	
.261 412 5046	21.102 499 8691	.047 387 7506	39	
.252 572 4682	21.355 072 3373	.046 827 2823	40	
.244 031 3702	21.599 103 7075	.046 298 2174	41	QUARTERLY
.235 779 1017	21.834 882 8092	.045 798 2765	42	If compounded
.227 805 8953	22.062 688 7046	.045 325 3914	43	*quarterly*
.220 102 3143	22.282 791 0189	.044 877 6816	44	nominal annual rate is
.212 659 2409	22.495 450 2598	.044 453 4334	45	**14%**
.205 467 8656	22.700 918 1254	.044 051 0817	46	
.198 519 6769	22.899 437 8023	.043 669 1944	47	
.191 806 4511	23.091 244 2535	.043 306 4580	48	
.185 320 2426	23.276 564 4961	.042 961 6665	49	
.179 053 3745	23.455 617 8706	.042 633 7096	50	
.172 998 4295	23.628 616 3001	.042 321 5641	51	MONTHLY
.167 148 2411	23.795 764 5412	.042 024 2854	52	If compounded
.161 495 8851	23.957 260 4263	.041 740 9997	53	*monthly*
.156 034 6716	24.113 295 0978	.041 470 8979	54	nominal annual rate is
.150 758 1368	24.264 053 2346	.041 213 2297	55	**42%**
.145 660 0355	24.409 713 2702	.040 967 2981	56	
.140 734 3339	24.550 447 6040	.040 732 4549	57	
.135 975 2018	24.686 422 8058	.040 508 0966	58	
.131 377 0066	24.817 799 8124	.040 293 6605	59	$i = .035$
.126 934 3059	24.944 734 1182	.040 088 6213	60	$j_{(2)} = .07$
$v^n = \dfrac{1}{(1+i)^n}$	$a_{\overline{n}} = \dfrac{1-v^n}{i}$	$\dfrac{1}{a_{\overline{n}}} = \dfrac{i}{1-v^n}$	n	$j_{(4)} = .14$ $j_{(12)} = .42$

49

P E R I O D S	AMOUNT OF 1 _How $1 left at compound interest will grow._	AMOUNT OF 1 PER PERIOD _How $1 deposited periodically will grow._	SINKING FUND _Periodic deposit that will grow to $1 at future date._
1	1.040 000 0000	1.000 000 0000	1.000 000 0000
2	1.081 600 0000	2.040 000 0000	.490 196 0784
3	1.124 864 0000	3.121 600 0000	.320 348 5392
4	1.169 858 5600	4.246 464 0000	.235 490 0454
5	1.216 652 9024	5.416 322 5600	.184 627 1135
6	1.265 319 0185	6.632 975 4624	.150 761 9025
7	1.315 931 7792	7.898 294 4809	.126 609 6120
8	1.368 569 0504	9.214 226 2601	.108 527 8320
9	1.423 311 8124	10.582 795 3105	.094 492 9927
10	1.480 244 2849	12.006 107 1230	.083 290 9443
11	1.539 454 0563	13.486 351 4079	.074 149 0393
12	1.601 032 2186	15.025 805 4642	.066 552 1727
13	1.665 073 5073	16.626 837 6828	.060 143 7278
14	1.731 676 4476	18.291 911 1901	.054 668 9731
15	1.800 943 5055	20.023 587 6377	.049 941 1004
16	1.872 981 2457	21.824 531 1432	.045 819 9992
17	1.947 900 4956	23.697 512 3889	.042 198 5221
18	2.025 816 5154	25.645 412 8845	.038 993 3281
19	2.106 849 1760	27.671 229 3998	.036 138 6184
20	2.191 123 1430	29.778 078 5758	.033 581 7503

P E R I O D S	AMOUNT OF 1	AMOUNT OF 1 PER PERIOD	SINKING FUND
21	2.278 768 0688	31.969 201 7189	.031 280 1054
22	2.369 918 7915	34.247 969 7876	.029 198 8111
23	2.464 715 5432	36.617 888 5791	.027 309 0568
24	2.563 304 1649	39.082 604 1223	.025 586 8313
25	2.665 836 3315	41.645 908 2872	.024 011 9628
26	2.772 469 7847	44.311 744 6187	.022 567 3805
27	2.883 368 5761	47.084 214 4034	.021 238 5406
28	2.998 703 3192	49.967 582 9796	.020 012 9752
29	3.118 651 4519	52.966 286 2987	.018 879 9342
30	3.243 397 5100	56.084 937 7507	.017 830 0991

P E R I O D S	AMOUNT OF 1	AMOUNT OF 1 PER PERIOD	SINKING FUND
31	3.373 133 4104	59.328 335 2607	.016 855 3524
32	3.508 058 7468	62.701 468 6711	.015 948 5897
33	3.648 381 0967	66.209 527 4180	.015 103 5665
34	3.794 316 3406	69.857 908 5147	.014 314 7715
35	3.946 088 9942	73.652 224 8553	.013 577 3224
36	4.103 932 5540	77.598 313 8495	.012 886 8780
37	4.268 089 8561	81.702 246 4035	.012 239 5655
38	4.438 813 4504	85.970 336 2596	.011 631 9191
39	4.616 365 9884	90.409 149 7100	.011 060 8274
40	4.801 020 6279	95.025 515 6984	.010 523 4893

P E R I O D S	AMOUNT OF 1	AMOUNT OF 1 PER PERIOD	SINKING FUND
41	4.993 061 4531	99.826 536 3264	.010 017 3765
42	5.192 783 9112	104.819 597 7794	.009 540 2007
43	5.400 495 2676	110.012 381 6906	.009 089 8859
44	5.616 515 0783	115.412 876 9582	.008 664 5444
45	5.841 175 6815	121.029 392 0365	.008 262 4558
46	6.074 822 7087	126.870 567 7180	.007 882 0488
47	6.317 815 6171	132.945 390 4267	.007 521 8855
48	6.570 528 2418	139.263 206 0438	.007 180 6476
49	6.833 349 3714	145.833 734 2855	.006 857 1240
50	7.106 683 3463	152.667 083 6570	.006 550 2004

P E R I O D S	AMOUNT OF 1	AMOUNT OF 1 PER PERIOD	SINKING FUND
51	7.390 950 6801	159.773 767 0032	.006 258 8497
52	7.686 588 7073	167.164 717 6834	.005 982 1236
53	7.994 052 2556	174.851 306 3907	.005 719 1451
54	8.313 814 3459	182.845 358 6463	.005 469 1025
55	8.646 366 9197	191.159 172 9922	.005 231 2426
56	8.992 221 5965	199.805 539 9119	.005 004 8662
57	9.351 910 4603	208.797 761 5083	.004 789 3234
58	9.725 986 8787	218.149 671 9687	.004 584 0087
59	10.115 026 3539	227.875 658 8474	.004 388 3581
60	10.519 627 4081	237.990 685 2013	.004 201 8451

n	$s=(1+i)^n$	$s_{\overline{n}|} = \dfrac{(1+i)^n-1}{i}$	$\dfrac{1}{s_{\overline{n}|}} = \dfrac{i}{(1+i)^n-1}$

PRESENT WORTH OF 1	PRESENT WORTH OF 1 PER PERIOD	PARTIAL PAYMENT	P E R I O D S	RATE
What $1 due in the future is worth today.	*What $1 payable periodically is worth today.*	*Annuity worth $1 today.* *Periodic payment necessary to pay off a loan of $1.*		**4%**

PRESENT WORTH OF 1	PRESENT WORTH OF 1 PER PERIOD	PARTIAL PAYMENT	PERIODS	RATE
.961 538 4615	.961 538 4615	1.040 000 0000	1	
.924 556 2130	1.886 094 6746	.530 196 0784	2	
.888 996 3587	2.775 091 0332	.360 348 5392	3	.04
.854 804 1910	3.629 895 2243	.275 490 0454	4	*per period*
.821 927 1068	4.451 822 3310	.224 627 1135	5	
.790 314 5257	5.242 136 8567	.190 761 9025	6	
.759 917 8132	6.002 054 6699	.166 609 6120	7	
.730 690 2050	6.732 744 8750	.148 527 8320	8	
.702 586 7356	7.435 331 6105	.134 492 9927	9	
.675 564 1688	8.110 895 7794	.123 290 9443	10	
.649 580 9316	8.760 476 7109	.114 149 0393	11	
.624 597 0496	9.385 073 7605	.106 552 1727	12	
.600 574 0861	9.985 647 8466	.100 143 7278	13	
.577 475 0828	10.563 122 9295	.094 668 9731	14	
.555 264 5027	11.118 387 4322	.089 941 1004	15	
.533 908 1757	11.652 295 6079	.085 819 9992	16	
.513 373 2459	12.165 668 8537	.082 198 5221	17	
.493 628 1210	12.659 296 9747	.078 993 3281	18	
.474 642 4240	13.133 939 3988	.076 138 6184	19	
.456 386 9462	13.590 326 3450	.073 581 7503	20	
.438 833 6021	14.029 159 9471	.071 280 1054	21	ANNUALLY
.421 955 3867	14.451 115 3337	.069 198 8111	22	If compounded
.405 726 3333	14.856 841 6671	.067 309 0568	23	*annually*
.390 121 4743	15.246 963 1414	.065 586 8313	24	nominal annual rate is
.375 116 8023	15.622 079 9437	.064 011 9628	25	**4%**
.360 689 2329	15.982 769 1766	.062 567 3805	26	
.346 816 5701	16.329 585 7467	.061 238 5406	27	
.333 477 4713	16.663 063 2180	.060 012 9752	28	
.320 651 4147	16.983 714 6327	.058 879 9342	29	
.308 318 6680	17.292 033 3007	.057 830 0991	30	
.296 460 2577	17.588 493 5583	.056 855 3524	31	SEMIANNUALLY
.285 057 9401	17.873 551 4984	.055 948 5897	32	If compounded
.274 094 1731	18.147 645 6715	.055 103 5665	33	*semiannually*
.263 552 0896	18.411 197 7611	.054 314 7715	34	nominal annual rate is
.253 415 4707	18.664 613 2318	.053 577 3224	35	**8%**
.243 668 7219	18.908 281 9537	.052 886 8780	36	
.234 296 8479	19.142 578 8016	.052 239 5655	37	
.225 285 4307	19.367 864 2323	.051 631 9191	38	
.216 620 6064	19.584 484 8388	.051 060 8274	39	
.208 289 0447	19.792 773 8834	.050 523 4893	40	
.200 277 9276	19.993 051 8110	.050 017 3765	41	QUARTERLY
.192 574 9303	20.185 626 7413	.049 540 2007	42	If compounded
.185 168 2023	20.370 794 9436	.049 089 8859	43	*quarterly*
.178 046 3483	20.548 841 2919	.048 664 5444	44	nominal annual rate is
.171 198 4118	20.720 039 7038	.048 262 4558	45	**16%**
.164 613 8575	20.884 653 5613	.047 882 0488	46	
.158 282 5553	21.042 936 1166	.047 521 8855	47	
.152 194 7647	21.195 130 8814	.047 180 6476	48	
.146 341 1199	21.341 472 0013	.046 857 1240	49	
.140 712 6153	21.482 184 6167	.046 550 2004	50	
.135 300 5917	21.617 485 2083	.046 258 8497	51	MONTHLY
.130 096 7228	21.747 581 9311	.045 982 1236	52	If compounded
.125 093 0027	21.872 674 9337	.045 719 1451	53	*monthly*
.120 281 7333	21.992 956 6671	.045 469 1025	54	nominal annual rate is
.115 655 5128	22.108 612 1799	.045 231 2426	55	**48%**
.111 207 2239	22.219 819 4037	.045 004 8662	56	
.106 930 0229	22.326 749 4267	.044 789 3234	57	
.102 817 3297	22.429 566 7564	.044 584 0087	58	i = .04
.098 862 8171	22.528 429 5735	.044 388 3581	59	$j_{(2)}$ = .08
.095 060 4010	22.623 489 9745	.044 201 8451	60	$j_{(4)}$ = .16
				$j_{(12)}$ = .48
$v^n=\dfrac{1}{(1+i)^n}$	$a_{\overline{n}|}=\dfrac{1-v^n}{i}$	$\dfrac{1}{a_{\overline{n}|}}=\dfrac{i}{1-v^n}$	**n**	

51

	P E R I O D S	AMOUNT OF 1 *How $1 left at compound interest will grow.*	AMOUNT OF 1 PER PERIOD *How $1 deposited periodically will grow.*	SINKING FUND *Periodic deposit that will grow to $1 at future date.*
	1	1.050 000 0000	1.000 000 0000	1.000 000 0000
	2	1.102 500 0000	2.050 000 0000	.487 804 8780
.05	3	1.157 625 0000	3.152 500 0000	.317 208 5646
per period	4	1.215 506 2500	4.310 125 0000	.232 011 8326
	5	1.276 281 5625	5.525 631 2500	.180 974 7981
	6	1.340 095 6406	6.801 912 8125	.147 017 4681
	7	1.407 100 4227	8.142 008 4531	.122 819 8184
	8	1.477 455 4438	9.549 108 8758	.104 721 8136
	9	1.551 328 2160	11.026 564 3196	.090 690 0800
	10	1.628 894 6268	12.577 892 5355	.079 504 5750
	11	1.710 339 3581	14.206 787 1623	.070 388 8915
	12	1.795 856 3260	15.917 126 5204	.062 825 4100
	13	1.885 649 1423	17.712 982 8465	.056 455 7652
	14	1.979 931 5994	19.598 631 9888	.051 023 9695
	15	2.078 928 1794	21.578 563 5882	.046 342 2876
	16	2.182 874 5884	23.657 491 7676	.042 269 9080
	17	2.292 018 3178	25.840 366 3560	.038 699 1417
	18	2.406 619 2337	28.132 384 6738	.035 546 2223
	19	2.526 950 1954	30.539 003 9075	.032 745 0104
	20	2.653 297 7051	33.065 954 1029	.030 242 5872
ANNUALLY *If compounded annually nominal annual rate is* 5%	21	2.785 962 5904	35.719 251 8080	.027 996 1071
	22	2.925 260 7199	38.505 214 3984	.025 970 5086
	23	3.071 523 7559	41.430 475 1184	.024 136 8219
	24	3.225 099 9437	44.501 998 8743	.022 470 9008
	25	3.386 354 9409	47.727 098 8180	.020 952 4573
	26	3.555 672 6879	51.113 453 7589	.019 564 3207
	27	3.733 456 3223	54.669 126 4468	.018 291 8599
	28	3.920 129 1385	58.402 582 7692	.017 122 5304
	29	4.116 135 5954	62.322 711 9076	.016 045 5149
	30	4.321 942 3752	66.438 847 5030	.015 051 4351
SEMIANNUALLY *If compounded semiannually nominal annual rate is* 10%	31	4.538 039 4939	70.760 789 8782	.014 132 1204
	32	4.764 941 4686	75.298 829 3721	.013 280 4189
	33	5.003 188 5420	80.063 770 8407	.012 490 0437
	34	5.253 347 9691	85.066 959 3827	.011 755 4454
	35	5.516 015 3676	90.320 307 3518	.011 071 7072
	36	5.791 816 1360	95.836 322 7194	.010 434 4571
	37	6.081 406 9428	101.628 138 8554	.009 839 7945
	38	6.385 477 2899	107.709 545 7982	.009 284 2282
	39	6.704 751 1544	114.095 023 0881	.008 764 6242
	40	7.039 988 7121	120.799 774 2425	.008 278 1612
QUARTERLY *If compounded quarterly nominal annual rate is* 20%	41	7.391 988 1477	127.839 762 9546	.007 822 2924
	42	7.761 587 5551	135.231 751 1023	.007 394 7131
	43	8.149 666 9329	142.993 338 6575	.006 993 3328
	44	8.557 150 2795	151.143 005 5903	.006 616 2506
	45	8.985 007 7935	159.700 155 8699	.006 261 7347
	46	9.434 258 1832	168.685 163 6633	.005 928 2036
	47	9.905 971 0923	178.119 421 8465	.005 614 2109
	48	10.401 269 6469	188.025 392 9388	.005 318 4306
	49	10.921 333 1293	198.426 662 5858	.005 039 6453
	50	11.467 399 7858	209.347 995 7151	.004 776 7355
MONTHLY *If compounded monthly nominal annual rate is* 60%	51	12.040 769 7750	220.815 395 5008	.004 528 6697
	52	12.642 808 2638	232.856 165 2759	.004 294 4966
	53	13.274 948 6770	245.498 973 5397	.004 073 3368
	54	13.938 696 1108	258.773 922 2166	.003 864 3770
	55	14.635 630 9164	272.712 618 3275	.003 666 8637
	56	15.367 412 4622	287.348 249 2439	.003 480 0978
$i = .05$ $j_{(2)} = .1$ $j_{(4)} = .2$ $j_{(12)} = .6$	57	16.135 783 0853	302.715 661 7060	.003 303 4300
	58	16.942 572 2396	318.851 444 7913	.003 136 2568
	59	17.789 700 8515	335.794 017 0309	.002 978 0161
	60	18.679 185 8941	353.583 717 8825	.002 828 1845
	n	$s=(1+i)^n$	$s_{\overline{n}\rceil}=\dfrac{(1+i)^n-1}{i}$	$\dfrac{1}{s_{\overline{n}\rceil}}=\dfrac{i}{(1+i)^n-1}$

PRESENT WORTH OF 1 — *What $1 due in the future is worth today.*	PRESENT WORTH OF 1 PER PERIOD — *What $1 payable periodically is worth today.*	PARTIAL PAYMENT — *Annuity worth $1 today. Periodic payment necessary to pay off a loan of $1.*	PERIODS	RATE
.952 380 9524	.952 380 9524	1.050 000 0000	1	**5%**
.907 029 4785	1.859 410 4308	.537 804 8780	2	
.863 837 5985	2.723 248 0294	.367 208 5646	3	.05
.822 702 4748	3.545 950 5042	.282 011 8326	4	
.783 526 1665	4.329 476 6706	.230 974 7981	5	*per period*
.746 215 3966	5.075 692 0673	.197 017 4681	6	
.710 681 3301	5.786 373 3974	.172 819 8184	7	
.676 839 3620	6.463 212 7594	.154 721 8136	8	
.644 608 9162	7.107 821 6756	.140 690 0800	9	
.613 913 2535	7.721 734 9292	.129 504 5750	10	
.584 679 2891	8.306 414 2183	.120 388 8915	11	
.556 837 4182	8.863 251 6364	.112 825 4100	12	
.530 321 3506	9.393 572 9871	.106 455 7652	13	
.505 067 9530	9.898 640 9401	.101 023 9695	14	
.481 017 0981	10.379 658 0382	.096 342 2876	15	
.458 111 5220	10.837 769 5602	.092 269 9080	16	
.436 296 6876	11.274 066 2478	.088 699 1417	17	
.415 520 6549	11.689 586 9027	.085 546 2223	18	
.395 733 9570	12.085 320 8597	.082 745 0104	19	
.376 889 4829	12.462 210 3425	.080 242 5872	20	
.358 942 3646	12.821 152 7072	.077 996 1071	21	**ANNUALLY** — If compounded *annually* nominal annual rate is **5%**
.341 849 8711	13.163 002 5783	.075 970 5086	22	
.325 571 3058	13.488 573 8841	.074 136 8219	23	
.310 067 9103	13.798 641 7943	.072 470 9008	24	
.295 302 7717	14.093 944 5660	.070 952 4573	25	
.281 240 7350	14.375 185 3010	.069 564 3207	26	
.267 848 3190	14.643 033 6200	.068 291 8599	27	
.255 093 6371	14.898 127 2571	.067 122 5304	28	
.242 946 3211	15.141 073 5782	.066 045 5149	29	
.231 377 4487	15.372 451 0269	.065 051 4351	30	
.220 359 4749	15.592 810 5018	.064 132 1204	31	**SEMIANNUALLY** — If compounded *semiannually* nominal annual rate is **10%**
.209 866 1666	15.802 676 6684	.063 280 4189	32	
.199 872 5396	16.002 549 2080	.062 490 0437	33	
.190 354 7996	16.192 904 0076	.061 755 4454	34	
.181 290 2854	16.374 194 2929	.061 071 7072	35	
.172 657 4146	16.546 851 7076	.060 434 4571	36	
.164 435 6330	16.711 287 3405	.059 839 7945	37	
.156 605 3647	16.867 892 7053	.059 284 2282	38	
.149 147 9664	17.017 040 6717	.058 764 6242	39	
.142 045 6823	17.159 086 3540	.058 278 1612	40	
.135 281 6022	17.294 367 9562	.057 822 2924	41	**QUARTERLY** — If compounded *quarterly* nominal annual rate is **20%**
.128 839 6211	17.423 207 5773	.057 394 7131	42	
.122 704 4011	17.545 911 9784	.056 993 3328	43	
.116 861 3344	17.662 773 3128	.056 616 2506	44	
.111 296 5089	17.774 069 8217	.056 261 7347	45	
.105 996 6752	17.880 066 4968	.055 928 2036	46	
.100 949 2144	17.981 015 7113	.055 614 2109	47	
.096 142 1090	18.077 157 8203	.055 318 4306	48	
.091 563 9133	18.168 721 7336	.055 039 6453	49	
.087 203 7270	18.255 925 4606	.054 776 7355	50	
.083 051 1685	18.338 976 6291	.054 528 6697	51	**MONTHLY** — If compounded *monthly* nominal annual rate is **60%**
.079 096 3510	18.418 072 9801	.054 294 4966	52	
.075 329 8581	18.493 402 8382	.054 073 3368	53	
.071 742 7220	18.565 145 5602	.053 864 3770	54	
.068 326 4019	18.633 471 9621	.053 666 8637	55	
.065 072 7637	18.698 544 7258	.053 480 0978	56	
.061 974 0607	18.760 518 7865	.053 303 4300	57	$i = .05$
.059 022 9149	18.819 541 7014	.053 136 2568	58	$j_{(2)} = .1$
.056 212 2999	18.875 754 0013	.052 978 0161	59	$j_{(4)} = .2$
.053 535 5237	18.929 289 5251	.052 828 1845	60	$j_{(12)} = .6$
$v^n = \dfrac{1}{(1+i)^n}$	$a_{\overline{n}\rvert} = \dfrac{1-v^n}{i}$	$\dfrac{1}{a_{\overline{n}\rvert}} = \dfrac{i}{1-v^n}$	n	

P E R I O D S	AMOUNT OF 1 *How $1 left at compound interest will grow.*	AMOUNT OF 1 PER PERIOD *How $1 deposited periodically will grow.*	SINKING FUND *Periodic deposit that will grow to $1 at future date.*
1	1.060 000 0000	1.000 000 0000	1.000 000 0000
2	1.123 600 0000	2.060 000 0000	.485 436 8932
3	1.191 016 0000	3.183 600 0000	.314 109 8128
4	1.262 476 9600	4.374 616 0000	.228 591 4924
5	1.338 225 5776	5.637 092 9600	.177 396 4004
6	1.418 519 1123	6.975 318 5376	.143 362 6285
7	1.503 630 2590	8.393 837 6499	.119 135 0181
8	1.593 848 0745	9.897 467 9088	.101 035 9426
9	1.689 478 9590	11.491 315 9834	.087 022 2350
10	1.790 847 6965	13.180 794 9424	.075 867 9582
11	1.898 298 5583	14.971 642 6389	.066 792 9381
12	2.012 196 4718	16.869 941 1973	.059 277 0294
13	2.132 928 2601	18.882 137 6691	.052 960 1053
14	2.260 903 9558	21.015 065 9292	.047 584 9090
15	2.396 558 1931	23.275 969 8850	.042 962 7640
16	2.540 351 6847	25.672 528 0781	.038 952 1436
17	2.692 772 7858	28.212 879 7628	.035 444 8042
18	2.854 339 1529	30.905 652 5485	.032 356 5406
19	3.025 599 5021	33.759 991 7015	.029 620 8604
20	3.207 135 4722	36.785 591 2035	.027 184 5570
21	3.399 563 6005	39.992 726 6758	.025 004 5467
22	3.603 537 4166	43.392 290 2763	.023 045 5685
23	3.819 749 6616	46.995 827 6929	.021 278 4847
24	4.048 934 6413	50.815 577 3545	.019 679 0050
25	4.291 870 7197	54.864 511 9957	.018 226 7182
26	4.549 382 9629	59.156 382 7155	.016 904 3467
27	4.822 345 9407	63.705 765 6784	.015 697 1663
28	5.111 686 6971	68.528 111 6191	.014 592 5515
29	5.418 387 8990	73.639 798 3162	.013 579 6135
30	5.743 491 1729	79.058 186 2152	.012 648 9115
31	6.088 100 6433	84.801 677 3881	.011 792 2196
32	6.453 386 6819	90.889 778 0314	.011 002 3374
33	6.840 589 8828	97.343 164 7133	.010 272 9350
34	7.251 025 2758	104.183 754 5961	.009 598 4254
35	7.686 086 7923	111.434 779 8719	.008 973 8590
36	8.147 251 9999	119.120 866 6642	.008 394 8348
37	8.636 087 1198	127.268 118 6640	.007 857 4274
38	9.154 252 3470	135.904 205 7839	.007 358 1240
39	9.703 507 4879	145.058 458 1309	.006 893 7724
40	10.285 717 9371	154.761 965 6188	.006 461 5359
41	10.902 861 0134	165.047 683 5559	.006 058 8551
42	11.557 032 6742	175.950 544 5692	.005 683 4152
43	12.250 454 6346	187.507 577 2434	.005 333 1178
44	12.985 481 9127	199.758 031 8780	.005 006 0565
45	13.764 610 8274	212.743 513 7907	.004 700 4958
46	14.590 487 4771	226.508 124 6181	.004 414 8527
47	15.465 916 7257	241.098 612 0952	.004 147 6805
48	16.393 871 7293	256.564 528 8209	.003 897 6549
49	17.377 504 0330	272.958 400 5502	.003 663 5619
50	18.420 154 2750	290.335 904 5832	.003 444 2864
51	19.525 363 5315	308.756 058 8582	.003 238 8028
52	20.696 885 3434	328.281 422 3897	.003 046 1669
53	21.938 698 4640	348.978 307 7331	.002 865 5076
54	23.255 020 3718	370.917 006 1970	.002 696 0209
55	24.650 321 5941	394.172 026 5689	.002 536 9634
56	26.129 340 8898	418.822 348 1630	.002 387 6472
57	27.697 101 3432	444.951 689 0528	.002 247 4350
58	29.358 927 4238	472.648 790 3959	.002 115 7359
59	31.120 463 0692	502.007 717 8197	.001 992 0012
60	32.987 690 8533	533.128 180 8889	.001 875 7215
n	$s=(1+i)^n$	$s_{\overline{n}\rceil} = \dfrac{(1+i)^n-1}{i}$	$\dfrac{1}{s_{\overline{n}\rceil}} = \dfrac{i}{(1+i)^n-1}$

.06
per period

ANNUALLY
If compounded
annually
nominal annual rate is
6%

SEMIANNUALLY
If compounded
semiannually
nominal annual rate is
12%

QUARTERLY
If compounded
quarterly
nominal annual rate is
24%

MONTHLY
If compounded
monthly
nominal annual rate is
72%

$i = .06$
$j_{(2)} = .12$
$j_{(4)} = .24$
$j_{(12)} = .72$

PRESENT WORTH OF 1	PRESENT WORTH OF 1 PER PERIOD	PARTIAL PAYMENT	P E R I O D S	RATE
What $1 due in the future is worth today.	*What $1 payable periodically is worth today.*	*Annuity worth $1 today.* *Periodic payment necessary to pay off a loan of $1.*		**6%**
.943 396 2264	.943 396 2264	1.060 000 0000	1	
.889 996 4400	1.833 392 6664	.545 436 8932	2	
.839 619 2830	2.673 011 9495	.374 109 8128	3	.06
.792 093 6632	3.465 105 6127	.288 591 4924	4	
.747 258 1729	4.212 363 7856	.237 396 4004	5	*per period*
.704 960 5404	4.917 324 3260	.203 362 6285	6	
.665 057 1136	5.582 381 4396	.179 135 0181	7	
.627 412 3713	6.209 793 8110	.161 035 9426	8	
.591 898 4635	6.801 692 2745	.147 022 2350	9	
.558 394 7769	7.360 087 0514	.135 867 9582	10	
.526 787 5254	7.886 874 5768	.126 792 9381	11	
.496 969 3636	8.383 843 9404	.119 277 0294	12	
.468 839 0222	8.852 682 9626	.112 960 1053	13	
.442 300 9644	9.294 983 9270	.107 584 9090	14	
.417 265 0607	9.712 248 9877	.102 962 7640	15	
.393 646 2837	10.105 895 2715	.098 952 1436	16	
.371 364 4186	10.477 259 6901	.095 444 8042	17	
.350 343 7911	10.827 603 4812	.092 356 5406	18	
.330 513 0105	11.158 116 4917	.089 620 8604	19	
.311 804 7269	11.469 921 2186	.087 184 5570	20	
.294 155 4027	11.764 076 6213	.085 004 5467	21	ANNUALLY *If compounded annually nominal annual rate is*
.277 505 0969	12.041 581 7182	.083 045 5685	22	
.261 797 2612	12.303 378 9794	.081 278 4847	23	
.246 978 5483	12.550 357 5278	.079 679 0050	24	
.232 998 6305	12.783 356 1583	.078 226 7182	25	**6%**
.219 810 0288	13.003 166 1870	.076 904 3467	26	
.207 367 9517	13.210 534 1387	.075 697 1663	27	
.195 630 1431	13.406 164 2818	.074 592 5515	28	
.184 556 7388	13.590 721 0206	.073 579 6135	29	
.174 110 1309	13.764 831 1515	.072 648 9115	30	
.164 254 8405	13.929 085 9920	.071 792 2196	31	SEMIANNUALLY *If compounded semiannually nominal annual rate is*
.154 957 3967	14.084 043 3887	.071 002 3374	32	
.146 186 2233	14.230 229 6119	.070 272 9350	33	
.137 911 5314	14.368 141 1433	.069 598 4254	34	
.130 105 2183	14.498 246 3616	.068 973 8590	35	**12%**
.122 740 7720	14.620 987 1336	.068 394 8348	36	
.115 793 1811	14.736 780 3147	.067 857 4274	37	
.109 238 8501	14.846 019 1648	.067 358 1240	38	
.103 055 5190	14.949 074 6838	.066 893 7724	39	
.097 222 1877	15.046 296 8715	.066 461 5359	40	
.091 719 0450	15.138 015 9165	.066 058 8551	41	QUARTERLY *If compounded quarterly nominal annual rate is*
.086 527 4010	15.224 543 3175	.065 683 4152	42	
.081 629 6235	15.306 172 9410	.065 333 1178	43	
.077 009 0788	15.383 182 0198	.065 006 0565	44	
.072 650 0743	15.455 832 0942	.064 700 4958	45	**24%**
.068 537 8060	15.524 369 9002	.064 414 8527	46	
.064 658 3075	15.589 028 2077	.064 147 6805	47	
.060 998 4033	15.650 026 6110	.063 897 6549	48	
.057 545 6635	15.707 572 2746	.063 663 5619	49	
.054 288 3618	15.761 860 6364	.063 444 2864	50	
.051 215 4357	15.813 076 0721	.063 238 8028	51	MONTHLY *If compounded monthly nominal annual rate is*
.048 316 4488	15.861 392 5208	.063 046 1669	52	
.045 581 5554	15.906 974 0762	.062 865 5076	53	
.043 001 4674	15.949 975 5436	.062 696 0209	54	
.040 567 4221	15.990 542 9657	.062 536 9634	55	**72%**
.038 271 1529	16.028 814 1186	.062 387 6472	56	
.036 104 8612	16.064 918 9798	.062 247 4350	57	
.034 061 1898	16.098 980 1696	.062 115 7359	58	$i = .06$
.032 133 1979	16.131 113 3676	.061 992 0012	59	$j_{(2)} = .12$
.030 314 3377	16.161 427 7052	.061 875 7215	60	$j_{(4)} = .24$ $j_{(12)} = .72$
$v^n = \dfrac{1}{(1+i)^n}$	$a_{\overline{n}\rceil} = \dfrac{1-v^n}{i}$	$\dfrac{1}{a_{\overline{n}\rceil}} = \dfrac{i}{1-v^n}$	**n**	

P E R I O D S	AMOUNT OF 1 *How $1 left at compound interest will grow.*	AMOUNT OF 1 PER PERIOD *How $1 deposited periodically will grow.*	SINKING FUND *Periodic deposit that will grow to $1 at future date.*
1	1.070 000 0000	1.000 000 0000	1.000 000 0000
2	1.144 900 0000	2.070 000 0000	.483 091 7874
3	1.225 043 0000	3.214 900 0000	.311 051 6657
4	1.310 796 0100	4.439 943 0000	.225 228 1167
5	1.402 551 7307	5.750 739 0100	.173 890 6944
6	1.500 730 3518	7.153 290 7407	.139 795 7998
7	1.605 781 4765	8.654 021 0925	.115 553 2196
8	1.718 186 1798	10.259 802 5690	.097 467 7625
9	1.838 459 2124	11.977 988 7489	.083 486 4701
10	1.967 151 3573	13.816 447 9613	.072 377 5027
11	2.104 851 9523	15.783 599 3186	.063 356 9048
12	2.252 191 5890	17.888 451 2709	.055 901 9887
13	2.409 845 0002	20.140 642 8598	.049 650 8481
14	2.578 534 1502	22.550 487 8600	.044 344 9386
15	2.759 031 5407	25.129 022 0102	.039 794 6247
16	2.952 163 7486	27.888 053 5509	.035 857 6477
17	3.158 815 2110	30.840 217 2995	.032 425 1931
18	3.379 932 2757	33.999 032 5105	.029 412 6017
19	3.616 527 5350	37.378 964 7862	.026 753 0148
20	3.869 684 4625	40.995 492 3212	.024 392 9257
21	4.140 562 3749	44.865 176 7837	.022 289 0017
22	4.430 401 7411	49.005 739 1586	.020 405 7732
23	4.740 529 8630	53.436 140 8997	.018 713 9263
24	5.072 366 9534	58.176 670 7627	.017 189 0207
25	5.427 432 6401	63.249 037 7160	.015 810 5172
26	5.807 352 9249	68.676 470 3562	.014 561 0279
27	6.213 867 6297	74.483 823 2811	.013 425 7340
28	6.648 838 3638	80.697 690 9108	.012 391 9283
29	7.114 257 0492	87.346 529 2745	.011 448 6518
30	7.612 255 0427	94.460 786 3237	.010 586 4035
31	8.145 112 8956	102.073 041 3664	.009 796 9061
32	8.715 270 7983	110.218 154 2621	.009 072 9155
33	9.325 339 7542	118.933 425 0604	.008 408 0653
34	9.978 113 5370	128.258 764 8146	.007 796 7381
35	10.676 581 4846	138.236 878 3516	.007 233 9596
36	11.423 942 1885	148.913 459 8363	.006 715 3097
37	12.223 618 1417	160.337 402 0248	.006 236 8480
38	13.079 271 4117	172.561 020 1665	.005 795 0515
39	13.994 820 4105	185.640 291 5782	.005 386 7616
40	14.974 457 8392	199.635 111 9887	.005 009 1389
41	16.022 669 8880	214.609 569 8279	.004 659 6245
42	17.144 256 7801	230.632 239 7158	.004 335 9072
43	18.344 354 7547	247.776 496 4959	.004 035 8953
44	19.628 459 5875	266.120 851 2507	.003 757 6913
45	21.002 451 7587	285.749 310 8382	.003 499 5710
46	22.472 623 3818	306.751 762 5969	.003 259 9650
47	24.045 707 0185	329.224 385 9787	.003 037 4421
48	25.728 906 5098	353.270 092 9972	.002 830 6953
49	27.529 929 9655	378.998 999 5070	.002 638 5294
50	29.457 025 0631	406.528 929 4724	.002 459 8495
51	31.519 016 8175	435.985 954 5355	.002 293 6519
52	33.725 347 9947	467.504 971 3530	.002 139 0147
53	36.086 122 3543	501.230 319 3477	.001 995 0908
54	38.612 150 9191	537.316 441 7021	.001 861 1007
55	41.315 001 4835	575.928 592 6212	.001 736 3264
56	44.207 051 5873	617.243 594 1047	.001 620 1059
57	47.301 545 1984	661.450 645 6920	.001 511 8286
58	50.612 653 3623	708.752 190 8905	.001 410 9304
59	54.155 539 0977	759.364 844 2528	.001 316 8900
60	57.946 426 8345	813.520 383 3505	.001 229 2255
n	$s=(1+i)^n$	$s_{\overline{n}|}=\dfrac{(1+i)^n-1}{i}$	$\dfrac{1}{s_{\overline{n}|}}=\dfrac{i}{(1+i)^n-1}$

.07
per period

ANNUALLY
If compounded
annually
nominal annual rate is
7%

SEMIANNUALLY
If compounded
semiannually
nominal annual rate is
14%

QUARTERLY
If compounded
quarterly
nominal annual rate is
28%

MONTHLY
If compounded
monthly
nominal annual rate is
84%

$i = .07$
$j_{(2)} = .14$
$j_{(4)} = .28$
$j_{(12)} = .84$

56

PRESENT WORTH OF 1 *What $1 due in the future is worth today.*	PRESENT WORTH OF 1 PER PERIOD *What $1 payable periodically is worth today.*	PARTIAL PAYMENT *Annuity worth $1 today.* *Periodic payment necessary to pay off a loan of $1.*	P E R I O D S	RATE 7%
.934 579 4393	.934 579 4393	1.070 000 0000	1	
.873 438 7283	1.808 018 1675	.553 091 7874	2	
.816 297 8769	2.624 316 0444	.381 051 6657	3	.07
.762 895 2120	3.387 211 2565	.295 228 1167	4	*per period*
.712 986 1795	4.100 197 4359	.243 890 6944	5	
.666 342 2238	4.766 539 6598	.209 795 7998	6	
.622 749 7419	5.389 289 4016	.185 553 2196	7	
.582 009 1046	5.971 298 5062	.167 467 7625	8	
.543 933 7426	6.515 232 2488	.153 486 4701	9	
.508 349 2921	7.023 581 5409	.142 377 5027	10	
.475 092 7964	7.498 674 3373	.133 356 9048	11	
.444 011 9592	7.942 686 2966	.125 901 9887	12	
.414 964 4479	8.357 650 7444	.119 650 8481	13	
.387 817 2410	8.745 467 9855	.114 344 9386	14	
.362 446 0196	9.107 914 0051	.109 794 6247	15	
.338 734 5978	9.446 648 6029	.105 857 6477	16	
.316 574 3905	9.763 222 9934	.102 425 1931	17	
.295 863 9163	10.059 086 9097	.099 412 6017	18	
.276 508 3330	10.335 595 2427	.096 753 0148	19	
.258 419 0028	10.594 014 2455	.094 392 9257	20	ANNUALLY If compounded *annually* nominal annual rate is
.241 513 0867	10.835 527 3323	.092 289 0017	21	
.225 713 1652	11.061 240 4974	.090 405 7732	22	
.210 946 8833	11.272 187 3808	.088 713 9263	23	7%
.197 146 6199	11.469 334 0007	.087 189 0207	24	
.184 249 1775	11.653 583 1783	.085 810 5172	25	
.172 195 4930	11.825 778 6713	.084 561 0279	26	
.160 930 3673	11.986 709 0386	.083 425 7340	27	
.150 402 2124	12.137 111 2510	.082 391 9283	28	
.140 562 8154	12.277 674 0664	.081 448 6518	29	
.131 367 1172	12.409 041 1835	.080 586 4035	30	SEMIANNUALLY If compounded *semiannually* nominal annual rate is
.122 773 0067	12.531 814 1902	.079 796 9061	31	
.114 741 1277	12.646 555 3179	.079 072 9155	32	
.107 234 6988	12.753 790 0168	.078 408 0653	33	
.100 219 3447	12.854 009 3615	.077 796 7381	34	
.093 662 9390	12.947 672 3004	.077 233 9596	35	14%
.087 535 4570	13.035 207 7574	.076 715 3097	36	
.081 808 8383	13.117 016 5957	.076 236 8480	37	
.076 456 8582	13.193 473 4539	.075 795 0515	38	
.071 455 0077	13.264 928 4616	.075 386 7616	39	
.066 780 3810	13.331 708 8426	.075 009 1389	40	QUARTERLY If compounded *quarterly* nominal annual rate is
.062 411 5710	13.394 120 4137	.074 659 6245	41	
.058 328 5711	13.452 448 9847	.074 335 9072	42	
.054 512 6832	13.506 961 6680	.074 035 8953	43	
.050 946 4329	13.557 908 1009	.073 757 6913	44	
.047 613 4887	13.605 521 5896	.073 499 5710	45	28%
.044 498 5876	13.650 020 1772	.073 259 9650	46	
.041 587 4650	13.691 607 6423	.073 037 4421	47	
.038 866 7898	13.730 474 4320	.072 830 6953	48	
.036 324 1026	13.766 798 5346	.072 638 5294	49	
.033 947 7594	13.800 746 2940	.072 459 8495	50	MONTHLY If compounded *monthly* nominal annual rate is
.031 726 8780	13.832 473 1720	.072 293 6519	51	
.029 651 2878	13.862 124 4598	.072 139 0147	52	
.027 711 4839	13.889 835 9437	.071 995 0908	53	
.025 898 5831	13.915 734 5269	.071 861 1007	54	
.024 204 2833	13.939 938 8102	.071 736 3264	55	84%
.022 620 8255	13.962 559 6357	.071 620 1059	56	
.021 140 9584	13.983 700 5941	.071 511 8286	57	
.019 757 9051	14.003 458 4991	.071 410 9304	58	$i = .07$
.018 465 3318	14.021 923 8310	.071 316 8900	59	$j_{(2)} = .14$
.017 257 3195	14.039 181 1504	.071 229 2255	60	$j_{(4)} = .28$ $j_{(12)} = .84$
$v^n = \dfrac{1}{(1+i)^n}$	$a_{\overline{n}|} = \dfrac{1-v^n}{i}$	$\dfrac{1}{a_{\overline{n}|}} = \dfrac{i}{1-v^n}$	n	

P E R I O D S	AMOUNT OF 1 *How $1 left at compound interest will grow.*	AMOUNT OF 1 PER PERIOD *How $1 deposited periodically will grow.*	SINKING FUND *Periodic deposit that will grow to $1 at future date.*
1	1.080 000 0000	1.000 000 0000	1.000 000 0000
2	1.166 400 0000	2.080 000 0000	.480 769 2308
3	1.259 712 0000	3.246 400 0000	.308 033 5140
4	1.360 488 9600	4.506 112 0000	.221 920 8045
5	1.469 328 0768	5.866 600 9600	.170 456 4546
6	1.586 874 3229	7.335 929 0368	.136 315 3862
7	1.713 824 2688	8.922 803 3597	.112 072 4014
8	1.850 930 2103	10.636 627 6285	.094 014 7606
9	1.999 004 6271	12.487 557 8388	.080 079 7092
10	2.158 924 9973	14.486 562 4659	.069 029 4887
11	2.331 638 9971	16.645 487 4632	.060 076 3421
12	2.518 170 1168	18.977 126 4602	.052 695 0169
13	2.719 623 7262	21.495 296 5771	.046 521 8052
14	2.937 193 6243	24.214 920 3032	.041 296 8528
15	3.172 169 1142	27.152 113 9275	.036 829 5449
16	3.425 942 6433	30.324 283 0417	.032 976 8720
17	3.700 018 0548	33.750 225 6850	.029 629 4315
18	3.996 019 4992	37.450 243 7398	.026 702 0959
19	4.315 701 0591	41.446 263 2390	.024 127 6275
20	4.660 957 1438	45.761 964 2981	.021 852 2088
21	5.033 833 7154	50.422 921 4420	.019 832 2503
22	5.436 540 4126	55.456 755 1573	.018 032 0684
23	5.871 463 6456	60.893 295 5699	.016 422 1692
24	6.341 180 7372	66.764 759 2155	.014 977 9616
25	6.848 475 1962	73.105 939 9527	.013 678 7791
26	7.396 353 2119	79.954 415 1490	.012 507 1267
27	7.988 061 4689	87.350 768 3609	.011 448 0962
28	8.627 106 3864	95.338 829 8297	.010 488 9057
29	9.317 274 8973	103.965 936 2161	.009 618 5350
30	10.062 656 8891	113.283 211 1134	.008 827 4334
31	10.867 669 4402	123.345 868 0025	.008 107 2841
32	11.737 082 9954	134.213 537 4427	.007 450 8132
33	12.676 049 6350	145.950 620 4381	.006 851 6324
34	13.690 133 6059	158.626 670 0732	.006 304 1101
35	14.785 344 2943	172.316 803 6790	.005 803 2646
36	15.968 171 8379	187.102 147 9733	.005 344 6741
37	17.245 625 5849	203.070 319 8112	.004 924 4025
38	18.625 275 6317	220.315 945 3961	.004 538 9361
39	20.115 297 6822	238.941 221 0278	.004 185 1297
40	21.724 521 4968	259.056 518 7100	.003 860 1615
41	23.462 483 2165	280.781 040 2068	.003 561 4940
42	25.339 481 8739	304.243 523 4233	.003 286 8407
43	27.366 640 4238	329.583 005 2972	.003 034 1370
44	29.555 971 6577	356.949 645 7210	.002 801 5156
45	31.920 449 3903	386.505 617 3787	.002 587 2845
46	34.474 085 3415	418.426 066 7690	.002 389 9085
47	37.232 012 1688	452.900 152 1105	.002 207 9922
48	40.210 573 1423	490.132 164 2793	.002 040 2660
49	43.427 418 9937	530.342 737 4217	.001 885 5731
50	46.901 612 5132	573.770 156 4154	.001 742 8582
51	50.653 741 5143	620.671 768 9286	.001 611 1575
52	54.706 040 8354	671.325 510 4429	.001 489 5903
53	59.082 524 1023	726.031 551 2783	.001 377 3506
54	63.809 126 0304	785.114 075 3806	.001 273 7003
55	68.913 856 1129	848.923 201 4111	.001 177 9629
56	74.426 964 6019	917.837 057 5239	.001 089 5180
57	80.381 121 7701	992.264 022 1259	.001 007 7963
58	86.811 611 5117	1072.645 143 8959	.000 932 2748
59	93.756 540 4326	1159.456 755 4076	.000 862 4729
60	101.257 063 6672	1253.213 295 8402	.000 797 9488
n	$s=(1+i)^n$	$s_{\overline{n}\rceil}=\dfrac{(1+i)^n-1}{i}$	$\dfrac{1}{s_{\overline{n}\rceil}}=\dfrac{i}{(1+i)^n-1}$

ANNUALLY
If compounded
annually
nominal annual rate is

8%

SEMIANNUALLY
If compounded
semiannually
nominal annual rate is

16%

QUARTERLY
If compounded
quarterly
nominal annual rate is

32%

MONTHLY
If compounded
monthly
nominal annual rate is

96%

$i \quad = .08$
$j_{(2)} = .16$
$j_{(4)} = .32$
$j_{(12)} = .96$

PRESENT WORTH OF 1 *What $1 due in the future is worth today.*	PRESENT WORTH OF 1 PER PERIOD *What $1 payable periodically is worth today.*	PARTIAL PAYMENT *Annuity worth $1 today.* *Periodic payment necessary to pay off a loan of $1.*	P E R I O D S	RATE **8%**
.925 925 9259	.925 925 9259	1.080 000 0000	1	
.857 338 8203	1.783 264 7462	.560 769 2308	2	
.793 832 2410	2.577 096 9872	.388 033 5140	3	.08
.735 029 8528	3.312 126 8400	.301 920 8045	4	
.680 583 1970	3.992 710 0371	.250 456 4546	5	*per period*
.630 169 6269	4.622 879 6640	.216 315 3862	6	
.583 490 3953	5.206 370 0592	.192 072 4014	7	
.540 268 8845	5.746 638 9437	.174 014 7606	8	
.500 248 9671	6.246 887 9109	.160 079 7092	9	
.463 193 4881	6.710 081 3989	.149 029 4887	10	
.428 882 8593	7.138 964 2583	.140 076 3421	11	
.397 113 7586	7.536 078 0169	.132 695 0169	12	
.367 697 9247	7.903 775 9416	.126 521 8052	13	
.340 461 0414	8.244 236 9830	.121 296 8528	14	
.315 241 7050	8.559 478 6879	.116 829 5449	15	
.291 890 4676	8.851 369 1555	.112 976 8720	16	
.270 268 9514	9.121 638 1069	.109 629 4315	17	
.250 249 0291	9.371 887 1360	.106 702 0959	18	
.231 712 0640	9.603 599 2000	.104 127 6275	19	
.214 548 2074	9.818 147 4074	.101 852 2088	20	
.198 655 7476	10.016 803 1550	.099 832 2503	21	ANNUALLY *If compounded annually* nominal annual rate is **8%**
.183 940 5070	10.200 743 6621	.098 032 0684	22	
.170 315 2843	10.371 058 9464	.096 422 1692	23	
.157 699 3373	10.528 758 2837	.094 977 9616	24	
.146 017 9049	10.674 776 1886	.093 678 7791	25	
.135 201 7638	10.809 977 9524	.092 507 1267	26	
.125 186 8183	10.935 164 7707	.091 448 0962	27	
.115 913 7207	11.051 078 4914	.090 488 9057	28	
.107 327 5192	11.158 406 0106	.089 618 5350	29	
.099 377 3325	11.257 783 3431	.088 827 4334	30	
.092 016 0487	11.349 799 3918	.088 107 2841	31	SEMIANNUALLY *If compounded semiannually* nominal annual rate is **16%**
.085 200 0451	11.434 999 4368	.087 450 8132	32	
.078 888 9306	11.513 888 3674	.086 851 6324	33	
.073 045 3061	11.586 933 6736	.086 304 1101	34	
.067 634 5427	11.654 568 2163	.085 803 2646	35	
.062 624 5766	11.717 192 7928	.085 344 6741	36	
.057 985 7190	11.775 178 5119	.084 924 4025	37	
.053 690 4806	11.828 868 9925	.084 538 9361	38	
.049 713 4080	11.878 582 4004	.084 185 1297	39	
.046 030 9333	11.924 613 3337	.083 860 1615	40	
.042 621 2345	11.967 234 5683	.083 561 4940	41	QUARTERLY *If compounded quarterly* nominal annual rate is **32%**
.039 464 1061	12.006 698 6743	.083 286 8407	42	
.036 540 8389	12.043 239 5133	.083 034 1370	43	
.033 834 1101	12.077 073 6234	.082 801 5156	44	
.031 327 8797	12.108 401 5032	.082 587 2845	45	
.029 007 2961	12.137 408 7992	.082 389 9085	46	
.026 858 6075	12.164 267 4067	.082 207 9922	47	
.024 869 0810	12.189 136 4877	.082 040 2660	48	
.023 026 9268	12.212 163 4145	.081 885 5731	49	
.021 321 2286	12.233 484 6431	.081 742 8582	50	
.019 741 8783	12.253 226 5214	.081 611 1575	51	MONTHLY *If compounded monthly* nominal annual rate is **96%**
.018 279 5169	12.271 506 0383	.081 489 5903	52	
.016 925 4786	12.288 431 5169	.081 377 3506	53	
.015 671 7395	12.304 103 2564	.081 273 7003	54	
.014 510 8699	12.318 614 1263	.081 177 9629	55	
.013 435 9906	12.332 050 1170	.081 089 5180	56	
.012 440 7321	12.344 490 8490	.081 007 7963	57	
.011 519 1964	12.356 010 0454	.080 932 2748	58	
.010 665 9226	12.366 675 9680	.080 862 4329	59	
.009 875 8542	12.376 551 8222	.080 797 9488	60	
$v^n = \dfrac{1}{(1+i)^n}$	$a_{\overline{n}|} = \dfrac{1-v^n}{i}$	$\dfrac{1}{a_{\overline{n}|}} = \dfrac{i}{1-v^n}$	n	$i = .08$ $j_{(2)} = .16$ $j_{(4)} = .32$ $j_{(12)} = .96$

Table 3

Auxiliary Tables

Time Interval	Amount of 1	Payment Equivalent to 1 per Period	Equivalent per Period to a Payment of 1
Fractional Parts of a Unit Period.	*How 1 left at compound interest will grow for a time interval which is a fractional part of a unit period.*	*Payment at the end of each time interval equivalent to 1 at the end of each period.*	*Payment at the end of each period equivalent to 1 at the end of each time interval.*

1/4% per Period $i = .0025$

1-12	1.000 208 0950	.083 237 9995	12.013 743 8011
1-6	1.000 416 2333	.166 493 3203	6.006 246 9656
1-4	1.000 624 4149	.249 765 9662	4.003 748 0493
1-3	1.000 832 6399	.333 055 9407	3.002 498 6128
1-2	1.001 249 2197	.499 687 8900	2.001 249 2197

1/3% per Period $i = .00333333$

1-12	1.000 277 3543	.083 206 2890	12.018 322 3177
1-6	1.000 554 7855	.166 435 6556	6.008 327 9411
1-4	1.000 832 2937	.249 688 1063	4.004 996 5336
1-3	1.001 109 8788	.332 963 6473	3.003 330 8683
1-2	1.001 665 2801	.499 584 0263	2.001 665 2801

5/12% per Period $i = .00416666$

1-12	1.000 346 5609	.083 174 6124	12.022 899 4619
1-6	1.000 693 2419	.166 378 0499	6.010 408 2448
1-4	1.001 040 0430	.249 610 3224	4.006 244 5859
1-3	1.001 386 9643	.332 871 4400	3.004 162 8167
1-2	1.002 081 1677	.499 480 2503	2.002 081 1677

1/2% per Period $i = .005$

1-12	1.000 415 7148	.083 142 9689	12.027 475 2355
1-6	1.000 831 6025	.166 320 5017	6.012 487 8775
1-4	1.001 247 6631	.249 532 6125	4.007 492 2070
1-3	1.001 663 8966	.332 779 3159	3.004 994 4583
1-2	1.002 496 8828	.499 376 5576	2.002 496 8828

3/4% per Period $i = .0075$

1-12	1.000 622 8618	.083 048 2402	12.041 194 3491
1-6	1.001 246 1116	.166 148 2079	6.018 722 7583
1-4	1.001 869 7495	.249 299 9354	4.011 232 4875
1-3	1.002 493 7759	.332 503 4550	3.007 487 5467
1-2	1.003 742 9950	.499 065 9992	2.003 742 9950

1% per Period $i = .01$

1-12	1.000 829 5381	.082 953 8114	12.054 901 1879
1-6	1.001 659 7644	.165 976 4362	6.024 951 6304
1-4	1.002 490 6793	.249 067 9314	4.014 968 9053
1-3	1.003 322 2835	.332 228 3542	3.009 977 8882
1-2	1.004 987 5621	.498 756 2112	2.004 987 5621

Table 3 (Continued)

Auxiliary Tables

Time Interval	Amount of 1	Payment Equivalent to 1 per Period	Equivalent per Period to a Payment of 1
Fractional Parts of a Unit Period.	*How 1 left at compound interest will grow for a time interval which is a fractional part of a unit period.*	*Payment at the end of each time interval equivalent to 1 at the end of each period.*	*Payment at the end of each period equivalent to 1 at the end of each time interval.*

1¼% per Period $i = .0125$

1-12	1.001 035 7460	.082 859 6812	12.068 595 7972
1-6	1.002 072 5648	.165 805 1839	6.031 174 5161
1-4	1.003 110 4575	.248 836 5972	4.018 701 4747
1-3	1.004 149 4251	.331 954 0099	3.012 465 4931
1-2	1.006 230 5899	.498 447 1900	2.006 230 5899

1½% per Period $i = .015$

1-12	1.001 241 4877	.082 765 8478	12.082 278 2225
1-6	1.002 484 5167	.165 634 4483	6.037 391 4376
1-4	1.003 729 0889	.248 605 9292	4.022 430 2099
1-3	1.004 975 2063	.331 680 4182	3.014 950 3715
1-2	1.007 472 0840	.498 138 9320	2.007 472 0840

1¾% per Period $i = .0175$

1-12	1.001 446 7654	.082 672 3096	12.095 948 5087
1-6	1.002 895 6240	.165 464 2266	6.043 602 4169
1-4	1.004 346 5787	.248 375 9242	4.026 155 1251
1-3	1.005 799 6326	.331 407 5755	3.017 432 5334
1-2	1.008 712 0501	.497 831 4338	2.008 712 0501

2% per Period $i = .02$

1-12	1.001 651 5813	.082 579 0651	12.109 606 7004
1-6	1.003 305 8903	.165 294 5162	6.049 807 4758
1-4	1.004 962 9316	.248 146 5787	4.029 876 2344
1-3	1.006 622 7096	.331 135 4780	3.019 911 9890
1-2	1.009 950 4938	.497 524 6918	2.009 950 4938

2¼% per Period $i = .0225$

1-12	1.001 855 9375	.082 486 1127	12.123 252 8421
1-6	1.003 715 3196	.165 125 3144	6.056 006 6360
1-4	1.005 578 1525	.247 917 8894	4.033 593 5518
1-3	1.007 444 4427	.330 864 1222	3.022 388 7480
1-2	1.011 187 4208	.497 218 7026	2.011 187 4208

2½% per Period $i = .025$

1-12	1.002 059 8363	.082 393 4508	12.136 886 9779
1-6	1.004 123 9155	.164 956 6186	6.062 199 9193
1-4	1.006 192 2463	.247 689 8530	4.037 307 0910
1-3	1.008 264 8376	.330 593 5044	3.024 862 8204
1-2	1.012 422 8366	.496 913 4626	2.012 422 8366

Table 3 (Continued)

Auxiliary Tables

Time Interval *Fractional Parts of a Unit Period.*	Amount of 1 *How 1 left at compound interest will grow for a time interval which is a fractional part of a unit period.*	Payment Equivalent to 1 per Period *Payment at the end of each time interval equivalent to 1 at the end of each period.*	Equivalent per Period to a Payment of 1 *Payment at the end of each period equivalent to 1 at the end of each time interval.*

3% per Period $i = .03$

1-12	1.002 466 2698	.082 208 9924	12.164 119 4069
1-6	1.004 938 6220	.164 620 7344	6.074 568 9406
1-4	1.007 417 0718	.247 235 7259	4.044 722 8905
1-3	1.009 901 6340	.330 054 4683	3.029 802 9445
1-2	1.014 889 1565	.496 305 2170	2.014 889 1565

3½% per Period $i = .035$

1-12	1.002 870 8987	.082 025 6777	12.191 304 3353
1-6	1.005 750 0395	.164 286 8428	6.086 914 7098
1-4	1.008 637 4460	.246 784 1714	4.052 123 7423
1-3	1.011 533 1419	.329 518 3414	3.034 732 4392
1-2	1.017 349 4975	.495 699 9277	2.017 349 4975

4% per Period $i = .04$

1-12	1.003 273 7398	.081 843 4946	12.218 442 1063
1-6	1.006 558 1969	.163 954 9234	6.099 237 3951
1-4	1.009 853 4065	.246 335 1637	4.059 509 7544
1-3	1.013 159 4038	.328 985 0955	3.039 651 3814
1-2	1.019 803 9027	.495 097 5680	2.019 803 9027

5% per Period $i = .05$

1-12	1.004 074 1238	.081 482 4757	12.272 577 5296
1-6	1.008 164 8461	.163 296 9210	6.123 814 1763
1-4	1.012 272 2344	.245 444 6886	4.074 237 6858
1-3	1.016 396 3568	.327 927 1363	3.049 457 9110
1-2	1.024 695 0766	.493 901 5319	2.024 695 0766

6% per Period $i = .06$

1-12	1.004 867 5506	.081 125 8428	12.326 528 3420
1-6	1.009 758 7942	.162 646 5697	6.148 300 5890
1-4	1.014 673 8462	.244 564 1028	4.088 907 5237
1-3	1.019 612 8224	.326 880 3737	3.059 223 1301
1-2	1.029 563 0141	.492 716 9016	2.029 563 0141

7% per Period $i = .07$

1-12	1.005 654 1454	.080 773 5055	12.380 297 1455
1-6	1.011 340 2601	.162 003 7162	6.172 697 9071
1-4	1.017 058 5250	.243 693 2143	4.103 520 0870
1-3	1.022 809 1218	.325 844 5967	3.068 947 6213
1-2	1.034 408 0433	.491 543 4754	2.034 408 0433

8% per Period $i = .08$

1-12	1.006 434 0301	.080 425 3764	12.433 886 4805
1-6	1.012 909 4570	.161 368 2120	6.197 007 3742
1-4	1.019 426 5469	.242 831 8364	4.118 076 1757
1-3	1.025 985 5680	.324 819 6001	3.078 631 9538
1-2	1.039 230 4845	.490 381 0568	2.039 230 4845

Table 4

Present Worth of 1

n	4%	6%	8%	10%	12%	14%	16%	18%	20%	22%	24%
1	.962	.943	.926	.909	.893	.877	.862	.847	.833	.820	.806
2	.925	.890	.857	.826	.797	.769	.743	.718	.694	.672	.650
3	.889	.840	.794	.751	.712	.675	.641	.609	.579	.551	.524
4	.855	.792	.735	.683	.636	.592	.552	.516	.482	.451	.423
5	.822	.747	.681	.621	.567	.519	.476	.437	.402	.370	.341
6	.790	.705	.630	.564	.507	.456	.410	.370	.335	.303	.275
7	.760	.665	.583	.513	.452	.400	.354	.314	.279	.249	.222
8	.731	.627	.540	.467	.404	.351	.305	.266	.233	.204	.179
9	.703	.592	.500	.424	.361	.308	.263	.225	.194	.167	.144
10	.676	.558	.463	.386	.322	.270	.227	.191	.162	.137	.116
11	.650	.527	.429	.350	.287	.237	.195	.162	.135	.112	.094
12	.625	.497	.397	.319	.257	.208	.168	.137	.112	.092	.076
13	.601	.469	.368	.290	.229	.182	.145	.116	.093	.075	.061
14	.577	.442	.340	.263	.205	.160	.125	.099	.078	.062	.049
15	.555	.417	.315	.239	.183	.140	.108	.084	.065	.051	.040
16	.534	.394	.292	.218	.163	.123	.093	.071	.054	.042	.032
17	.513	.371	.270	.198	.146	.108	.080	.060	.045	.034	.026
18	.494	.350	.250	.180	.130	.095	.069	.051	.038	.028	.021
19	.475	.331	.232	.164	.116	.083	.060	.043	.031	.023	.017
20	.456	.312	.215	.149	.104	.073	.051	.037	.026	.019	.014

n	25%	30%	35%	40%	45%	50%	60%	70%	80%	90%	100%
1	.800	.769	.741	.714	.690	.667	.625	.588	.556	.526	.500
2	.640	.592	.549	.510	.476	.444	.391	.346	.309	.277	.250
3	.512	.455	.406	.364	.328	.296	.244	.204	.171	.146	.125
4	.410	.350	.301	.260	.226	.198	.153	.120	.095	.077	.063
5	.328	.269	.223	.186	.156	.132	.095	.070	.053	.040	.031
6	.262	.207	.165	.133	.108	.088	.060	.041	.029	.021	.016
7	.210	.159	.122	.095	.074	.059	.037	.024	.016	.011	.008
8	.168	.123	.091	.068	.051	.039	.023	.014	.009	.006	.004
9	.134	.094	.067	.048	.035	.026	.015	.008	.005	.003	.002
10	.107	.073	.050	.035	.024	.017	.009	.005	.003	.002	.001

Present Worth of 1 Per Period

n	4%	6%	8%	10%	12%	14%	16%	18%	20%	22%	24%
1	.962	.943	.926	.909	.893	.877	.862	.847	.833	.820	.806
2	1.886	1.833	1.783	1.736	1.690	1.647	1.605	1.566	1.528	1.492	1.457
3	2.775	2.673	2.577	2.487	2.402	2.322	2.246	2.174	2.106	2.042	1.981
4	3.630	3.465	3.312	3.170	3.037	2.914	2.798	2.690	2.589	2.494	2.404
5	4.452	4.212	3.993	3.791	3.605	3.433	3.274	3.127	2.991	2.864	2.745
6	5.242	4.917	4.623	4.355	4.111	3.889	3.685	3.498	3.326	3.167	3.020
7	6.002	5.582	5.206	4.868	4.564	4.288	4.039	3.812	3.605	3.416	3.242
8	6.733	6.210	5.747	5.335	4.968	4.639	4.344	4.078	3.837	3.619	3.421
9	7.435	6.802	6.247	5.759	5.328	4.946	4.607	4.303	4.031	3.786	3.566
10	8.111	7.360	6.710	6.145	5.650	5.216	4.833	4.494	4.192	3.923	3.682
11	8.760	7.887	7.139	6.495	5.938	5.453	5.029	4.656	4.327	4.035	3.776
12	9.385	8.384	7.536	6.814	6.194	5.660	5.197	4.793	4.439	4.127	3.851
13	9.986	8.853	7.904	7.103	6.424	5.842	5.342	4.910	4.533	4.203	3.912
14	10.563	9.295	8.244	7.367	6.628	6.002	5.468	5.008	4.611	4.265	3.962
15	11.118	9.712	8.559	7.606	6.811	6.142	5.575	5.092	4.675	4.315	4.001
16	11.652	10.106	8.851	7.824	6.974	6.265	5.668	5.162	4.730	4.357	4.033
17	12.166	10.477	9.122	8.022	7.120	6.373	5.749	5.222	4.775	4.391	4.059
18	12.659	10.828	9.372	8.201	7.250	6.467	5.818	5.273	4.812	4.419	4.080
19	13.134	11.158	9.604	8.365	7.366	6.550	5.877	5.316	4.843	4.442	4.097
20	13.590	11.470	9.818	8.514	7.469	6.623	5.929	5.353	4.870	4.460	4.110

n	25%	30%	35%	40%	45%	50%	60%	70%	80%	90%	100%
1	.800	.769	.741	.714	.690	.667	.625	.588	.556	.526	.500
2	1.440	1.361	1.289	1.224	1.165	1.111	1.016	.934	.864	.803	.750
3	1.952	1.816	1.696	1.589	1.493	1.407	1.260	1.138	1.036	.949	.875
4	2.362	2.166	1.997	1.849	1.720	1.605	1.412	1.258	1.131	1.026	.938
5	2.689	2.436	2.220	2.035	1.876	1.737	1.508	1.328	1.184	1.066	.969
6	2.951	2.643	2.385	2.168	1.983	1.824	1.567	1.369	1.213	1.087	.984
7	3.161	2.802	2.508	2.263	2.057	1.883	1.605	1.394	1.230	1.099	.992
8	3.329	2.925	2.598	2.331	2.109	1.922	1.628	1.408	1.239	1.105	.996
9	3.463	3.019	2.665	2.379	2.144	1.948	1.642	1.417	1.244	1.108	.998
10	3.571	3.092	2.715	2.414	2.168	1.965	1.652	1.421	1.246	1.109	.999

Table 5

1958 Commissioners Standard Ordinary (CSO) Mortality Table

Values for females age 0 to 14 are in the complete tables of the Society of Actuaries from which these data are reproduced with permission of the Society.

Age x M	F	Number Living l_x	Number Dying d_x	Deaths per 1000 $1000q_x$	Age x M	F	Number Living l_x	Number Dying d_x	Deaths per 1000 $1000q_x$
0		10 000 000	70 800	7.08	50	53	8 762 306	72 902	8.32
1		9 929 200	17 475	1.76	51	54	8 689 404	79 160	9.11
2		9 911 725	15 066	1.52	52	55	8 610 244	85 758	9.96
3		9 896 659	14 449	1.46	53	56	8 524 486	92 832	10.89
4		9 882 210	13 835	1.40	54	57	8 431 654	100 337	11.90
5		9 868 375	13 322	1.35	55	58	8 331 317	108 307	13.00
6		9 855 053	12 812	1.30	56	59	8 223 010	116 849	14.21
7		9 842 241	12 401	1.26	57	60	8 106 161	125 970	15.54
8		9 829 840	12 091	1.23	58	61	7 980 191	135 663	17.00
9		9 817 749	11 879	1.21	59	62	7 844 528	145 830	18.59
10		9 805 870	11 865	1.21	60	63	7 698 698	156 592	20.34
11		9 794 005	12 047	1.23	61	64	7 542 106	167 736	22.24
12	15	9 781 958	12 325	1.26	62	65	7 374 370	179 271	24.31
13	16	9 769 633	12 896	1.32	63	66	7 195 099	191 174	26.57
14	17	9 756 737	13 562	1.39	64	67	7 003 925	203 394	29.04
15	18	9 743 175	14 225	1.46	65	68	6 800 531	215 917	31.75
16	19	9 728 950	14 983	1.54	66	69	6 584 614	228 749	34.74
17	20	9 713 967	15 737	1.62	67	70	6 355 865	241 777	38.04
18	21	9 698 230	16 390	1.69	68	71	6 114 088	254 835	41.68
19	22	9 681 840	16 846	1.74	69	72	5 859 253	267 241	45.61
20	23	9 664 994	17 300	1.79	70	73	5 592 012	278 426	49.79
21	24	9 647 694	17 655	1.83	71	74	5 313 586	287 731	54.15
22	25	9 630 039	17 912	1.86	72	75	5 025 855	294 766	58.65
23	26	9 612 127	18 167	1.89	73	76	4 731 089	299 289	63.26
24	27	9 593 960	18 324	1.91	74	77	4 431 800	301 894	68.12
25	28	9 575 636	18 481	1.93	75	78	4 129 906	303 011	73.37
26	29	9 557 155	18 732	1.96	76	79	3 826 895	303 014	79.18
27	30	9 538 423	18 981	1.99	77	80	3 523 881	301 997	85.70
28	31	9 519 442	19 324	2.03	78	81	3 221 884	299 829	93.06
29	32	9 500 118	19 760	2.08	79	82	2 922 055	295 683	101.19
30	33	9 480 358	20 193	2.13	80	83	2 626 372	288 848	109.98
31	34	9 460 165	20 718	2.19	81	84	2 337 524	278 983	119.35
32	35	9 439 447	21 239	2.25	82	85	2 058 541	265 902	129.17
33	36	9 418 208	21 850	2.32	83	86	1 792 639	249 858	139.38
34	37	9 396 358	22 551	2.40	84	87	1 542 781	231 433	150.01
35	38	9 373 807	23 528	2.51	85	88	1 311 348	211 311	161.14
36	39	9 350 279	24 685	2.64	86	89	1 100 037	190 108	172.82
37	40	9 325 594	26 112	2.80	87	90	909 929	168 455	185.13
38	41	9 299 482	27 991	3.01	88	91	741 474	146 997	198.25
39	42	9 271 491	30 132	3.25	89	92	594 477	126 303	212.46
40	43	9 241 359	32 622	3.53	90	93	468 174	106 809	228.14
41	44	9 208 737	35 362	3.84	91	94	361 365	88 813	245.77
42	45	9 173 375	38 253	4.17	92	95	272 552	72 480	265.93
43	46	9 135 122	41 382	4.53	93	96	200 072	57 881	289.30
44	47	9 093 740	44 741	4.92	94	97	142 191	45 026	316.66
45	48	9 048 999	48 412	5.35	95	98	97 165	34 128	351.24
46	49	9 000 587	52 473	5.83	96	99	63 037	25 250	400.56
47	50	8 948 114	56 910	6.36	97	100	37 787	18 456	488.42
48	51	8 891 204	61 794	6.95	98	101	19 331	12 916	668.15
49	52	8 829 410	67 104	7.60	99	102	6 415	6 415	1000.00

Table 6

Commutation Columns, Interest at 2½%

Values for females age 0 to 14 are in the complete tables of the Society of Actuaries from which these data are reproduced with permission of the Society.

Age						Annuity Due	Life Insurance
x							
M	F	D_x	N_x	C_x	M_x	$\ddot{a}_x$	$1000A_x$
0		10 000 000.0	324 850 105.9	69 073.171	2 076 826.724	32.48 5011	207.68 267
1		9 687 024.4	314 850 105.9	16 632.957	2 007 753.553	32.50 2252	207.26 216
2		9 434 122.6	305 163 081.5	13 990.279	1 991 120.596	32.34 6737	211.05 520
3		9 190 031.7	295 728 958.9	13 090.081	1 977 130.317	32.17 9319	215.13 857
4		8 952 794.5	286 538 927.2	12 228.124	1 964 040.236	32.00 5529	219.37 734
5		8 722 205.6	277 586 132.7	11 487.519	1 951 812.112	31.82 5222	223.77 506
6		8 497 981.4	268 863 927.1	10 778.290	1 940 324.593	31.63 8564	228.32 771
7		8 279 935.2	260 365 945.7	10 178.078	1 929 546.303	31.44 5409	233.03 882
8		8 067 807.5	252 086 010.5	9 681.607	1 919 368.225	31.24 5913	237.90 456
9		7 861 350.1	244 018 203.0	9 279.856	1 909 686.618	31.04 0241	242.92 095
10		7 660 330.0	236 156 852.9	9 042.848	1 900 406.762	30.82 8548	248.08 419
11		7 464 449.8	228 496 522.9	8 957.618	1 891 363.914	30.61 1301	253.38 290
12	15	7 273 432.5	221 032 073.1	8 940.806	1 882 406.296	30.38 8963	258.80 577
13	16	7 087 090.9	213 758 640.6	9 126.850	1 873 465.490	30.16 1690	264.34 901
14	17	6 905 108.2	206 671 549.7	9 364.094	1 864 338.640	29.93 0241	269.99 412
15	18	6 727 326.8	199 766 441.5	9 582.315	1 854 974.546	29.69 4773	275.73 724
16	19	6 553 663.3	193 039 114.7	9 846.754	1 845 392.231	29.45 5147	281.58 179
17	20	6 383 971.1	186 485 451.4	10 090.028	1 835 545.477	29.21 1512	287.52 409
18	21	6 218 174.5	180 101 480.3	10 252.399	1 825 455.449	28.96 3722	293.56 774
19	22	6 056 259.3	173 883 305.8	10 280.624	1 815 203.050	28.71 1338	299.72 347
20	23	5 898 265.0	167 827 046.5	10 300.183	1 804 922.426	28.45 3629	306.00 904
21	24	5 744 104.7	161 928 781.5	10 255.166	1 794 622.243	28.19 0430	312.42 854
22	25	5 593 749.4	156 184 676.8	10 150.681	1 784 367.077	27.92 1286	318.99 303
23	26	5 447 165.0	150 590 927.4	10 044.086	1 774 216.396	27.64 5740	325.71 368
24	27	5 304 264.0	145 143 761.6	9 883.793	1 764 172.310	27.36 3601	332.59 512
25	28	5 165 008.0	139 839 497.6	9 725.344	1 754 288.517	27.07 4401	339.64 875
26	29	5 029 306.8	134 674 489.6	9 617.004	1 744 563.173	26.77 7943	346.87 945
27	30	4 897 023.8	129 645 182.8	9 507.161	1 734 946.169	26.47 4281	354.28 584
28	31	4 768 077.0	124 748 159.0	9 442.890	1 725 439.008	26.16 3201	361.87 314
29	32	4 642 339.5	119 980 082.0	9 420.436	1 715 996.118	25.84 4745	369.64 038
30	33	4 519 691.4	115 337 742.5	9 392.064	1 706 575.682	25.51 8942	377.58 677
31	34	4 400 062.9	110 818 051.1	9 401.218	1 697 183.618	25.18 5561	385.71 804
32	35	4 283 343.1	106 417 988.2	9 402.569	1 687 782.400	24.84 4610	394.03 390
33	36	4 169 468.7	102 134 645.1	9 437.132	1 678 379.831	24.49 5842	402.54 046
34	37	4 058 337.2	97 965 176.4	9 502.339	1 668 942.699	24.13 9240	411.23 806
35	38	3 949 851.1	93 906 839.2	9 672.213	1 659 440.360	23.77 4780	420.12 732
36	39	3 843 841.0	89 956 988.1	9 900.340	1 649 768.147	23.40 2890	429.19 781
37	40	3 740 188.5	86 113 147.1	10 217.232	1 639 867.807	23.02 3745	438.44 523
38	41	3 638 747.1	82 372 958.6	10 685.323	1 629 650.575	22.63 7726	447.86 036
39	42	3 539 311.9	78 734 211.5	11 222.079	1 618 965.252	22.24 5627	457.42 373
40	43	3 441 765.1	75 194 899.6	11 853.104	1 607 743.173	21.84 7772	467.12 751
41	44	3 345 966.5	71 753 134.5	12 535.293	1 595 890.069	21.44 4666	476.95 937
42	45	3 251 822.3	68 407 168.0	13 229.374	1 583 354.776	21.03 6564	486.91 307
43	46	3 159 280.2	65 155 345.7	13 962.442	1 570 125.402	20.62 3478	496.98 833
44	47	3 068 262.1	61 996 065.5	14 727.592	1 556 162.960	20.20 5596	507.18 058
45	48	2 978 698.8	58 927 803.4	15 547.309	1 541 435.368	19.78 3069	517.48 615
46	49	2 890 500.4	55 949 104.6	16 440.470	1 525 888.059	19.35 6200	527.89 754
47	50	2 803 559.9	53 058 604.2	17 395.746	1 509 447.589	18.92 5440	538.40 390
48	51	2 717 784.6	50 255 044.3	18 427.945	1 492 051.843	18.49 1180	548.99 562
49	52	2 633 069.2	47 537 259.7	19 523.386	1 473 623.898	18.05 3935	559.66 015

Table 6 (*Continued*)

Commutation Columns, Interest at 2½%

Age x						Annuity Due	Life Insurance
M	F	D_x	N_x	C_x	M_x	$\ddot{a}_x$	$1000A_x$
50	53	2 549 324.7	44 904 190.5	20 692.945	1 454 100.512	17.61 4151	570.38 655
51	54	2 466 453.1	42 354 865.8	21 921.223	1 433 407.567	17.17 2378	581.16 149
52	55	2 384 374.4	39 888 412.7	23 169.133	1 411 486.344	16.72 9089	591.97 345
53	56	2 303 049.8	37 504 038.3	24 468.592	1 388 317.211	16.28 4510	602.81 684
54	57	2 222 409.3	35 200 988.5	25 801.712	1 363 848.619	15.83 9111	613.68 022
55	58	2 142 402.5	32 978 579.2	27 171.903	1 338 046.907	15.39 3270	624.55 440
56	59	2 062 976.8	30 836 176.7	28 599.910	1 310 875.004	14.94 7418	635.42 886
57	60	1 984 060.4	28 773 199.9	30 080.354	1 282 275.094	14.50 2179	646.28 834
58	61	1 905 588.4	26 789 139.5	31 604.823	1 252 194.740	14.05 8198	657.11 711
59	62	1 827 505.8	24 883 551.1	33 144.766	1 220 589.917	13.61 6127	667.89 934
60	63	1 749 787.7	23 056 045.3	34 722.724	1 187 445.151	13.17 6482	678.62 241
61	64	1 672 387.3	21 306 257.6	36 286.629	1 152 722.427	12.74 0026	689.26 763
62	65	1 595 310.7	19 633 870.3	37 836.114	1 116 435.798	12.30 7239	699.82 342
63	66	1 518 564.6	18 038 559.6	39 364.201	1 078 599.684	11.87 8691	710.27 580
64	67	1 442 162.2	16 519 995.0	40 858.920	1 039 235.483	11.45 5019	720.60 929
65	68	1 366 128.5	15 077 832.8	42 316.694	998 376.563	11.03 6907	730.80 721
66	69	1 290 491.7	13 711 704.3	43 738.131	956 059.869	10.62 5178	740.84 930
67	70	1 215 278.1	12 421 212.6	45 101.621	912 321.738	10.22 0881	750.71 026
68	71	1 140 535.6	11 205 934.5	46 378.038	867 220.117	9.82 5151	760.36 216
69	72	1 066 339.6	10 065 398.9	47 449.596	820 842.079	9.43 9206	769.77 548
70	73	992 881.8	8 999 059.3	48 229.787	773 392.483	9.06 3576	778.93 711
71	74	920 435.3	8 006 177.5	48 625.978	725 162.696	8.69 8251	787.84 755
72	75	849 359.7	7 085 742.2	48 599.883	676 536.718	8.34 2452	796.52 557
73	76	780 043.7	6 236 382.5	48 142.066	627 936.835	7.99 4914	805.00 212
74	77	712 876.2	5 456 338.8	47 376.675	579 794.769	7.65 3978	813.31 761
75	78	648 112.3	4 743 462.6	46 392.163	532 418.094	7.31 8890	821.49 049
76	79	585 912.5	4 095 350.3	45 261.095	486 025.931	6.98 9696	829.51 965
77	80	526 360.9	3 509 437.8	44 008.963	440 764.836	6.66 7360	837.38 142
78	81	469 513.8	2 983 076.9	42 627.343	396 755.873	6.35 3545	845.03 559
79	82 ●	415 434.9	2 513 563.1	41 012.583	354 128.530	6.05 0438	852.42 846
80	83	364 289.8	2 098 128.2	39 087.353	313 115.947	5.75 9503	859.52 433
81	84	316 317.3	1 733 838.4	36 831.617	274 028.594	5.48 1327	866.30 922
82	85	271 770.7	1 417 521.1	34 248.438	237 196.977	5.21 5872	872.78 348
83	86	230 893.7	1 145 750.4	31 397.029	202 948.539	4.96 2242	878.96 958
84	87	193 865.1	914 856.7	28 372.443	171 551.510	4.71 9038	884.90 146
85	88	160 764.2	720 991.6	25 273.751	143 179.067	4.48 4777	890.61 537
86	89	131 569.4	560 227.4	22 183.195	117 905.316	4.25 8037	896.14 543
87	90	106 177.2	428 658.0	19 177.136	95 722.121	4.03 7194	901.53 179
88	91	84 410.4	322 480.8	16 326.175	76 544.985	3.82 0392	906.81 936
89	92	66 025.4	238 070.4	13 685.661	60 218.810	3.60 5740	912.05 521
90	93	50 729.4	172 045.0	11 291.096	46 533.149	3.39 1426	917.28 167
91	94	38 201.0	121 315.6	9 159.693	35 242.053	3.17 5718	922.54 268
92	95	28 109.5	83 114.6	7 292.874	26 082.360	2.95 6815	927.88 417
93	96	20 131.1	55 005.1	5 681.888	18 789.486	2.73 2344	933.35 615
94	97	13 958.2	34 874.0	4 312.173	13 107.598	2.49 8460	939.06 077
95	98	9 305.6	20 915.8	3 188.745	8 795.425	2.24 7657	945.17 549
96	99	5 889.9	11 610.2	2 301.688	5 606.680	1.97 1205	951.91 429
97	100	3 444.5	5 720.3	1 641.341	3 304.992	1.66 0705	959.49 833
98	101	1 719.2	2 275.8	1 120.638	1 663.651	1.32 3755	967.68 904
99	102	556.6	556.6	543.013	543.013	1.00 0000	975.58 929

Table 7

Six-Place Logarithms of Numbers 100–1,000

N	0	1	2	3	4	5	6	7	8	9	D
100	00 0000	00 0434	00 0868	00 1301	00 1734	00 2166	00 2598	00 3029	00 3461	00 3891	432
101	4321	4751	5181	5609	6038	6466	6894	7321	7748	8174	428
102	8600	9026	9451	9876	01 0300	01 0724	01 1147	01 1570	01 1993	01 2415	424
103	01 2837	01 3259	01 3680	01 4100	4521	4940	5360	5779	6197	6616	420
104	7033	7451	7868	8284	8700	9116	9532	9947	02 0361	02 0775	416
105	02 1189	02 1603	02 2016	02 2428	02 2841	02 3252	02 3664	02 4075	4486	4896	412
106	5306	5715	6125	6533	6942	7350	7757	8164	8571	8978	408
107	9384	9789	03 0195	03 0600	03 1004	03 1408	03 1812	03 2216	03 2619	03 3021	404
108	03 3424	03 3826	4227	4628	5029	5430	5830	6230	6629	7028	400
109	7426	7825	8223	8620	9017	9414	9811	04 0207	04 0602	04 0998	397
110	04 1393	04 1787	04 2182	04 2576	04 2969	04 3362	04 3755	4148	4540	4932	393
111	5323	5714	6105	6495	6885	7275	7664	8053	8442	8830	390
112	9218	9606	9993	05 0380	05 0766	05 1153	05 1538	05 1924	05 2309	05 2694	386
113	05 3078	05 3463	05 3846	4230	4613	4996	5378	5760	6142	6524	383
114	6905	7286	7666	8046	8426	8805	9185	9563	9942	06 0320	379
115	06 0698	06 1075	06 1452	06 1829	06 2206	06 2582	06 2958	06 3333	06 3709	4083	376
116	4458	4832	5206	5580	5953	6326	6699	7071	7443	7815	373
117	8186	8557	8928	9298	9668	07 0038	07 0407	07 0776	07 1145	07 1514	370
118	07 1882	07 2250	07 2617	07 2985	07 3352	3718	4085	4451	4816	5182	366
119	5547	5912	6276	6640	7004	7368	7731	8094	8457	8819	363
120	9182	9543	9904	08 0266	08 0626	08 0987	08 1347	08 1707	08 2067	08 2426	360
121	08 2785	08 3144	08 3503	3861	4219	4576	4934	5291	5647	6004	357
122	6360	6716	7071	7426	7781	8136	8490	8845	9198	9552	355
123	9905	09 0258	09 0611	09 0963	09 1315	09 1667	09 2018	09 2370	09 2721	09 3071	352
124	09 3422	3772	4122	4471	4820	5169	5518	5866	6215	6562	349
125	6910	7257	7604	7951	8298	8644	8990	9335	9681	10 0026	346
126	10 0371	10 0715	10 1059	10 1403	10 1747	10 2091	10 2434	10 2777	10 3119	3462	343
127	3804	4146	4487	4828	5169	5510	5851	6191	6531	6871	341
128	7210	7549	7888	8227	8565	8903	9241	9579	9916	11 0253	338
129	11 0590	11 0926	11 1263	11 1599	11 1934	11 2270	11 2605	11 2940	11 3275	3609	335
130	3943	4277	4611	4944	5278	5611	5943	6276	6608	6940	333
131	7271	7603	7934	8265	8595	8926	9256	9586	9915	12 0245	330
132	12 0574	12 0903	12 1231	12 1560	12 1888	12 2216	12 2544	12 2871	12 3198	3525	328
133	3852	4178	4504	4830	5156	5481	5806	6131	6456	6781	325
134	7105	7429	7753	8076	8399	8722	9045	9368	9690	13 0012	323
135	13 0334	13 0655	13 0977	13 1298	13 1619	13 1939	13 2260	13 2580	13 2900	3219	321
136	3539	3858	4177	4496	4814	5133	5451	5769	6086	6403	318
137	6721	7037	7354	7671	7987	8303	8618	8934	9249	9564	316
138	9879	14 0194	14 0508	14 0822	14 1136	14 1450	14 1763	14 2076	14 2389	14 2702	314
139	14 3015	3327	3639	3951	4263	4574	4885	5196	5507	5818	311
140	6128	6438	6748	7058	7367	7676	7985	8294	8603	8911	309
141	9219	9527	9835	15 0142	15 0449	15 0756	15 1063	15 1370	15 1676	15 1982	307
142	15 2288	15 2594	15 2900	3205	3510	3815	4120	4424	4728	5032	305
143	5336	5640	5943	6246	6549	6852	7154	7457	7759	8061	303
144	8362	8664	8965	9266	9567	9868	16 0168	16 0469	16 0769	16 1068	301
145	16 1368	16 1667	16 1967	16 2266	16 2564	16 2863	3161	3460	3758	4055	299
146	4353	4650	4947	5244	5541	5838	6134	6430	6726	7022	297
147	7317	7613	7908	8203	8497	8792	9086	9380	9674	9968	295
148	17 0262	17 0555	17 0848	17 1141	17 1434	17 1726	17 2019	17 2311	17 2603	17 2895	293
149	3186	3478	3769	4060	4351	4641	4932	5222	5512	5802	291
150	6091	6381	6670	6959	7248	7536	7825	8113	8401	8689	289

Proportional Part[s]

n\d	435	430	425	42[0]
1	44	43	43	
2	87	86	85	
3	131	129	128	
4	174	172	170	
5	218	215	213	
6	261	258	255	
7	305	301	298	
8	348	344	340	
9	392	387	383	

n\d	415	410	405	4[00]
1	42	41	41	
2	83	82	81	
3	125	123	122	
4	166	164	162	
5	208	205	203	
6	249	246	243	
7	291	287	284	
8	332	328	324	
9	374	369	365	

n\d	395	390	385	3[80]
1	40	39	39	
2	79	78	77	
3	119	117	116	
4	158	156	154	
5	198	195	193	
6	237	234	231	
7	277	273	270	
8	316	312	308	
9	356	351	347	

n\d	375	370	365	3[60]
1	38	37	37	
2	75	74	73	
3	113	111	110	
4	150	148	146	
5	188	185	183	
6	225	222	219	
7	263	259	256	
8	300	296	292	
9	338	333	329	

n\d	355	350	345	3[40]
1	36	35	35	
2	71	70	69	
3	107	105	104	
4	142	140	138	
5	178	175	173	
6	213	210	207	
7	249	245	242	
8	284	280	276	
9	320	315	311	

n\d	335	330	325	3[20]
1	34	33	33	
2	67	66	65	
3	101	99	98	
4	134	132	130	
5	168	165	163	
6	201	198	195	
7	235	231	228	
8	268	264	260	
9	302	297	293	

n\d	315	310	305	3[00]
1	32	31	31	
2	63	62	61	
3	95	93	92	
4	126	124	122	
5	158	155	153	
6	189	186	183	
7	221	217	214	
8	252	248	244	
9	284	279	275	

Six-Place Logarithms of Numbers 150-200

N	0	1	2	3	4	5	6	7	8	9	D
150	17 6091	17 6381	17 6670	17 6959	17 7248	17 7536	17 7825	17 8113	17 8401	17 8689	289
151	8977	9264	9552	9839	18 0126	18 0413	18 0699	18 0986	18 1272	18 1558	287
152	18 1844	18 2129	18 2415	18 2700	2985	3270	3555	3839	4123	4407	285
153	4691	4975	5259	5542	5825	6108	6391	6674	6956	7239	283
154	7521	7803	8084	8366	8647	8928	9209	9490	9771	19 0051	281
155	19 0332	19 0612	19 0892	19 1171	19 1451	19 1730	19 2010	19 2289	19 2567	2846	279
156	3125	3403	3681	3959	4237	4514	4792	5069	5346	5623	278
157	5900	6176	6453	6729	7005	7281	7556	7832	8107	8382	276
158	8657	8932	9206	9481	9755	20 0029	20 0303	20 0577	20 0850	20 1124	274
159	20 1397	20 1670	20 1943	20 2216	20 2488	2761	3033	3305	3577	3848	272
160	4120	4391	4663	4934	5204	5475	5746	6016	6286	6556	271
161	6826	7096	7365	7634	7904	8173	8441	8710	8979	9247	269
162	9515	9783	21 0051	21 0319	21 0586	21 0853	21 1121	21 1388	21 1654	21 1921	267
163	21 2188	21 2454	2720	2986	3252	3518	3783	4049	4314	4579	266
164	4844	5109	5373	5638	5902	6166	6430	6694	6957	7221	264
165	7484	7747	8010	8273	8536	8798	9060	9323	9585	9846	262
166	22 0108	22 0370	22 0631	22 0892	22 1153	22 1414	22 1675	22 1936	22 2196	22 2456	261
167	2716	2976	3236	3496	3755	4015	4274	4533	4792	5051	259
168	5309	5568	5826	6084	6342	6600	6858	7115	7372	7630	258
169	7887	8144	8400	8657	8913	9170	9426	9682	9938	23 0193	256
170	23 0449	23 0704	23 0960	23 1215	23 1470	23 1724	23 1979	23 2234	23 2488	2742	255
171	2996	3250	3504	3757	4011	4264	4517	4770	5023	5276	253
172	5528	5781	6033	6285	6537	6789	7041	7292	7544	7795	252
173	8046	8297	8548	8799	9049	9299	9550	9800	24 0050	24 0300	250
174	24 0549	24 0799	24 1048	24 1297	24 1546	24 1795	24 2044	24 2293	2541	2790	249
175	3038	3286	3534	3782	4030	4277	4525	4772	5019	5266	248
176	5513	5759	6006	6252	6499	6745	6991	7237	7482	7728	246
177	7973	8219	8464	8709	8954	9198	9443	9687	9932	25 0176	245
178	25 0420	25 0664	25 0908	25 1151	25 1395	25 1638	25 1881	25 2125	25 2368	2610	243
179	2853	3096	3338	3580	3822	4064	4306	4548	4790	5031	242
180	5273	5514	5755	5996	6237	6477	6718	6958	7198	7439	241
181	7679	7918	8158	8398	8637	8877	9116	9355	9594	9833	239
182	26 0071	26 0310	26 0548	26 0787	26 1025	26 1263	26 1501	26 1739	26 1976	26 2214	238
183	2451	2688	2925	3162	3399	3636	3873	4109	4346	4582	237
184	4818	5054	5290	5525	5761	5996	6232	6467	6702	6937	235
185	7172	7406	7641	7875	8110	8344	8578	8812	9046	9279	234
186	9513	9746	9980	27 0213	27 0446	27 0679	27 0912	27 1144	27 1377	27 1609	233
187	27 1842	27 2074	27 2306	2538	2770	3001	3233	3464	3696	3927	232
188	4158	4389	4620	4850	5081	5311	5542	5772	6002	6232	230
189	6462	6692	6921	7151	7380	7609	7838	8067	8296	8525	229
190	8754	8982	9211	9439	9667	9895	28 0123	28 0351	28 0578	28 0806	228
191	28 1033	28 1261	28 1488	28 1715	28 1942	28 2169	2396	2622	2849	3075	227
192	3301	3527	3753	3979	4205	4431	4656	4882	5107	5332	226
193	5557	5782	6007	6232	6456	6681	6905	7130	7354	7578	225
194	7802	8026	8249	8473	8696	8920	9143	9366	9589	9812	223
195	29 0035	29 0257	29 0480	29 0702	29 0925	29 1147	29 1369	29 1591	29 1813	29 2034	222
196	2256	2478	2699	2920	3141	3363	3584	3804	4025	4246	221
197	4466	4687	4907	5127	5347	5567	5787	6007	6226	6446	220
198	6665	6884	7104	7323	7542	7761	7979	8198	8416	8635	219
199	8853	9071	9289	9507	9725	9943	30 0161	30 0378	30 0595	30 0813	218
200	30 1030	30 1247	30 1464	30 1681	30 1898	30 2114	2331	2547	2764	2980	217

Proportional Parts

n\d	295	290	285	280
1	30	29	29	28
2	59	58	57	56
3	89	87	86	84
4	118	116	114	112
5	148	145	143	140
6	177	174	171	168
7	207	203	200	196
8	236	232	228	224
9	266	261	257	252

n\d	275	270	265	260
1	28	27	27	26
2	55	54	53	52
3	83	81	80	78
4	110	108	106	104
5	138	135	133	130
6	165	162	159	156
7	193	189	186	182
8	220	216	212	208
9	248	243	239	234

n\d	255	250	248	246
1	26	25	25	25
2	51	50	50	49
3	77	75	74	74
4	102	100	99	98
5	128	125	124	123
6	153	150	149	148
7	179	175	174	172
8	204	200	198	197
9	230	225	223	221

n\d	244	242	240	238
1	24	24	24	24
2	49	48	48	48
3	73	73	72	71
4	98	97	96	95
5	122	121	120	119
6	146	145	144	143
7	171	169	168	167
8	195	194	192	190
9	220	218	216	214

n\d	236	234	232	230
1	24	23	23	23
2	47	47	46	46
3	71	70	70	69
4	94	94	93	92
5	118	117	116	115
6	142	140	139	138
7	165	164	162	161
8	189	187	186	184
9	212	211	209	207

n\d	228	226	224	222
1	23	23	22	22
2	46	45	45	44
3	68	68	67	67
4	91	90	90	89
5	114	113	112	111
6	137	136	134	133
7	160	158	157	155
8	182	181	179	178
9	205	203	202	200

n\d	220	218	216	214
1	22	22	22	21
2	44	44	43	43
3	66	65	65	64
4	88	87	86	86
5	110	109	108	107
6	132	131	130	128
7	154	153	151	150
8	176	174	173	171
9	198	196	194	193

N	0	1	2	3	4	5	6	7	8	9	D
200	30 1030	30 1247	30 1464	30 1681	30 1898	30 2114	30 2331	30 2547	30 2764	30 2980	217
201	3196	3412	3628	3844	4059	4275	4491	4706	4921	5136	216
202	5351	5566	5781	5996	6211	6425	6639	6854	7068	7282	215
203	7496	7710	7924	8137	8351	8564	8778	8991	9204	9417	213
204	9630	9843	31 0056	31 0268	31 0481	31 0693	31 0906	31 1118	31 1330	31 1542	212
205	31 1754	31 1966	2177	2389	2600	2812	3023	3234	3445	3656	211
206	3867	4078	4289	4499	4710	4920	5130	5340	5551	5760	210
207	5970	6180	6390	6599	6809	7018	7227	7436	7646	7854	209
208	8063	8272	8481	8689	8898	9106	9314	9522	9730	9938	208
209	32 0146	32 0354	32 0562	32 0769	32 0977	32 1184	32 1391	32 1598	32 1805	32 2012	207
210	2219	2426	2633	2839	3046	3252	3458	3665	3871	4077	206
211	4282	4488	4694	4899	5105	5310	5516	5721	5926	6131	205
212	6336	6541	6745	6950	7155	7359	7563	7767	7972	8176	204
213	8380	8583	8787	8991	9194	9398	9601	9805	33 0008	33 0211	203
214	33 0414	33 0617	33 0819	33 1022	33 1225	33 1427	33 1630	33 1832	2034	2236	202
215	2438	2640	2842	3044	3246	3447	3649	3850	4051	4253	202
216	4454	4655	4856	5057	5257	5458	5658	5859	6059	6260	201
217	6460	6660	6860	7060	7260	7459	7659	7858	8058	8257	200
218	8456	8656	8855	9054	9253	9451	9650	9849	34 0047	34 0246	199
219	34 0444	34 0642	34 0841	34 1039	34 1237	34 1435	34 1632	34 1830	2028	2225	198
220	2423	2620	2817	3014	3212	3409	3606	3802	3999	4196	197
221	4392	4589	4785	4981	5178	5374	5570	5766	5962	6157	196
222	6353	6549	6744	6939	7135	7330	7525	7720	7915	8110	195
223	8305	8500	8694	8889	9083	9278	9472	9666	9860	35 0054	194
224	35 0248	35 0442	35 0636	35 0829	35 1023	35 1216	35 1410	35 1603	35 1796	1989	193
225	2183	2375	2568	2761	2954	3147	3339	3532	3724	3916	193
226	4108	4301	4493	4685	4876	5068	5260	5452	5643	5834	192
227	6026	6217	6408	6599	6790	6981	7172	7363	7554	7744	191
228	7935	8125	8316	8506	8696	8886	9076	9266	9456	9646	190
229	9835	36 0025	36 0215	36 0404	36 0593	36 0783	36 0972	36 1161	36 1350	36 1539	189
230	36 1728	1917	2105	2294	2482	2671	2859	3048	3236	3424	188
231	3612	3800	3988	4176	4363	4551	4739	4926	5113	5301	188
232	5488	5675	5862	6049	6236	6423	6610	6796	6983	7169	187
233	7356	7542	7729	7915	8101	8287	8473	8659	8845	9030	186
234	9216	9401	9587	9772	9958	37 0143	37 0328	37 0513	37 0698	37 0883	185
235	37 1068	37 1253	37 1437	37 1622	37 1806	1991	2175	2360	2544	2728	184
236	2912	3096	3280	3464	3647	3831	4015	4198	4382	4565	184
237	4748	4932	5115	5298	5481	5664	5846	6029	6212	6394	183
238	6577	6759	6942	7124	7306	7488	7670	7852	8034	8216	182
239	8398	8580	8761	8943	9124	9306	9487	9668	9849	38 0030	181
240	38 0211	38 0392	38 0573	38 0754	38 0934	38 1115	38 1296	38 1476	38 1656	1837	181
241	2017	2197	2377	2557	2737	2917	3097	3277	3456	3636	180
242	3815	3995	4174	4353	4533	4712	4891	5070	5249	5428	179
243	5606	5785	5964	6142	6321	6499	6677	6856	7034	7212	178
244	7390	7568	7746	7923	8101	8279	8456	8634	8811	8989	178
245	9166	9343	9520	9698	9875	39 0051	39 0228	39 0405	39 0582	39 0759	177
246	39 0935	39 1112	39 1288	39 1464	39 1641	1817	1993	2169	2345	2521	176
247	2697	2873	3048	3224	3400	3575	3751	3926	4101	4277	176
248	4452	4627	4802	4977	5152	5326	5501	5676	5850	6025	175
249	6199	6374	6548	6722	6896	7071	7245	7419	7592	7766	174
250	7940	8114	8287	8461	8634	8808	8981	9154	9328	9501	173

Proportional Parts

n\d	220	218	216	214
1	22	22	22	21
2	44	44	43	43
3	66	65	65	64
4	88	87	86	86
5	110	109	108	107
6	132	131	130	128
7	154	153	151	150
8	176	174	173	171
9	198	196	194	193

n\d	212	210	208	206
1	21	21	21	21
2	42	42	42	41
3	64	63	62	62
4	85	84	83	82
5	106	105	104	103
6	127	126	125	124
7	148	147	146	144
8	170	168	166	165
9	191	189	187	185

n\d	204	202	200	198
1	20	20	20	20
2	41	40	40	40
3	61	61	60	59
4	82	81	80	79
5	102	101	100	99
6	122	121	120	119
7	143	141	140	139
8	163	162	160	158
9	184	182	180	178

n\d	196	194	192	190
1	20	19	19	19
2	39	39	38	38
3	59	58	58	57
4	78	78	77	76
5	98	97	96	95
6	118	116	115	114
7	137	136	134	133
8	157	155	154	152
9	176	175	173	171

n\d	188	186	184	182
1	19	19	18	18
2	38	37	37	36
3	56	56	55	55
4	75	74	74	73
5	94	93	92	91
6	113	112	110	109
7	132	130	129	127
8	150	149	147	146
9	169	167	166	164

n\d	180	178	176	174
1	18	18	18	17
2	36	36	35	35
3	54	53	53	52
4	72	71	70	70
5	90	89	88	87
6	108	107	106	104
7	126	125	123	122
8	144	142	141	139
9	162	160	158	157

n\d	174	173	172	171
1	17	17	17	17
2	35	35	34	34
3	52	52	52	51
4	70	69	69	68
5	87	87	86	86
6	104	104	103	103
7	122	121	120	120
8	139	138	138	137
9	157	156	155	154

N	0	1	2	3	4	5	6	7	8	9	D
250	39 7940	39 8114	39 8287	39 8461	39 8634	39 8808	39 8981	39 9154	39 9328	39 9501	173
251	9674	9847	40 0020	40 0192	40 0365	40 0538	40 0711	40 0883	40 1056	40 1228	173
252	40 1401	40 1573	1745	1917	2089	2261	2433	2605	2777	2949	172
253	3121	3292	3464	3635	3807	3978	4149	4320	4492	4663	171
254	4834	5005	5176	5346	5517	5688	5858	6029	6199	6370	171
255	6540	6710	6881	7051	7221	7391	7561	7731	7901	8070	170
256	8240	8410	8579	8749	8918	9087	9257	9426	9595	9764	169
257	9933	41 0102	41 0271	41 0440	41 0609	41 0777	41 0946	41 1114	41 1283	41 1451	169
258	41 1620	1788	1956	2124	2293	2461	2629	2796	2964	3132	168
259	3300	3467	3635	3803	3970	4137	4305	4472	4639	4806	167
260	4973	5140	5307	5474	5641	5808	5974	6141	6308	6474	167
261	6641	6807	6973	7139	7306	7472	7638	7804	7970	8135	166
262	8301	8467	8633	8798	8964	9129	9295	9460	9625	9791	165
263	9956	42 0121	42 0286	42 0451	42 0616	42 0781	42 0945	42 1110	42 1275	42 1439	165
264	42 1604	1768	1933	2097	2261	2426	2590	2754	2918	3082	164
265	3246	3410	3574	3737	3901	4065	4228	4392	4555	4718	164
266	4882	5045	5208	5371	5534	5697	5860	6023	6186	6349	163
267	6511	6674	6836	6999	7161	7324	7486	7648	7811	7973	162
268	8135	8297	8459	8621	8783	8944	9106	9268	9429	9591	162
269	9752	9914	43 0075	43 0236	43 0398	43 0559	43 0720	43 0881	43 1042	43 1203	161
270	43 1364	43 1525	1685	1846	2007	2167	2328	2488	2649	2809	161
271	2969	3130	3290	3450	3610	3770	3930	4090	4249	4409	160
272	4569	4729	4888	5048	5207	5367	5526	5685	5844	6004	159
273	6163	6322	6481	6640	6799	6957	7116	7275	7433	7592	159
274	7751	7909	8067	8226	8384	8542	8701	8859	9017	9175	158
275	9333	9491	9648	9806	9964	44 0122	44 0279	44 0437	44 0594	44 0752	158
276	44 0909	44 1066	44 1224	44 1381	44 1538	1695	1852	2009	2166	2323	157
277	2480	2637	2793	2950	3106	3263	3419	3576	3732	3889	157
278	4045	4201	4357	4513	4669	4825	4981	5137	5293	5449	156
279	5604	5760	5915	6071	6226	6382	6537	6692	6848	7003	155
280	7158	7313	7468	7623	7778	7933	8088	8242	8397	8552	155
281	8706	8861	9015	9170	9324	9478	9633	9787	9941	45 0095	154
282	45 0249	45 0403	45 0557	45 0711	45 0865	45 1018	45 1172	45 1326	45 1479	1633	154
283	1786	1940	2093	2247	2400	2553	2706	2859	3012	3165	153
284	3318	3471	3624	3777	3930	4082	4235	4387	4540	4692	153
285	4845	4997	5150	5302	5454	5606	5758	5910	6062	6214	152
286	6366	6518	6670	6821	6973	7125	7276	7428	7579	7731	152
287	7882	8033	8184	8336	8487	8638	8789	8940	9091	9242	151
288	9392	9543	9694	9845	9995	46 0146	46 0296	46 0447	46 0597	46 0748	151
289	46 0898	46 1048	46 1198	46 1348	46 1499	1649	1799	1948	2098	2248	150
290	2398	2548	2697	2847	2997	3146	3296	3445	3594	3744	150
291	3893	4042	4191	4340	4490	4639	4788	4936	5085	5234	149
292	5383	5532	5680	5829	5977	6126	6274	6423	6571	6719	149
293	6868	7016	7164	7312	7460	7608	7756	7904	8052	8200	148
294	8347	8495	8643	8790	8938	9085	9233	9380	9527	9675	148
295	9822	9969	47 0116	47 0263	47 0410	47 0557	47 0704	47 0851	47 0998	47 1145	147
296	47 1292	47 1438	1585	1732	1878	2025	2171	2318	2464	2610	146
297	2756	2903	3049	3195	3341	3487	3633	3779	3925	4071	146
298	4216	4362	4508	4653	4799	4944	5090	5235	5381	5526	146
299	5671	5816	5962	6107	6252	6397	6542	6687	6832	6976	145
300	7121	7266	7411	7555	7700	7844	7989	8133	8278	8422	145

Proportional Parts

n\d	170	169	168	167
1	17	17	17	17
2	34	34	34	33
3	51	51	50	50
4	68	68	67	67
5	85	85	84	84
6	102	101	101	100
7	119	118	118	117
8	136	135	134	134
9	153	152	151	150

n\d	166	165	164	163
1	17	17	16	16
2	33	33	33	33
3	50	50	49	49
4	66	66	66	65
5	83	83	82	82
6	100	99	98	98
7	116	116	115	114
8	133	132	131	130
9	149	149	148	147

n\d	162	161	160	159
1	16	16	16	16
2	32	32	32	32
3	49	48	48	48
4	65	64	64	64
5	81	81	80	80
6	97	97	96	95
7	113	113	112	111
8	130	129	128	127
9	146	145	144	143

n\d	158	157	156	155
1	16	16	16	16
2	32	31	31	31
3	47	47	47	47
4	63	63	62	62
5	79	79	78	78
6	95	94	94	93
7	111	110	109	109
8	126	126	125	124
9	142	141	140	140

n\d	154	153	152	151
1	15	15	15	15
2	31	31	30	30
3	46	46	46	45
4	62	61	61	60
5	77	77	76	76
6	92	92	91	91
7	108	107	106	106
8	123	122	122	121
9	139	138	137	136

n\d	150	149	148	147
1	15	15	15	15
2	30	30	30	29
3	45	45	44	44
4	60	60	59	59
5	75	75	74	74
6	90	89	89	88
7	105	104	104	103
8	120	119	118	118
9	135	134	133	132

n\d	146	145	144
1	15	15	14
2	29	29	29
3	44	44	43
4	58	58	58
5	73	73	72
6	88	87	86
7	102	102	101
8	117	116	115
9	131	131	130

Proportional Parts

N	0	1	2	3	4	5	6	7	8	9	D
300	47 7121	47 7266	47 7411	47 7555	47 7700	47 7844	47 7989	47 8133	47 8278	47 8422	145
301	8566	8711	8855	8999	9143	9287	9431	9575	9719	9863	144
302	48 0007	48 0151	48 0294	48 0438	48 0582	48 0725	48 0869	48 1012	48 1156	48 1299	144
303	1443	1586	1729	1872	2016	2159	2302	2445	2588	2731	143
304	2874	3016	3159	3302	3445	3587	3730	3872	4015	4157	143
305	4300	4442	4585	4727	4869	5011	5153	5295	5437	5579	142
306	5721	5863	6005	6147	6289	6430	6572	6714	6855	6997	142
307	7138	7280	7421	7563	7704	7845	7986	8127	8269	8410	141
308	8551	8692	8833	8974	9114	9255	9396	9537	9677	9818	141
309	9958	49 0099	49 0239	49 0380	49 0520	49 0661	49 0801	49 0941	49 1081	49 1222	140
310	49 1362	1502	1642	1782	1922	2062	2201	2341	2481	2621	140
311	2760	2900	3040	3179	3319	3458	3597	3737	3876	4015	139
312	4155	4294	4433	4572	4711	4850	4989	5128	5267	5406	139
313	5544	5683	5822	5960	6099	6238	6376	6515	6653	6791	139
314	6930	7068	7206	7344	7483	7621	7759	7897	8035	8173	138
315	8311	8448	8586	8724	8862	8999	9137	9275	9412	9550	138
316	9687	9824	9962	50 0099	50 0236	50 0374	50 0511	50 0648	50 0785	50 0922	137
317	50 1059	50 1196	50 1333	1470	1607	1744	1880	2017	2154	2291	137
318	2427	2564	2700	2837	2973	3109	3246	3382	3518	3655	136
319	3791	3927	4063	4199	4335	4471	4607	4743	4878	5014	136
320	5150	5286	5421	5557	5693	5828	5964	6099	6234	6370	136
321	6505	6640	6776	6911	7046	7181	7316	7451	7586	7721	135
322	7856	7991	8126	8260	8395	8530	8664	8799	8934	9068	135
323	9203	9337	9471	9606	9740	9874	51 0009	51 0143	51 0277	51 0411	134
324	51 0545	51 0679	51 0813	51 0947	51 1081	51 1215	1349	1482	1616	1750	134
325	1883	2017	2151	2284	2418	2551	2684	2818	2951	3084	133
326	3218	3351	3484	3617	3750	3883	4016	4149	4282	4415	133
327	4548	4681	4813	4946	5079	5211	5344	5476	5609	5741	133
328	5874	6006	6139	6271	6403	6535	6668	6800	6932	7064	132
329	7196	7328	7460	7592	7724	7855	7987	8119	8251	8382	132
330	8514	8646	8777	8909	9040	9171	9303	9434	9566	9697	131
331	9828	9959	52 0090	52 0221	52 0353	52 0484	52 0615	52 0745	52 0876	52 1007	131
332	52 1138	52 1269	1400	1530	1661	1792	1922	2053	2183	2314	131
333	2444	2575	2705	2835	2966	3096	3226	3356	3486	3616	130
334	3746	3876	4006	4136	4266	4396	4526	4656	4785	4915	130
335	5045	5174	5304	5434	5563	5693	5822	5951	6081	6210	129
336	6339	6469	6598	6727	6856	6985	7114	7243	7372	7501	129
337	7630	7759	7888	8016	8145	8274	8402	8531	8660	8788	129
338	8917	9045	9174	9302	9430	9559	9687	9815	9943	53 0072	128
339	53 0200	53 0328	53 0456	53 0584	53 0712	53 0840	53 0968	53 1096	53 1223	1351	128
340	1479	1607	1734	1862	1990	2117	2245	2372	2500	2627	128
341	2754	2882	3009	3136	3264	3391	3518	3645	3772	3899	127
342	4026	4153	4280	4407	4534	4661	4787	4914	5041	5167	127
343	5294	5421	5547	5674	5800	5927	6053	6180	6306	6432	126
344	6558	6685	6811	6937	7063	7189	7315	7441	7567	7693	126
345	7819	7945	8071	8197	8322	8448	8574	8699	8825	8951	126
346	9076	9202	9327	9452	9578	9703	9829	9954	54 0079	54 0204	125
347	54 0329	54 0455	54 0580	54 0705	54 0830	54 0955	54 1080	54 1205	1330	1454	125
348	1579	1704	1829	1953	2078	2203	2327	2452	2576	2701	125
349	2825	2950	3074	3199	3323	3447	3571	3696	3820	3944	124
350	4068	4192	4316	4440	4564	4688	4812	4936	5060	5183	124

n\d	145	144	143	142
1	15	14	14	14
2	29	29	29	28
3	44	43	43	43
4	58	58	57	57
5	73	72	72	71
6	87	86	86	85
7	102	101	100	99
8	116	115	114	114
9	131	130	129	128

n\d	141	140	139	138
1	14	14	14	14
2	28	28	28	28
3	42	42	42	41
4	56	56	56	55
5	71	70	70	69
6	85	84	83	83
7	99	98	97	97
8	113	112	111	110
9	127	126	125	124

n\d	137	136	135	134
1	14	14	14	1
2	27	27	27	2
3	41	41	41	4
4	55	54	54	5
5	69	68	68	6
6	82	82	81	8
7	96	95	95	9
8	110	109	108	10
9	123	122	122	12

n\d	133	132	131	13
1	13	13	13	1
2	27	26	26	2
3	40	40	39	3
4	53	53	52	5
5	67	66	66	6
6	80	79	79	7
7	93	92	92	9
8	106	106	105	10
9	120	119	118	11

n\d	129	128	127
1	13	13	13
2	26	26	25
3	39	38	38
4	52	51	51
5	65	64	64
6	77	77	76
7	90	90	89
8	103	102	102
9	116	115	114

n\d	126	125	124
1	13	13	12
2	25	25	25
3	38	38	37
4	50	50	50
5	63	63	62
6	76	75	74
7	88	88	87
8	101	100	99
9	113	113	112

N	0	1	2	3	4	5	6	7	8	9	D
350	54 4068	54 4192	54 4316	54 4440	54 4564	54 4688	54 4812	54 4936	54 5060	54 5183	124
351	5307	5431	5555	5678	5802	5925	6049	6172	6296	6419	124
352	6543	6666	6789	6913	7036	7159	7282	7405	7529	7652	123
353	7775	7898	8021	8144	8267	8389	8512	8635	8758	8881	123
354	9003	9126	9249	9371	9494	9616	9739	9861	9984	55 0106	123
355	55 0228	55 0351	55 0473	55 0595	55 0717	55 0840	55 0962	55 1084	55 1206	1328	122
356	1450	1572	1694	1816	1938	2060	2181	2303	2425	2547	122
357	2668	2790	2911	3033	3155	3276	3398	3519	3640	3762	121
358	3883	4004	4126	4247	4368	4489	4610	4731	4852	4973	121
359	5094	5215	5336	5457	5578	5699	5820	5940	6061	6182	121
360	6303	6423	6544	6664	6785	6905	7026	7146	7267	7387	120
361	7507	7627	7748	7868	7988	8108	8228	8349	8469	8589	120
362	8709	8829	8948	9068	9188	9308	9428	9548	9667	9787	120
363	9907	56 0026	56 0146	56 0265	56 0385	56 0504	56 0624	56 0743	56 0863	56 0982	119
364	56 1101	1221	1340	1459	1578	1698	1817	1936	2055	2174	119
365	2293	2412	2531	2650	2769	2887	3006	3125	3244	3362	119
366	3481	3600	3718	3837	3955	4074	4192	4311	4429	4548	119
367	4666	4784	4903	5021	5139	5257	5376	5494	5612	5730	118
368	5848	5966	6084	6202	6320	6437	6555	6673	6791	6909	118
369	7026	7144	7262	7379	7497	7614	7732	7849	7967	8084	118
370	8202	8319	8436	8554	8671	8788	8905	9023	9140	9257	117
371	9374	9491	9608	9725	9842	9959	57 0076	57 0193	57 0309	57 0426	117
372	57 0543	57 0660	57 0776	57 0893	57 1010	57 1126	1243	1359	1476	1592	117
373	1709	1825	1942	2058	2174	2291	2407	2523	2639	2755	116
374	2872	2988	3104	3220	3336	3452	3568	3684	3800	3915	116
375	4031	4147	4263	4379	4494	4610	4726	4841	4957	5072	116
376	5188	5303	5419	5534	5650	5765	5880	5996	6111	6226	115
377	6341	6457	6572	6687	6802	6917	7032	7147	7262	7377	115
378	7492	7607	7722	7836	7951	8066	8181	8295	8410	8525	115
379	8639	8754	8868	8983	9097	9212	9326	9441	9555	9669	114
380	9784	9898	58 0012	58 0126	58 0241	58 0355	58 0469	58 0583	58 0697	58 0811	114
381	58 0925	58 1039	1153	1267	1381	1495	1608	1722	1836	1950	114
382	2063	2177	2291	2404	2518	2631	2745	2858	2972	3085	114
383	3199	3312	3426	3539	3652	3765	3879	3992	4105	4218	113
384	4331	4444	4557	4670	4783	4896	5009	5122	5235	5348	113
385	5461	5574	5686	5799	5912	6024	6137	6250	6362	6475	113
386	6587	6700	6812	6925	7037	7149	7262	7374	7486	7599	112
387	7711	7823	7935	8047	8160	8272	8384	8496	8608	8720	112
388	8832	8944	9056	9167	9279	9391	9503	9615	9726	9838	112
389	9950	59 0061	59 0173	59 0284	59 0396	59 0507	59 0619	59 0730	59 0842	59 0953	112
390	59 1065	1176	1287	1399	1510	1621	1732	1843	1955	2066	111
391	2177	2288	2399	2510	2621	2732	2843	2954	3064	3175	111
392	3286	3397	3508	3618	3729	3840	3950	4061	4171	4282	111
393	4393	4503	4614	4724	4834	4945	5055	5165	5276	5386	110
394	5496	5606	5717	5827	5937	6047	6157	6267	6377	6487	110
395	6597	6707	6817	6927	7037	7146	7256	7366	7476	7586	110
396	7695	7805	7914	8024	8134	8243	8353	8462	8572	8681	110
397	8791	8900	9009	9119	9228	9337	9446	9556	9665	9774	109
398	9883	9992	60 0101	60 0210	60 0319	60 0428	60 0537	60 0646	60 0755	60 0864	109
399	60 0973	60 1082	1191	1299	1408	1517	1625	1734	1843	1951	109
400	2060	2169	2277	2386	2494	2603	2711	2819	2928	3036	108

n\d	124	123	122
1	12	12	12
2	25	25	24
3	37	37	37
4	50	49	49
5	62	62	61
6	74	74	73
7	87	86	85
8	99	98	98
9	112	111	110

n\d	121	120	119
1	12	12	12
2	24	24	24
3	36	36	36
4	48	48	48
5	61	60	60
6	73	72	71
7	85	84	83
8	97	96	95
9	109	108	107

n\d	118	117	116
1	12	12	12
2	24	23	23
3	35	35	35
4	47	47	46
5	59	59	58
6	71	70	70
7	83	82	81
8	94	94	93
9	106	105	104

n\d	115	114	113
1	12	11	11
2	23	23	23
3	35	34	34
4	46	46	45
5	58	57	57
6	69	68	68
7	81	80	79
8	92	91	90
9	104	103	102

n\d	112	111	110
1	11	11	11
2	22	22	22
3	34	33	33
4	45	44	44
5	56	56	55
6	67	67	66
7	78	78	77
8	90	89	88
9	101	100	99

n\d	109	108
1	11	11
2	22	22
3	33	32
4	44	43
5	55	54
6	65	65
7	76	76
8	87	86
9	98	97

Proportional Part

N	0	1	2	3	4	5	6	7	8	9	D
400	60 2060	60 2169	60 2277	60 2386	60 2494	60 2603	60 2711	60 2819	60 2928	60 3036	108
401	3144	3253	3361	3469	3577	3686	3794	3902	4010	4118	108
402	4226	4334	4442	4550	4658	4766	4874	4982	5089	5197	108
403	5305	5413	5521	5628	5736	5844	5951	6059	6166	6274	108
404	6381	6489	6596	6704	6811	6919	7026	7133	7241	7348	107
405	7455	7562	7669	7777	7884	7991	8098	8205	8312	8419	107
406	8526	8633	8740	8847	8954	9061	9167	9274	9381	9488	107
407	9594	9701	9808	9914	61 0021	61 0128	61 0234	61 0341	61 0447	61 0554	107
408	61 0660	61 0767	61 0873	61 0979	1086	1192	1298	1405	1511	1617	106
409	1723	1829	1936	2042	2148	2254	2360	2466	2572	2678	106
410	2784	2890	2996	3102	3207	3313	3419	3525	3630	3736	106
411	3842	3947	4053	4159	4264	4370	4475	4581	4686	4792	106
412	4897	5003	5108	5213	5319	5424	5529	5634	5740	5845	105
413	5950	6055	6160	6265	6370	6476	6581	6686	6790	6895	105
414	7000	7105	7210	7315	7420	7525	7629	7734	7839	7943	105
415	8048	8153	8257	8362	8466	8571	8676	8780	8884	8989	105
416	9093	9198	9302	9406	9511	9615	9719	9824	9928	62 0032	104
417	62 0136	62 0240	62 0344	62 0448	62 0552	62 0656	62 0760	62 0864	62 0968	1072	104
418	1176	1280	1384	1488	1592	1695	1799	1903	2007	2110	104
419	2214	2318	2421	2525	2628	2732	2835	2939	3042	3146	104
420	3249	3353	3456	3559	3663	3766	3869	3973	4076	4179	103
421	4282	4385	4488	4591	4695	4798	4901	5004	5107	5210	103
422	5312	5415	5518	5621	5724	5827	5929	6032	6135	6238	103
423	6340	6443	6546	6648	6751	6853	6956	7058	7161	7263	103
424	7366	7468	7571	7673	7775	7878	7980	8082	8185	8287	102
425	8389	8491	8593	8695	8797	8900	9002	9104	9206	9308	102
426	9410	9512	9613	9715	9817	9919	63 0021	63 0123	63 0224	63 0326	102
427	63 0428	63 0530	63 0631	63 0733	63 0835	63 0936	1038	1139	1241	1342	102
428	1444	1545	1647	1748	1849	1951	2052	2153	2255	2356	101
429	2457	2559	2660	2761	2862	2963	3064	3165	3266	3367	101
430	3468	3569	3670	3771	3872	3973	4074	4175	4276	4376	101
431	4477	4578	4679	4779	4880	4981	5081	5182	5283	5383	101
432	5484	5584	5685	5785	5886	5986	6087	6187	6287	6388	100
433	6488	6588	6688	6789	6889	6989	7089	7189	7290	7390	100
434	7490	7590	7690	7790	7890	7990	8090	8190	8290	8389	100
435	8489	8589	8689	8789	8888	8988	9088	9188	9287	9387	100
436	9486	9586	9686	9785	9885	9984	64 0084	64 0183	64 0283	64 0382	99
437	64 0481	64 0581	64 0680	64 0779	64 0879	64 0978	1077	1177	1276	1375	99
438	1474	1573	1672	1771	1871	1970	2069	2168	2267	2366	99
439	2465	2563	2662	2761	2860	2959	3058	3156	3255	3354	99
440	3453	3551	3650	3749	3847	3946	4044	4143	4242	4340	98
441	4439	4537	4636	4734	4832	4931	5029	5127	5226	5324	98
442	5422	5521	5619	5717	5815	5913	6011	6110	6208	6306	98
443	6404	6502	6600	6698	6796	6894	6992	7089	7187	7285	98
444	7383	7481	7579	7676	7774	7872	7969	8067	8165	8262	98
445	8360	8458	8555	8653	8750	8848	8945	9043	9140	9237	97
446	9335	9432	9530	9627	9724	9821	9919	65 0016	65 0113	65 0210	97
447	65 0308	65 0405	65 0502	65 0599	65 0696	65 0793	65 0890	0987	1084	1181	97
448	1278	1375	1472	1569	1666	1762	1859	1956	2053	2150	97
449	2246	2343	2440	2536	2633	2730	2826	2923	3019	3116	97
450	3213	3309	3405	3502	3598	3695	3791	3888	3984	4080	96

Proportional Parts (right margin, partly cut off):

n\d	109	108	10_
1	11	11	
2	22	22	
3	33	32	
4	44	43	
5	55	54	
6	65	65	
7	76	76	
8	87	86	
9	98	97	

n\d	106	105	
1	11	11	
2	21	21	
3	32	32	
4	42	42	
5	53	53	
6	64	63	
7	74	74	
8	85	84	
9	95	95	

n\d	103	102
1	10	10
2	21	20
3	31	31
4	41	41
5	52	51
6	62	61
7	72	71
8	82	82
9	93	92

n\d	101	100
1	10	10
2	20	20
3	30	30
4	40	40
5	51	50
6	61	60
7	71	70
8	81	80
9	91	90

n\d	99	98
1	9.9	9.8
2	19.8	19.6
3	29.7	29.4
4	39.6	39.2
5	49.5	49.0
6	59.4	58.8
7	69.3	68.6
8	79.2	78.4
9	89.1	88.2

n\d	97	96
1	9.7	9.6
2	19.4	19._
3	29.1	28.8
4	38.8	38._
5	48.5	48._
6	58.2	57._
7	67.9	67._
8	77.6	76._
9	87.3	86._

N	0	1	2	3	4	5	6	7	8	9	D
450	65 3213	65 3309	65 3405	65 3502	65 3598	65 3695	65 3791	65 3888	65 3984	65 4080	96
451	4177	4273	4369	4465	4562	4658	4754	4850	4946	5042	96
452	5138	5235	5331	5427	5523	5619	5715	5810	5906	6002	96
453	6098	6194	6290	6386	6482	6577	6673	6769	6864	6960	96
454	7056	7152	7247	7343	7438	7534	7629	7725	7820	7916	96
455	8011	8107	8202	8298	8393	8488	8584	8679	8774	8870	95
456	8965	9060	9155	9250	9346	9441	9536	9631	9726	9821	95
457	9916	66 0011	66 0106	66 0201	66 0296	66 0391	66 0486	66 0581	66 0676	66 0771	95
458	66 0865	0960	1055	1150	1245	1339	1434	1529	1623	1718	95
459	1813	1907	2002	2096	2191	2286	2380	2475	2569	2663	95
460	2758	2852	2947	3041	3135	3230	3324	3418	3512	3607	94
461	3701	3795	3889	3983	4078	4172	4266	4360	4454	4548	94
462	4642	4736	4830	4924	5018	5112	5206	5299	5393	5487	94
463	5581	5675	5769	5862	5956	6050	6143	6237	6331	6424	94
464	6518	6612	6705	6799	6892	6986	7079	7173	7266	7360	94
465	7453	7546	7640	7733	7826	7920	8013	8106	8199	8293	93
466	8386	8479	8572	8665	8759	8852	8945	9038	9131	9224	93
467	9317	9410	9503	9596	9689	9782	9875	9967	67 0060	67 0153	93
468	67 0246	67 0339	67 0431	67 0524	67 0617	67 0710	67 0802	67 0895	0988	1080	93
469	1173	1265	1358	1451	1543	1636	1728	1821	1913	2005	93
470	2098	2190	2283	2375	2467	2560	2652	2744	2836	2929	92
471	3021	3113	3205	3297	3390	3482	3574	3666	3758	3850	92
472	3942	4034	4126	4218	4310	4402	4494	4586	4677	4769	92
473	4861	4953	5045	5137	5228	5320	5412	5503	5595	5687	92
474	5778	5870	5962	6053	6145	6236	6328	6419	6511	6602	92
475	6694	6785	6876	6968	7059	7151	7242	7333	7424	7516	91
476	7607	7698	7789	7881	7972	8063	8154	8245	8336	8427	91
477	8518	8609	8700	8791	8882	8973	9064	9155	9246	9337	91
478	9428	9519	9610	9700	9791	9882	9973	68 0063	68 0154	68 0245	91
479	68 0336	68 0426	68 0517	68 0607	68 0698	68 0789	68 0879	0970	1060	1151	91
480	1241	1332	1422	1513	1603	1693	1784	1874	1964	2055	90
481	2145	2235	2326	2416	2506	2596	2686	2777	2867	2957	90
482	3047	3137	3227	3317	3407	3497	3587	3677	3767	3857	90
483	3947	4037	4127	4217	4307	4396	4486	4576	4666	4756	90
484	4845	4935	5025	5114	5204	5294	5383	5473	5563	5652	90
485	5742	5831	5921	6010	6100	6189	6279	6368	6458	6547	89
486	6636	6726	6815	6904	6994	7083	7172	7261	7351	7440	89
487	7529	7618	7707	7796	7886	7975	8064	8153	8242	8331	89
488	8420	8509	8598	8687	8776	8865	8953	9042	9131	9220	89
489	9309	9398	9486	9575	9664	9753	9841	9930	69 0019	69 0107	89
490	69 0196	69 0285	69 0373	69 0462	69 0550	69 0639	69 0728	69 0816	0905	0993	89
491	1081	1170	1258	1347	1435	1524	1612	1700	1789	1877	88
492	1965	2053	2142	2230	2318	2406	2494	2583	2671	2759	88
493	2847	2935	3023	3111	3199	3287	3375	3463	3551	3639	88
494	3727	3815	3903	3991	4078	4166	4254	4342	4430	4517	88
495	4605	4693	4781	4868	4956	5044	5131	5219	5307	5394	88
496	5482	5569	5657	5744	5832	5919	6007	6094	6182	6269	87
497	6356	6444	6531	6618	6706	6793	6880	6968	7055	7142	87
498	7229	7317	7404	7491	7578	7665	7752	7839	7926	8014	87
499	8101	8188	8275	8362	8449	8535	8622	8709	8796	8883	87
500	8970	9057	9144	9231	9317	9404	9491	9578	9664	9751	87

n\d	97	96
1	9.7	9.6
2	19.4	19.2
3	29.1	28.8
4	38.8	38.4
5	48.5	48.0
6	58.2	57.6
7	67.9	67.2
8	77.6	76.8
9	87.3	86.4

n\d	95	94
1	9.5	9.4
2	19.0	18.8
3	28.5	28.2
4	38.0	37.6
5	47.5	47.0
6	57.0	56.4
7	66.5	65.8
8	76.0	75.2
9	85.5	84.6

n\d	93	92
1	9.3	9.2
2	18.6	18.4
3	27.9	27.6
4	37.2	36.8
5	46.5	46.0
6	55.8	55.2
7	65.1	64.4
8	74.4	73.6
9	83.7	82.8

n\d	91	90
1	9.1	9.0
2	18.2	18.0
3	27.3	27.0
4	36.4	36.0
5	45.5	45.0
6	54.6	54.0
7	63.7	63.0
8	72.8	72.0
9	81.9	81.0

n\d	89	88
1	8.9	8.8
2	17.8	17.6
3	26.7	26.4
4	35.6	35.2
5	44.5	44.0
6	53.4	52.8
7	62.3	61.6
8	71.2	70.4
9	80.1	79.2

n\d	87	86
1	8.7	8.6
2	17.4	17.2
3	26.1	25.8
4	34.8	34.4
5	43.5	43.0
6	52.2	51.6
7	60.9	60.2
8	69.6	68.8
9	78.3	77.4

N	0	1	2	3	4	5	6	7	8	9	D
500	69 8970	69 9057	69 9144	69 9231	69 9317	69 9404	69 9491	69 9578	69 9664	69 9751	87
501	9838	9924	70 0011	70 0098	70 0184	70 0271	70 0358	70 0444	70 0531	70 0617	87
502	70 0704	70 0790	0877	0963	1050	1136	1222	1309	1395	1482	86
503	1568	1654	1741	1827	1913	1999	2086	2172	2258	2344	86
504	2431	2517	2603	2689	2775	2861	2947	3033	3119	3205	86
505	3291	3377	3463	3549	3635	3721	3807	3893	3979	4065	86
506	4151	4236	4322	4408	4494	4579	4665	4751	4837	4922	86
507	5008	5094	5179	5265	5350	5436	5522	5607	5693	5778	86
508	5864	5949	6035	6120	6206	6291	6376	6462	6547	6632	85
509	6718	6803	6888	6974	7059	7144	7229	7315	7400	7485	85
510	7570	7655	7740	7826	7911	7996	8081	8166	8251	8336	85
511	8421	8506	8591	8676	8761	8846	8931	9015	9100	9185	85
512	9270	9355	9440	9524	9609	9694	9779	9863	9948	71 0033	85
513	71 0117	71 0202	71 0287	71 0371	71 0456	71 0540	71 0625	71 0710	71 0794	0879	85
514	0963	1048	1132	1217	1301	1385	1470	1554	1639	1723	84
515	1807	1892	1976	2060	2144	2229	2313	2397	2481	2566	84
516	2650	2734	2818	2902	2986	3070	3154	3238	3323	3407	84
517	3491	3575	3659	3742	3826	3910	3994	4078	4162	4246	84
518	4330	4414	4497	4581	4665	4749	4833	4916	5000	5084	84
519	5167	5251	5335	5418	5502	5586	5669	5753	5836	5920	84
520	6003	6087	6170	6254	6337	6421	6504	6588	6671	6754	83
521	6838	6921	7004	7088	7171	7254	7338	7421	7504	7587	83
522	7671	7754	7837	7920	8003	8086	8169	8253	8336	8419	83
523	8502	8585	8668	8751	8834	8917	9000	9083	9165	9248	83
524	9331	9414	9497	9580	9663	9745	9828	9911	9994	72 0077	83
525	72 0159	72 0242	72 0325	72 0407	72 0490	72 0573	72 0655	72 0738	72 0821	0903	83
526	0986	1068	1151	1233	1316	1398	1481	1563	1646	1728	82
527	1811	1893	1975	2058	2140	2222	2305	2387	2469	2552	82
528	2634	2716	2798	2881	2963	3045	3127	3209	3291	3374	82
529	3456	3538	3620	3702	3784	3866	3948	4030	4112	4194	82
530	4276	4358	4440	4522	4604	4685	4767	4849	4931	5013	82
531	5095	5176	5258	5340	5422	5503	5585	5667	5748	5830	82
532	5912	5993	6075	6156	6238	6320	6401	6483	6564	6646	82
533	6727	6809	6890	6972	7053	7134	7216	7297	7379	7460	81
534	7541	7623	7704	7785	7866	7948	8029	8110	8191	8273	81
535	8354	8435	8516	8597	8678	8759	8841	8922	9003	9084	81
536	9165	9246	9327	9408	9489	9570	9651	9732	9813	9893	81
537	9974	73 0055	73 0136	73 0217	73 0298	73 0378	73 0459	73 0540	73 0621	73 0702	81
538	73 0782	0863	0944	1024	1105	1186	1266	1347	1428	1508	81
539	1589	1669	1750	1830	1911	1991	2072	2152	2233	2313	81
540	2394	2474	2555	2635	2715	2796	2876	2956	3037	3117	80
541	3197	3278	3358	3438	3518	3598	3679	3759	3839	3919	80
542	3999	4079	4160	4240	4320	4400	4480	4560	4640	4720	80
543	4800	4880	4960	5040	5120	5200	5279	5359	5439	5519	80
544	5599	5679	5759	5838	5918	5998	6078	6157	6237	6317	80
545	6397	6476	6556	6635	6715	6795	6874	6954	7034	7113	80
546	7193	7272	7352	7431	7511	7590	7670	7749	7829	7908	79
547	7987	8067	8146	8225	8305	8384	8463	8543	8622	8701	79
548	8781	8860	8939	9018	9097	9177	9256	9335	9414	9493	79
549	9572	9651	9731	9810	9889	9968	74 0047	74 0126	74 0205	74 0284	79
550	74 0363	74 0442	74 0521	74 0600	74 0678	74 0757	0836	0915	0994	1073	79

n\d	87	86
1	8.7	8.6
2	17.4	17.2
3	26.1	25.8
4	34.8	34.4
5	43.5	43.0
6	52.2	51.6
7	60.9	60.2
8	69.6	68.8
9	78.3	77.4

n\d	85	84
1	8.5	8.4
2	17.0	16.8
3	25.5	25.2
4	34.0	33.6
5	42.5	42.0
6	51.0	50.4
7	59.5	58.8
8	68.0	67.2
9	76.5	75.6

n\d	83	82
1	8.3	8.2
2	16.6	16.4
3	24.9	24.6
4	33.2	32.8
5	41.5	41.0
6	49.8	49.2
7	58.1	57.4
8	66.4	65.6
9	74.7	73.8

n\d	81	80
1	8.1	8.0
2	16.2	16.0
3	24.3	24.0
4	32.4	32.0
5	40.5	40.0
6	48.6	48.0
7	56.7	56.0
8	64.8	64.0
9	72.9	72.0

n\d	79
1	7.9
2	15.8
3	23.7
4	31.6
5	39.5
6	47.4
7	55.3
8	63.2
9	71.1

N	0	1	2	3	4	5	6	7	8	9	D
550	74 0363	74 0442	74 0521	74 0600	74 0678	74 0757	74 0836	74 0915	74 0994	74 1073	79
551	1152	1230	1309	1388	1467	1546	1624	1703	1782	1860	79
552	1939	2018	2096	2175	2254	2332	2411	2489	2568	2647	79
553	2725	2804	2882	2961	3039	3118	3196	3275	3353	3431	79
554	3510	3588	3667	3745	3823	3902	3980	4058	4136	4215	78
555	4293	4371	4449	4528	4606	4684	4762	4840	4919	4997	78
556	5075	5153	5231	5309	5387	5465	5543	5621	5699	5777	78
557	5855	5933	6011	6089	6167	6245	6323	6401	6479	6556	78
558	6634	6712	6790	6868	6945	7023	7101	7179	7256	7334	78
559	7412	7489	7567	7645	7722	7800	7878	7955	8033	8110	78
560	8188	8266	8343	8421	8498	8576	8653	8731	8808	8885	77
561	8963	9040	9118	9195	9272	9350	9427	9504	9582	9659	77
562	9736	9814	9891	9968	75 0045	75 0123	75 0200	75 0277	75 0354	75 0431	77
563	75 0508	75 0586	75 0663	75 0740	0817	0894	0971	1048	1125	1202	77
564	1279	1356	1433	1510	1587	1664	1741	1818	1895	1972	77
565	2048	2125	2202	2279	2356	2433	2509	2586	2663	2740	77
566	2816	2893	2970	3047	3123	3200	3277	3353	3430	3506	77
567	3583	3660	3736	3813	3889	3966	4042	4119	4195	4272	77
568	4348	4425	4501	4578	4654	4730	4807	4883	4960	5036	76
569	5112	5189	5265	5341	5417	5494	5570	5646	5722	5799	76
570	5875	5951	6027	6103	6180	6256	6332	6408	6484	6560	76
571	6636	6712	6788	6864	6940	7016	7092	7168	7244	7320	76
572	7396	7472	7548	7624	7700	7775	7851	7927	8003	8079	76
573	8155	8230	8306	8382	8458	8533	8609	8685	8761	8836	76
574	8912	8988	9063	9139	9214	9290	9366	9441	9517	9592	76
575	9668	9743	9819	9894	9970	76 0045	76 0121	76 0196	76 0272	76 0347	75
576	76 0422	76 0498	76 0573	76 0649	76 0724	0799	0875	0950	1025	1101	75
577	1176	1251	1326	1402	1477	1552	1627	1702	1778	1853	75
578	1928	2003	2078	2153	2228	2303	2378	2453	2529	2604	75
579	2679	2754	2829	2904	2978	3053	3128	3203	3278	3353	75
580	3428	3503	3578	3653	3727	3802	3877	3952	4027	4101	75
581	4176	4251	4326	4400	4475	4550	4624	4699	4774	4848	75
582	4923	4998	5072	5147	5221	5296	5370	5445	5520	5594	75
583	5669	5743	5818	5892	5966	6041	6115	6190	6264	6338	74
584	6413	6487	6562	6636	6710	6785	6859	6933	7007	7082	74
585	7156	7230	7304	7379	7453	7527	7601	7675	7749	7823	74
586	7898	7972	8046	8120	8194	8268	8342	8416	8490	8564	74
587	8638	8712	8786	8860	8934	9008	9082	9156	9230	9303	74
588	9377	9451	9525	9599	9673	9746	9820	9894	9968	77 0042	74
589	77 0115	77 0189	77 0263	77 0336	77 0410	77 0484	77 0557	77 0631	77 0705	0778	74
590	0852	0926	0999	1073	1146	1220	1293	1367	1440	1514	74
591	1587	1661	1734	1808	1881	1955	2028	2102	2175	2248	73
592	2322	2395	2468	2542	2615	2688	2762	2835	2908	2981	73
593	3055	3128	3201	3274	3348	3421	3494	3567	3640	3713	73
594	3786	3860	3933	4006	4079	4152	4225	4298	4371	4444	73
595	4517	4590	4663	4736	4809	4882	4955	5028	5100	5173	73
596	5246	5319	5392	5465	5538	5610	5683	5756	5829	5902	73
597	5974	6047	6120	6193	6265	6338	6411	6483	6556	6629	73
598	6701	6774	6846	6919	6992	7064	7137	7209	7282	7354	73
599	7427	7499	7572	7644	7717	7789	7862	7934	8006	8079	72
600	8151	8224	8296	8368	8441	8513	8585	8658	8730	8802	72

n\d	79	78
1	7.9	7.8
2	15.8	15.6
3	23.7	23.4
4	31.6	31.2
5	39.5	39.0
6	47.4	46.8
7	55.3	54.6
8	63.2	62.4
9	71.1	70.2

n\d	77	76
1	7.7	7.6
2	15.4	15.2
3	23.1	22.8
4	30.8	30.4
5	38.5	38.0
6	46.2	45.6
7	53.9	53.2
8	61.6	60.8
9	69.3	68.4

n\d	75	74
1	7.5	7.4
2	15.0	14.8
3	22.5	22.2
4	30.0	29.6
5	37.5	37.0
6	45.0	44.4
7	52.5	51.8
8	60.0	59.2
9	67.5	66.6

n\d	73
1	7.3
2	14.6
3	21.9
4	29.2
5	36.5
6	43.8
7	51.1
8	58.4
9	65.7

n\d	72
1	7.2
2	14.4
3	21.6
4	28.8
5	36.0
6	43.2
7	50.4
8	57.6
9	64.8

N	0	1	2	3	4	5	6	7	8	9	D
600	77 8151	77 8224	77 8296	77 8368	77 8441	77 8513	77 8585	77 8658	77 8730	77 8802	72
601	8874	8947	9019	9091	9163	9236	9308	9380	9452	9524	72
602	9596	9669	9741	9813	9885	9957	78 0029	78 0101	78 0173	78 0245	72
603	78 0317	78 0389	78 0461	78 0533	78 0605	78 0677	0749	0821	0893	0965	72
604	1037	1109	1181	1253	1324	1396	1468	1540	1612	1684	72
605	1755	1827	1899	1971	2042	2114	2186	2258	2329	2401	72
606	2473	2544	2616	2688	2759	2831	2902	2974	3046	3117	72
607	3189	3260	3332	3403	3475	3546	3618	3689	3761	3832	71
608	3904	3975	4046	4118	4189	4261	4332	4403	4475	4546	71
609	4617	4689	4760	4831	4902	4974	5045	5116	5187	5259	71
610	5330	5401	5472	5543	5615	5686	5757	5828	5899	5970	71
611	6041	6112	6183	6254	6325	6396	6467	6538	6609	6680	71
612	6751	6822	6893	6964	7035	7106	7177	7248	7319	7390	71
613	7460	7531	7602	7673	7744	7815	7885	7956	8027	8098	71
614	8168	8239	8310	8381	8451	8522	8593	8663	8734	8804	71
615	8875	8946	9016	9087	9157	9228	9299	9369	9440	9510	71
616	9581	9651	9722	9792	9863	9933	79 0004	79 0074	79 0144	79 0215	70
617	79 0285	79 0356	79 0426	79 0496	79 0567	79 0637	0707	0778	0848	0918	70
618	0988	1059	1129	1199	1269	1340	1410	1480	1550	1620	70
619	1691	1761	1831	1901	1971	2041	2111	2181	2252	2322	70
620	2392	2462	2532	2602	2672	2742	2812	2882	2952	3022	70
621	3092	3162	3231	3301	3371	3441	3511	3581	3651	3721	70
622	3790	3860	3930	4000	4070	4139	4209	4279	4349	4418	70
623	4488	4558	4627	4697	4767	4836	4906	4976	5045	5115	70
624	5185	5254	5324	5393	5463	5532	5602	5672	5741	5811	70
625	5880	5949	6019	6088	6158	6227	6297	6366	6436	6505	69
626	6574	6644	6713	6782	6852	6921	6990	7060	7129	7198	69
627	7268	7337	7406	7475	7545	7614	7683	7752	7821	7890	69
628	7960	8029	8098	8167	8236	8305	8374	8443	8513	8582	69
629	8651	8720	8789	8858	8927	8996	9065	9134	9203	9272	69
630	9341	9409	9478	9547	9616	9685	9754	9823	9892	9961	69
631	80 0029	80 0098	80 0167	80 0236	80 0305	80 0373	80 0442	80 0511	80 0580	80 0648	69
632	0717	0786	0854	0923	0992	1061	1129	1198	1266	1335	69
633	1404	1472	1541	1609	1678	1747	1815	1884	1952	2021	69
634	2089	2158	2226	2295	2363	2432	2500	2568	2637	2705	68
635	2774	2842	2910	2979	3047	3116	3184	3252	3321	3389	68
636	3457	3525	3594	3662	3730	3798	3867	3935	4003	4071	68
637	4139	4208	4276	4344	4412	4480	4548	4616	4685	4753	68
638	4821	4889	4957	5025	5093	5161	5229	5297	5365	5433	68
639	5501	5569	5637	5705	5773	5841	5908	5976	6044	6112	68
640	6180	6248	6316	6384	6451	6519	6587	6655	6723	6790	68
641	6858	6926	6994	7061	7129	7197	7264	7332	7400	7467	68
642	7535	7603	7670	7738	7806	7873	7941	8008	8076	8143	68
643	8211	8279	8346	8414	8481	8549	8616	8684	8751	8818	67
644	8886	8953	9021	9088	9156	9223	9290	9358	9425	9492	67
645	9560	9627	9694	9762	9829	9896	9964	81 0031	81 0098	81 0165	67
646	81 0233	81 0300	81 0367	81 0434	81 0501	81 0569	81 0636	0703	0770	0837	67
647	0904	0971	1039	1106	1173	1240	1307	1374	1441	1508	67
648	1575	1642	1709	1776	1843	1910	1977	2044	2111	2178	67
649	2245	2312	2379	2445	2512	2579	2646	2713	2780	2847	67
650	2913	2980	3047	3114	3181	3247	3314	3381	3448	3514	67

n\d	73	72
1	7.3	7.2
2	14.6	14.4
3	21.9	21.6
4	29.2	28.8
5	36.5	36.0
6	43.8	43.2
7	51.1	50.4
8	58.4	57.6
9	65.7	64.8

n\d	71	70
1	7.1	7.0
2	14.2	14.0
3	21.3	21.0
4	28.4	28.0
5	35.5	35.0
6	42.6	42.0
7	49.7	49.0
8	56.8	56.0
9	63.9	63.0

n\d	69	68
1	6.9	6.8
2	13.8	13.6
3	20.7	20.4
4	27.6	27.2
5	34.5	34.0
6	41.4	40.8
7	48.3	47.6
8	55.2	54.4
9	62.1	61.2

n\d	67
1	6.7
2	13.4
3	20.1
4	26.8
5	33.5
6	40.2
7	46.9
8	53.6
9	60.3

n\d	66
1	6.6
2	13.2
3	19.8
4	26.4
5	33.0
6	39.6
7	46.2
8	52.8
9	59.4

N	0	1	2	3	4	5	6	7	8	9	D
650	81 2913	81 2980	81 3047	81 3114	81 3181	81 3247	81 3314	81 3381	81 3448	81 3514	67
651	3581	3648	3714	3781	3848	3914	3981	4048	4114	4181	67
652	4248	4314	4381	4447	4514	4581	4647	4714	4780	4847	67
653	4913	4980	5046	5113	5179	5246	5312	5378	5445	5511	66
654	5578	5644	5711	5777	5843	5910	5976	6042	6109	6175	66
655	6241	6308	6374	6440	6506	6573	6639	6705	6771	6838	66
656	6904	6970	7036	7102	7169	7235	7301	7367	7433	7499	66
657	7565	7631	7698	7764	7830	7896	7962	8028	8094	8160	66
658	8226	8292	8358	8424	8490	8556	8622	8688	8754	8820	66
659	8885	8951	9017	9083	9149	9215	9281	9346	9412	9478	66
660	9544	9610	9676	9741	9807	9873	9939	82 0004	82 0070	82 0136	66
661	82 0201	82 0267	82 0333	82 0399	82 0464	82 0530	82 0595	0661	0727	0792	66
662	0858	0924	0989	1055	1120	1186	1251	1317	1382	1448	66
663	1514	1579	1645	1710	1775	1841	1906	1972	2037	2103	65
664	2168	2233	2299	2364	2430	2495	2560	2626	2691	2756	65
665	2822	2887	2952	3018	3083	3148	3213	3279	3344	3409	65
666	3474	3539	3605	3670	3735	3800	3865	3930	3996	4061	65
667	4126	4191	4256	4321	4386	4451	4516	4581	4646	4711	65
668	4776	4841	4906	4971	5036	5101	5166	5231	5296	5361	65
669	5426	5491	5556	5621	5686	5751	5815	5880	5945	6010	65
670	6075	6140	6204	6269	6334	6399	6464	6528	6593	6658	65
671	6723	6787	6852	6917	6981	7046	7111	7175	7240	7305	65
672	7369	7434	7499	7563	7628	7692	7757	7821	7886	7951	65
673	8015	8080	8144	8209	8273	8338	8402	8467	8531	8595	64
674	8660	8724	8789	8853	8918	8982	9046	9111	9175	9239	64
675	9304	9368	9432	9497	9561	9625	9690	9754	9818	9882	64
676	9947	83 0011	83 0075	83 0139	83 0204	83 0268	83 0332	83 0396	83 0460	83 0525	64
677	83 0589	0653	0717	0781	0845	0909	0973	1037	1102	1166	64
678	1230	1294	1358	1422	1486	1550	1614	1678	1742	1806	64
679	1870	1934	1998	2062	2126	2189	2253	2317	2381	2445	64
680	2509	2573	2637	2700	2764	2828	2892	2956	3020	3083	64
681	3147	3211	3275	3338	3402	3466	3530	3593	3657	3721	64
682	3784	3848	3912	3975	4039	4103	4166	4230	4294	4357	64
683	4421	4484	4548	4611	4675	4739	4802	4866	4929	4993	64
684	5056	5120	5183	5247	5310	5373	5437	5500	5564	5627	63
685	5691	5754	5817	5881	5944	6007	6071	6134	6197	6261	63
686	6324	6387	6451	6514	6577	6641	6704	6767	6830	6894	63
687	6957	7020	7083	7146	7210	7273	7336	7399	7462	7525	63
688	7588	7652	7715	7778	7841	7904	7967	8030	8093	8156	63
689	8219	8282	8345	8408	8471	8534	8597	8660	8723	8786	63
690	8849	8912	8975	9038	9101	9164	9227	9289	9352	9415	63
691	9478	9541	9604	9667	9729	9792	9855	9918	9981	84 0043	63
692	84 0106	84 0169	84 0232	84 0294	84 0357	84 0420	84 0482	84 0545	84 0608	0671	63
693	0733	0796	0859	0921	0984	1046	1109	1172	1234	1297	63
694	1359	1422	1485	1547	1610	1672	1735	1797	1860	1922	63
695	1985	2047	2110	2172	2235	2297	2360	2422	2484	2547	62
696	2609	2672	2734	2796	2859	2921	2983	3046	3108	3170	62
697	3233	3295	3357	3420	3482	3544	3606	3669	3731	3793	62
698	3855	3918	3980	4042	4104	4166	4229	4291	4353	4415	62
699	4477	4539	4601	4664	4726	4788	4850	4912	4974	5036	62
700	5098	5160	5222	5284	5346	5408	5470	5532	5594	5656	62

Proportional Parts

n\d 67		n\d 66		n\d 65		n\d 64		n\d 63		n\d 62	
1	6.7	1	6.6	1	6.5	1	6.4	1	6.3	1	6.2
2	13.4	2	13.2	2	13.0	2	12.8	2	12.6	2	12.4
3	20.1	3	19.8	3	19.5	3	19.2	3	18.9	3	18.6
4	26.8	4	26.4	4	26.0	4	25.6	4	25.2	4	24.8
5	33.5	5	33.0	5	32.5	5	32.0	5	31.5	5	31.0
6	40.2	6	39.6	6	39.0	6	38.4	6	37.8	6	37.2
7	46.9	7	46.2	7	45.5	7	44.8	7	44.1	7	43.4
8	53.6	8	52.8	8	52.0	8	51.2	8	50.4	8	49.6
9	60.3	9	59.4	9	58.5	9	57.6	9	56.7	9	55.8

Proportional Part

N	0	1	2	3	4	5	6	7	8	9	D
700	84 5098	84 5160	84 5222	84 5284	84 5346	84 5408	84 5470	84 5532	84 5594	84 5656	62
701	5718	5780	5842	5904	5966	6028	6090	6151	6213	6275	62
702	6337	6399	6461	6523	5685	6646	6708	6770	6832	6894	62
703	6955	7017	7079	7141	7202	7264	7326	7388	7449	7511	62
704	7573	7634	7696	7758	7819	7881	7943	8004	8066	8128	62
705	8189	8251	8312	8374	8435	8497	8559	8620	8682	8743	62
706	8805	8866	8928	8989	9051	9112	9174	9235	9297	9358	61
707	9419	9481	9542	9604	9665	9726	9788	9849	9911	9972	61
708	85 0033	85 0095	85 0156	85 0217	85 0279	85 0340	85 0401	85 0462	85 0524	85 0585	61
709	0646	0707	0769	0830	0891	0952	1014	1075	1136	1197	61
710	1258	1320	1381	1442	1503	1564	1625	1686	1747	1809	61
711	1870	1931	1992	2053	2114	2175	2236	2297	2358	2419	61
712	2480	2541	2602	2663	2724	2785	2846	2907	2968	3029	61
713	3090	3150	3211	3272	3333	3394	3455	3516	3577	3637	61
714	3698	3759	3820	3881	3941	4002	4063	4124	4185	4245	61
715	4306	4367	4428	4488	4549	4610	4670	4731	4792	4852	61
716	4913	4974	5034	5095	5156	5216	5277	5337	5398	5459	61
717	5519	5580	5640	5701	5761	5822	5882	5943	6003	6064	61
718	6124	6185	6245	6306	6366	6427	6487	6548	6608	6668	60
719	6729	6789	6850	6910	6970	7031	7091	7152	7212	7272	60
720	7332	7393	7453	7513	7574	7634	7694	7755	7815	7875	60
721	7935	7995	8056	8116	8176	8236	8297	8357	8417	8477	60
722	8537	8597	8657	8718	8778	8838	8898	8958	9018	9078	60
723	9138	9198	9258	9318	9379	9439	9499	9559	9619	9679	60
724	9739	9799	9859	9918	9978	86 0038	86 0098	86 0158	86 0218	86 0278	60
725	86 0338	86 0398	86 0458	86 0518	86 0578	0637	0697	0757	0817	0877	60
726	0937	0996	1056	1116	1176	1236	1295	1355	1415	1475	60
727	1534	1594	1654	1714	1773	1833	1893	1952	2012	2072	60
728	2131	2191	2251	2310	2370	2430	2489	2549	2608	2668	60
729	2728	2787	2847	2906	2966	3025	3085	3144	3204	3263	60
730	3323	3382	3442	3501	3561	3620	3680	3739	3799	3858	59
731	3917	3977	4036	4096	4155	4214	4274	4333	4392	4452	59
732	4511	4570	4630	4689	4748	4808	4867	4926	4985	5045	59
733	5104	5163	5222	5282	5341	5400	5459	5519	5578	5637	59
734	5696	5755	5814	5874	5933	5992	6051	6110	6169	6228	59
735	6287	6346	6405	6465	6524	6583	6642	6701	6760	6819	59
736	6878	6937	6996	7055	7114	7173	7232	7291	7350	7409	59
737	7467	7526	7585	7644	7703	7762	7821	7880	7939	7998	59
738	8056	8115	8174	8233	8292	8350	8409	8468	8527	8586	59
739	8644	8703	8762	8821	8879	8938	8997	9056	9114	9173	59
740	9232	9290	9349	9408	9466	9525	9584	9642	9701	9760	59
741	9818	9877	9935	9994	87 0053	87 0111	87 0170	87 0228	87 0287	87 0345	59
742	87 0404	87 0462	87 0521	87 0579	0638	0696	0755	0813	0872	0930	58
743	0989	1047	1106	1164	1223	1281	1339	1398	1456	1515	58
744	1573	1631	1690	1748	1806	1865	1923	1981	2040	2098	58
745	2156	2215	2273	2331	2389	2448	2506	2564	2622	2681	58
746	2739	2797	2855	2913	2972	3030	3088	3146	3204	3262	58
747	3321	3379	3437	3495	3553	3611	3669	3727	3785	3844	58
748	3902	3960	4018	4076	4134	4192	4250	4308	4366	4424	58
749	4482	4540	4598	4656	4714	4772	4830	4888	4945	5003	58
750	5061	5119	5177	5235	5293	5351	5409	5466	5524	5582	58

n\d	62	61
1	6.2	6.1
2	12.4	12.2
3	18.6	18.3
4	24.8	24.4
5	31.0	30.5
6	37.2	36.6
7	43.4	42.7
8	49.6	48.8
9	55.8	54.9

n\d	60
1	6.0
2	12.0
3	18.0
4	24.0
5	30.0
6	36.0
7	42.0
8	48.0
9	54.0

n\d	59
1	5.9
2	11.8
3	17.7
4	23.6
5	29.5
6	35.4
7	41.3
8	47.2
9	53.1

n\d	58
1	5.8
2	11.6
3	17.4
4	23.2
5	29.0
6	34.8
7	40.6
8	46.4
9	52.2

n\d	57
1	5.7
2	11.4
3	17.1
4	22.8
5	28.5
6	34.2
7	39.9
8	45.6
9	51.3

Six-Place Logarithms of Numbers 750-800

N	0	1	2	3	4	5	6	7	8	9	D
750	87 5061	87 5119	87 5177	87 5235	87 5293	87 5351	87 5409	87 5466	87 5524	87 5582	58
751	5640	5698	5756	5813	5871	5929	5987	6045	6102	6160	58
752	6218	6276	6333	6391	6449	6507	6564	6622	6680	6737	58
753	6795	6853	6910	6968	7026	7083	7141	7199	7256	7314	58
754	7371	7429	7487	7544	7602	7659	7717	7774	7832	7889	58
755	7947	8004	8062	8119	8177	8234	8292	8349	8407	8464	57
756	8522	8579	8637	8694	8752	8809	8866	8924	8981	9039	57
757	9096	9153	9211	9268	9325	9383	9440	9497	9555	9612	57
758	9669	9726	9784	9841	9898	9956	88 0013	88 0070	88 0127	88 0185	57
759	88 0242	88 0299	88 0356	88 0413	88 0471	88 0528	0585	0642	0699	0756	57
760	0814	0871	0928	0985	1042	1099	1156	1213	1271	1328	57
761	1385	1442	1499	1556	1613	1670	1727	1784	1841	1898	57
762	1955	2012	2069	2126	2183	2240	2297	2354	2411	2468	57
763	2525	2581	2638	2695	2752	2809	2866	2923	2980	3037	57
764	3093	3150	3207	3264	3321	3377	3434	3491	3548	3605	57
765	3661	3718	3775	3832	3888	3945	4002	4059	4115	4172	57
766	4229	4285	4342	4399	4455	4512	4569	4625	4682	4739	57
767	4795	4852	4909	4965	5022	5078	5135	5192	5248	5305	57
768	5361	5418	5474	5531	5587	5644	5700	5757	5813	5870	57
769	5926	5983	6039	6096	6152	6209	6265	6321	6378	6434	56
770	6491	6547	6604	6660	6716	6773	6829	6885	6942	6998	56
771	7054	7111	7167	7223	7280	7336	7392	7449	7505	7561	56
772	7617	7674	7730	7786	7842	7898	7955	8011	8067	8123	56
773	8179	8236	8292	8348	8404	8460	8516	8573	8629	8685	56
774	8741	8797	8853	8909	8965	9021	9077	9134	9190	9246	56
775	9302	9358	9414	9470	9526	9582	9638	9694	9750	9806	56
776	9862	9918	9974	89 0030	89 0086	89 0141	89 0197	89 0253	89 0309	89 0365	56
777	89 0421	89 0477	89 0533	0589	0645	0700	0756	0812	0868	0924	56
778	0980	1035	1091	1147	1203	1259	1314	1370	1426	1482	56
779	1537	1593	1649	1705	1760	1816	1872	1928	1983	2039	56
780	2095	2150	2206	2262	2317	2373	2429	2484	2540	2595	56
781	2651	2707	2762	2818	2873	2929	2985	3040	3096	3151	56
782	3207	3262	3318	3373	3429	3484	3540	3595	3651	3706	56
783	3762	3817	3873	3928	3984	4039	4094	4150	4205	4261	55
784	4316	4371	4427	4482	4538	4593	4648	4704	4759	4814	55
785	4870	4925	4980	5036	5091	5146	5201	5257	5312	5367	55
786	5423	5478	5533	5588	5644	5699	5754	5809	5864	5920	55
787	5975	6030	6085	6140	6195	6251	6306	6361	6416	6471	55
788	6526	6581	6636	6692	6747	6802	6857	6912	6967	7022	55
789	7077	7132	7187	7242	7297	7352	7407	7462	7517	7572	55
790	7627	7682	7737	7792	7847	7902	7957	8012	8067	8122	55
791	8176	8231	8286	8341	8396	8451	8506	8561	8615	8670	55
792	8725	8780	8835	8890	8944	8999	9054	9109	9164	9218	55
793	9273	9328	9383	9437	9492	9547	9602	9656	9711	9766	55
794	9821	9875	9930	9985	90 0039	90 0094	90 0149	90 0203	90 0258	90 0312	55
795	90 0367	90 0422	90 0476	90 0531	0586	0640	0695	0749	0804	0859	55
796	0913	0968	1022	1077	1131	1186	1240	1295	1349	1404	55
797	1458	1513	1567	1622	1676	1731	1785	1840	1894	1948	54
798	2003	2057	2112	2166	2221	2275	2329	2384	2438	2492	54
799	2547	2601	2655	2710	2764	2818	2873	2927	2981	3036	54
800	3090	3144	3199	3253	3307	3361	3416	3470	3524	3578	54

Proportional Parts

n\d 58	n\d 57	n\d 56	n\d 55	n\d 54
1 5.8	1 5.7	1 5.6	1 5.5	1 5.4
2 11.6	2 11.4	2 11.2	2 11.0	2 10.8
3 17.4	3 17.1	3 16.8	3 16.5	3 16.2
4 23.2	4 22.8	4 22.4	4 22.0	4 21.6
5 29.0	5 28.5	5 28.0	5 27.5	5 27.0
6 34.8	6 34.2	6 33.6	6 33.0	6 32.4
7 40.6	7 39.9	7 39.2	7 38.5	7 37.8
8 46.4	8 45.6	8 44.8	8 44.0	8 43.2
9 52.2	9 51.3	9 50.4	9 49.5	9 48.6

Proportional Parts

N	0	1	2	3	4	5	6	7	8	9	D
800	90 3090	90 3144	90 3199	90 3253	90 3307	90 3361	90 3416	90 3470	90 3524	90 3578	54
801	3633	3687	3741	3795	3849	3904	3958	4012	4066	4120	54
802	4174	4229	4283	4337	4391	4445	4499	4553	4607	4661	54
803	4716	4770	4824	4878	4932	4986	5040	5094	5148	5202	54
804	5256	5310	5364	5418	5472	5526	5580	5634	5688	5742	54
805	5796	5850	5904	5958	6012	6066	6119	6173	6227	6281	54
806	6335	6389	6443	6497	6551	6604	6658	6712	6766	6820	54
807	6874	6927	6981	7035	7089	7143	7196	7250	7304	7358	54
808	7411	7465	7519	7573	7626	7680	7734	7787	7841	7895	54
809	7949	8002	8056	8110	8163	8217	8270	8324	8378	8431	54
810	8485	8539	8592	8646	8699	8753	8807	8860	8914	8967	54
811	9021	9074	9128	9181	9235	9289	9342	9396	9449	9503	54
812	9556	9610	9663	9716	9770	9823	9877	9930	9984	91 0037	53
813	91 0091	91 0144	91 0197	91 0251	91 0304	91 0358	91 0411	91 0464	91 0518	0571	53
814	0624	0678	0731	0784	0838	0891	0944	0998	1051	1104	53
815	1158	1211	1264	1317	1371	1424	1477	1530	1584	1637	53
816	1690	1743	1797	1850	1903	1956	2009	2063	2116	2169	53
817	2222	2275	2328	2381	2435	2488	2541	2594	2647	2700	53
818	2753	2806	2859	2913	2966	3019	3072	3125	3178	3231	53
819	3284	3337	3390	3443	3496	3549	3602	3655	3708	3761	53
820	3814	3867	3920	3973	4026	4079	4132	4184	4237	4290	53
821	4343	4396	4449	4502	4555	4608	4660	4713	4766	4819	53
822	4872	4925	4977	5030	5083	5136	5189	5241	5294	5347	53
823	5400	5453	5505	5558	5611	5664	5716	5769	5822	5875	53
824	5927	5980	6033	6085	6138	6191	6243	6296	6349	6401	53
825	6454	6507	6559	6612	6664	6717	6770	6822	6875	6927	53
826	6980	7033	7085	7138	7190	7243	7295	7348	7400	7453	53
827	7506	7558	7611	7663	7716	7768	7820	7873	7925	7978	52
828	8030	8083	8135	8188	8240	8293	8345	8397	8450	8502	52
829	8555	8607	8659	8712	8764	8816	8869	8921	8973	9026	52
830	9078	9130	9183	9235	9287	9340	9392	9444	9496	9549	52
831	9601	9653	9706	9758	9810	9862	9914	9967	92 0019	92 0071	52
832	92 0123	92 0176	92 0228	92 0280	92 0332	92 0384	92 0436	92 0489	0541	0593	52
833	0645	0697	0749	0801	0853	0906	0958	1010	1062	1114	52
834	1166	1218	1270	1322	1374	1426	1478	1530	1582	1634	52
835	1686	1738	1790	1842	1894	1946	1998	2050	2102	2154	52
836	2206	2258	2310	2362	2414	2466	2518	2570	2622	2674	52
837	2725	2777	2829	2881	2933	2985	3037	3089	3140	3192	52
838	3244	3296	3348	3399	3451	3503	3555	3607	3658	3710	52
839	3762	3814	3865	3917	3969	4021	4072	4124	4176	4228	52
840	4279	4331	4383	4434	4486	4538	4589	4641	4693	4744	52
841	4796	4848	4899	4951	5003	5054	5106	5157	5209	5261	52
842	5312	5364	5415	5467	5518	5570	5621	5673	5725	5776	52
843	5828	5879	5931	5982	6034	6085	6137	6188	6240	6291	51
844	6342	6394	6445	6497	6548	6600	6651	6702	6754	6805	51
845	6857	6908	6959	7011	7062	7114	7165	7216	7268	7319	51
846	7370	7422	7473	7524	7576	7627	7678	7730	7781	7832	51
847	7883	7935	7986	8037	8088	8140	8191	8242	8293	8345	51
848	8396	8447	8498	8549	8601	8652	8703	8754	8805	8857	51
849	8908	8959	9010	9061	9112	9163	9215	9266	9317	9368	51
850	9419	9470	9521	9572	9623	9674	9725	9776	9827	9879	51

n\d	55
1	5.5
2	11.0
3	16.5
4	22.0
5	27.5
6	33.0
7	38.5
8	44.0
9	49.5

n\d	54
1	5.4
2	10.8
3	16.2
4	21.6
5	27.0
6	32.4
7	37.8
8	43.2
9	48.6

n\d	53
1	5.3
2	10.6
3	15.9
4	21.2
5	26.5
6	31.8
7	37.1
8	42.4
9	47.7

n\d	52
1	5.2
2	10.4
3	15.6
4	20.8
5	26.0
6	31.2
7	36.4
8	41.6
9	46.8

n\d	51
1	5.1
2	10.2
3	15.3
4	20.4
5	25.5
6	30.6
7	35.7
8	40.8
9	45.9

N	0	1	2	3	4	5	6	7	8	9	D
950	97 7724	97 7769	97 7815	97 7861	97 7906	97 7952	97 7998	97 8043	97 8089	97 8135	46
951	8181	8226	8272	8317	8363	8409	8454	8500	8546	8591	46
952	8637	8683	8728	8774	8819	8865	8911	8956	9002	9047	46
953	9093	9138	9184	9230	9275	9321	9366	9412	9457	9503	46
954	9548	9594	9639	9685	9730	9776	9821	9867	9912	9958	46
955	98 0003	98 0049	98 0094	98 0140	98 0185	98 0231	98 0276	98 0322	98 0367	98 0412	45
956	0458	0503	0549	0594	0640	0685	0730	0776	0821	0867	45
957	0912	0957	1003	1048	1093	1139	1184	1229	1275	1320	45
958	1366	1411	1456	1501	1547	1592	1637	1683	1728	1773	45
959	1819	1864	1909	1954	2000	2045	2090	2135	2181	2226	45
960	2271	2316	2362	2407	2452	2497	2543	2588	2633	2678	45
961	2723	2769	2814	2859	2904	2949	2994	3040	3085	3130	45
962	3175	3220	3265	3310	3356	3401	3446	3491	3536	3581	45
963	3626	3671	3716	3762	3807	3852	3897	3942	3987	4032	45
964	4077	4122	4167	4212	4257	4302	4347	4392	4437	4482	45
965	4527	4572	4617	4662	4707	4752	4797	4842	4887	4932	45
966	4977	5022	5067	5112	5157	5202	5247	5292	5337	5382	45
967	5426	5471	5516	5561	5606	5651	5696	5741	5786	5830	45
968	5875	5920	5965	6010	6055	6100	6144	6189	6234	6279	45
969	6324	6369	6413	6458	6503	6548	6593	6637	6682	6727	45
970	6772	6817	6861	6906	6951	6996	7040	7085	7130	7175	45
971	7219	7264	7309	7353	7398	7443	7488	7532	7577	7622	45
972	7666	7711	7756	7800	7845	7890	7934	7979	8024	8068	45
973	8113	8157	8202	8247	8291	8336	8381	8425	8470	8514	45
974	8559	8604	8648	8693	8737	8782	8826	8871	8916	8960	45
975	9005	9049	9094	9138	9183	9227	9272	9316	9361	9405	45
976	9450	9494	9539	9583	9628	9672	9717	9761	9806	9850	44
977	9895	9939	9983	99 0028	99 0072	99 0117	99 0161	99 0206	99 0250	99 0294	44
978	99 0339	99 0383	99 0428	0472	0516	0561	0605	0650	0694	0738	44
979	0783	0827	0871	0916	0960	1004	1049	1093	1137	1182	44
980	1226	1270	1315	1359	1403	1448	1492	1536	1580	1625	44
981	1669	1713	1758	1802	1846	1890	1935	1979	2023	2067	44
982	2111	2156	2200	2244	2288	2333	2377	2421	2465	2509	44
983	2554	2598	2642	2686	2730	2774	2819	2863	2907	2951	44
984	2995	3039	3083	3127	3172	3216	3260	3304	3348	3392	44
985	3436	3480	3524	3568	3613	3657	3701	3745	3789	3833	44
986	3877	3921	3965	4009	4053	4097	4141	4185	4229	4273	44
987	4317	4361	4405	4449	4493	4537	4581	4625	4669	4713	44
988	4757	4801	4845	4889	4933	4977	5021	5065	5108	5152	44
989	5196	5240	5284	5328	5372	5416	5460	5504	5547	5591	44
990	5635	5679	5723	5767	5811	5854	5898	5942	5986	6030	44
991	6074	6117	6161	6205	6249	6293	6337	6380	6424	6468	44
992	6512	6555	6599	6643	6687	6731	6774	6818	6862	6906	44
993	6949	6993	7037	7080	7124	7168	7212	7255	7299	7343	44
994	7386	7430	7474	7517	7561	7605	7648	7692	7736	7779	44
995	7823	7867	7910	7954	7998	8041	8085	8129	8172	8216	44
996	8259	8303	8347	8390	8434	8477	8521	8564	8608	8652	44
997	8695	8739	8782	8826	8869	8913	8956	9000	9043	9087	44
998	9131	9174	9218	9261	9305	9348	9392	9435	9479	9522	44
999	9565	9609	9652	9696	9739	9783	9826	9870	9913	9957	43
1000	00 0000	00 0043	00 0087	00 0130	00 0174	00 0217	00 0260	00 0304	00 0347	00 0391	43

Proportional Parts

n\d	46
1	4.6
2	9.2
3	13.8
4	18.4
5	23.0
6	27.6
7	32.2
8	36.8
9	41.4

n\d	45
1	4.5
2	9.0
3	13.5
4	18.0
5	22.5
6	27.0
7	31.5
8	36.0
9	40.5

n\d	44
1	4.4
2	8.8
3	13.2
4	17.6
5	22.0
6	26.4
7	30.8
8	35.2
9	39.6

n\d	43
1	4.3
2	8.6
3	12.9
4	17.2
5	21.5
6	25.8
7	30.1
8	34.4
9	38.7

Table 8

Reciprocals

n	$1/n$	n	$1/n$ .0	n	$1/n$ .0	n	$1/n$ .00	n	$1/n$ .00
0	∞	50	2000000	100	10000000	150	6666667	200	5000000
1	1.0000000	51	1960784	101	09900990	151	6622517	201	4975124
2	.5000000	52	1923077	102	09803922	152	6578947	202	4950495
3	.3333333	53	1886792	103	09708738	153	6535948	203	4926108
4	.2500000	54	1851852	104	09615385	154	6493506	204	4901961
5	.2000000	55	1818182	105	09523810	155	6451613	205	4878049
6	.1666667	56	1785714	106	09433962	156	6410256	206	4854369
7	.1428571	57	1754386	107	09345794	157	6369427	207	4830918
8	.1250000	58	1724138	108	09259259	158	6329114	208	4807692
9	.1111111	59	1694915	109	09174312	159	6289308	209	4784689
10	.1000000	60	1666667	110	09090909	160	6250000	210	4761905
11	.09090909	61	1639344	111	09009009	161	6211180	211	4739336
12	.08333333	62	1612903	112	08928571	162	6172840	212	4716981
13	.07692308	63	1587302	113	08849558	163	6134969	213	4694836
14	.07142857	64	1562500	114	08771930	164	6097561	214	4672897
15	.06666667	65	1538462	115	08695652	165	6060606	215	4651163
16	.06250000	66	1515152	116	08620690	166	6024096	216	4629630
17	.05882353	67	1492537	117	08547009	167	5988024	217	4608295
18	.05555556	68	1470588	118	08474576	168	5952381	218	4587156
19	.05263158	69	1449275	119	08403361	169	5917160	219	4566210
20	.05000000	70	1428571	120	08333333	170	5882353	220	4545455
21	.04761905	71	1408451	121	08264463	171	5847953	221	4524887
22	.04545455	72	1388889	122	08196721	172	5813953	222	4504505
23	.04347826	73	1369863	123	08130081	173	5780347	223	4484305
24	.04166667	74	1351351	124	08064516	174	5747126	224	4464286
25	.04000000	75	1333333	125	08000000	175	5714286	225	4444444
26	.03846154	76	1315789	126	07936508	176	5681818	226	4424779
27	.03703704	77	1298701	127	07874016	177	5649718	227	4405286
28	.03571429	78	1282051	128	07812500	178	5617978	228	4385965
29	.03448276	79	1265823	129	07751938	179	5586592	229	4366812
30	.03333333	80	1250000	130	07692308	180	5555556	230	4347826
31	.03225806	81	1234568	131	07633588	181	5524862	231	4329004
32	.03125000	82	1219512	132	07575758	182	5494505	232	4310345
33	.03030303	83	1204819	133	07518797	183	5464481	233	4291845
34	.02941176	84	1190476	134	07462687	184	5434783	234	4273504
35	.02857143	85	1176471	135	07407407	185	5405405	235	4255319
36	.02777778	86	1162791	136	07352941	186	5376344	236	4237288
37	.02702703	87	1149425	137	07299270	187	5347594	237	4219409
38	.02631579	88	1136364	138	07246377	188	5319149	238	4201681
39	.02564103	89	1123596	139	07194245	189	5291005	239	4184100
40	.02500000	90	1111111	140	07142857	190	5263158	240	4166667
41	.02439024	91	1098901	141	07092199	191	5235602	241	4149378
42	.02380952	92	1086957	142	07042254	192	5208333	242	4132231
43	.02325581	92	1075269	143	06993007	193	5181347	243	4115226
44	.02272727	94	1063830	144	06944444	194	5154639	244	4098361
45	.02222222	95	1052632	145	06896552	195	5128205	245	4081633
46	.02173913	96	1041667	146	06849315	196	5102041	246	4065041
47	.02127660	97	1030928	147	06802721	197	5076142	247	4048583
48	.02083333	98	1020408	148	06756757	198	5050505	248	4032258
49	.02040816	99	1010101	149	06711409	199	5025126	249	4016064
50	.02000000	100	1000000	150	06666667	200	5000000	250	4000000

Table 8 (*Continued*)

n	1/n .00	n	1/n .00	n	1/n .00	n	1/n .00	n	1/n .00
250	4000000	300	3333333	350	2857143	400	2500000	450	2222222
251	3984064	301	3322259	351	2849003	401	2493766	451	2217295
252	3968254	302	3311258	352	2840909	402	2487562	452	2212389
253	3952569	303	3300330	353	2832861	403	2481390	453	2207506
254	3937008	304	3289474	354	2824859	404	2475248	454	2202643
255	3921569	305	3278689	355	2816901	405	2469136	455	2197802
256	3906250	306	3267974	356	2808989	406	2463054	456	2192982
257	3891051	307	3257329	357	2801120	407	2457002	457	2188184
258	3875969	308	3246753	358	2793296	408	2450980	458	2183406
259	3861004	309	3236246	359	2785515	409	2444988	459	2178649
260	3846154	310	3225806	360	2777778	410	2439024	460	2173913
261	3831418	311	3215434	361	2770083	411	2433090	461	2169197
262	3816794	312	3205128	362	2762431	412	2427184	462	2164502
263	3802281	313	3194888	363	2754821	413	2421308	463	2159827
264	3787879	314	3184713	364	2747253	414	2415459	464	2155172
265	3773585	315	3174603	365	2739726	415	2409639	465	2150538
266	3759398	316	3164557	376	2732240	416	2403846	466	2145923
267	3745318	317	3154574	367	2724796	417	2398082	467	2141328
268	3731343	318	3144654	368	2717391	418	2392344	468	2136752
269	3717472	319	3134796	369	2710027	419	2386635	469	2132196
270	3703704	320	3125000	370	2702703	420	2380952	470	2127660
271	3690037	321	3115265	371	2695418	421	2375297	471	2123142
272	3676471	322	3105590	372	2688172	422	2369668	472	2118644
273	3663004	323	3095975	373	2680965	423	2364066	473	2114165
274	3649635	324	3086420	374	2673797	424	2358491	474	2109705
275	3636364	325	3076923	375	2666667	425	2352941	475	2105263
276	3623188	326	3067485	376	2659574	426	2347418	476	2100840
277	3610108	327	3058104	377	2652520	427	2341920	477	2096436
278	3597122	328	3048780	378	2645503	428	2336449	478	2092050
279	3584229	329	3039514	379	2638522	429	2331002	479	2087683
280	3571429	330	3030303	380	2631579	430	2325581	480	2083333
281	3558719	331	3021148	381	2624672	431	2320186	481	2079002
282	3546099	332	3012048	382	2617801	432	2314815	482	2074689
283	3533569	333	3003003	383	2610966	433	2309469	483	2070393
284	3521127	334	2994012	384	2604167	434	2304147	484	2066116
285	3508772	335	2985075	385	2597403	435	2298851	485	2061856
286	3496503	336	2976190	386	2590674	436	2293578	486	2057613
287	3484321	337	2967359	387	2583979	437	2288330	487	2053388
288	3472222	338	2958580	388	2577320	438	2283105	488	2049180
289	3460208	339	2949853	389	2570694	439	2277904	489	2044990
290	3448276	340	2941176	390	2564103	440	2272727	490	2040816
291	3436426	341	2932551	391	2557545	441	2267574	491	2036660
292	3424658	342	2923977	392	2551020	442	2262443	492	2032520
293	3412969	343	2915452	393	2544529	443	2257336	493	2028398
294	3401361	344	2906977	394	2538071	444	2252252	494	2024291
295	3389831	345	2898551	395	2531646	445	2247191	495	2020202
296	3378378	346	2890173	396	2525253	446	2242152	496	2016129
297	3367003	347	2881844	397	2518892	447	2237136	497	2012072
298	3355705	348	2873563	398	2512563	448	2232143	498	2008032
299	3344482	349	2865330	399	2506266	449	2227171	499	2004008
300	3333333	350	2857143	400	2500000	450	2222222	500	2000000

Table 8 (*Continued*)

n	$1/n$ .00	n	$1/n$ .00	n	$1/n$ .00	n	$1/n$ .00	n	$1/n$ .00
500	2000000	550	1818182	600	1666667	650	1538462	700	1428571
501	1996008	551	1814882	601	1663894	651	1536098	701	1426534
502	1992032	552	1811594	602	1661130	652	1533742	702	1424501
503	1988072	553	1808318	603	1658375	653	1531394	703	1422475
504	1984127	554	1805054	604	1655629	654	1529052	704	1420455
505	1980198	555	1801802	605	1652893	655	1526718	705	1418440
506	1976285	556	1798561	606	1650165	656	1524390	706	1416431
507	1972387	557	1795332	607	1647446	657	1522070	707	1414427
508	1968504	558	1792115	608	1644737	658	1519757	708	1412429
509	1964637	559	1788909	609	1642036	659	1517451	709	1410437
510	1960784	560	1785714	610	1639344	660	1515152	710	1408451
511	1956947	561	1782531	611	1636661	661	1512859	711	1406470
512	1953125	562	1779359	612	1633987	662	1510574	712	1404494
513	1949318	563	1776199	613	1631321	663	1508296	713	1402525
514	1945525	564	1773050	614	1628664	664	1506024	714	1400560
515	1941748	565	1769912	615	1626016	665	1503759	715	1398601
516	1937934	566	1766784	616	1623377	666	1501502	716	1396648
517	1934236	567	1763668	617	1620746	667	1499250	717	1394700
518	1930502	568	1760563	618	1618123	668	1497006	718	1392758
519	1926782	569	1757469	619	1615509	669	1494768	719	1390821
520	1923077	570	1754386	620	1612903	670	1492537	720	1388889
521	1919386	571	1751313	621	1610306	671	1490313	721	1386963
522	1915709	572	1748252	622	1607717	672	1488095	722	1385042
523	1912046	573	1745201	623	1605136	673	1485884	723	1383126
524	1908397	574	1742160	624	1602564	674	1483680	724	1381215
525	1904762	575	1739130	625	1600000	675	1481481	725	1379310
526	1901141	576	1736111	626	1597444	676	1479290	726	1377410
527	1897533	577	1733102	627	1594896	677	1477105	727	1375516
528	1893939	578	1730104	628	1592357	678	1474926	728	1373626
529	1890359	579	1727116	629	1589825	679	1472754	729	1371742
530	1886792	580	1724138	630	1587302	680	1470588	730	1369863
531	1883239	581	1721170	631	1584786	681	1468429	731	1367989
532	1879699	582	1718213	632	1582278	682	1466276	732	1366120
533	1876173	583	1715266	633	1579779	673	1464129	733	1364256
534	1872659	584	1712329	634	1577287	684	1461988	734	1362398
535	1869159	585	1709402	635	1574803	685	1459854	735	1360544
536	1865672	586	1706485	636	1572327	686	1457726	736	1358696
537	1862197	587	1703578	637	1569859	687	1455604	737	1356852
538	1858736	588	1700680	638	1567398	688	1453488	738	1355014
539	1855288	589	1697793	639	1564945	689	1451379	739	1353180
540	1851852	590	1694915	640	1562500	690	1449275	740	1351351
541	1848429	591	1692047	641	1560062	691	1447178	741	1349528
542	1845018	592	1689189	642	1557632	692	1445087	742	1347709
543	1841621	593	1686341	643	1555210	693	1443001	743	1345895
544	1838235	594	1683502	644	1552795	694	1440922	744	1344086
545	1834862	595	1680672	645	1550388	695	1438849	745	1342282
546	1831502	596	1677852	646	1547988	696	1436782	746	1340483
547	1828154	597	1675042	647	1545595	697	1434720	747	1338688
548	1824818	598	1672241	648	1543210	698	1432665	748	1336898
549	1821494	599	1669449	649	1540832	699	1430615	749	1335113
550	1818182	600	1666667	650	1538462	700	1428571	750	1333333

Table 8 (*Continued*)

n	1/n .00	n	1/n .00	n	1/n .00	n	1/n .00	n	1/n .00
750	1333333	800	1250000	850	1176471	900	1111111	950	1052632
751	1331558	801	1248439	851	1175088	901	1109878	951	1051525
752	1329787	802	1246883	852	1173709	902	1108647	952	1050420
753	1328021	803	1245330	853	1172333	903	1107420	953	1049318
754	1326260	804	1243781	854	1170960	904	1106195	954	1048218
755	1324503	805	1242236	855	1169591	905	1104972	955	1047120
756	1322751	806	1240695	856	1168224	906	1103753	956	1046025
757	1321104	807	1239157	857	1166861	907	1102536	957	1044932
758	1319261	808	1237624	858	1165501	908	1101322	958	1043841
759	1317523	809	1236094	859	1164144	909	1100110	959	1042753
760	1315789	810	1234568	860	1162791	910	1098901	960	1041667
761	1314060	811	1233046	861	1161440	911	1097695	961	1040583
762	1312336	812	1231527	862	1160093	912	1096491	962	1039501
763	1310616	813	1230012	863	1158749	913	1095290	963	1038422
764	1308901	814	1228501	864	1157407	914	1094092	964	1037344
765	1307190	815	1226994	865	1156069	915	1092896	965	1036269
766	1035483	816	1225490	866	1154734	916	1091703	966	1035197
767	1303781	817	1223990	867	1153403	917	1090513	967	1034126
768	1302083	818	1222494	868	1152074	918	1089325	968	1033058
769	1300390	819	1221001	869	1150748	919	1088139	969	1031992
770	1298701	820	1219512	870	1149425	920	1086957	970	1030928
771	1297017	821	1218027	871	1148106	921	1085776	971	1029866
772	1295337	822	1216545	872	1146789	922	1084599	972	1028807
773	1293661	823	1215067	873	1145475	923	1083424	973	1027749
774	1291990	824	1213592	874	1144165	924	1082251	974	1026694
775	1290323	825	1212121	875	1142857	925	1081081	975	1025641
776	1288660	826	1210654	876	1141553	926	1079914	976	1024590
777	1287001	827	1209190	877	1140251	927	1078749	977	1023541
778	1285347	828	1207729	878	1138952	928	1077586	978	1022495
779	1283697	829	1206273	879	1137656	929	1076426	979	1021450
780	1282051	830	1204819	880	1136364	930	1075269	980	1020408
781	1280410	831	1203369	881	1135074	931	1074114	981	1019368
782	1278772	832	1201923	882	1133787	932	1072961	982	1018330
783	1277139	833	1200480	883	1132503	933	1071811	983	1017294
784	1275510	834	1199041	884	1131222	934	1070664	984	1016260
785	1273885	835	1197605	885	1129944	935	1069519	985	1015228
786	1272265	836	1196172	886	1128668	936	1068376	986	1014199
787	1270648	837	1194743	887	1127396	937	1067236	987	1013171
788	1269036	838	1193317	888	1126126	938	1066098	988	1012146
789	1267427	839	1191895	889	1124859	939	1064936	989	1011122
790	1265823	840	1190476	890	1123596	940	1063830	990	1010101
791	1264223	841	1189061	891	1122334	941	1062699	991	1009082
792	1262626	842	1187648	892	1121076	942	1061571	992	1008065
793	1261034	843	1186240	893	1119821	943	1060445	993	1007049
794	1259446	844	1184834	894	1118568	944	1059322	994	1006036
795	1257862	845	1183432	895	1117318	945	1058201	995	1005025
796	1256281	846	1182033	896	1116071	946	1057082	996	1004016
797	1254705	847	1180638	897	1114827	947	1055966	997	1003009
798	1253133	848	1179245	898	1113586	948	1054852	998	1002004
799	1251564	849	1177856	899	1112347	949	1053741	999	1001001
800	1250000	850	1176471	900	1111111	950	1052632	1000	1000000

INDEX

(Numbers refer to pages)